MATHIEU'S EQUATION FOR COMPLEX PARAMETERS

Tables of Characteristic Values

by

G. Blanch and D. S. Clemm

1969

AEROSPACE RESEARCH LABORATORIES

Office of Aerospace Research

United States Air Force

For sale by the Superintendent of Documents, U.S. Government Printing Office
Washington, D.C. 20402 - Price $4.50

Library of Congress Catalog Card Number: 78–602165

CONTENTS

INTRODUCTION

1. Background

Mathieu's equation

1.00)
$$\frac{d^2y}{dx^2} + (a - 2q\cos 2x)y = 0$$

admits of periodic solutions of period π and 2π for four countable sets of *characteristic* values, $a(q)$, for each assigned value of q. There are extensive tabulations for real values of q [10] but very little is available in the complex plane. Power series expansions for the characteristic values (eigenvalues) were first developed by Mathieu [6] and an algorithm, suitable for computers, appeared in [12] which enables one to generate successively the coefficients of the power series. The radii of convergence of these expansions, however, has remained largely unknown, since these depend on a knowledge of the multiple eigenvalues for complex values of q. These multiple eigenvalues occur at branch points, q, where $|da/dq| = \infty$; they will be termed singular points or double points, interchangeably.

In [9] Mulholland and Goldstein tabulated six sets of characteristic values for purely imaginary values of q, namely $q = is$, $s \leq 2$. (The tabulation comprised 61 values.) They found that $a_0(q)$ and $a_2(q)$ have a common value when $s = 1.468 \ldots$, thus establishing that the power series for these two orders is valid at most up to $s = 1.468 \ldots$ Bouwkamp [3] improved on this value of s, giving it as 1.468769, and he gave the corresponding value of $a(q)$ to only three decimals, as 2.088.

The present work provides a tabulation in the complex plane (tables I and II) for $q = \rho\exp(i\phi)$, $\phi = 5°(5°)90°$, $\rho = 0(.5)25$, and additional tables on the 90°-ray for ρ up to 100 (tables III, IV, V). In tables I and II the intervals in ρ and ϕ are not small enough for satisfactory interpolation, but the table does exhibit the main features of these eigenvalues over the range covered. Actually many more values were available, especially in regions near the singular points. Now that high-speed computing equipment is at the disposal of investigators in almost every scientific establishment, it was deemed that the need for interpolable tables is not paramount, as it was a generation ago. A smaller table, that presents a general overview of a function, may in fact be more serviceable. These considerations prompted the present authors to limit the tabulations. An exception was made in the case of the 90°-ray because of the importance of this ray in both theoretical and applied problems. For this one ray, the tabulation is interpolable and extends beyond the singular point (if there is one) for each order, and always at least up to $\rho = 100$. [In one of the sets the last entry is for $\rho = 130$.]

In addition, the double points in the complex plane for orders $r \leq 15$ are tabulated; hence the radii of convergence of the power series for these orders are now known.* The present tabulation confirms the fact that the singular point found in [9] is indeed the one closest to the origin in Euclidean distance. The method used to obtain the double points gave the eigenvalue itself to as high an accuracy as the values of ρ and ϕ at the double point; it is a general method which can be used in other problems as well. Details are given in Section 5. The graphs given here show the behavior of $a_r(q)$ near the singularities.

It is believed that the values in the present tabulation are accurate to within a unit in the last place.

------

2. Derivation of the Basic Equations

When $q=0$, the solutions of (1.00) assume simple forms. Thus if $a=q=0$, the periodic solution is the constant, $y=C$ and we regard $a=a_0=0$ as the first eigenvalue corresponding to $q=0$. The second independent solution of (1.00) is $y=x$. Other solutions corresponding to $q=0$ are

$$(2.00) \qquad\qquad y_1=\cos rx,\ y_2=\sin rx,$$

associated with $a_r(q)=r^2$, $r=1,\ 2,\ \ldots$. [We may adjoin $r=0$ to this set, to include a_0. Corresponding to $r=0$, $y_2=0$ is a trivial solution and so it is not considered. For the odd orders, the *order* r begins with 1.]

The solutions corresponding to $q=0$ are exceptional in this respect: if $r\geq 1$, both solutions of (1.00) are periodic and of the required period, π or 2π. It will turn out that if $q\neq 0$, then an eigenvalue $a(q)$ gives rise to one and only one periodic solution. On the other hand, it is known that there are periodic solutions of period $m\pi$, for positive integers $m\geq 3$, corresponding to special values of a. In this case all solutions of (1.00) are periodic, if one is. See [5]. For our purposes, only the values giving rise to solutions of period π or 2π will be termed characteristic values or eigenvalues.

Let us now consider the case when $q\neq 0$. A solution of period π or 2π, which is twice differentiable with respect to x, can be put into the form

$$(2.01) \qquad\qquad y(x,q,a)=\sum_{j=0}^{\infty}(A_j\cos jx+B_j\sin jx),\ B_0=0.$$

If (2.01) is substituted into (1.00) and the coefficients of $\cos jx$ and of $\sin jx$ are equated to zero, for every j, the following recurrence relations are obtained:

$$(2.02) \qquad\qquad aA_0-qA_2=0,$$
$$(2.03) \qquad\qquad (a-4)A_2-q(2A_0+A_4)=0,$$
$$(2.04) \qquad\qquad (a-j^2)A_j-q(A_{j-2}+A_{j+2})=0,\ j\geq 3,$$
$$(2.05) \qquad\qquad (a-1)A_1-q(A_1+A_3)=0,$$
$$(2.06) \qquad\qquad (a-1)B_1-q(-B_1+B_3)=0,$$
$$(2.07) \qquad\qquad (a-4)B_2-qB_4=0,$$
$$(2.08) \qquad\qquad (a-j^2)B_j-q(B_{j-2}+B_{j+2})=0,\ j\geq 3.$$

Equations (2.02)–(2.08) lead to the observations (a) and (b) below.

(a) No coefficient B_j is connected in any way with the coefficients A_j. It follows that the solutions associated with these parameters are distinct. Let us designate the eigenvalues $a(q)$ that lead to the even and odd solutions by $a_r(q)$ and $b_r(q)$, respectively, $r=0,1,2.$.—with the understanding that $r=0$ applies only to the even solutions.

(b) No coefficient A_{2j}—or B_{2j}—is interrelated in any way with an A_{2j+1}—or B_{2j+1}. It follows that the solutions again separate into those of period π and 2π. The four types of solutions, with the associated sets of characteristic values, will hereafter be referred to as of types 0,1,2, or 3 as follows:

$$(2.10) \qquad y(x,q,a_{2m})=\sum_{k=0}^{\infty}A_{2k}\cos 2kx,\ a=a_{2m}(q),\ m=0,1,2,\ \ldots\ \text{(Type 0)}.$$

$$(2.11) \qquad y(x,q,a_{2m+1})=\sum_{k=0}^{\infty}A_{2k+1}\cos (2k+1)x,\ a=a_{2m+1}(q),\ m=0,1,2,\ \ldots\ \text{(Type 1)}.$$

$$(2.12) \qquad y(x,q,b_{2m})=\sum_{k=1}^{\infty}B_{2k}\sin 2kx,\ a=b_{2m}(q),\ m=1,\ 2,\ \ldots\ \text{(Type 2)}.$$

(2.13) $\quad y(x, q, b_{2m+1}) = \sum_{k=0}^{\infty} B_{2k+1} \sin(2k+1)x, \ a = b_{2m+1}(q), \ m = 0,1,2 \ldots$ (Type 3).

The coefficients A_j and B_j are functions of both q and the order, r; they are different in the various sets. The following properties can be established, for all complex values of q.

Property 1. As $q \to 0$, $a_r(q) \to r^2$, $r = 0,1,2 \ldots$, $b_r(q) \to r^2$, $r = 1,2, \ldots$.

Property 2. $a_{2m}(-q) = a_{2m}(q)$, $b_{2m}(-q) = b_{2m}(q)$, $a_{2m+1}(-q) = b_{2m+1}(q)$. See [7], [8], [10].

If, in addition, q is real, it is worth mentioning two other properties.

Property 3. If q is real and different from zero, the eigenvalues are simple ones and they can be ordered as follows:

$$a_0 < b_1 < a_1 < b_2 < a_2 < \ldots b_r < a_r \ldots, \ q > 0$$
$$a_0 < a_1 < b_1 < b_2 < a_2 < a_3 < b_3 < \ldots a_{2m-1} < b_{2m-1} < b_{2m} < a_{2m} < \ldots, \ q < 0.$$

Property 4. If q is real, the solutions associated with $a_r(q)$ and $b_r(q)$ have r zeros in the semi-open interval $0 \le x < \pi$.

An examination of the present tabulations shows that the ordering principle of Property 3, for either the real or imaginary component of $a_r(q)$, does not hold in general for complex values of q. Similarly, Property 4 no longer holds in the complex plane. For at a singular point—say q_1—where $a_r(q_1) = a_{r+2}(q_1)$, $y(x,q_1,a_r)$ is necessarily proportional to $y(x,q_1,a_{r+2})$ for all x. Hence there cannot be, simultaneously, r and $r+2$ zeros of these functions in the same interval. It follows that Property 1, coupled with continuity of the function $a_r(q)$, is the only criterion available so far for distinguishing between eigenvalues of various orders in the complex plane.

If $y(x,q,a_r)$ satisfies (1.00), then it can be readily verified that $\bar{y}(x,q,a_r)$, when associated with $\bar{q}$ and $\bar{a}_r(q)$, also satisfies (1.00); similarly for $\bar{y}(x,q,b_r)$, in association with $\bar{q}$ and $\bar{b}_r(q)$. In view of Property 2, it is enough to study the solutions for q in the first quadrant of the complex plane. Moreover, it is easy to prove from Property 2 that on the imaginary axis, $a_{2m+1}(q)$ and $b_{2m+1}(q)$ are complex conjugates.

Define

(2.14) $\qquad V_m(a,q) = V_m = (a-m^2)/q, \ q \ne 0.$

For any assigned value of the pair (a,q), with the value, a, not necessarily an eigenvalue, it is always possible to find an m_3 such that

(2.15) $\qquad |V_m| > 2, \ m \ge m_3.$

Let

(2.16) $\qquad G_{m,2}(a, q) = \cfrac{1}{V_m - \cfrac{1}{V_{m+2} - \ldots}}, \ m \ge m_3 \ge 4.$

For brevity $G_{m,2}$ will be used as an abbreviation for $G_{m,2}(a,q)$ when no ambiguity is likely to arise. It is known that if the V_m satisfy (2.15), then (2.16) converges to a unique value, numerically no greater than unity. If, in addition, m_2 is such that $|V_m| \ge 3$ for $m \ge m_2$ then

(2.18) $\qquad |G_{m,2}| < 0.4, \ m \ge m_2.$

Such an m_2 can always be attained if q is different from zero.

For all $m < m_3$, define

$$\text{(2.19)} \qquad G_{m,2}(a,\,q) = \frac{c_m}{V_m - G_{m+2,\,2}}, \quad c_m = 2, \text{ if } m = 2; \ c_m = 1 \text{ otherwise.}$$

$$\text{(2.20)} \qquad G_{m,2}(a,\,q)H_{m,2}(a,\,q) = 1.$$

Equation (2.20) thus defines $H_{m,2}$. It may happen that $|G_{m,2}|$ is infinite. In such a case $H_{m,2} = 0$ and

$$\text{(2.21)} \qquad G_{m-2,\,2} = \frac{c_{m-2}}{V_{m-2} - G_{m,\,2}} = 0, \text{ when } H_{m,2} = 0.$$

Let us multiply the numerator and denominator on the right-hand side of (2.19) by $H_{m+2,2}$; we obtain form which is sometimes more convenient than (2.19). Thus

$$\text{(2.22)} \qquad G_{m,2}(a,\,q) = \frac{c_m H_{m+2,\,2}}{V_m H_{m+2,\,2} - 1}.$$

Using (2.22) with m replaced by $m-2$, and multiplying both sides by $G_{m,2}$, one obtains, for the case when (2.21) holds,

$$\text{(2.23)} \qquad \lim_{H_{m,2} \to 0} G_{m-2,\,2}G_{m,\,2} = \lim_{H_{m,2} \to 0} \frac{c_{m-2}}{V_{m-2}H_{m,\,2} - 1} = -c_{m-2}.$$

Equation (2.23) shows that it is possible to define all members of the set $\{G_{m,2}\}$, $m \geq 2$, even when som members of the set are not finite.

Now let us define another set of functions, $G_{m,1}(a,q)$—to be abbreviated to $G_{m,1}$ at times—s follows:

$$\text{(2.24)} \qquad G_{2,1} = a/q, \quad H_{2,1}G_{2,1} = 1,$$

$$\text{(2.241)} \qquad G_{4,1} = V_2 - 2H_{2,1}.$$

Equations (2.24) and (2.241) will be used only in connection with developing eigenvalues of type (through a sequence of values, a, that may not be eigenvalues. Similarly, define

$$\text{(2.25)} \qquad G_{4,1} = V_2,$$

when developing eigenvalues of type 2. Finally, for types 1 and 3, let

$$\text{(2.26)} \qquad G_{3,1} = V_1 + \sigma, \qquad \sigma = \begin{cases} -1, \text{ for type 1} \\ 1, \text{ for type 3.} \end{cases}$$

For all $m \geq 5$, in all sets

$$\text{(2.27)} \qquad G_{m,1} = V_{m-2} - H_{m-2,1}.$$

Again, only if $G_{m-2,1} = 0$ is $|G_{m,1}|$ infinite, and in this case, it is easy to verify by a development simila to (2.22) that $G_{m+2,1} = V_m$. In this manner all the required $G_{m,1}$ can be developed, even if some inter mediate member is not finite. Define

$$\text{(2.30)} \qquad T_m(a,q) = G_{m,2}(a,q) - G_{m,1}(a,q).$$

It is shown in [2] that a necessary and sufficient condition for $a(q)$ to be an eigenvalue is that $T_m(a,\,q) =$ for some m. Moreover, if this is true for any m then it is true for all m provided non-finite quantities if they exist, are interpreted as noted previously.

When $T_m(a,\,q) = 0$, then the $G_{m,1}$ and $G_{m,2}$, which are the same, can be interpreted as the ratio A_m/A_{m-2}—or for types 2 and 3, as B_m/B_{m-2}. In practice, therefore, one method of obtaining an eigenvalu s to approach it through a sequence of values, a, such that $T_m(a, q)$ approaches 0. Having obtained such a value to sufficient accuracy, one may assign the value of some one coefficient, and develop all the rest through the ratios $G_{m, j}$, $j = 1, 2$ as convenient. Complete details will be found in [2], where it is shown how a desirable value of m can be chosen at which to "chain" the $G_{k, 1}$ and $G_{k, 2}$, to obtain a value of $T_m(a, q)$ that is numerically significant. A subroutine using this method is included in the Clemm code [4], to which we shall refer later.

Let us assume that a set of coefficients $\{A_{2k+p}\}$ or $\{B_{2k+p}\}$, $p = 0$ or 1 is available, corresponding to an eigenvalue $a_r(q)$, $q \neq 0$. It is shown in [10], Section V that it is possible to develop an auxiliary set of coefficients, say C_{2m+p}, which depend on the $\{A_{2k+p}\}$, such that

$$\text{(2.31)} \qquad U = x[y(x, q, a_r)] + \sum_{k=0}^{\infty} C_{2k+p} \sin (2k+p) x$$

is a second, independent solution of (1.00), associated with the same parameters, $a_r(q)$ and q. The development* is valid for complex values of q. Similarly, one may find coefficients E_{2m+p}, based on the B_{2k+p}, such that

$$\text{(2.32)} \qquad V = x[y(x, q, b_r)] + \sum_{k=0}^{\infty} E_{2m+p} \cos (2k+p) x$$

satisfies (1.00), associated with the parameters b_r, q. Since neither U nor V is periodic, it follows that if q is different from zero, no eigenvalue of one type can simultaneously be an eigenvalue corresponding to any of the other three types. For if that were possible, every solution corresponding to those eigenvalues would be periodic—and that contradicts (2.31) and (2.32). In seeking multiple eigenvalues, it is therefore enough to seek them among members of the same set.

The multiple eigenvalues for orders $r \leq 15$ are given in Table VI. Several features of these are worth noting. On the 90°-ray, there are multiple eigenvalues $a_{4m}(q) = a_{4m+2}(q)$, $m = 0, 1, \ldots$ as well as $b_{4m-2}(q) = b_{4m}(q)$, $m = 1, 2, \ldots$. At the origin and up to these singular points, the eigenvalues on the 90°-ray, for even orders, are all real; thereafter they become complex conjugates. There are no singular points on the 90°-ray in the sets of eigenvalues of odd order. The multiple eigenvalues elsewhere in the complex plane are not complex conjugates; it is interesting to note that both the real and imaginary components of the eigenvalue are non-negative at singular points of the first quadrant. One more fact is of interest: $b_1(q)$ has no singular points in the first quadrant of the complex plane. However, since $b_1(-q) = a_1(q)$, there is a singular point in the third quadrant, and its conjugate in the second quadrant. The radius of convergence of the power series for $b_1(q)$ is the same as for $a_1(q)$.

3. Method of Computation

There is now in existence an extensive computer program [4] for generating not only the eigenvalues, but also both the periodic and the associated radial solutions of (1.00), for positive values of q. The basic method used in this code is that of the continued fraction, which is developed with much detail in [2]. The program dealing with the eigenvalues contained in [4] was the basis in the present computations. Modifications had to be made to operate with complex arithmetic—a minor change; other changes became necessary, since it could no longer be assumed that all eigenvalues would be simple ones. The necessary modifications will be explained. In what follows, the symbol $a_r(q)$ or a_r will be used to indicate both $a_r(q)$ and $b_r(q)$, since the same developments apply to both. Whenever a distinction must be made between the two, the fact will be stated. The symbol $a_r(\rho, \phi)$ will at times be used in place of $a_r(q)$, where

---

*The methods of obtaining the auxiliary coefficients will also be found in [7], Sections 7.50–7.55 and in [13].

(3.00)
$$q = \rho \exp i\phi.$$

In practice ϕ was kept fixed and computations proceeded beginning with $\rho = 0$, at sufficiently small int ervals, h, to allow successful extrapolation of a first approximation. Since the power series expansions are valid for sufficiently small values of $|q|$, the routine in [4] for obtaining initial approximations for $\rho \le 4h$ was used without change. For larger values of ρ, the first approximation was extrapolated, very much as in [4], for values of $a_r(q)$ sufficiently far from a singular point. The procedure for regions near a singularity will be explained in Section 4. Let us assume, therefore, that there is an approximation (say the sth, $s = 0, 1, \ldots$) which we denote by $a_r^s(q) = a_r^s$. We shall be dealing with functions related to $T_m(a, q)$ which were defined in (2.30). For brevity let

(3.01)
$$T_m(a_r^s, q) = P_o,$$

(3.02)
$$\frac{\partial T_m(a, q)}{\partial a} = P_1, \ a = a_r^s,$$

(3.03)
$$\frac{\partial^2 T_m(a, q)}{\partial a^2} = P_2, \ a = a_r^s.$$

In the case of positive values of q, it is known that $|P_1| \ge 1/q$. This no longer holds everywhere in the complex plane, since a multiple eigenvalue is characterized precisely by $P_o = P_1 = 0$. However, whenever P_1 is sufficiently different from zero, a modification of Newton's approximation can be used, namely

(3.04)
$$a_r^{s+1} = a_r^s + (-P_0/P_1), \ s = 0, 1 \ \ldots.$$

Let us assume that P_2 is a continuous function of the parameter, a, for a fixed q, in the neighborhood of an eigenvalue. The Taylor series for P_o is

(3.05)
$$P_0(a + \Delta a, q) = P_0 + \Delta a P_1 + \tfrac{1}{2}(\Delta a)^2 P_2 + \ldots$$

Dropping terms beyond P_2 and solving for a zero of the right-hand side of (3.05), one obtains

(3.06)
$$\Delta a = -\frac{P_1}{P_2} + \sigma \sqrt{\left(\frac{P_1}{P_2}\right)^2 - \frac{2P_0}{P_2}}, \ \sigma = \pm 1.$$

(3.07)
$$a_r^{s+1} = a_r^s + \Delta a.$$

The functions in (3.06) are in general complex-valued and the choice of the sign of σ is more difficult than in the real case. However, since in the limit $|\Delta a| \to 0$ as $a \to a_r(q)$, it is reasonable to choose the smaller of the two possible values of $|\Delta a|$ derived from (3.06). Ambiguity, when both values of Δa are of the same magnitude, occurred only very close to a singular point. The method of dealing with such situations on the 90°-ray is given later in this section. For other rays, the problem is treated in Sections 4 and 5.

The procedure used to calculate most of the values of tables I and II can be summarized as follows:

Given an approximation a_r^s, values of P_k, $k = 0, 1, 2$ were computed. The next iteration depended on the magnitude of P_1 as follows:

For $|P_1| \ge 0.1$, (3.04) was used; otherwise (3.06) was used. Convergence was obtained after about 4 iterations; rarely were more than 9 necessary.

It remains to explain the ambiguous $|\Delta a|$ of (3.06) on the 90°-ray. It occurred for the even orders; here $a_r(\rho, \phi)$ is real up to the singular point and thereafter, $a_r(\rho, \phi)$ and $a_{r+2}(\rho, \phi)$ become complex conjugates. Consider the case when $a(\rho - h, \phi)$ is still real but $a_r(\rho, \phi)$ is complex. Let us assume that a first approximation to $a_r(\rho, \phi)$—say a_r^o—has been obtained by extrapolation, based on available values corresponding to $\rho-kh$, $k=1,2,3,4$. This value will be real. Corresponding to it, as explained before, P_0, P_1, and P_2 were obtained—all of them necessarily real, and (3.06) was used to obtain the next approximation, since in this region $|P_1|$ is less than 0.1. The expression under the radical sign is real, but it is negative when $|P_1|^2$ is small relative to $|P_0|$. In this manner $\triangle a$ acquires an imaginary component and the two values of $\triangle a$ are of the same magnitude. In such cases a subroutine was developed which generated the values of $a_r(\rho,\phi_1)$, $\phi_1=89.99°$. The aim of this calculation was to make the value on the 90°-ray continuous with that on ϕ_1. In this way the ambiguity was resolved. It was found *a posteriori* that in all cases the imaginary component of $a_{4m}(\rho,\phi)$ and of $b_{4m-2}(\rho,\phi)$ were negative near the singular point, while those for $a_{4m+2}(\rho,\phi)$ and $b_{4m}(\rho,\phi)$ were positive. This fact was made use of in subsequent calculations relating to Table VI, when the singular points were obtained.

When generating the eigenvalues of odd order on the 90°-ray and all the other eigenvalues on other rays, provision was made in the subroutines to read out a warning when an ambiguity occurred which could not be resolved. No such warnings that would have affected the published values were found.

4. Auxiliary Functions Useful near a Singular Point

Let q_1 be a point at which $a_r(q_1)=a_{r+2}(q_1)$. At such a point

$$T_m(a, q_1)=\frac{\partial T_m(a, q_1)}{\partial a}=0, a=a_r(q_1).$$

Both $a_r(q)$ and $a_{r+2}(q)$ are continuous functions of ρ, for a fixed ϕ, but $|da/d\rho|$ is not well behaved—it is infinite at q_1—and the closer one approaches the singularity, the more difficult it is to determine $a_r(q)$ and $a_{r+2}(q)$ by the iterative methods (3.04) and (3.06). Fortunately it is not necessary to use these methods too close to a singular point. It turns out that the eigenvalues and the coordinates of the singular point itself can all be determined by interpolation in well behaved functions. These will now be obtained.

Consider (3.06) in a region where

(4.01)
$$|(P_1/P_2)^2|>>|-2P_0P_2|, \text{ (Case 1)},$$

where P_k, $k=0,1,2$ are defined in (3.01)–(3.03) corresponding to a given value of a. In this instance one may factor the dominant term from the radical in (3.06), and expand the latter by the binomial theorem. Even the sign of σ is determined in this case, from continuity considerations, and one obtains

(4.02)
$$\triangle a=-\frac{P_0}{P_1}\left[1+\frac{1}{2}\frac{P_0P_2}{(P_1)^2}+\ \cdot\ \cdot\ \cdot\right].$$

It follows that when (4.01) holds, $\triangle a$ as determined from (3.06) differs but little in nature from that obtained in (3.04). This happens when $|P_1|$ is large relative to $|P_0|$. On the other hand, let us consider another region where

(4.03)
$$|2P_0/P_2|>>|(P_1/P_2)^2|, \text{ (Case 2)}.$$

Again factoring the dominant term of the radical, (3.06) assumes the form

(4.04)
$$\triangle a=-\frac{P_1}{P_2}+\sigma\sqrt{-2P_0/P_2}\cdot\sqrt{1-[(P_1)^2/2P_0P_2]}.$$

When (4.03) holds, the second radical on the right-hand side of (4.04) is well behaved and can be expanded into a smooth function. The first radical in (4.04) gives an insight into the nature of the singularity at a double point, as $a_r(q)$ and $a_{r+2}(q)$ acquire increments of the type (4.04). Let $\triangle_1 a$ and

$\Delta_2 a$ be the two possible values of (4.04), depending on the phase chosen for the radical. If $\Delta_1 a$ is th
appropriate increment for $a_r{}^s(q)$, then it is to be expected that $\Delta_2 a$ will be appropriate as an incremen
to $a_{r+2}(q)$, as $q \to q_1$. Assume that P_2 is a continuous function of a, and bounded away from zero in
sufficiently small neighborhood of q_1. (If P_2 were zero, then the singularity would be a triple point an
not a double point; no such were detected.) An examination of (3.06) shows that the following tw
functions can be expected to be free of the singularities due to the radical:

$$(4.05) \qquad FA(\rho,\phi) = \tfrac{1}{2}[a_r(\rho,\phi) + a_{r+2}(\rho,\phi)] = u_1 + iu_2, \text{ say};$$

$$(4.06) \qquad FB(\rho,\phi) = [a_{r+2}(\rho,\phi) - a_r(\rho,\phi)]^2 = v_1 + iv_2, \text{ say}.$$

The fact that $FA(\rho,\phi)$ and $FB(\rho,\phi)$ are smooth functions near the singularity connecting the order
r and $r+2$ is easily verified from the tabulations. It is clear that q_1 is a singular point if and only if bot
components of $FB(\rho,\phi)$ vanish. In this instance $a_r(q_1) = a_{r+2}(q_1) = FA(\rho,\phi)$. Moreover, the inverse func
tion, q, is a well behaved function of the arguments $FB(\rho,\phi)$ considered as the independent variable.

Conversely, given $FA(\rho,\phi)$ and $FB(\rho,\phi)$, the functions $a_r(\rho,\phi)$ and $a_{r+2}(\rho,\phi)$ are determined, excep
for the subscript. For let

$$(4.07) \qquad a_r(q) = c_1 + id_1, \ a_{r+2}(q) = c_2 + id_2.$$

From (4.05) and (4.06) it follows that

$$(4.08) \qquad u_1 = \tfrac{1}{2}(c_1 + c_2), \ u_2 = \tfrac{1}{2}(d_1 + d_2)$$

$$(4.09) \qquad v_1 = (c_2 - c_1)^2 - (d_2 - d_1)^2, \ v_2 = 2(c_2 - c_1)(d_2 - d_1).$$

Three cases arise:

Case 1. $v_2 \ne 0$. In this case both $(c_2 - c_1)$ and $(d_2 - d_1)$ are different from zero. Define

$$(4.10) \qquad d_2 - d_1 = \lambda(c_2 - c_1).$$

Substituting (4.10) into (4.09) one obtains

$$(4.11) \qquad v_1 = (1 - \lambda^2)(c_2 - c_1)^2, \ v_2 = 2\lambda(c_2 - c_1)^2.$$

Observe that λ must have the sign of v_2. From (4.11) λ is known; namely

$$(4.12) \qquad \lambda = -(v_1/v_2) + p\sqrt{1 + (v_1/v_2)^2}, \ p = \pm 1.$$

Since the radical in (4.12) is always greater than $|v_1/v_2|$, the sign of λ is the same as the sign of p. How-
ever, it has already been noted that λ must have the sign of v_2. It follows that p is uniquely determined
and so is λ. With λ known, (4.11) now yields

$$(4.13) \qquad c_2 - c_1 = \tau g, \ d_2 - d_1 = \tau \lambda g,$$

$$(4.14) \qquad g = \sqrt{\tfrac{1}{2}(v_2/\lambda)}, \ \tau = \pm 1$$

Using (4.07), (4.13), and (4.14), one obtains

$$(4.15) \qquad c_1 = u_1 - \tfrac{1}{2}\tau g, \ d_1 = u_2 - \tfrac{1}{2}\tau \lambda g,$$

$$(4.16) \qquad c_2 = u_1 + \tfrac{1}{2}\tau g, \ d_2 = u_2 + \tfrac{1}{2}\tau \lambda g.$$

It is clear from (4.15) and (4.16) that changing the sign of τ merely interchanges $a_r(q)$ with $a_{r+2}(q)$.

Case 2. $v_2 = 0$, $v_1 \ne 0$. Either $c_2 - c_1 = 0$ or else $d_2 - d_1 = 0$.

If $v_1 < 0$, the first equation of (4.09) shows that $c_2 - c_1 = 0$. Similarly, if $v_1 > 0$, then $d_2 - d_1 = 0$. Thus
when $v_1 < 0$, $c_2 - c_1 = 0$, $d_2 - d_1 = \tau \sqrt{-v_1}$,
when $v_1 > 0$, $d_2 - d_1 = 0$, $c_2 - c_1 = \tau \sqrt{v_1}$.

One may again solve for the c_k and d_k, $k = 1,2$ as in (4.15)–(4.16).

Case 3. $v_1 = v_2 = 0$. This is a necessary and sufficient condition that q be a singular point, and $a_r(q) = a_{r+2}(q)$
$= FA(\rho,\phi)$.

The auxiliary functions $FA(\rho, \phi)$ and $FB(\rho, \phi)$ are of great importance in determining the double
points. They are also useful in generating eigenvalues in the immediate vicinity of double points, as
we shall see in the next section. However, these functions do have singularities in other regions. For

example, let q_2 be a singular point at which $a_{r-2}(q)=a_r(q)$. In such a region $FA(\rho, \phi)$ and $FB(\rho, \phi)$ which depend on $a_{r+2}(q)$ (and not $a_{r-2}(q)$) along with $a_r(q)$ will mirror the singularity at $a_r(q_2)$, since $a_{r+2}(q_2)$ is regular at q_2. We may conclude from this fact that in an effective computing routine, these auxiliary functions should be used only in a region close to the singular point; in any event, in a region that does not contain any other singular point.

The functions $FA(\rho, \phi)$ and $FB(\rho, \phi)$ are also useful for interpolation purposes. This fact has been used in Table III and Table IV, relating to the even orders on the 90°-ray. As noted previously, the functions $a_{4r}(i\rho)$, $a_{4r+2}(i\rho)$ and $b_{4r-2}(i\rho)$, $b_{4r}(i\rho)$ are real before the singular point and are complex conjugates after the singular point. Thus $FA(i\rho)$ is always real and is continuous with the real part of $a_{4r}(i\rho)$— or $b_{4r}(i\rho)$ after the singular point. Immediately before a singular point, $a_{4r}(i\rho)$ and $a_{4r+2}(i\rho)$—as well as $b_{4r-2}(i\rho)$ and $b_{4r}(i\rho)$—are not interpolable; but $FA(i\rho)$ and its continuation in the real part of $a_{4r}(i\rho)$— or $b_{4r}(i\rho)$—is an interpolable function. An example is provided in Section 6.

5. Method of Determining the Singular Points

The first task was a coarse tabulation of the eigenvalues, by single precision arithmetic, over the range from $\rho=0$ to 100, but unlike the tabulations of tables I and II, the functions $FA(\rho,\phi)$ and $FB(\rho,\phi)$, defined in Section 4, were generated along with $a_r(q)$ and $a_{r+2}(q)$, which were computed simultaneously. This meant that each set of eigenvalues, $a_r(q)$, $r\geq 2$ was generated twice; once with $a_{r-2}(q)$ and again with $a_{r+2}(q)$. It was deemed that this much exploratory computation was necessary. Since the double points form but a countable set and the tabulation was over a fairly coarse grid, it was not to be expected that an area unreasonably close to a singular point would be encountered—although the possibility was not ruled out. There was a subprogram to halt the computations if an ambiguity could not be resolved, but in practice the entire tabulation was obtained without too much difficulty. The range in ϕ was 90°(−5°)5°. To find the areas where there were singular points, it was only necessary to examine the tabulations for changes in sign of v_1 (as defined in (4.06)) and to note whether v_2 also changed sign in such an area. If one such region was found, the following information was read into the computer: ϕ_o (initial value of ϕ), ϕ_t (final value of ϕ), ρ_o (initial value of ρ), ρ_t (final value of ρ), $h=\Delta\rho$, and $d\phi=\Delta\phi$. It will be easiest to explain the details by an example.

Example. An examination of the coarse tabulation showed that there is a singular point connecting $r=2$ and $r=4$ in the following range: $46°>\phi>44°$, $6.9<\rho<7.5$.

The information read into the computer was as follows:

$$\phi_o \text{ (initial } \phi)=46.°, \ \phi_t \text{ (final } \phi)=44.°, \ d\phi=\Delta\phi=-0.2,$$
$$\rho_o \text{ (initial } \rho)=6.9, \ \rho_t \text{ (final } \rho)=7.5, \ h=\Delta\rho=.05.$$

The computer program was provided with double precision arithmetic, and it proceeded as follows:
1. Beginning with the initial ϕ_o, the values of $a_r(q)$ and $a_{r+2}(q)$ were generated for $\rho=0(.1)\rho_o$, along with $FA(\rho,\phi)$ and $FB(\rho,\phi)$. This range will be called Range 1. In this range $a_r(q)$ and $a_{r+2}(q)$ have no singularities and the method of Section 3 is adequate.
2. When $\rho_o=6.9$ was reached, values corresponding to $\rho=6.75$, 6.80, 6.85 were obtained by interpolation. [These would be useful in extrapolating first approximations to $a_r(q)$ and $a_{r+2}(q)$ in the new range.]
3. The next phase was to compute the required functions in the range from $\rho=\rho_o$ to $\rho=\rho_t$. This range will be referred to as Range 2. This time, the first approximation to $a_r(q)$ and $a_{r+2}(q)$ was obtained by extrapolating values of $FA(\rho, \phi)$ and $FB(\rho, \phi)$, and using (4.15)−(4.16) to obtain $a^o_r(\rho, \phi)$ and $a^o_{r+2}(\rho, \phi)$. This initial approximation was iterated, through (3.04) or (3.06), as explained in Section 3, until

convergence was obtained. It remains to explain how τ was determined. On the 90°-ray, it was known what the sign of the imaginary component should be near a singularity; this information was read into the computer, along with other basic information. On other rays, no similar information was available. The procedure was therefore the following. Tentatively, values of d_2-d_1 of (4.13) were extrapolated from known values corresponding to $\Delta\rho=kh$, $k=1, \ldots, 4$. In this range such extrapolation can be only tentative, since the functions are not smooth very close to the singular point. With this initial approximation, the iterative procedure was used to generate $a_{r+2}(q)$ first. Thereafter, this value, combined with the extrapolated value of $FA(\rho, \phi)$, provided an approximation to the companion eigenvalue, $a°_r(q)$. After both were obtained to a sufficient accuracy, two tests were performed:

a) $FA(\rho, \phi)$, as derived from the values of $a_{r+2}(q)$ and $a_r(q)$ that were just obtained, was compared with the extrapolated value. If the two differed by more than a pre-set, small tolerance, based on the expected accuracy of the extrapolation, the values were discarded, and a warning to this effect read out for *a posteriori* examination. [It turned out that no such warnings were read out.]

b) It has been noted that the choice in the incorrect sign would merely interchange $a_{r+2}(q)$ with $a_r(q)$. It has already been pointed out that the only criterion that is available for determining the order is continuity with other values. It was reasonable to expect that the correct value of $a_r(\rho, \phi)$ should be closer in distance to $a_r(\rho-h, \phi)$ than $a_{r+2}(\rho, \phi)$; similarly for the relation between $a_{r+2}(\rho-h, \phi)$ and $a_{r+2}(\rho, \phi)$. The test performed was the following.

Let

$$(5.01) \qquad S_1 = |a_{r+2}(\rho, \phi) - a_{r+2}(\rho-h, \phi)|^2 + |a_r(\rho, \phi) - a_r(\rho-h, \phi)|^2,$$

$$(5.02) \qquad S_2 = |a_r(\rho, \phi) - a_{r+2}(\rho-h, \phi)|^2 + |a_{r+2}(\rho, \phi) - a_r(\rho-h, \phi)|^2.$$

If $S_1 \leq S_2$, the choice of τ was accepted as correct.

If $S_1 > S_2$, a_r and a_{r+2} were interchanged, and a warning to this effect was read out for *a posteriori* examination. In practice, several such warnings were recorded and closer scrutiny showed that the interchange was necessary.

Proceeding with the example, we now list part of the computations on the first ray, namely $\phi=46.°$

SCHEDULE 1: $\phi=46°$, $r=2$, $r+2=4$

ρ	$a_r(q)$, real part	$a_{r+2}(q)$, real part	$a_r(q)$, imag. part	$a_{r+2}(q)$, imag. part
6. 90	10. 90664 80791 568	14. 19745 72621 910	3. 78398 98015 941	1. 71447 31598 588
6. 95	11. 05453 28631 683	14. 10314 70191 303	3. 79200 93615 848	1. 73677 81368 712
7. 00	11. 21094 61287 695	14. 00038 50103 847	3. 80309 50625 754	1. 75580 47252 027
7. 05	11. 37704 73642 281	13. 88801 12744 952	3. 81908 69221 083	1. 76971 31254 332
7. 10	11. 55382 37457 409	13. 76503 81749 751	3. 84281 88112 033	1. 77566 96920 288
7. 15	11. 74143 59397 184	13. 63130 45977 319	3. 87849 39152 429	1. 76947 14727 104
7. 20	11. 93786 21713 932	13. 48883 18821 814	3. 93162 99029 224	1. 74560 10397 508
7. 25	12. 13718 47908 430	13. 34353 72549 610	4. 00742 44700 492	1. 69886 09464 145
7. 30	12. 32988 71489 920	13. 20493 69536 769	4. 10701 90802 205	1. 62810 99865 143
7. 35	12. 50732 50891 744	13. 08167 47351 037	4. 22523 53264 208	1. 53852 68330 408

ρ	$FB(\rho,\phi)$, real part	$FB(\rho,\phi)$, imag. part
6.90	6.54652 59487 2308	−13.62076 87381 292
6.95	5.07007 28848 9359	−12.53121 40108 737
7.00	3.58957 15487 6717	−11.42158 25380 457
7.05	2.10500 68001 6522	−10.29180 72841 963
7.10	0.61636 37711 4919	−9.14181 99193 951
7.15	−0.87637 21185 6400	−7.97155 08263 788
7.20	−2.37321 51468 3705	−6.78092 91073 758
7.25	−3.87417 92749 7293	−5.56988 25906 195
7.30	−5.37927 81341 8019	−4.33833 78365 582
7.35	−6.88852 50126 2126	−3.08622 01437 759

By 8-point inverse interpolation, $FB(\rho_s,\phi)$, real part, $=0$ when $\rho_s=7.12066208771319$.

In Range 2, the real component of $FB(\rho,\phi)$ was examined for a change in sign, beginning with the fourth entry; in this case, with $\rho = 7.05$. When a change of sign was found, only 4 additional values of ρ were processed—and so the computations ended with entries corresponding to $\rho=7.35$. The value of $\rho_s(\phi)$—at which $FB(\rho_s,\phi)$, real part, changed sign—was obtained by inverse interpolation. Corresponding to ρ_s, interpolation in $FA(\rho,\phi)$ and $FB(\rho,\phi)$, imaginary part, led to values of $a_r(\rho_s,\phi)$ and $a_{r+2}(\rho_s,\phi)$ through (4.15) and (4.16). These approximations were processed through iteration in the usual manner, so that one ended up with the following data: $\phi,\rho_s(\phi)$, $FB(\rho_s,\phi)$, imaginary part—the real part is zero—$FA(\rho_s,\phi)$, as well as $a_j(\rho_s,\phi)$, $j=r,r+2$. This ended the computations for $\phi=46.°$

The same procedure was used to process the other rays in sequence, 45.8°, 45.6°, 45.4°. Beginning with the fourth ray (in this case 45.4°) the entries $FB(\rho_s,\phi)$, imaginary part, were examined for a change in sign. After one such a change in sign was found, only four additional values of ϕ were processed. We list in Schedule 3 part of this data.

SCHEDULE 3

ϕ (degrees)	$\rho_s(\phi)$	$FB(\rho_s,\phi)$, imag. part$=v_2$
46.0	7.12066 20878	−8.66067 87724
45.8	7.14036 08474	−7.45755 07724
45.6	7.16054 35855	−6.24116 58185
45.4	7.18122 53687	−5.01088 18645
45.2	7.20242 20793	−3.76601 98444
45.0	7.22415 04760	−2.50586 07340
44.8	7.24642 82588	−1.22964 23176
44.6	7.26927 41417	+0.06344 43726
44.4	7.29270 79314	1.37425 89890
44.2	7.31675 06150	2.70371 62166
44.0	7.34142 44559	4.05279 05937

The entries in Schedule 3 can be regarded as grid points on the curve $FB(\rho,\phi)$, real part$=0$. By inverse interpolation in $FB(\rho_s,\phi)$, imaginary part, the value of ϕ at which $FB(\rho,\phi)=0$ was found. We shall refer to this value as ϕ_d. In the present instance the interpolation gave

$$\phi_d=44.60975\ 03877\ 721 \quad \text{(8-pt. interpolation)}.$$

Corresponding to ϕ_d $\quad \rho_d=7.26814\ 68935\ 1669 \quad \text{(8-pt. interpolation)}.$

Within the computer, all values were carried to double precision (equivalent to about 15 significant digits). In most cases either 14 or 15 were printed out. We list only 10 decimal places in Schedule 3 for ease in presentation. All interpolations were also made by 7-point formulas; the results differed in the last two places from those obtained above. Finally, the value of $FA(\rho_d,\phi_d)$ was obtained by interpolation this gave

$$a_r(\rho_d,\phi_d)=a_{r+2}(\rho_d,\phi_d)=12.79971\ 62446\ 345+i\ 2.76304\ 49169\ 2944.$$

Corresponding to this value of a, values of P_0, P_1, and P_2 as defined in (3.01)—(3.03) were computed. The orders of magnitude of these quantities are noted below.

$$P_0=10^{-14}(.83-i.033),\ P_1=10^{-15}(.11-i.66),\ P_2=-.049-i.014.$$

Corresponding to the value of a obtained by 7-point formulas, we obtained in this instance:

$$P_0=10^{-13}(-.94+i.46),\ P_1=10^{-13}(.17+i.14),\ P_2=-.049-i.014.$$

The fact that P_0 and P_1 are as small as they turned out to be was further verification that the double point was obtained to the required accuracy.

In practice, the closeness of the interpolated values, as found by 8-point and 7-point interpolation were tested. Whenever the last place of the tabulated entries would have been affected, the computations were done over at a smaller interval in ϕ, ρ, or in both.

A further test was made. The entries on which interpolation was based were differenced—some by divided differences and others by ordinary differences as follows:

Argument	Dependent function	Type of differences
$FB(\rho,\phi)$, imag.pt.	ϕ	divided differences
ϕ	$\rho_s(\phi)$	ordinary differences
ϕ	$FA(\rho_s,\phi)$, both components	ordinary differences

The numerically largest differences of all these functions, for orders 2, 4, 6, 7, and 8 were printed out. Whenever the 8th difference would have affected the 8th decimal place of the various functions, the computations were again discarded and recomputed at finer intervals in ϕ and ρ.

The advantage of this method of obtaining the double point is two-fold. In the first place, it is not necessary to get too close to the singular point, and so fewer difficulties are encountered; the true value can be obtained as accurately as required by interpolation in smooth functions. If, in some problems, one accidentally came too close to a singular point, the grid could always be changed, and the entries recomputed by a more favorable grid.

Another advantage is in the confidence one may place in the results. For example, suppose one had obtained the value of ρ_d and of ϕ_d only from computations based on either (3.04) or (3.06). The uncertainty in the value of $a_r(\rho,\phi)$, if judged from (4.04), is of the order of magnitude of $\sqrt{|2P_0/P_2|}$. If, then, P_0 is obtained to about 14 decimal places, and P_2 is less than 0.1 in magnitude, then the uncertainty in $a_r(q)$ is of the order of magnitude of 10^{-6}. Moreover, the iterative procedure itself breaks down close to a singular point—as one may find by trying the method. In obtaining ϕ_d by the present method, in contrast, the uncertainty in ϕ_d is measured by $|d\phi/dv_2|$. If the values of $\rho_s(\phi)$ are correct to 10 decimals, then the interpolated value is also correct to within $c(10^{-10})$, where c is a small integer, provided the interpolation formula is accurate; the latter can of course be verified. The inverse function, ϕ, is accurate to within $w(|d\phi/dv_2|)$, where w is the uncertainty in v_2. When v_2 is correct to 10 decimal places—and these places were actually certain—w is less than 10^{-10}. Schedule 3 shows that $|d\phi/dv_2|$ is less than 0.2.

The present example is typical of all other cases; namely, $|d\phi/dv_2|$ was always less than 1. Thus, the values of ϕ_d are at least as accurate as the values v_2. In a similar way, with trustworthy values of ϕ_d and of ρ_d, the interpolation for $FA(\rho_d, \phi_d)$ was an accurate procedure. This fact is borne out by the very small values of $|P_1|$ that were obtained.

The method is general and can be used in other problems, where the equivalent of P_2 is regular around the singular point.

6. Interpolation

In tables III, IV and V, the upper bound of the truncation error in linear interpolation is three units in the second decimal place, while interpolation performed with a 4-point Lagrangian formula will yield five decimal places with an error no greater than one unit in the fifth place. A 6-point formula will give results to the full accuracy of the tabulations in tables III and IV and to at least seven decimal places in Table V. To the above errors must be added the errors introduced due to round-off. As noted in a previous section, tables I and II are not interpolable at the given intervals.

Throughout much of the tables, one can interpolate directly for the real and imaginary parts of the characteristic values. If, however, it is desired to interpolate in tables III or IV in the vicinity of a double point, it will be necessary to use the auxiliary functions FA and FB. We will illustrate their use by means of an example in which interpolation is required for a value of $\rho < \rho_d$, where ρ_d is the value of ρ at the double point. The details are given here using Lagrangian interpolation coefficients, $A^6_k(p)$, from [11] and functional values of FA and FB from page 192 of this volume.

Example 1. Suppose it is required to find the values of $a_0(q)$ and $a_2(q)$, for $q = i\,0.8437$, correct to seven decimal places. From definitions (4.05) and (4.06) we see that $a_0(q) = FA - \sqrt{FB}/2$ and $a_2(q) = FA + \sqrt{FB}/2$. We therefore interpolate for FA and FB using a 6-point formula and then use these relations to get the results.

$$\rho = \rho_0 + p(\rho_1 - \rho_0), \quad p = (\rho - \rho_0)/(\rho_1 - \rho_0) = 0.437$$

k	ρ_k	$A^6_k(p)$	$FA(i\rho_k)$	$FB(i\rho_k)$
-2	0. 6	0. 01180 24709	2. 01496 714	13. 35497 711
-1	0. 7	$-0.$ 10007 87111	2. 02035 576	12. 39736 260
0	0. 8	0. 65818 35599	2. 02656 270	11. 29079 725
1	0. 9	0. 51088 13778	2. 03358 336	10. 03458 567
2	1. 0	$-0.$ 09201 09455	2. 04141 250	8. 62794 061
3	1. 1	0. 01122 22480	2. 05004 425	7. 06998 344

$$FA(i\rho) = \Sigma A^6_k(p) FA(i\rho_k) = 2.02953\ 092 \text{ and } FB(i\rho) = 10.76028\ 587$$

Using these values, we get the following results:

$$a_0(q) = FA - \sqrt{FB}/2 = 2.02953\ 092 - 1.64014\ 373 = 0.38938\ 719$$

$$a_2(q) = FA + \sqrt{FB}/2 = 3.66967\ 465$$

These results are correct to seven decimal places.

If interpolation is required for a value of ρ near to but greater than ρ_d, the value of U (the real part) can be obtained by interpolating directly in the tabulated entries, but V (the imaginary part) should be calculated from the relation $V = -\sqrt{-FB/4}$. This is derived from definition (4.06) and the fact that, for $\rho > \rho_d$ on the 90°-ray, a_{4m} and $a_{4m+2}(b_{4m+2}$ and $b_{4m+4})$, $m = 0, 1, \ldots$, are complex conjugates.

A case may occasionally arise in which it is required to interpolate for $a_r(q)$, $q=i\rho$, where both ρ and ρ_d lie between the same tabulated entries. The important thing to note here is the function FA (tabulated for $\rho<\rho_d$) is continuous with U (tabulated for $\rho>\rho_d$) and should be treated as the same function for interpolation purposes. We give here an example to clarify the point.

Example 2. Let it be required to find $b_6(q)$ and $b_8(q)$ for $q=i\,30.0986$, correct to five decimal places. From an inspection of Table IV, page 227, we note that this is in the same interval as a double point, namely, $\rho_d=30.09677284$. We further note that $\rho>\rho_d$ and, therefore, the values we seek are complex conjugates. The imposed accuracy dictates the use of a 4-point interpolation formula. The details of calculation follow, with the tabular entries being found on pages 227 and 228 of this volume and the $A_k^4(p)$ in [11].

$$p=(\rho-\rho_0)/(\rho_1-\rho_0)=0.986$$

k	ρ_k	$A_k^4(p)$	$U(i\rho_k)$	$FB(i\rho_k)$
−1	29. 9	−0. 00233 2876	50. 39054 934*	17. 68427 548
0	30. 0	0. 01409 6628	50. 43332 238*	8. 72088 136
1	30. 1	0. 99280 5372	50. 47641 165	−0. 29161 738
2	30. 2	−0. 00456 9124	50. 51981 638	−9. 35347 978

$U(i\rho)=50.47580\ 622$, $FB(i\rho)=-0.16510\ 229$, and $V=-\sqrt{-FB/4}=-0.20316\ 391$

From these values we get:

$$b_6(q)=U+iV=50.47580\ 622-i\ 0.20316\ 391$$

$$b_8(q)=U-iV=50.47580\ 622+i\ 0.20316\ 391$$

These results are correct to at least five decimal places.

————

*Tabulated as function FA on page 227.

REFERENCES

1. G. Blanch and D. S. Clemm. Tables Relating to the Radial Mathieu Functions. Vol. 1 (1962); Vol. 2 (1965). U.S. Govt. Printing Office, Washington, D.C.

2. G. Blanch. Numerical aspects of Mathieu eigenvalues. Rend. Circ. Mat. Palermo, Ser. II, Tomo XV, pp. 51–97, (1966).

3. C. J. Bouwkamp. A note on Mathieu functions. Kon. Nederl. Akad. Wetensch., Proc. 51, pp. 891–893, (1948).

4. D. S. Clemm. A comprehensive code for Mathieu's equation. (To be published in a forthcoming Aerospace Research Laboratories Report, (1969)).

5. Wilhelm Magnus and Stanley Winkler. Hill's Equation. Interscience Publishers, New York, N.Y. (1966).

6. É. Mathieu. Mémoire sur le mouvement vibratoire d'une membrane de forme elliptique. J. Math. Pures Appl. 13, pp. 137–203, (1868).

7. N. W. McLachlan. Theory and Application of Mathieu Functions. Clarendon Press, Oxford, England. (1947).

8. J. Meixner and F. W. Schäfke. Mathieusche Funktionen und Sphäroidfunktionen. Springer, Berlin, (1954).

9. H. P. Mulholland and S. Goldstein. The characteristic numbers of the Mathieu equation with purely imaginary parameters. Phil. Mag. 8, pp. 834–840, (1929).

10. National Bureau of Standards. Tables Relating to Mathieu Functions. Second edition, AMS 59. U.S. Govt. Printing Office, Washington, D.C., (1967).

11. National Bureau of Standards. Tables of Lagrangian Interpolation Coefficients. Columbia Univ. Press, N.Y. (second printing) 1948.

12. Hanan Rubin. Anecdote on power series expansions of Mathieu functions. J. Math. and Phys. No. 4, pp. 339–341, (1964).

13. J. A. Stratton, P. M. Morse, L. J. Chu, and R. A. Hutner. Elliptic Cylinder and Spheroidal Wave Functions, Wiley, New York, (1941).

More complete bibliographies relating to Mathieu functions will be found in [8] and [7].

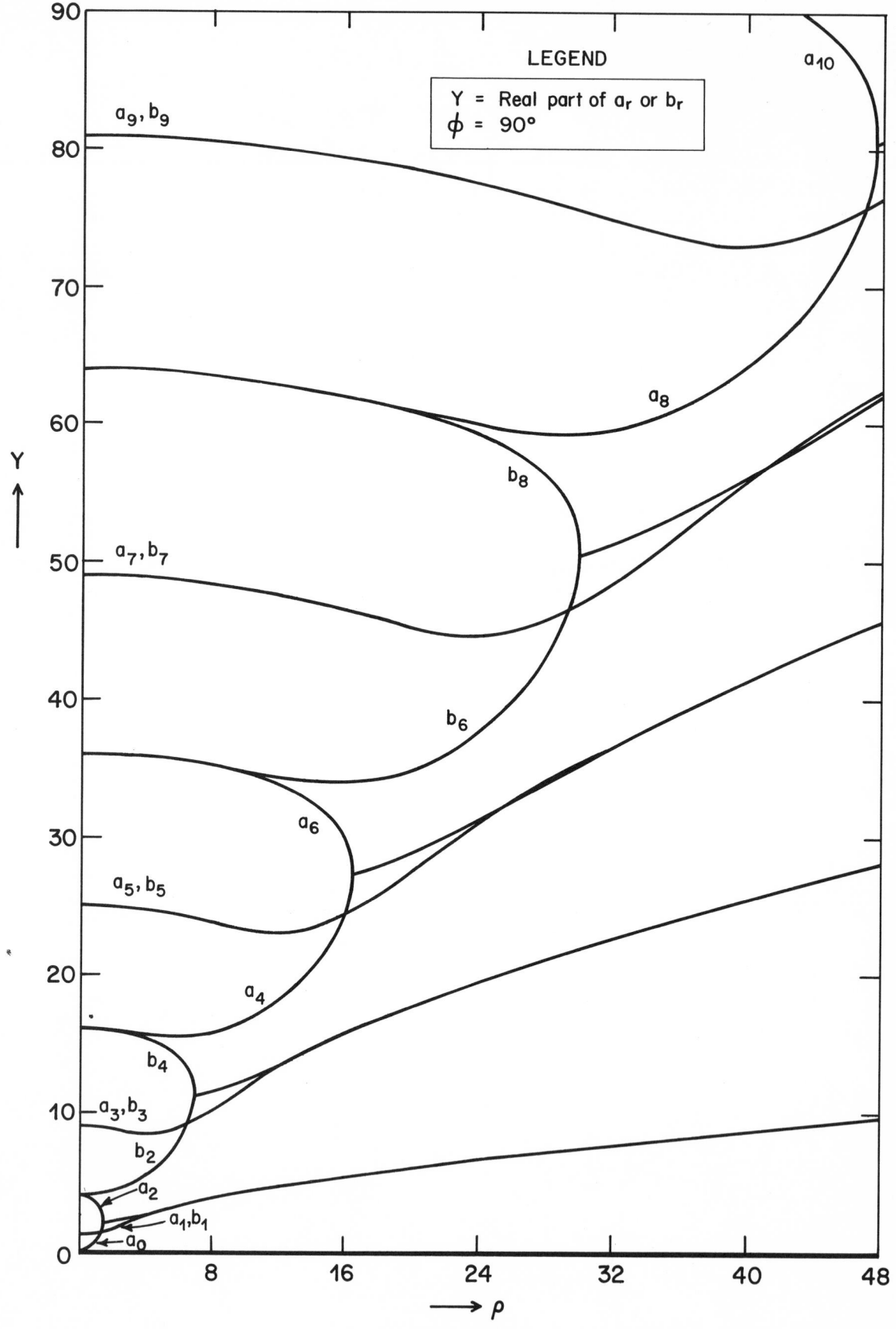

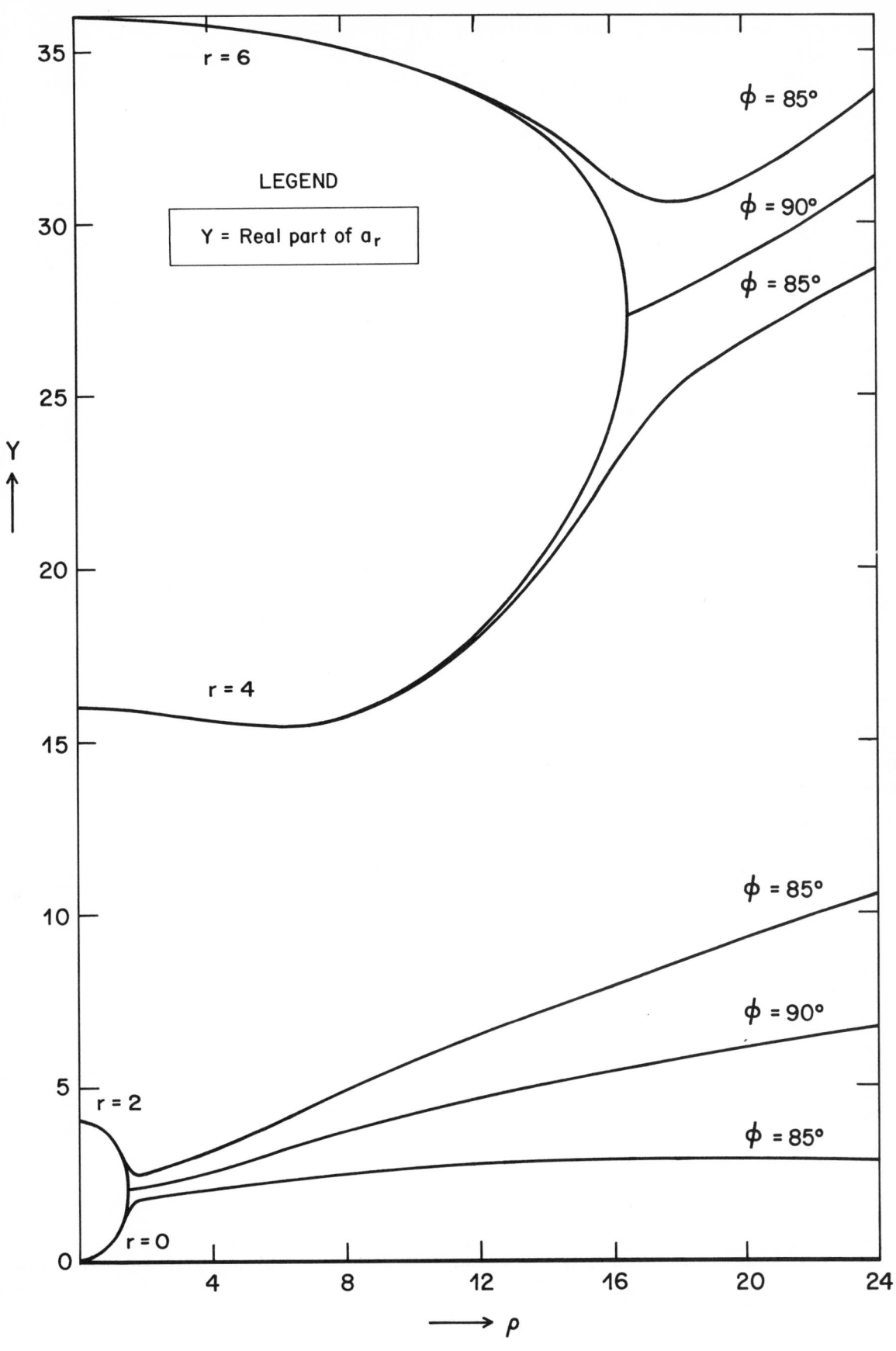

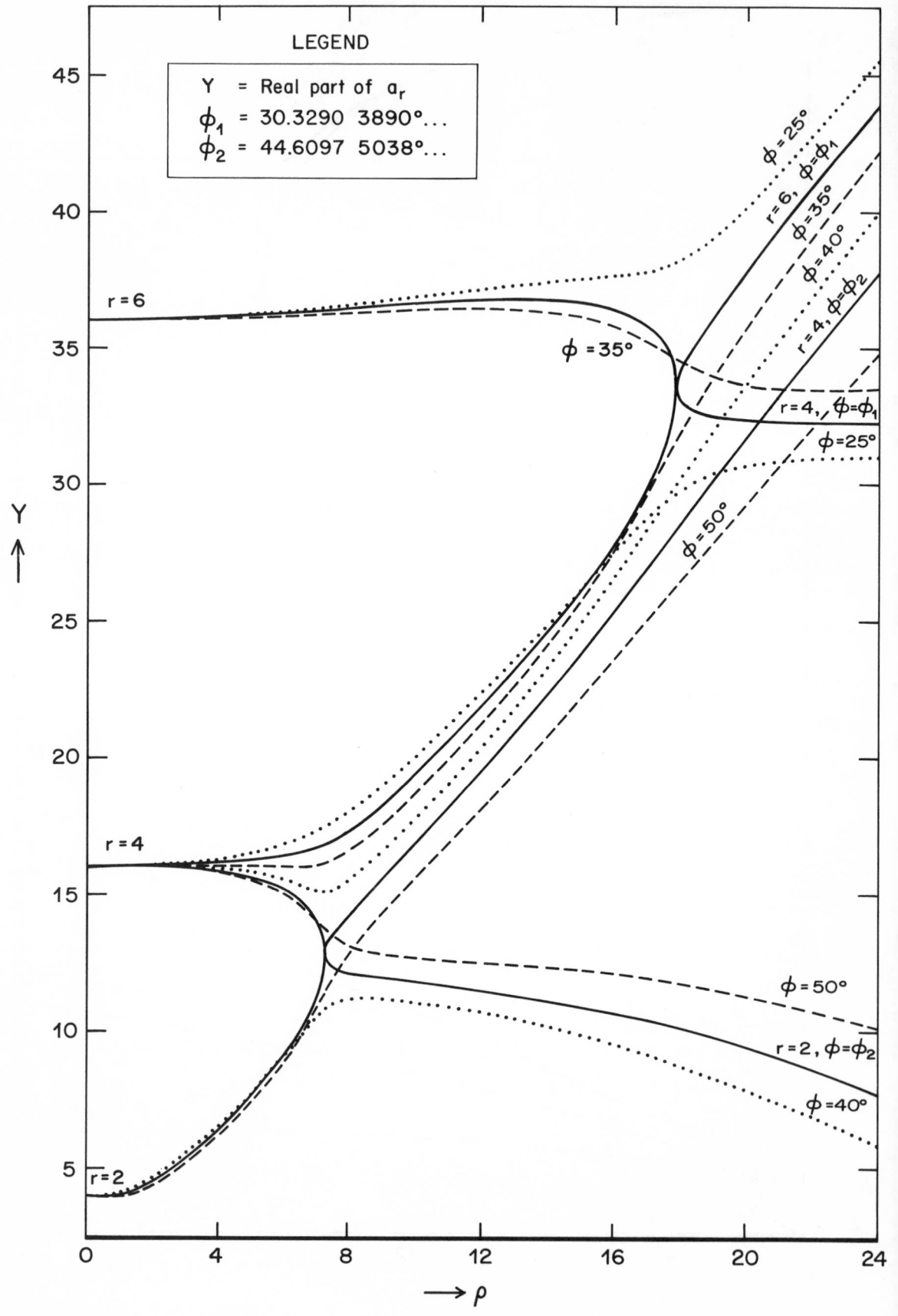

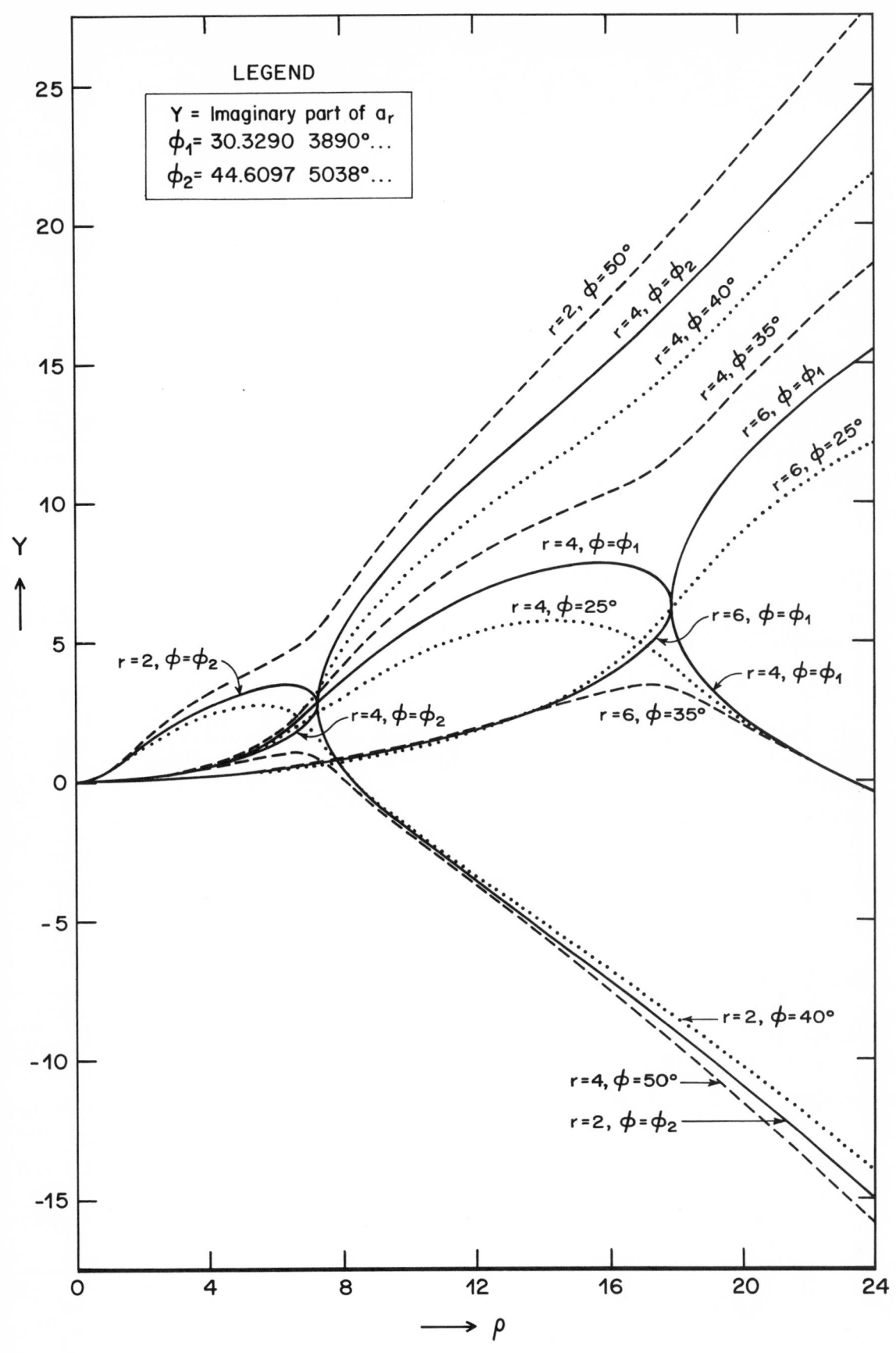

TABLE I. VALUES OF $a_r(q)$

Associated with even periodic solutions

$$a_r(q) = U + iV$$

$$q = \rho e^{i\phi}$$

TABLE I. $a_r(q) = U + iV$, $q = \rho e^{i\phi}$ $r = 0$

| ρ | $\phi = 5°$ | | $\phi = 10°$ | | $\phi = 15°$ | |
	U	V	U	V	U	V
0.0	0.0000	0.0000	0.0000	0.0000	0.0000	0.0000
0.5	-0.1200	-0.0206	-0.1149	-0.0407	-0.1066	-0.0597
1.0	-0.4497	-0.0727	-0.4335	-0.1441	-0.4068	-0.2126
1.5	-0.9275	-0.1401	-0.8996	-0.2782	-0.8532	-0.4124
2.0	-1.5009	-0.2133	-1.4619	-0.4241	-1.3973	-0.6300
2.5	-2.1365	-0.2887	-2.0869	-0.5743	-2.0047	-0.8538
3.0	-2.8144	-0.3649	-2.7544	-0.7261	-2.6550	-1.0801
3.5	-3.5225	-0.4416	-3.4522	-0.8789	-3.3356	-1.3078
4.0	-4.2535	-0.5187	-4.1727	-1.0325	-4.0389	-1.5366
4.5	-5.0025	-0.5962	-4.9112	-1.1868	-4.7599	-1.7665
5.0	-5.7660	-0.6740	-5.6642	-1.3417	-5.4954	-1.9972
5.5	-6.5417	-0.7521	-6.4292	-1.4973	-6.2428	-2.2290
6.0	-7.3277	-0.8305	-7.2045	-1.6535	-7.0004	-2.4616
6.5	-8.1226	-0.9092	-7.9887	-1.8102	-7.7669	-2.6951
7.0	-8.9254	-0.9881	-8.7808	-1.9675	-8.5410	-2.9293
7.5	-9.7352	-1.0674	-9.5797	-2.1253	-9.3221	-3.1643
8.0	-10.5512	-1.1468	-10.3849	-2.2835	-10.1093	-3.4000
8.5	-11.3728	-1.2264	-11.1957	-2.4421	-10.9021	-3.6364
9.0	-12.1996	-1.3063	-12.0116	-2.6012	-11.7000	-3.8733
9.5	-13.0311	-1.3863	-12.8322	-2.7606	-12.5025	-4.1109
10.0	-13.8669	-1.4666	-13.6570	-2.9204	-13.3093	-4.3489
10.5	-14.7067	-1.5470	-14.4859	-3.0805	-14.1200	-4.5875
11.0	-15.5502	-1.6275	-15.3185	-3.2410	-14.9345	-4.8265
11.5	-16.3971	-1.7082	-16.1545	-3.4017	-15.7523	-5.0659
12.0	-17.2473	-1.7890	-16.9937	-3.5626	-16.5734	-5.3057
12.5	-18.1005	-1.8699	-17.8360	-3.7239	-17.3974	-5.5460
13.0	-18.9566	-1.9510	-18.6810	-3.8854	-18.2243	-5.7866
13.5	-19.8153	-2.0322	-19.5288	-4.0471	-19.0538	-6.0275
14.0	-20.6766	-2.1135	-20.3791	-4.2090	-19.8859	-6.2688
14.5	-21.5403	-2.1949	-21.2318	-4.3711	-20.7203	-6.5103
15.0	-22.4062	-2.2763	-22.0867	-4.5334	-21.5570	-6.7522
15.5	-23.2743	-2.3579	-22.9438	-4.6960	-22.3958	-6.9943
16.0	-24.1445	-2.4396	-23.8029	-4.8586	-23.2366	-7.2367
16.5	-25.0166	-2.5214	-24.6640	-5.0215	-24.0794	-7.4794
17.0	-25.8906	-2.6032	-25.5270	-5.1845	-24.9241	-7.7223
17.5	-26.7664	-2.6851	-26.3917	-5.3477	-25.7705	-7.9654
18.0	-27.6439	-2.7671	-27.2582	-5.5110	-26.6187	-8.2088
18.5	-28.5231	-2.8491	-28.1263	-5.6745	-27.4684	-8.4523
19.0	-29.4038	-2.9313	-28.9959	-5.8381	-28.3198	-8.6961
19.5	-30.2860	-3.0135	-29.8671	-6.0018	-29.1726	-8.9400
20.0	-31.1697	-3.0957	-30.7397	-6.1656	-30.0269	-9.1842
20.5	-32.0548	-3.1780	-31.6137	-6.3296	-30.8825	-9.4285
21.0	-32.9412	-3.2604	-32.4891	-6.4937	-31.7395	-9.6730
21.5	-33.8289	-3.3428	-33.3657	-6.6579	-32.5978	-9.9177
22.0	-34.7179	-3.4253	-34.2436	-6.8222	-33.4573	-10.1626
22.5	-35.6081	-3.5079	-35.1228	-6.9867	-34.3181	-10.4076
23.0	-36.4995	-3.5904	-36.0031	-7.1512	-35.1800	-10.6527
23.5	-37.3920	-3.6731	-36.8845	-7.3158	-36.0430	-10.8980
24.0	-38.2856	-3.7558	-37.7670	-7.4805	-36.9072	-11.1434
24.5	-39.1803	-3.8385	-38.6506	-7.6453	-37.7723	-11.3890
25.0	-40.0760	-3.9213	-39.5352	-7.8102	-38.6385	-11.6347

TABLE I. $a_r(q) = U + iV,\ q = \rho e^{i\phi}$ $r = 0$

ρ	$\phi = 20°$		$\phi = 25°$		$\phi = 30°$	
	U	V	U	V	U	V
0.0	0.0000	0.0000	0.0000	0.0000	0.0000	0.0000
0.5	-0.0951	-0.0771	-0.0808	-0.0925	-0.0640	-0.1053
1.0	-0.3697	-0.2770	-0.3229	-0.3359	-0.2668	-0.3879
1.5	-0.7888	-0.5406	-0.7069	-0.6609	-0.6079	-0.7713
2.0	-1.3073	-0.8284	-1.1927	-1.0169	-1.0542	-1.1934
2.5	-1.8905	-1.1243	-1.7451	-1.3830	-1.5695	-1.6270
3.0	-2.5169	-1.4234	-2.3412	-1.7526	-2.1293	-2.0643
3.5	-3.1736	-1.7242	-2.9677	-2.1240	-2.7196	-2.5034
4.0	-3.8530	-2.0263	-3.6167	-2.4969	-3.3319	-2.9440
4.5	-4.5500	-2.3297	-4.2830	-2.8714	-3.9613	-3.3864
5.0	-5.2611	-2.6344	-4.9633	-3.2474	-4.6044	-3.8306
5.5	-5.9841	-2.9403	-5.6552	-3.6250	-5.2588	-4.2766
6.0	-6.7171	-3.2475	-6.3569	-4.0040	-5.9229	-4.7243
6.5	-7.4588	-3.5557	-7.0672	-4.3845	-6.5953	-5.1738
7.0	-8.2082	-3.8650	-7.7850	-4.7662	-7.2751	-5.6249
7.5	-8.9644	-4.1753	-8.5096	-5.1493	-7.9614	-6.0774
8.0	-9.7267	-4.4866	-9.2401	-5.5335	-8.6537	-6.5314
8.5	-10.4944	-4.7987	-9.9761	-5.9188	-9.3513	-6.9867
9.0	-11.2673	-5.1116	-10.7170	-6.3051	-10.0538	-7.4433
9.5	-12.0447	-5.4253	-11.4625	-6.6923	-10.7608	-7.9009
10.0	-12.8263	-5.7396	-12.2122	-7.0805	-11.4719	-8.3596
10.5	-13.6119	-6.0547	-12.9658	-7.4694	-12.1868	-8.8194
11.0	-14.4012	-6.3703	-13.7230	-7.8592	-12.9053	-9.2800
11.5	-15.1938	-6.6866	-14.4835	-8.2496	-13.6271	-9.7415
12.0	-15.9896	-7.0033	-15.2472	-8.6408	-14.3520	-10.2039
12.5	-16.7884	-7.3206	-16.0138	-9.0325	-15.0799	-10.6670
13.0	-17.5900	-7.6384	-16.7832	-9.4249	-15.8105	-11.1308
13.5	-18.3942	-7.9566	-17.5552	-9.8179	-16.5436	-11.5953
14.0	-19.2009	-8.2753	-18.3297	-10.2114	-17.2792	-12.0605
14.5	-20.0100	-8.5943	-19.1065	-10.6054	-18.0172	-12.5263
15.0	-20.8213	-8.9138	-19.8855	-10.9998	-18.7573	-12.9926
15.5	-21.6347	-9.2336	-20.6667	-11.3948	-19.4995	-13.4595
16.0	-22.4502	-9.5538	-21.4498	-11.7902	-20.2437	-13.9270
16.5	-23.2676	-9.8743	-22.2349	-12.1860	-20.9897	-14.3949
17.0	-24.0868	-10.1951	-23.0218	-12.5822	-21.7376	-14.8633
17.5	-24.9078	-10.5163	-23.8105	-12.9788	-22.4872	-15.3322
18.0	-25.7305	-10.8377	-24.6008	-13.3758	-23.2385	-15.8015
18.5	-26.5548	-11.1594	-25.3927	-13.7731	-23.9914	-16.2713
19.0	-27.3807	-11.4814	-26.1862	-14.1707	-24.7457	-16.7414
19.5	-28.2080	-11.8037	-26.9811	-14.5687	-25.5016	-17.2120
20.0	-29.0368	-12.1262	-27.7775	-14.9670	-26.2588	-17.6829
20.5	-29.8670	-12.4489	-28.5752	-15.3656	-27.0174	-18.1542
21.0	-30.6985	-12.7719	-29.3742	-15.7645	-27.7773	-18.6258
21.5	-31.5313	-13.0951	-30.1746	-16.1637	-28.5385	-19.0977
22.0	-32.3653	-13.4185	-30.9761	-16.5631	-29.3009	-19.5700
22.5	-33.2005	-13.7422	-31.7789	-16.9628	-30.0644	-20.0426
23.0	-34.0369	-14.0660	-32.5827	-17.3628	-30.8291	-20.5155
23.5	-34.8744	-14.3900	-33.3877	-17.7629	-31.5949	-20.9887
24.0	-35.7129	-14.7143	-34.1938	-18.1634	-32.3617	-21.4622
24.5	-36.5526	-15.0387	-35.0009	-18.5640	-33.1296	-21.9359
25.0	-37.3932	-15.3632	-35.8090	-18.9649	-33.8985	-22.4099

TABLE I. $a_r(q) = U + iV$, $q = \rho e^{i\phi}$ $\qquad\qquad r = 0$

ρ	$\phi = 35°$		$\phi = 40°$		$\phi = 45°$	
	U	V	U	V	U	V
0.0	0.0000	0.0000	0.0000	0.0000	0.0000	0.0000
0.5	−0.0452	−0.1152	−0.0248	−0.1218	−0.0034	−0.1248
1.0	−0.2023	−0.4315	−0.1301	−0.4655	−0.0514	−0.4885
1.5	−0.4925	−0.8699	−0.3615	−0.9549	−0.2156	−1.0241
2.0	−0.8927	−1.3555	−0.7091	−1.5012	−0.5044	−1.6286
2.5	−1.3650	−1.8539	−1.1331	−2.0612	−0.8753	−2.2468
3.0	−1.8829	−2.3556	−1.6038	−2.6235	−1.2944	−2.8656
3.5	−2.4311	−2.8587	−2.1048	−3.1867	−1.7434	−3.4842
4.0	−3.0011	−3.3634	−2.6270	−3.7512	−2.2129	−4.1035
4.5	−3.5877	−3.8699	−3.1653	−4.3175	−2.6977	−4.7248
5.0	−4.1876	−4.3785	−3.7163	−4.8860	−3.1947	−5.3484
5.5	−4.7984	−4.8891	−4.2779	−5.4569	−3.7017	−5.9746
6.0	−5.4186	−5.4018	−4.8485	−6.0302	−4.2173	−6.6036
6.5	−6.0470	−5.9165	−5.4269	−6.6057	−4.7404	−7.2351
7.0	−6.6825	−6.4331	−6.0124	−7.1835	−5.2702	−7.8692
7.5	−7.3245	−6.9514	−6.6040	−7.7633	−5.8061	−8.5056
8.0	−7.9722	−7.4714	−7.2013	−8.3450	−6.3474	−9.1442
8.5	−8.6252	−7.9930	−7.8037	−8.9285	−6.8937	−9.7848
9.0	−9.2829	−8.5160	−8.4108	−9.5137	−7.4446	−10.4273
9.5	−9.9451	−9.0403	−9.0223	−10.1004	−7.9997	−11.0716
10.0	−10.6113	−9.5659	−9.6377	−10.6885	−8.5588	−11.7175
10.5	−11.2814	−10.0926	−10.2568	−11.2780	−9.1214	−12.3649
11.0	−11.9549	−10.6205	−10.8793	−11.8687	−9.6875	−13.0137
11.5	−12.6316	−11.1493	−11.5051	−12.4606	−10.2567	−13.6638
12.0	−13.3115	−11.6791	−12.1339	−13.0536	−10.8288	−14.3151
12.5	−13.9942	−12.2098	−12.7655	−13.6476	−11.4037	−14.9676
13.0	−14.6796	−12.7414	−13.3998	−14.2425	−11.9813	−15.6212
13.5	−15.3676	−13.2737	−14.0366	−14.8384	−12.5613	−16.2758
14.0	−16.0580	−13.8068	−14.6758	−15.4351	−13.1437	−16.9314
14.5	−16.7507	−14.3406	−15.3172	−16.0327	−13.7283	−17.5879
15.0	−17.4455	−14.8751	−15.9607	−16.6310	−14.3149	−18.2452
15.5	−18.1424	−15.4102	−16.6063	−17.2301	−14.9036	−18.9034
16.0	−18.8412	−15.9459	−17.2538	−17.8298	−15.4942	−19.5624
16.5	−19.5420	−16.4823	−17.9032	−18.4302	−16.0866	−20.2221
17.0	−20.2445	−17.0192	−18.5543	−19.0313	−16.6807	−20.8825
17.5	−20.9487	−17.5566	−19.2071	−19.6330	−17.2764	−21.5436
18.0	−21.6545	−18.0945	−19.8615	−20.2352	−17.8738	−22.2053
18.5	−22.3619	−18.6329	−20.5175	−20.8380	−18.4726	−22.8677
19.0	−23.0709	−19.1718	−21.1749	−21.4413	−19.0730	−23.5306
19.5	−23.7812	−19.7112	−21.8337	−22.0452	−19.6747	−24.1942
20.0	−24.4930	−20.2510	−22.4940	−22.6495	−20.2777	−24.8583
20.5	−25.2061	−20.7912	−23.1555	−23.2544	−20.8821	−25.5229
21.0	−25.9204	−21.3318	−23.8183	−23.8597	−21.4877	−26.1881
21.5	−26.6360	−21.8728	−24.4823	−24.4654	−22.0945	−26.8537
22.0	−27.3529	−22.4141	−25.1476	−25.0715	−22.7025	−27.5198
22.5	−28.0708	−22.9559	−25.8139	−25.6781	−23.3116	−28.1864
23.0	−28.7899	−23.4979	−26.4814	−26.2851	−23.9218	−28.8534
23.5	−29.5101	−24.0404	−27.1499	−26.8924	−24.5330	−29.5209
24.0	−30.2313	−24.5831	−27.8195	−27.5002	−25.1453	−30.1888
24.5	−30.9536	−25.1262	−28.4900	−28.1082	−25.7585	−30.8570
25.0	−31.6768	−25.6696	−29.1616	−28.7167	−26.3727	−31.5257

TABLE I. $a_r(q) = U + iV$, $q = \rho e^{i\phi}$ $r = 0$

ρ	$\phi = 50°$		$\phi = 55°$		$\phi = 60°$	
	U	V	U	V	U	V
0.0	0.0000	0.0000	0.0000	0.0000	0.0000	0.0000
0.5	0.0184	-0.1241	0.0400	-0.1195	0.0606	-0.1112
1.0	0.0325	-0.4989	0.1201	-0.4953	0.2093	-0.4764
1.5	-0.0556	-1.0757	0.1180	-1.1076	0.3047	-1.1172
2.0	-0.2796	-1.7360	-0.0356	-1.8220	0.2269	-1.8856
2.5	-0.5934	-2.4089	-0.2894	-2.5461	0.0348	-2.6573
3.0	-0.9570	-3.0796	-0.5944	-3.2635	-0.2096	-3.4159
3.5	-1.3499	-3.7483	-0.9278	-3.9768	-0.4808	-4.1675
4.0	-1.7624	-4.4173	-1.2793	-4.6894	-0.7682	-4.9173
4.5	-2.1891	-5.0880	-1.6440	-5.4035	-1.0671	-5.6684
5.0	-2.6272	-5.7612	-2.0189	-6.1204	-1.3752	-6.4224
5.5	-3.0747	-6.4373	-2.4025	-6.8405	-1.6910	-7.1801
6.0	-3.5304	-7.1165	-2.7937	-7.5640	-2.0136	-7.9416
6.5	-3.9931	-7.7987	-3.1916	-8.2909	-2.3425	-8.7070
7.0	-4.4623	-8.4837	-3.5955	-9.0210	-2.6771	-9.4760
7.5	-4.9373	-9.1713	-4.0050	-9.7542	-3.0169	-10.2484
8.0	-5.4176	-9.8615	-4.4195	-10.4901	-3.3616	-11.0240
8.5	-5.9027	-10.5539	-4.8388	-11.2286	-3.7109	-11.8024
9.0	-6.3923	-11.2485	-5.2624	-11.9695	-4.0643	-12.5835
9.5	-6.8860	-11.9450	-5.6900	-12.7126	-4.4217	-13.3671
10.0	-7.3835	-12.6434	-6.1213	-13.4577	-4.7827	-14.1529
10.5	-7.8845	-13.3434	-6.5562	-14.2047	-5.1471	-14.9407
11.0	-8.3889	-14.0451	-6.9942	-14.9535	-5.5148	-15.7304
11.5	-8.8964	-14.7481	-7.4353	-15.7038	-5.8854	-16.5219
12.0	-9.4068	-15.4526	-7.8793	-16.4556	-6.2587	-17.3150
12.5	-9.9199	-16.1583	-8.3259	-17.2089	-6.6348	-18.1097
13.0	-10.4356	-16.8652	-8.7751	-17.9634	-7.0132	-18.9058
13.5	-10.9537	-17.5733	-9.2266	-18.7192	-7.3941	-19.7032
14.0	-11.4741	-18.2824	-9.6804	-19.4762	-7.7771	-20.5019
14.5	-11.9967	-18.9925	-10.1363	-20.2342	-8.1622	-21.3018
15.0	-12.5213	-19.7036	-10.5942	-20.9934	-8.5493	-22.1029
15.5	-13.0479	-20.4156	-11.0541	-21.7535	-8.9382	-22.9050
16.0	-13.5764	-21.1285	-11.5158	-22.5145	-9.3290	-23.7081
16.5	-14.1066	-21.8422	-11.9792	-23.2765	-9.7214	-24.5122
17.0	-14.6385	-22.5567	-12.4443	-24.0393	-10.1155	-25.3172
17.5	-15.1721	-23.2719	-12.9110	-24.8029	-10.5111	-26.1231
18.0	-15.7072	-23.9879	-13.3791	-25.5674	-10.9082	-26.9299
18.5	-16.2438	-24.7045	-13.8488	-26.3325	-11.3068	-27.7375
19.0	-16.7818	-25.4218	-14.3199	-27.0984	-11.7067	-28.5458
19.5	-17.3212	-26.1397	-14.7922	-27.8650	-12.1079	-29.3549
20.0	-17.8620	-26.8583	-15.2659	-28.6323	-12.5104	-30.1648
20.5	-18.4040	-27.5774	-15.7409	-29.4002	-12.9141	-30.9753
21.0	-18.9472	-28.2971	-16.2170	-30.1687	-13.3189	-31.7865
21.5	-19.4916	-29.0174	-16.6943	-30.9378	-13.7249	-32.5984
22.0	-20.0371	-29.7381	-17.1727	-31.7075	-14.1320	-33.4108
22.5	-20.5838	-30.4594	-17.6522	-32.4778	-14.5401	-34.2239
23.0	-21.1315	-31.1812	-18.1327	-33.2486	-14.9493	-35.0376
23.5	-21.6802	-31.9035	-18.6142	-34.0199	-15.3594	-35.8518
24.0	-22.2299	-32.6262	-19.0967	-34.7917	-15.7705	-36.6666
24.5	-22.7806	-33.3494	-19.5802	-35.5640	-16.1825	-37.4819
25.0	-23.3323	-34.0730	-20.0645	-36.3368	-16.5954	-38.2977

TABLE I. $a_r(q) = U + iV$, $q = \rho e^{i\phi}$ $r = 0$

ρ	$\phi = 65°$		$\phi = 70°$		$\phi = 75°$	
	U	V	U	V	U	V
0.0	0.0000	0.0000	0.0000	0.0000	0.0000	0.0000
0.5	0.0796	-0.0992	0.0962	-0.0839	0.1100	-0.0657
1.0	0.2976	-0.4405	0.3816	-0.3865	0.4570	-0.3135
1.5	0.5048	-1.1017	0.7195	-1.0573	0.9522	-0.9785
2.0	0.5074	-1.9262	0.8058	-1.9445	1.1222	-1.9423
2.5	0.3770	-2.7421	0.7346	-2.8007	1.1048	-2.8340
3.0	0.1941	-3.5359	0.6130	-3.6227	1.0431	-3.6764
3.5	-0.0129	-4.3189	0.4713	-4.4297	0.9672	-4.4992
4.0	-0.2337	-5.0988	0.3192	-5.2323	0.8849	-5.3163
4.5	-0.4639	-5.8799	0.1599	-6.0358	0.7985	-6.1343
5.0	-0.7019	-6.6641	-0.0051	-6.8428	0.7084	-6.9563
5.5	-0.9464	-7.4525	-0.1756	-7.6546	0.6145	-7.7838
6.0	-1.1970	-8.2452	-0.3511	-8.4715	0.5165	-8.6173
6.5	-1.4533	-9.0424	-0.5317	-9.2934	0.4143	-9.4566
7.0	-1.7149	-9.8437	-0.7171	-10.1200	0.3077	-10.3014
7.5	-1.9814	-10.6488	-0.9072	-10.9511	0.1966	-11.1513
8.0	-2.2526	-11.4575	-1.1018	-11.7861	0.0813	-12.0057
8.5	-2.5282	-12.2695	-1.3006	-12.6248	-0.0382	-12.8642
9.0	-2.8079	-13.0844	-1.5034	-13.4667	-0.1616	-13.7263
9.5	-3.0914	-13.9019	-1.7100	-14.3116	-0.2888	-14.5917
10.0	-3.3785	-14.7219	-1.9202	-15.1592	-0.4195	-15.4599
10.5	-3.6689	-15.5442	-2.1336	-16.0092	-0.5535	-16.3308
11.0	-3.9625	-16.3685	-2.3501	-16.8615	-0.6906	-17.2040
11.5	-4.2590	-17.1948	-2.5695	-17.7157	-0.8305	-18.0794
12.0	-4.5583	-18.0228	-2.7916	-18.5719	-0.9730	-18.9568
12.5	-4.8601	-18.8524	-3.0162	-19.4298	-1.1181	-19.8361
13.0	-5.1643	-19.6836	-3.2432	-20.2894	-1.2655	-20.7171
13.5	-5.4708	-20.5162	-3.4724	-21.1505	-1.4150	-21.5996
14.0	-5.7795	-21.3502	-3.7038	-22.0130	-1.5666	-22.4838
14.5	-6.0902	-22.1855	-3.9371	-22.8769	-1.7202	-23.3693
15.0	-6.4028	-23.0220	-4.1723	-23.7421	-1.8758	-24.2562
15.5	-6.7173	-23.8596	-4.4093	-24.6085	-2.0327	-25.1444
16.0	-7.0335	-24.6983	-4.6480	-25.4761	-2.1915	-26.0338
16.5	-7.3514	-25.5381	-4.8883	-26.3448	-2.3518	-26.9244
17.0	-7.6709	-26.3789	-5.1301	-27.2145	-2.5136	-27.8160
17.5	-7.9919	-27.2206	-5.3734	-28.0853	-2.6769	-28.7088
18.0	-8.3143	-28.0632	-5.6181	-28.9570	-2.8415	-29.6026
18.5	-8.6381	-28.9067	-5.8642	-29.8296	-3.0074	-30.4974
19.0	-8.9632	-29.7511	-6.1115	-30.7032	-3.1745	-31.3931
19.5	-9.2897	-30.5962	-6.3601	-31.5776	-3.3429	-32.2897
20.0	-9.6173	-31.4422	-6.6099	-32.4528	-3.5124	-33.1872
20.5	-9.9461	-32.2888	-6.8609	-33.3289	-3.6830	-34.0856
21.0	-10.2761	-33.1362	-7.1129	-34.2057	-3.8547	-34.9848
21.5	-10.6072	-33.9843	-7.3660	-35.0832	-4.0274	-35.8847
22.0	-10.9393	-34.8331	-7.6201	-35.9615	-4.2011	-36.7855
22.5	-11.2725	-35.6825	-7.8753	-36.8404	-4.3758	-37.6869
23.0	-11.6066	-36.5325	-8.1314	-37.7200	-4.5514	-38.5891
23.5	-11.9417	-37.3832	-8.3884	-38.6003	-4.7279	-39.4919
24.0	-12.2777	-38.2344	-8.6463	-39.4812	-4.9052	-40.3954
24.5	-12.6147	-39.0862	-8.9051	-40.3627	-5.0834	-41.2996
25.0	-12.9524	-39.9386	-9.1647	-41.2448	-5.2625	-42.2044

TABLE I. $a_r(q) = U + iV$, $q = \rho e^{i\phi}$ $r = 0$

ρ	$\phi=80°$		$\phi=85°$		$\phi=90°$	
	U	V	U	V	U	V
0.0	0.0000	0.0000	0.0000	0.0000	0.0000	0.0000
0.5	0.1202	−0.0451	0.1265	−0.0230	0.1286	0.0000
1.0	0.5181	−0.2223	0.5585	−0.1157	0.5727	0.0000
1.5	1.2122	−0.8554	1.5287	−0.6675	2.0925	−0.4170
2.0	1.4563	−1.9240	1.8055	−1.8964	2.1626	−1.8675
2.5	1.4839	−2.8435	1.8675	−2.8312	2.2503	−2.7988
3.0	1.4799	−3.6972	1.9186	−3.6858	2.3539	−3.6431
3.5	1.4695	−4.5271	1.9727	−4.5133	2.4712	−4.4583
4.0	1.4576	−5.3500	2.0314	−5.3331	2.5996	−5.2654
4.5	1.4453	−6.1740	2.0936	−6.1542	2.7363	−6.0743
5.0	1.4318	−7.0028	2.1577	−6.9810	2.8786	−6.8900
5.5	1.4163	−7.8381	2.2221	−7.8155	3.0237	−7.7150
6.0	1.3980	−8.6803	2.2851	−8.6585	3.1693	−8.5501
6.5	1.3762	−9.5295	2.3456	−9.5096	3.3135	−9.3953
7.0	1.3506	−10.3851	2.4026	−10.3684	3.4547	−10.2497
7.5	1.3208	−11.2465	2.4558	−11.2341	3.5922	−11.1122
8.0	1.2868	−12.1131	2.5047	−12.1058	3.7253	−11.9818
8.5	1.2487	−12.9843	2.5495	−12.9826	3.8539	−12.8573
9.0	1.2065	−13.8596	2.5901	−13.8640	3.9780	−13.7378
9.5	1.1607	−14.7383	2.6268	−14.7491	4.0980	−14.6225
10.0	1.1112	−15.6203	2.6598	−15.6377	4.2141	−15.5107
10.5	1.0585	−16.5049	2.6895	−16.5291	4.3265	−16.4019
11.0	1.0027	−17.3922	2.7160	−17.4232	4.4357	−17.2958
11.5	0.9440	−18.2816	2.7396	−18.3196	4.5420	−18.1920
12.0	0.8827	−19.1732	2.7606	−19.2182	4.6456	−19.0903
12.5	0.8190	−20.0667	2.7792	−20.1186	4.7468	−19.9905
13.0	0.7529	−20.9620	2.7955	−21.0209	4.8458	−20.8925
13.5	0.6847	−21.8589	2.8098	−21.9250	4.9428	−21.7962
14.0	0.6145	−22.7574	2.8221	−22.8306	5.0380	−22.7015
14.5	0.5425	−23.6574	2.8326	−23.7377	5.1314	−23.6084
15.0	0.4686	−24.5588	2.8413	−24.6463	5.2232	−24.5167
15.5	0.3931	−25.4616	2.8485	−25.5563	5.3135	−25.4265
16.0	0.3160	−26.3656	2.8542	−26.4676	5.4024	−26.3376
16.5	0.2374	−27.2709	2.8585	−27.3802	5.4899	−27.2500
17.0	0.1574	−28.1773	2.8613	−28.2940	5.5761	−28.1637
17.5	0.0760	−29.0849	2.8629	−29.2089	5.6612	−29.0786
18.0	−0.0067	−29.9935	2.8632	−30.1251	5.7450	−29.9947
18.5	−0.0907	−30.9032	2.8624	−31.0422	5.8277	−30.9120
19.0	−0.1758	−31.8138	2.8603	−31.9605	5.9094	−31.8303
19.5	−0.2621	−32.7255	2.8572	−32.8797	5.9899	−32.7498
20.0	−0.3496	−33.6380	2.8530	−33.8000	6.0695	−33.6702
20.5	−0.4380	−34.5515	2.8478	−34.7212	6.1481	−34.5916
21.0	−0.5276	−35.4658	2.8417	−35.6432	6.2258	−35.5140
21.5	−0.6181	−36.3809	2.8345	−36.5662	6.3025	−36.4374
22.0	−0.7095	−37.2969	2.8264	−37.4900	6.3784	−37.3616
22.5	−0.8019	−38.2136	2.8175	−38.4146	6.4534	−38.2866
23.0	−0.8952	−39.1311	2.8077	−39.3400	6.5276	−39.2125
23.5	−0.9894	−40.0493	2.7970	−40.2662	6.6010	−40.1393
24.0	−1.0844	−40.9682	2.7856	−41.1931	6.6736	−41.0667
24.5	−1.1802	−41.8878	2.7733	−42.1208	6.7455	−41.9950
25.0	−1.2768	−42.8080	2.7603	−43.0491	6.8166	−42.9240

ρ	$\phi = 5°$		$\phi = 10°$		$\phi = 15°$	
	U	V	U	V	U	V
0.0	1.0000	0.0000	1.0000	0.0000	1.0000	0.0000
0.5	1.4654	0.0376	1.4613	0.0751	1.4545	0.1124
1.0	1.8577	0.0614	1.8536	0.1230	1.8464	0.1851
1.5	2.1662	0.0685	2.1667	0.1384	2.1670	0.2106
2.0	2.3826	0.0580	2.3925	0.1187	2.4081	0.1847
2.5	2.5035	0.0308	2.5261	0.0655	2.5630	0.1083
3.0	2.5313	−0.0104	2.5680	−0.0159	2.6285	−0.0115
3.5	2.4731	−0.0616	2.5234	−0.1180	2.6071	−0.1635
4.0	2.3390	−0.1194	2.4018	−0.2333	2.5064	−0.3362
4.5	2.1399	−0.1809	2.2138	−0.3563	2.3369	−0.5206
5.0	1.8862	−0.2445	1.9702	−0.4833	2.1099	−0.7109
5.5	1.5867	−0.3091	1.6801	−0.6123	1.8353	−0.9037
6.0	1.2485	−0.3743	1.3510	−0.7422	1.5211	−1.0978
6.5	0.8776	−0.4398	0.9891	−0.8728	1.1738	−1.2923
7.0	0.4786	−0.5055	0.5990	−1.0037	0.7985	−1.4873
7.5	0.0552	−0.5715	0.1846	−1.1350	0.3990	−1.6828
8.0	−0.3896	−0.6377	−0.2510	−1.2668	−0.0216	−1.8788
8.5	−0.8534	−0.7041	−0.7055	−1.3991	−0.4608	−2.0756
9.0	−1.3341	−0.7709	−1.1769	−1.5319	−0.9166	−2.2732
9.5	−1.8302	−0.8379	−1.6635	−1.6653	−1.3875	−2.4716
10.0	−2.3402	−0.9053	−2.1639	−1.7993	−1.8720	−2.6710
10.5	−2.8629	−0.9730	−2.6769	−1.9340	−2.3689	−2.8713
11.0	−3.3974	−1.0410	−3.2016	−2.0693	−2.8774	−3.0726
11.5	−3.9427	−1.1093	−3.7370	−2.2053	−3.3965	−3.2749
12.0	−4.4980	−1.1779	−4.2825	−2.3419	−3.9255	−3.4781
12.5	−5.0628	−1.2468	−4.8373	−2.4791	−4.4638	−3.6823
13.0	−5.6364	−1.3161	−5.4008	−2.6169	−5.0107	−3.8874
13.5	−6.2183	−1.3856	−5.9726	−2.7553	−5.5657	−4.0933
14.0	−6.8079	−1.4554	−6.5521	−2.8943	−6.1285	−4.3002
14.5	−7.4049	−1.5255	−7.1389	−3.0338	−6.6984	−4.5078
15.0	−8.0088	−1.5958	−7.7327	−3.1738	−7.2753	−4.7163
15.5	−8.6193	−1.6664	−8.3330	−3.3144	−7.8586	−4.9255
16.0	−9.2361	−1.7373	−8.9395	−3.4554	−8.4482	−5.1354
16.5	−9.8589	−1.8084	−9.5520	−3.5969	−9.0437	−5.3461
17.0	−10.4873	−1.8797	−10.1702	−3.7389	−9.6447	−5.5575
17.5	−11.1212	−1.9512	−10.7937	−3.8813	−10.2512	−5.7695
18.0	−11.7603	−2.0229	−11.4225	−4.0242	−10.8628	−5.9822
18.5	−12.4044	−2.0949	−12.0562	−4.1674	−11.4794	−6.1955
19.0	−13.0532	−2.1670	−12.6947	−4.3111	−12.1006	−6.4093
19.5	−13.7066	−2.2394	−13.3377	−4.4551	−12.7265	−6.6238
20.0	−14.3645	−2.3119	−13.9852	−4.5995	−13.3567	−6.8388
20.5	−15.0266	−2.3846	−14.6368	−4.7442	−13.9910	−7.0543
21.0	−15.6927	−2.4574	−15.2925	−4.8893	−14.6295	−7.2704
21.5	−16.3628	−2.5305	−15.9522	−5.0348	−15.2718	−7.4869
22.0	−17.0367	−2.6037	−16.6156	−5.1805	−15.9179	−7.7039
22.5	−17.7143	−2.6770	−17.2827	−5.3266	−16.5677	−7.9214
23.0	−18.3954	−2.7505	−17.9534	−5.4729	−17.2209	−8.1393
23.5	−19.0799	−2.8241	−18.6274	−5.6195	−17.8776	−8.3577
24.0	−19.7678	−2.8979	−19.3048	−5.7665	−18.5376	−8.5765
24.5	−20.4589	−2.9718	−19.9854	−5.9137	−19.2007	−8.7957
25.0	−21.1531	−3.0459	−20.6690	−6.0611	−19.8669	−9.0153

TABLE I. $a_r(q) = U + iV$, $q = \rho e^{i\phi}$ $\qquad\qquad r = 1$

ρ	$\phi=20°$		$\phi=25°$		$\phi=30°$	
	U	V	U	V	U	V
0.0	1.0000	0.0000	1.0000	0.0000	1.0000	0.0000
0.5	1.4449	0.1492	1.4326	0.1855	1.4174	0.2210
1.0	1.8359	0.2479	1.8218	0.3114	1.8035	0.3757
1.5	2.1663	0.2864	2.1635	0.3667	2.1571	0.4520
2.0	2.4281	0.2584	2.4508	0.3422	2.4734	0.4383
2.5	2.6126	0.1632	2.6730	0.2344	2.7411	0.3263
3.0	2.7120	0.0081	2.8171	0.0486	2.9418	0.1164
3.5	2.7239	-0.1926	2.8734	-0.1991	3.0556	-0.1763
4.0	2.6529	-0.4227	2.8415	-0.4869	3.0733	-0.5232
4.5	2.5092	-0.6687	2.7309	-0.7953	3.0026	-0.8958
5.0	2.3050	-0.9220	2.5552	-1.1118	2.8602	-1.2761
5.5	2.0515	-1.1781	2.3277	-1.4303	2.6626	-1.6562
6.0	1.7576	-1.4350	2.0589	-1.7486	2.4227	-2.0339
6.5	1.4304	-1.6921	1.7566	-2.0663	2.1495	-2.4095
7.0	1.0753	-1.9495	1.4267	-2.3836	1.8494	-2.7837
7.5	0.6963	-2.2072	1.0734	-2.7011	1.5266	-3.1577
8.0	0.2965	-2.4656	0.6999	-3.0192	1.1844	-3.5321
8.5	-0.1216	-2.7249	0.3086	-3.3382	0.8252	-3.9075
9.0	-0.5559	-2.9852	-0.0985	-3.6585	0.4508	-4.2844
9.5	-1.0050	-3.2466	-0.5199	-3.9803	0.0627	-4.6630
10.0	-1.4674	-3.5093	-0.9543	-4.3036	-0.3379	-5.0436
10.5	-1.9421	-3.7733	-1.4006	-4.6286	-0.7500	-5.4262
11.0	-2.4280	-4.0386	-1.8579	-4.9552	-1.1728	-5.8109
11.5	-2.9245	-4.3052	-2.3255	-5.2835	-1.6055	-6.1976
12.0	-3.4306	-4.5731	-2.8025	-5.6135	-2.0474	-6.5863
12.5	-3.9459	-4.8422	-3.2885	-5.9450	-2.4981	-6.9771
13.0	-4.4697	-5.1126	-3.7829	-6.2781	-2.9570	-7.3697
13.5	-5.0015	-5.3842	-4.2852	-6.6127	-3.4236	-7.7642
14.0	-5.5409	-5.6570	-4.7949	-6.9488	-3.8975	-8.1605
14.5	-6.0875	-5.9308	-5.3117	-7.2864	-4.3783	-8.5586
15.0	-6.6409	-6.2057	-5.8352	-7.6252	-4.8658	-8.9583
15.5	-7.2007	-6.4817	-6.3651	-7.9654	-5.3595	-9.3595
16.0	-7.7666	-6.7587	-6.9010	-8.3069	-5.8591	-9.7623
16.5	-8.3384	-7.0366	-7.4427	-8.6495	-6.3645	-10.1666
17.0	-8.9158	-7.3154	-7.9899	-8.9933	-6.8753	-10.5723
17.5	-9.4985	-7.5952	-8.5423	-9.3383	-7.3913	-10.9793
18.0	-10.0863	-7.8758	-9.0998	-9.6843	-7.9123	-11.3876
18.5	-10.6790	-8.1572	-9.6622	-10.0313	-8.4380	-11.7972
19.0	-11.2764	-8.4394	-10.2292	-10.3793	-8.9684	-12.2080
19.5	-11.8783	-8.7224	-10.8007	-10.7283	-9.5032	-12.6199
20.0	-12.4845	-9.0061	-11.3764	-11.0782	-10.0422	-13.0329
20.5	-13.0949	-9.2905	-11.9563	-11.4290	-10.5853	-13.4470
21.0	-13.7093	-9.5756	-12.5402	-11.7807	-11.1323	-13.8621
21.5	-14.3276	-9.8613	-13.1279	-12.1331	-11.6831	-14.2782
22.0	-14.9497	-10.1477	-13.7193	-12.4864	-12.2376	-14.6953
22.5	-15.5753	-10.4348	-14.3143	-12.8405	-12.7956	-15.1133
23.0	-16.2044	-10.7224	-14.9127	-13.1953	-13.3571	-15.5322
23.5	-16.8370	-11.0106	-15.5145	-13.5508	-13.9218	-15.9519
24.0	-17.4727	-11.2994	-16.1196	-13.9071	-14.4898	-16.3726
24.5	-18.1117	-11.5887	-16.7277	-14.2640	-15.0609	-16.7940
25.0	-18.7537	-11.8785	-17.3390	-14.6216	-15.6349	-17.2162

-9-

TABLE I. $a_r(q) = U+iV$, $q=\rho e^{i\phi}$ $r=1$

ρ	$\phi=35°$ U	$\phi=35°$ V	$\phi=40°$ U	$\phi=40°$ V	$\phi=45°$ U	$\phi=45°$ V
0.0	1.0000	0.0000	1.0000	0.0000	1.0000	0.0000
0.5	1.3994	0.2555	1.3786	0.2889	1.3550	0.3209
1.0	1.7806	0.4406	1.7524	0.5058	1.7186	0.5708
1.5	2.1456	0.5427	2.1270	0.6388	2.0996	0.7395
2.0	2.4928	0.5483	2.5051	0.6732	2.5058	0.8129
2.5	2.8128	0.4433	2.8821	0.5896	2.9408	0.7682
3.0	3.0832	0.2190	3.2365	0.3656	3.3932	0.5679
3.5	3.2707	−0.1156	3.5199	−0.0061	3.8057	0.1694
4.0	3.3506	−0.5251	3.6783	−0.4860	4.0677	−0.3988
4.5	3.3263	−0.9663	3.7053	−1.0046	4.1460	−1.0121
5.0	3.2201	−1.4121	3.6352	−1.5190	4.1055	−1.5993
5.5	3.0547	−1.8529	3.5017	−2.0191	4.0000	−2.1556
6.0	2.8463	−2.2875	3.3258	−2.5067	3.8556	−2.6908
6.5	2.6054	−2.7173	3.1193	−2.9863	3.6848	−3.2137
7.0	2.3388	−3.1446	2.8893	−3.4614	3.4940	−3.7303
7.5	2.0508	−3.5708	2.6400	−3.9347	3.2867	−4.2445
8.0	1.7446	−3.9972	2.3742	−4.4082	3.0652	−4.7588
8.5	1.4225	−4.4248	2.0937	−4.8829	2.8309	−5.2747
9.0	1.0860	−4.8541	1.8002	−5.3597	2.5849	−5.7933
9.5	0.7366	−5.2856	1.4945	−5.8391	2.3280	−6.3152
10.0	0.3753	−5.7194	1.1778	−6.3214	2.0609	−6.8406
10.5	0.0030	−6.1556	0.8507	−6.8066	1.7840	−7.3696
11.0	−0.3795	−6.5944	0.5138	−7.2949	1.4980	−7.9024
11.5	−0.7716	−7.0356	0.1678	−7.7863	1.2033	−8.4388
12.0	−1.1727	−7.4793	−0.1868	−8.2805	0.9003	−8.9786
12.5	−1.5822	−7.9254	−0.5497	−8.7776	0.5894	−9.5219
13.0	−1.9997	−8.3738	−0.9202	−9.2775	0.2711	−10.0684
13.5	−2.4247	−8.8245	−1.2982	−9.7800	−0.0545	−10.6180
14.0	−2.8570	−9.2773	−1.6831	−10.2850	−0.3868	−11.1705
14.5	−3.2960	−9.7321	−2.0746	−10.7925	−0.7257	−11.7258
15.0	−3.7414	−10.1889	−2.4725	−11.3022	−1.0708	−12.2838
15.5	−4.1930	−10.6476	−2.8765	−11.8141	−1.4218	−12.8443
16.0	−4.6505	−11.1081	−3.2862	−12.3281	−1.7784	−13.4071
16.5	−5.1136	−11.5704	−3.7014	−12.8441	−2.1405	−13.9722
17.0	−5.5821	−12.0343	−4.1219	−13.3620	−2.5078	−14.5395
17.5	−6.0557	−12.4997	−4.5474	−13.8818	−2.8801	−15.1089
18.0	−6.5342	−12.9667	−4.9778	−14.4033	−3.2571	−15.6802
18.5	−7.0174	−13.4351	−5.4129	−14.9264	−3.6388	−16.2534
19.0	−7.5051	−13.9050	−5.8524	−15.4512	−4.0248	−16.8284
19.5	−7.9972	−14.3762	−6.2961	−15.9775	−4.4150	−17.4052
20.0	−8.4935	−14.8487	−6.7440	−16.5052	−4.8093	−17.9836
20.5	−8.9938	−15.3224	−7.1959	−17.0344	−5.2075	−18.5636
21.0	−9.4980	−15.7973	−7.6516	−17.5650	−5.6095	−19.1452
21.5	−10.0059	−16.2734	−8.1110	−18.0969	−6.0151	−19.7282
22.0	−10.5175	−16.7506	−8.5740	−18.6301	−6.4242	−20.3126
22.5	−11.0325	−17.2289	−9.0404	−19.1645	−6.8367	−20.8985
23.0	−11.5510	−17.7083	−9.5102	−19.7001	−7.2525	−21.4856
23.5	−12.0727	−18.1886	−9.9832	−20.2368	−7.6715	−22.0741
24.0	−12.5975	−18.6699	−10.4592	−20.7747	−8.0935	−22.6638
24.5	−13.1255	−19.1522	−10.9383	−21.3136	−8.5185	−23.2547
25.0	−13.6564	−19.6354	−11.4204	−21.8536	−8.9464	−23.8468

TABLE I. $a_r(q) = U + iV$, $q = \rho e^{i\phi}$ $\qquad\qquad r = 1$

| ρ | $\phi = 50°$ | | $\phi = 55°$ | | $\phi = 60°$ | |
	U	V	U	V	U	V
0.0	1.0000	0.0000	1.0000	0.0000	1.0000	0.0000
0.5	1.3285	0.3513	1.2994	0.3797	1.2676	0.4060
1.0	1.6786	0.6350	1.6320	0.6977	1.5787	0.7581
1.5	2.0615	0.8438	2.0111	0.9501	1.9472	1.0564
2.0	2.4901	0.9661	2.4533	1.1300	2.3915	1.2999
2.5	2.9783	0.9802	2.9821	1.2224	2.9405	1.4854
3.0	3.5372	0.8393	3.6381	1.1891	3.6521	1.6046
3.5	4.1316	0.4428	4.4884	0.8888	4.7096	1.6428
4.0	4.5446	-0.2573	5.1777	-0.0750	6.4276	2.6725
4.5	4.6577	-0.9993	5.2455	-0.9955	6.9998	3.8670
5.0	4.6291	-1.6607	5.1969	-1.7166	7.4892	4.7847
5.5	4.5435	-2.2659	5.1213	-2.3548	7.9691	5.5960
6.0	4.4283	-2.8399	5.0329	-2.9548	8.4541	6.3502
6.5	4.2937	-3.3977	4.9353	-3.5364	8.9496	7.0696
7.0	4.1442	-3.9478	4.8296	-4.1103	9.4578	7.7671
7.5	3.9822	-4.4953	4.7161	-4.6824	9.9801	8.4511
8.0	3.8088	-5.0433	4.5947	-5.2561	10.5165	9.1280
8.5	3.6249	-5.5937	4.4653	-5.8334	11.0667	9.8028
9.0	3.4310	-6.1477	4.3278	-6.4155	11.6297	10.4795
9.5	3.2275	-6.7058	4.1823	-7.0030	12.2040	11.1614
10.0	3.0147	-7.2683	4.0287	-7.5962	12.7875	11.8512
10.5	2.7931	-7.8354	3.8670	-8.1950	13.3776	12.5506
11.0	2.5629	-8.4069	3.6973	-8.7993	13.9718	13.2608
11.5	2.3244	-8.9829	3.5199	-9.4088	14.5675	13.9816
12.0	2.0781	-9.5630	3.3349	-10.0234	15.1623	14.7127
12.5	1.8241	-10.1471	3.1425	-10.6427	15.7545	15.4527
13.0	1.5629	-10.7350	2.9430	-11.2665	16.3427	16.2002
13.5	1.2947	-11.3265	2.7367	-11.8943	16.9264	16.9536
14.0	1.0198	-11.9214	2.5238	-12.5261	17.5052	17.7116
14.5	0.7385	-12.5194	2.3046	-13.1614	18.0794	18.4727
15.0	0.4511	-13.1205	2.0793	-13.8002	18.6493	19.2361
15.5	0.1579	-13.7244	1.8483	-14.4421	19.2155	20.0009
16.0	-0.1409	-14.3311	1.6117	-15.0871	19.7785	20.7665
16.5	-0.4451	-14.9402	1.3699	-15.7348	20.3388	21.5327
17.0	-0.7543	-15.5518	1.1229	-16.3853	20.8970	22.2992
17.5	-1.0685	-16.1657	0.8712	-17.0383	21.4536	23.0658
18.0	-1.3874	-16.7818	0.6148	-17.6936	22.0089	23.8327
18.5	-1.7108	-17.4000	0.3539	-18.3513	22.5632	24.5997
19.0	-2.0385	-18.0201	0.0888	-19.0112	23.1169	25.3672
19.5	-2.3704	-18.6422	-0.1804	-19.6731	23.6701	26.1350
20.0	-2.7063	-19.2662	-0.4536	-20.3371	24.2229	26.9033
20.5	-3.0460	-19.8919	-0.7305	-21.0029	24.7755	27.6723
21.0	-3.3894	-20.5193	-1.0111	-21.6707	25.3279	28.4421
21.5	-3.7365	-21.1483	-1.2952	-22.3402	25.8802	29.2127
22.0	-4.0869	-21.7789	-1.5826	-23.0114	26.4323	29.9842
22.5	-4.4407	-22.4111	-1.8734	-23.6843	26.9843	30.7567
23.0	-4.7977	-23.0447	-2.1673	-24.3588	27.5361	31.5303
23.5	-5.1578	-23.6797	-2.4642	-25.0348	28.0877	32.3049
24.0	-5.5210	-24.3161	-2.7641	-25.7123	28.6390	33.0806
24.5	-5.8870	-24.9539	-3.0669	-26.3913	29.1901	33.8574
25.0	-6.2559	-25.5929	-3.3724	-27.0717	29.7408	34.6352

TABLE I. $a_r(q) = U + iV$, $q = \rho e^{i\phi}$ $r = 1$

ρ	$\phi = 65°$		$\phi = 70°$		$\phi = 75°$	
	U	V	U	V	U	V
0.0	1.0000	0.0000	1.0000	0.0000	1.0000	0.0000
0.5	1.2333	0.4298	1.1966	0.4508	1.1578	0.4688
1.0	1.5185	0.8151	1.4515	0.8678	1.3781	0.9152
1.5	1.8690	1.1602	1.7763	1.2589	1.6695	1.3500
2.0	2.3024	1.4703	2.1856	1.6350	2.0422	1.7881
2.5	2.8463	1.7548	2.6996	2.0150	2.5064	2.2529
3.0	3.5500	2.0387	3.3437	2.4401	3.0647	2.7848
3.5	4.5031	2.4295	4.1187	3.0054	3.6854	3.4405
4.0	5.5503	3.2722	4.8850	3.8076	4.2794	4.2386
4.5	6.2224	4.2908	5.4858	4.7217	4.7822	5.1107
5.0	6.7345	5.2065	5.9712	5.6163	5.2085	5.9900
5.5	7.2026	6.0487	6.4064	6.4733	5.5916	6.8544
6.0	7.6595	6.8462	6.8219	7.3010	5.9530	7.7029
6.5	8.1168	7.6157	7.2310	8.1089	6.3043	8.5391
7.0	8.5798	8.3677	7.6400	8.9042	6.6518	9.3672
7.5	9.0507	9.1094	8.0520	9.6921	6.9986	10.1907
8.0	9.5303	9.8460	8.4682	10.4766	7.3462	11.0124
8.5	10.0183	10.5816	8.8888	11.2607	7.6953	11.8343
9.0	10.5142	11.3190	9.3136	12.0467	8.0459	12.6579
9.5	11.0167	12.0608	9.7418	12.8361	8.3976	13.4845
10.0	11.5243	12.8084	10.1725	13.6300	8.7501	14.3146
10.5	12.0355	13.5630	10.6048	14.4290	9.1028	15.1487
11.0	12.5486	14.3249	11.0377	15.2333	9.4552	15.9869
11.5	13.0621	15.0941	11.4703	16.0429	9.8068	16.8291
12.0	13.5748	15.8702	11.9020	16.8576	10.1572	17.6753
12.5	14.0857	16.6525	12.3322	17.6768	10.5061	18.5250
13.0	14.5941	17.4402	12.7605	18.5002	10.8534	19.3782
13.5	15.0996	18.2324	13.1867	19.3273	11.1989	20.2343
14.0	15.6020	19.0284	13.6106	20.1574	11.5426	21.0931
14.5	16.1014	19.8274	14.0323	20.9903	11.8844	21.9544
15.0	16.5979	20.6287	14.4519	21.8255	12.2245	22.8178
15.5	17.0918	21.4320	14.8695	22.6626	12.5628	23.6832
16.0	17.5834	22.2367	15.2851	23.5015	12.8994	24.5503
16.5	18.0728	23.0427	15.6991	24.3419	13.2346	25.4189
17.0	18.5605	23.8496	16.1115	25.1836	13.5683	26.2891
17.5	19.0466	24.6575	16.5224	26.0265	13.9007	27.1605
18.0	19.5315	25.4662	16.9321	26.8706	14.2318	28.0333
18.5	20.0153	26.2757	17.3407	27.7157	14.5619	28.9071
19.0	20.4981	27.0860	17.7483	28.5618	14.8908	29.7822
19.5	20.9801	27.8970	18.1549	29.4090	15.2188	30.6583
20.0	21.4615	28.7089	18.5607	30.2570	15.5458	31.5354
20.5	21.9422	29.5216	18.9657	31.1061	15.8720	32.4135
21.0	22.4225	30.3351	19.3700	31.9560	16.1973	33.2926
21.5	22.9022	31.1496	19.7736	32.8070	16.5219	34.1727
22.0	23.3815	31.9650	20.1766	33.6588	16.8457	35.0537
22.5	23.8603	32.7813	20.5790	34.5115	17.1689	35.9356
23.0	24.3387	33.5985	20.9808	35.3652	17.4913	36.8184
23.5	24.8167	34.4167	21.3820	36.2197	17.8131	37.7020
24.0	25.2943	35.2358	21.7827	37.0751	18.1342	38.5865
24.5	25.7714	36.0559	22.1828	37.9314	18.4548	39.4719
25.0	26.2480	36.8769	22.5824	38.7886	18.7747	40.3580

TABLE I. $a_r(q) = U + iV$, $q = \rho e^{i\phi}$ $\qquad\qquad r=1$

ρ	$\phi=80°$		$\phi=85°$		$\phi=90°$	
	U	V	U	V	U	V
0.0	1.0000	0.0000	1.0000	0.0000	1.0000	0.0000
0.5	1.1171	0.4834	1.0748	0.4946	1.0312	0.5020
1.0	1.2986	0.9563	1.2137	0.9901	1.1243	1.0159
1.5	1.5497	1.4311	1.4183	1.5000	1.2770	1.5549
2.0	1.8750	1.9245	1.6876	2.0405	1.4838	2.1334
2.5	2.2752	2.4600	2.0149	2.6318	1.7332	2.7663
3.0	2.7386	3.0687	2.3820	3.2942	2.0057	3.4648
3.5	3.2286	3.7779	2.7570	4.0372	2.2760	4.2286
4.0	3.6910	4.5818	3.1068	4.8482	2.5235	5.0442
4.5	4.0952	5.4386	3.4157	5.6994	2.7401	5.8918
5.0	4.4473	6.3102	3.6870	6.5670	2.9281	6.7555
5.5	4.7648	7.1792	3.9308	7.4383	3.0938	7.6259
6.0	5.0620	8.0414	4.1565	8.3086	3.2435	8.4988
6.5	5.3477	8.8975	4.3708	9.1770	3.3822	9.3726
7.0	5.6273	9.7492	4.5777	10.0440	3.5130	10.2471
7.5	5.9038	10.5986	4.7800	10.9106	3.6384	11.1226
8.0	6.1788	11.4476	4.9792	11.7777	3.7596	11.9995
8.5	6.4531	12.2974	5.1761	12.6463	3.8775	12.8783
9.0	6.7269	13.1490	5.3714	13.5168	3.9928	13.7593
9.5	7.0004	14.0032	5.5651	14.3898	4.1058	14.6426
10.0	7.2733	14.8604	5.7573	15.2655	4.2166	15.5284
10.5	7.5454	15.7209	5.9480	16.1439	4.3253	16.4168
11.0	7.8166	16.5846	6.1371	17.0253	4.4321	17.3077
11.5	8.0864	17.4517	6.3247	17.9094	4.5369	18.2011
12.0	8.3549	18.3220	6.5106	18.7962	4.6399	19.0969
12.5	8.6219	19.1953	6.6948	19.6857	4.7410	19.9950
13.0	8.8871	20.0714	6.8773	20.5775	4.8402	20.8952
13.5	9.1507	20.9500	7.0580	21.4717	4.9377	21.7976
14.0	9.4126	21.8311	7.2371	22.3680	5.0335	22.7018
14.5	9.6729	22.7143	7.4146	23.2663	5.1276	23.6079
15.0	9.9314	23.5995	7.5905	24.1664	5.2201	24.5157
15.5	10.1884	24.4866	7.7648	25.0682	5.3110	25.4251
16.0	10.4439	25.3754	7.9377	25.9717	5.4005	26.3361
16.5	10.6980	26.2657	8.1091	26.8767	5.4885	27.2485
17.0	10.9507	27.1575	8.2792	27.7831	5.5752	28.1622
17.5	11.2021	28.0507	8.4480	28.6908	5.6606	29.0772
18.0	11.4522	28.9451	8.6156	29.5998	5.7447	29.9934
18.5	11.7013	29.8407	8.7820	30.5100	5.8277	30.9108
19.0	11.9492	30.7375	8.9473	31.4213	5.9095	31.8294
19.5	12.1961	31.6354	9.1116	32.3337	5.9902	32.7489
20.0	12.4420	32.5344	9.2748	33.2472	6.0698	33.6695
20.5	12.6870	33.4344	9.4371	34.1617	6.1485	34.5911
21.0	12.9312	34.3353	9.5984	35.0771	6.2262	35.5136
21.5	13.1745	35.2372	9.7589	35.9935	6.3029	36.4371
22.0	13.4169	36.1401	9.9184	36.9108	6.3788	37.3614
22.5	13.6586	37.0438	10.0772	37.8290	6.4538	38.2865
23.0	13.8996	37.9484	10.2352	38.7480	6.5279	39.2125
23.5	14.1398	38.8538	10.3924	39.6678	6.6013	40.1392
24.0	14.3794	39.7601	10.5489	40.5884	6.6739	41.0668
24.5	14.6182	40.6672	10.7046	41.5099	6.7457	41.9950
25.0	14.8565	41.5750	10.8597	42.4320	6.8168	42.9240

TABLE I. $a_r(q) = U + iV$, $q = \rho e^{i\phi}$ $\qquad\qquad r = 2$

ρ	$\phi = 5°$		$\phi = 10°$		$\phi = 15°$	
	U	V	U	V	U	V
0.0	4.0000	0.0000	4.0000	0.0000	4.0000	0.0000
0.5	4.0995	0.0170	4.0953	0.0336	4.0885	0.0493
1.0	4.3672	0.0581	4.3548	0.1152	4.3344	0.1705
1.5	4.7404	0.1067	4.7214	0.2125	4.6896	0.3164
2.0	5.1652	0.1527	5.1426	0.3051	5.1045	0.4564
2.5	5.6055	0.1917	5.5826	0.3839	5.5438	0.5768
3.0	6.0387	0.2216	6.0190	0.4448	5.9848	0.6714
3.5	6.4499	0.2409	6.4368	0.4853	6.4130	0.7364
4.0	6.8284	0.2490	6.8254	0.5035	6.8179	0.7690
4.5	7.1663	0.2454	7.1769	0.4985	7.1914	0.7673
5.0	7.4583	0.2301	7.4849	0.4702	7.5264	0.7304
5.5	7.7004	0.2040	7.7449	0.4197	7.8166	0.6590
6.0	7.8911	0.1683	7.9537	0.3491	8.0571	0.5558
6.5	8.0300	0.1245	8.1104	0.2618	8.2445	0.4255
7.0	8.1187	0.0745	8.2153	0.1614	8.3776	0.2738
7.5	8.1597	0.0199	8.2707	0.0515	8.4577	0.1068
8.0	8.1563	−0.0378	8.2798	−0.0647	8.4879	−0.0699
8.5	8.1120	−0.0974	8.2465	−0.1846	8.4724	−0.2519
9.0	8.0308	−0.1581	8.1749	−0.3066	8.4162	−0.4364
9.5	7.9160	−0.2194	8.0688	−0.4294	8.3239	−0.6215
10.0	7.7710	−0.2808	7.9319	−0.5523	8.1998	−0.8060
10.5	7.5987	−0.3422	7.7673	−0.6750	8.0475	−0.9896
11.0	7.4018	−0.4036	7.5779	−0.7974	7.8702	−1.1722
11.5	7.1825	−0.4648	7.3662	−0.9193	7.6705	−1.3539
12.0	6.9427	−0.5259	7.1340	−1.0409	7.4507	−1.5349
12.5	6.6843	−0.5869	6.8833	−1.1623	7.2126	−1.7153
13.0	6.4087	−0.6478	6.6156	−1.2836	6.9578	−1.8955
13.5	6.1172	−0.7088	6.3322	−1.4049	6.6876	−2.0755
14.0	5.8110	−0.7699	6.0342	−1.5262	6.4031	−2.2556
14.5	5.4911	−0.8310	5.7226	−1.6477	6.1054	−2.4360
15.0	5.1583	−0.8922	5.3984	−1.7695	5.7952	−2.6168
15.5	4.8135	−0.9536	5.0623	−1.8915	5.4735	−2.7980
16.0	4.4574	−1.0152	4.7149	−2.0139	5.1407	−2.9797
16.5	4.0906	−1.0770	4.3570	−2.1367	4.7976	−3.1621
17.0	3.7136	−1.1389	3.9891	−2.2599	4.4447	−3.3451
17.5	3.3271	−1.2011	3.6117	−2.3836	4.0824	−3.5287
18.0	2.9314	−1.2635	3.2252	−2.5077	3.7112	−3.7131
18.5	2.5269	−1.3262	2.8300	−2.6323	3.3315	−3.8982
19.0	2.1142	−1.3891	2.4267	−2.7573	2.9436	−4.0841
19.5	1.6935	−1.4522	2.0154	−2.8828	2.5480	−4.2707
20.0	1.2651	−1.5155	1.5965	−3.0088	2.1449	−4.4580
20.5	0.8295	−1.5791	1.1704	−3.1353	1.7347	−4.6460
21.0	0.3868	−1.6429	0.7373	−3.2623	1.3175	−4.8348
21.5	−0.0626	−1.7069	0.2975	−3.3897	0.8937	−5.0242
22.0	−0.5186	−1.7712	−0.1487	−3.5176	0.4635	−5.2144
22.5	−0.9808	−1.8357	−0.6012	−3.6459	0.0271	−5.4052
23.0	−1.4491	−1.9004	−1.0598	−3.7747	−0.4153	−5.5968
23.5	−1.9232	−1.9653	−1.5241	−3.9039	−0.8634	−5.7889
24.0	−2.4030	−2.0305	−1.9941	−4.0335	−1.3171	−5.9818
24.5	−2.8883	−2.0958	−2.4695	−4.1635	−1.7762	−6.1752
25.0	−3.3788	−2.1614	−2.9502	−4.2940	−2.2405	−6.3693

TABLE I. $a_r(q) = U + iV$, $q = \rho e^{i\phi}$ $r = 2$

ρ	$\phi=20°$		$\phi=25°$		$\phi=30°$	
	U	V	U	V	U	V
0.0	4.0000	0.0000	4.0000	0.0000	4.0000	0.0000
0.5	4.0791	0.0637	4.0674	0.0765	4.0536	0.0872
1.0	4.3058	0.2230	4.2694	0.2716	4.2254	0.3153
1.5	4.6447	0.4176	4.5868	0.5147	4.5154	0.6067
2.0	5.0505	0.6062	4.9798	0.7537	4.8915	0.8977
2.5	5.4878	0.7705	5.4132	0.9648	5.3184	1.1588
3.0	5.9342	0.9023	5.8646	1.1383	5.7731	1.3790
3.5	6.3755	0.9969	6.3204	1.2687	6.2427	1.5525
4.0	6.8019	1.0503	6.7716	1.3512	6.7197	1.6741
4.5	7.2052	1.0591	7.2110	1.3809	7.1987	1.7379
5.0	7.5779	1.0210	7.6314	1.3529	7.6746	1.7362
5.5	7.9119	0.9352	8.0236	1.2633	8.1394	1.6601
6.0	8.1992	0.8035	8.3762	1.1105	8.5801	1.5010
6.5	8.4329	0.6311	8.6764	0.8981	8.9761	1.2546
7.0	8.6083	0.4262	8.9126	0.6363	9.3018	0.9289
7.5	8.7245	0.1985	9.0789	0.3402	9.5377	0.5481
8.0	8.7843	-0.0429	9.1771	0.0260	9.6817	0.1434
8.5	8.7930	-0.2906	9.2144	-0.2941	9.7474	-0.2614
9.0	8.7570	-0.5400	9.2007	-0.6126	9.7528	-0.6553
9.5	8.6823	-0.7885	9.1450	-0.9262	9.7128	-1.0356
10.0	8.5744	-1.0348	9.0548	-1.2341	9.6382	-1.4037
10.5	8.4378	-1.2786	8.9357	-1.5368	9.5361	-1.7619
11.0	8.2763	-1.5202	8.7922	-1.8350	9.4115	-2.1127
11.5	8.0926	-1.7599	8.6275	-2.1299	9.2678	-2.4583
12.0	7.8893	-1.9982	8.4442	-2.4223	9.1072	-2.8002
12.5	7.6682	-2.2355	8.2441	-2.7132	8.9316	-3.1400
13.0	7.4310	-2.4722	8.0288	-3.0032	8.7422	-3.4786
13.5	7.1789	-2.7087	7.7995	-3.2928	8.5402	-3.8169
14.0	6.9131	-2.9453	7.5572	-3.5826	8.3263	-4.1554
14.5	6.6345	-3.1822	7.3029	-3.8727	8.1013	-4.4946
15.0	6.3439	-3.4196	7.0371	-4.1636	7.8656	-4.8349
15.5	6.0420	-3.6576	6.7607	-4.4554	7.6200	-5.1764
16.0	5.7295	-3.8965	6.4741	-4.7483	7.3648	-5.5195
16.5	5.4070	-4.1361	6.1778	-5.0423	7.1004	-5.8641
17.0	5.0749	-4.3767	5.8723	-5.3375	6.8272	-6.2104
17.5	4.7337	-4.6183	5.5580	-5.6341	6.5456	-6.5583
18.0	4.3838	-4.8608	5.2353	-5.9320	6.2559	-6.9081
18.5	4.0256	-5.1044	4.9045	-6.2312	5.9584	-7.2595
19.0	3.6594	-5.3489	4.5660	-6.5317	5.6534	-7.6127
19.5	3.2856	-5.5945	4.2200	-6.8336	5.3412	-7.9676
20.0	2.9044	-5.8411	3.8668	-7.1368	5.0219	-8.3241
20.5	2.5162	-6.0887	3.5068	-7.4413	4.6959	-8.6823
21.0	2.1212	-6.3372	3.1400	-7.7471	4.3634	-9.0421
21.5	1.7196	-6.5868	2.7669	-8.0541	4.0246	-9.4035
22.0	1.3118	-6.8373	2.3875	-8.3624	3.6797	-9.7664
22.5	0.8978	-7.0887	2.0021	-8.6718	3.3288	-10.1307
23.0	0.4780	-7.3411	1.6109	-8.9825	2.9723	-10.4965
23.5	0.0524	-7.5943	1.2141	-9.2942	2.6102	-10.8637
24.0	-0.3787	-7.8484	0.8118	-9.6071	2.2428	-11.2323
24.5	-0.8151	-8.1034	0.4043	-9.9211	1.8701	-11.6022
25.0	-1.2567	-8.3592	-0.0083	-10.2361	1.4924	-11.9734

TABLE I. $a_r(q) = U + iV, \ q = \rho e^{i\phi}$ $r = 2$

ρ	φ=35°		φ=40°		φ=45°	
	U	V	U	V	U	V
0.0	4.0000	0.0000	4.0000	0.0000	4.0000	0.0000
0.5	4.0381	0.0956	4.0212	0.1012	4.0034	0.1040
1.0	4.1742	0.3529	4.1161	0.3833	4.0519	0.4051
1.5	4.4303	0.6921	4.3313	0.7693	4.2182	0.8366
2.0	4.7848	1.0370	4.6588	1.1700	4.5125	1.2951
2.5	5.2016	1.3514	5.0610	1.5410	4.8952	1.7255
3.0	5.6565	1.6233	5.5117	1.8694	5.3358	2.1141
3.5	6.1371	1.8475	5.9980	2.1513	5.8207	2.4595
4.0	6.6375	2.0193	6.5159	2.3839	6.3464	2.7616
4.5	7.1553	2.1326	7.0658	2.5627	6.9156	3.0195
5.0	7.6894	2.1784	7.6519	2.6802	7.5361	3.2305
5.5	8.2374	2.1432	8.2812	2.7233	8.2223	3.3896
6.0	8.7915	2.0076	8.9632	2.6676	9.0012	3.4877
6.5	9.3291	1.7470	9.7045	2.4625	9.9310	3.5060
7.0	9.8000	1.3470	10.4629	2.0009	11.2054	3.4000
7.5	10.1393	0.8409	10.9964	1.2335	13.3117	4.3163
8.0	10.3295	0.3059	11.1797	0.4663	14.1316	5.5373
8.5	10.4085	−0.2051	11.2111	−0.1708	14.8141	6.4467
9.0	10.4177	−0.6805	11.1882	−0.7193	15.4630	7.2271
9.5	10.3826	−1.1257	11.1397	−1.2147	16.1018	7.9324
10.0	10.3173	−1.5485	11.0749	−1.6777	16.7402	8.5873
10.5	10.2294	−1.9554	10.9979	−2.1204	17.3830	9.2058
11.0	10.1233	−2.3516	10.9103	−2.5505	18.0335	9.7965
11.5	10.0018	−2.7407	10.8128	−2.9729	18.6937	10.3659
12.0	9.8665	−3.1254	10.7061	−3.3911	19.3653	10.9186
12.5	9.7188	−3.5076	10.5902	−3.8073	20.0494	11.4586
13.0	9.5595	−3.8887	10.4654	−4.2233	20.7471	11.9894
13.5	9.3892	−4.2698	10.3318	−4.6402	21.4589	12.5142
14.0	9.2085	−4.6516	10.1896	−5.0587	22.1853	13.0362
14.5	9.0179	−5.0346	10.0388	−5.4793	22.9263	13.5585
15.0	8.8177	−5.4193	9.8795	−5.9026	23.6813	14.0842
15.5	8.6083	−5.8058	9.7120	−6.3286	24.4491	14.6162
16.0	8.3900	−6.1944	9.5364	−6.7575	25.2281	15.1573
16.5	8.1632	−6.5852	9.3527	−7.1894	26.0156	15.7096
17.0	7.9280	−6.9782	9.1613	−7.6242	26.8088	16.2747
17.5	7.6849	−7.3735	8.9622	−8.0620	27.6044	16.8532
18.0	7.4339	−7.7710	8.7557	−8.5027	28.3993	17.4445
18.5	7.1755	−8.1707	8.5420	−8.9462	29.1906	18.0473
19.0	6.9037	−8.5726	8.3212	−9.3924	29.9765	18.6599
19.5	6.6370	−8.9766	8.0936	−9.8413	30.7555	19.2798
20.0	6.3574	−9.3827	7.8593	−10.2927	31.5272	19.9051
20.5	6.0713	−9.7908	7.6185	−10.7465	32.2916	20.5335
21.0	5.7787	−10.2009	7.3715	−11.2027	33.0493	21.1635
21.5	5.4800	−10.6129	7.1184	−11.6612	33.8010	21.7939
22.0	5.1753	−11.0268	6.8594	−12.1219	34.5475	22.4235
22.5	4.8647	−11.4424	6.5946	−12.5847	35.2899	23.0517
23.0	4.5486	−11.8597	6.3244	−13.0495	36.0289	23.6783
23.5	4.2270	−12.2788	6.0487	−13.5163	36.7655	24.3028
24.0	3.9001	−12.6994	5.7678	−13.9850	37.5003	24.9254
24.5	3.5681	−13.1216	5.4818	−14.4555	38.2341	25.5461
25.0	3.2311	−13.5454	5.1909	−14.9278	38.9673	26.1650

TABLE I. $a_r(q) = U + iV$, $q = \rho e^{i\phi}$ $r = 2$

ρ	$\phi=50°$ U	$\phi=50°$ V	$\phi=55°$ U	$\phi=55°$ V	$\phi=60°$ U	$\phi=60°$ V
0.0	4.0000	0.0000	4.0000	0.0000	4.0000	0.0000
0.5	3.9852	0.1036	3.9672	0.1000	3.9498	0.0932
1.0	3.9824	0.4170	3.9088	0.4174	3.8326	0.4046
1.5	4.0906	0.8920	3.9482	0.9330	3.7903	0.9570
2.0	4.3452	1.4104	4.1559	1.5139	3.9440	1.6039
2.5	4.7028	1.9024	4.4831	2.0692	4.2359	2.2234
3.0	5.1268	2.3539	4.8837	2.5847	4.6064	2.8023
3.5	5.6015	2.7666	5.3386	3.0658	5.0323	3.3504
4.0	6.1230	3.1437	5.8427	3.5195	5.5061	3.8783
4.5	6.6940	3.4887	6.3969	3.9530	6.0264	4.3957
5.0	7.3226	3.8054	7.0061	4.3750	6.5941	4.9134
5.5	8.0226	4.0995	7.6775	4.7974	7.2095	5.4439
6.0	8.8163	4.3839	8.4181	5.2400	7.8694	6.0027
6.5	9.7376	4.6923	9.2275	5.7332	8.5636	6.6063
7.0	10.8109	5.1203	10.0817	6.3151	9.2718	7.2660
7.5	11.9118	5.8085	10.9250	7.0005	9.9694	7.9798
8.0	12.8285	6.6526	11.7077	7.7558	10.6385	8.7324
8.5	13.5932	7.4823	12.4233	8.5327	11.2741	9.5046
9.0	14.2841	8.2633	13.0894	9.3036	11.8806	10.2821
9.5	14.9407	9.0012	13.7243	10.0589	12.4653	11.0568
10.0	15.5818	9.7050	14.3411	10.7975	13.0351	11.8256
10.5	16.2173	10.3825	14.9484	11.5209	13.5955	12.5875
11.0	16.8529	11.0395	15.5515	12.2318	14.1504	13.3431
11.5	17.4922	11.6808	16.1541	12.9327	14.7026	14.0934
12.0	18.1374	12.3102	16.7584	13.6259	15.2541	14.8396
12.5	18.7899	12.9309	17.3659	14.3138	15.8060	15.5830
13.0	19.4506	13.5458	17.9775	14.9983	16.3593	16.3246
13.5	20.1198	14.1574	18.5936	15.6810	16.9144	17.0656
14.0	20.7977	14.7680	19.2141	16.3635	17.4713	17.8069
14.5	21.4839	15.3797	19.8390	17.0471	18.0301	18.5493
15.0	22.1776	15.9944	20.4677	17.7328	18.5906	19.2933
15.5	22.8779	16.6136	21.0997	18.4216	19.1524	20.0395
16.0	23.5836	17.2385	21.7343	19.1141	19.7153	20.7882
16.5	24.2932	17.8700	22.3707	19.8105	20.2788	21.5396
17.0	25.0053	18.5085	23.0081	20.5112	20.8426	22.2939
17.5	25.7183	19.1540	23.6459	21.2161	21.4063	23.0509
18.0	26.4310	19.8064	24.2834	21.9251	21.9697	23.8106
18.5	27.1421	20.4649	24.9201	22.6378	22.5324	24.5729
19.0	27.8509	21.1288	25.5555	23.3540	23.0943	25.3377
19.5	28.5567	21.7973	26.1895	24.0732	23.6552	26.1046
20.0	29.2592	22.4693	26.8217	24.7950	24.2150	26.8736
20.5	29.9583	23.1441	27.4520	25.5189	24.7736	27.6443
21.0	30.6541	23.8209	28.0806	26.2447	25.3311	28.4167
21.5	31.3467	24.4990	28.7074	26.9720	25.8874	29.1904
22.0	32.0366	25.1779	29.3325	27.7005	26.4425	29.9654
22.5	32.7240	25.8571	29.9561	28.4300	26.9966	30.7415
23.0	33.4093	26.5365	30.5783	29.1602	27.5497	31.5186
23.5	34.0928	27.2157	31.1993	29.8910	28.1019	32.2966
24.0	34.7750	27.8948	31.8192	30.6224	28.6532	33.0754
24.5	35.4561	28.5735	32.4383	31.3542	29.2037	33.8550
25.0	36.1365	29.2520	33.0565	32.0864	29.7535	34.6352

TABLE I. $a_r(q) = U + iV$, $q = \rho e^{i\phi}$ $\qquad\qquad r=2$

ρ	$\phi=65°$		$\phi=70°$		$\phi=75°$	
	U	V	U	V	U	V
0.0	4.0000	0.0000	4.0000	0.0000	4.0000	0.0000
0.5	3.9338	0.0833	3.9197	0.0705	3.9081	0.0553
1.0	3.7561	0.3772	3.6822	0.3334	3.6150	0.2723
1.5	3.6162	0.9606	3.4237	0.9394	3.2089	0.8870
2.0	3.7084	1.6789	3.4482	1.7383	3.1624	1.7828
2.5	3.9616	2.3629	3.6611	2.4858	3.3364	2.5911
3.0	4.2961	3.0026	3.9548	3.1822	3.5857	3.3381
3.5	4.6843	3.6140	4.2981	3.8511	3.8783	4.0572
4.0	5.1168	4.2106	4.6802	4.5087	4.2031	4.7669
4.5	5.5897	4.8035	5.0958	5.1665	4.5544	5.4786
5.0	6.1006	5.4031	5.5404	5.8339	4.9270	6.2002
5.5	6.6457	6.0199	6.0088	6.5184	5.3158	6.9375
6.0	7.2185	6.6637	6.4941	7.2260	5.7147	7.6935
6.5	7.8085	7.3420	6.9884	7.9597	6.1181	8.4695
7.0	8.4029	8.0573	7.4833	8.7191	6.5206	9.2644
7.5	8.9893	8.8056	7.9723	9.5009	6.9183	10.0756
8.0	9.5595	9.5788	8.4509	10.3001	7.3088	10.8998
8.5	10.1108	10.3672	8.9177	11.1113	7.6910	11.7338
9.0	10.6445	11.1631	9.3730	11.9300	8.0652	12.5746
9.5	11.1635	11.9613	9.8182	12.7528	8.4320	13.4201
10.0	11.6714	12.7591	10.2551	13.5777	8.7926	14.2688
10.5	12.1713	13.5549	10.6857	14.4034	9.1478	15.1196
11.0	12.6659	14.3485	11.1114	15.2292	9.4988	15.9719
11.5	13.1570	15.1401	11.5335	16.0551	9.8464	16.8254
12.0	13.6462	15.9301	11.9531	16.8810	10.1913	17.6801
12.5	14.1343	16.7191	12.3709	17.7072	10.5340	18.5358
13.0	14.6220	17.5077	12.7875	18.5340	10.8750	19.3926
13.5	15.1099	18.2965	13.2031	19.3615	11.2145	20.2506
14.0	15.5980	19.0860	13.6181	20.1900	11.5528	21.1100
14.5	16.0865	19.8766	14.0326	21.0198	11.8901	21.9707
15.0	16.5754	20.6687	14.4466	21.8510	12.2264	22.8328
15.5	17.0645	21.4625	14.8601	22.6838	12.5618	23.6964
16.0	17.5536	22.2582	15.2732	23.5181	12.8963	24.5615
16.5	18.0428	23.0560	15.6857	24.3542	13.2299	25.4281
17.0	18.5316	23.8558	16.0976	25.1920	13.5627	26.2962
17.5	19.0201	24.6577	16.5089	26.0314	13.8946	27.1657
18.0	19.5081	25.4616	16.9194	26.8725	14.2257	28.0368
18.5	19.9954	26.2675	17.3292	27.7152	14.5559	28.9092
19.0	20.4820	27.0752	17.7383	28.5595	14.8853	29.7830
19.5	20.9677	27.8847	18.1465	29.4052	15.2138	30.6581
20.0	21.4526	28.6959	18.5539	30.2524	15.5415	31.5345
20.5	21.9365	29.5085	18.9605	31.1008	15.8684	32.4121
21.0	22.4196	30.3226	19.3662	31.9506	16.1944	33.2908
21.5	22.9017	31.1379	19.7712	32.8015	16.5196	34.1706
22.0	23.3830	31.9545	20.1753	33.6536	16.8440	35.0515
22.5	23.8633	32.7721	20.5786	34.5067	17.1677	35.9334
23.0	24.3429	33.5908	20.9812	35.3608	17.4906	36.8163
23.5	24.8217	34.4105	21.3830	36.2159	17.8128	37.7001
24.0	25.2997	35.2310	21.7842	37.0719	18.1342	38.5848
24.5	25.7770	36.0524	22.1846	37.9288	18.4550	39.4703
25.0	26.2536	36.8747	22.5844	38.7865	18.7752	40.3567

TABLE I. $a_r(q) = U + iV$, $q = \rho e^{i\phi}$ $r = 2$

ρ	$\phi = 80°$		$\phi = 85°$		$\phi = 90°$	
	U	V	U	V	U	V
0.0	4.0000	0.0000	4.0000	0.0000	4.0000	0.0000
0.5	3.8994	0.0380	3.8940	0.0194	3.8922	0.0000
1.0	3.5599	0.1941	3.5231	0.1014	3.5101	0.0000
1.5	2.9621	0.7930	2.6535	0.6358	2.0925	0.4170
2.0	2.8507	1.8153	2.5150	1.8414	2.1626	1.8675
2.5	2.9902	2.6785	2.6265	2.7477	2.2503	2.7988
3.0	3.1928	3.4680	2.7805	3.5701	2.3539	3.6431
3.5	3.4300	4.2287	2.9590	4.3630	2.4712	4.4583
4.0	3.6925	4.9808	3.1556	5.1476	2.5996	5.2654
4.5	3.9748	5.7354	3.3660	5.9344	2.7363	6.0743
5.0	4.2722	6.4992	3.5863	6.7294	2.8786	6.8900
5.5	4.5800	7.2764	3.8127	7.5355	3.0237	7.7150
6.0	4.8937	8.0689	4.0419	8.3540	3.1693	8.5501
6.5	5.2090	8.8770	4.2710	9.1849	3.3135	9.3953
7.0	5.5226	9.6994	4.4977	10.0272	3.4547	10.2497
7.5	5.8321	10.5343	4.7206	10.8794	3.5922	11.1122
8.0	6.1359	11.3796	4.9387	11.7400	3.7253	11.9818
8.5	6.4336	12.2329	5.1517	12.6075	3.8539	12.8573
9.0	6.7251	13.0924	5.3597	13.4805	3.9780	13.7378
9.5	7.0109	13.9565	5.5630	14.3581	4.0980	14.6225
10.0	7.2916	14.8243	5.7618	15.2392	4.2141	15.5107
10.5	7.5678	15.6948	5.9568	16.1233	4.3265	16.4019
11.0	7.8403	16.5675	6.1483	17.0100	4.4357	17.2958
11.5	8.1095	17.4421	6.3367	17.8988	4.5420	18.1920
12.0	8.3760	18.3183	6.5225	18.7897	4.6456	19.0903
12.5	8.6402	19.1962	6.7058	19.6823	4.7468	19.9905
13.0	8.9024	20.0755	6.8871	20.5767	4.8458	20.8925
13.5	9.1629	20.9563	7.0664	21.4727	4.9428	21.7962
14.0	9.4218	21.8385	7.2440	22.3703	5.0380	22.7015
14.5	9.6793	22.7222	7.4200	23.2693	5.1314	23.6084
15.0	9.9356	23.6074	7.5945	24.1699	5.2232	24.5167
15.5	10.1906	24.4940	7.7677	25.0718	5.3135	25.4265
16.0	10.4446	25.3821	7.9395	25.9752	5.4024	26.3376
16.5	10.6974	26.2716	8.1101	26.8800	5.4899	27.2500
17.0	10.9492	27.1624	8.2796	27.7860	5.5761	28.1637
17.5	11.2000	28.0547	8.4479	28.6934	5.6612	29.0786
18.0	11.4498	28.9482	8.6151	29.6020	5.7450	29.9947
18.5	11.6987	29.8431	8.7812	30.5118	5.8277	30.9120
19.0	11.9466	30.7392	8.9464	31.4227	5.9094	31.8303
19.5	12.1936	31.6364	9.1106	32.3348	5.9899	32.7498
20.0	12.4397	32.5349	9.2738	33.2480	6.0695	33.6702
20.5	12.6849	33.4345	9.4361	34.1622	6.1481	34.5916
21.0	12.9293	34.3351	9.5975	35.0775	6.2258	35.5140
21.5	13.1729	35.2368	9.7580	35.9937	6.3025	36.4374
22.0	13.4156	36.1394	9.9177	36.9108	6.3784	37.3616
22.5	13.6576	37.0431	10.0765	37.8289	6.4534	38.2866
23.0	13.8988	37.9476	10.2346	38.7478	6.5276	39.2125
23.5	14.1392	38.8530	10.3919	39.6676	6.6010	40.1393
24.0	14.3790	39.7593	10.5485	40.5882	6.6736	41.0667
24.5	14.6180	40.6664	10.7043	41.5096	6.7455	41.9950
25.0	14.8563	41.5743	10.8594	42.4317	6.8166	42.9240

ρ	$\phi = 5°$		$\phi = 10°$		$\phi = 15°$	
	U	V	U	V	U	V
0.0	9.0000	0.0000	9.0000	0.0000	9.0000	0.0000
0.5	9.0173	0.0032	9.0164	0.0063	9.0149	0.0092
1.0	9.0769	0.0149	9.0725	0.0293	9.0654	0.0425
1.5	9.1895	0.0377	9.1783	0.0739	9.1601	0.1072
2.0	9.3632	0.0727	9.3419	0.1427	9.3071	0.2075
2.5	9.6011	0.1188	9.5679	0.2341	9.5131	0.3423
3.0	9.9006	0.1731	9.8558	0.3424	9.7810	0.5040
3.5	10.2541	0.2314	10.1998	0.4596	10.1084	0.6810
4.0	10.6509	0.2901	10.5901	0.5780	10.4873	0.8613
4.5	11.0792	0.3460	11.0154	0.6913	10.9069	1.0350
5.0	11.5279	0.3970	11.4643	0.7952	11.3555	1.1952
5.5	11.9870	0.4418	11.9268	0.8868	11.8228	1.3378
6.0	12.4481	0.4793	12.3942	0.9643	12.3000	1.4598
6.5	12.9039	0.5089	12.8594	1.0262	12.7798	1.5594
7.0	13.3484	0.5300	13.3162	1.0714	13.2562	1.6349
7.5	13.7762	0.5423	13.7594	1.0992	13.7239	1.6849
8.0	14.1830	0.5455	14.1842	1.1089	14.1782	1.7082
8.5	14.5650	0.5396	14.5866	1.1002	14.6147	1.7037
9.0	14.9189	0.5247	14.9628	1.0733	15.0291	1.6709
9.5	15.2423	0.5013	15.3097	1.0285	15.4169	1.6098
10.0	15.5334	0.4700	15.6246	0.9671	15.7741	1.5214
10.5	15.7908	0.4316	15.9053	0.8905	16.0969	1.4075
11.0	16.0141	0.3871	16.1507	0.8009	16.3822	1.2712
11.5	16.2033	0.3376	16.3601	0.7005	16.6280	1.1162
12.0	16.3591	0.2842	16.5338	0.5915	16.8335	0.9469
12.5	16.4824	0.2277	16.6728	0.4764	16.9993	0.7675
13.0	16.5747	0.1692	16.7785	0.3571	17.1271	0.5818
13.5	16.6376	0.1093	16.8527	0.2352	17.2194	0.3929
14.0	16.6728	0.0486	16.8976	0.1121	17.2790	0.2033
14.5	16.6821	-0.0125	16.9153	-0.0114	17.3089	0.0143
15.0	16.6672	-0.0736	16.9077	-0.1346	17.3119	-0.1729
15.5	16.6297	-0.1345	16.8769	-0.2570	17.2906	-0.3580
16.0	16.5713	-0.1952	16.8247	-0.3786	17.2474	-0.5408
16.5	16.4933	-0.2554	16.7527	-0.4991	17.1841	-0.7213
17.0	16.3971	-0.3153	16.6625	-0.6187	17.1027	-0.8997
17.5	16.2839	-0.3749	16.5552	-0.7373	17.0044	-1.0763
18.0	16.1548	-0.4340	16.4321	-0.8550	16.8907	-1.2512
18.5	16.0107	-0.4929	16.2943	-0.9721	16.7627	-1.4248
19.0	15.8526	-0.5515	16.1425	-1.0885	16.6212	-1.5974
19.5	15.6813	-0.6099	15.9778	-1.2045	16.4671	-1.7691
20.0	15.4974	-0.6681	15.8008	-1.3201	16.3012	-1.9402
20.5	15.3018	-0.7262	15.6122	-1.4354	16.1240	-2.1108
21.0	15.0949	-0.7842	15.4125	-1.5505	15.9363	-2.2812
21.5	14.8773	-0.8422	15.2023	-1.6656	15.7384	-2.4515
22.0	14.6495	-0.9002	14.9821	-1.7807	15.5308	-2.6218
22.5	14.4120	-0.9582	14.7524	-1.8958	15.3140	-2.7922
23.0	14.1651	-1.0162	14.5135	-2.0110	15.0883	-2.9628
23.5	13.9093	-1.0743	14.2658	-2.1263	14.8541	-3.1337
24.0	13.6450	-1.1325	14.0097	-2.2419	14.6117	-3.3049
24.5	13.3724	-1.1909	13.7455	-2.3577	14.3614	-3.4765
25.0	13.0919	-1.2493	13.4734	-2.4737	14.1035	-3.6486

TABLE I. $a_r(q) = U + iV$, $q = \rho e^{i\phi}$ $r = 3$

ρ	$\phi=20°$		$\phi=25°$		$\phi=30°$	
	U	V	U	V	U	V
0.0	9.0000	0.0000	9.0000	0.0000	9.0000	0.0000
0.5	9.0130	0.0118	9.0105	0.0139	9.0078	0.0155
1.0	9.0559	0.0540	9.0444	0.0633	9.0313	0.0701
1.5	9.1355	0.1361	9.1057	0.1594	9.0717	0.1761
2.0	9.2597	0.2645	9.2013	0.3111	9.1340	0.3448
2.5	9.4374	0.4395	9.3422	0.5217	9.2295	0.5845
3.0	9.6762	0.6535	9.5414	0.7857	9.3771	0.8945
3.5	9.9787	0.8916	9.8090	1.0865	9.5970	1.2593
4.0	10.3402	1.1371	10.1455	1.4015	9.8988	1.6499
4.5	10.7505	1.3755	10.5419	1.7106	10.2756	2.0373
5.0	11.1975	1.5972	10.9850	2.0003	10.7115	2.4028
5.5	11.6701	1.7964	11.4620	2.2633	11.1910	2.7374
6.0	12.1591	1.9697	11.9630	2.4958	11.7023	3.0378
6.5	12.6571	2.1147	12.4805	2.6958	12.2377	3.3028
7.0	13.1584	2.2294	13.0093	2.8611	12.7924	3.5313
7.5	13.6582	2.3120	13.5453	2.9898	13.3638	3.7218
8.0	14.1521	2.3602	14.0854	3.0791	13.9504	3.8720
8.5	14.6358	2.3719	14.6265	3.1256	14.5516	3.9781
9.0	15.1047	2.3451	15.1651	3.1249	15.1675	4.0348
9.5	15.5535	2.2780	15.6966	3.0723	15.7977	4.0343
10.0	15.9760	2.1699	16.2140	2.9625	16.4406	3.9652
10.5	16.3657	2.0217	16.7073	2.7909	17.0907	3.8110
11.0	16.7157	1.8365	17.1630	2.5564	17.7319	3.5498
11.5	17.0201	1.6197	17.5648	2.2639	18.3266	3.1617
12.0	17.2753	1.3791	17.8990	1.9268	18.8122	2.6567
12.5	17.4808	1.1230	18.1598	1.5644	19.1451	2.0987
13.0	17.6387	0.8589	18.3510	1.1953	19.3440	1.5586
13.5	17.7531	0.5930	18.4829	0.8322	19.4550	1.0646
14.0	17.8290	0.3291	18.5669	0.4815	19.5127	0.6158
14.5	17.8713	0.0695	18.6132	0.1449	19.5367	0.2031
15.0	17.8845	−0.1848	18.6293	−0.1784	19.5373	−0.1820
15.5	17.8725	−0.4336	18.6208	−0.4898	19.5205	−0.5465
16.0	17.8383	−0.6773	18.5919	−0.7915	19.4894	−0.8956
16.5	17.7845	−0.9165	18.5454	−1.0851	19.4463	−1.2335
17.0	17.7131	−1.1517	18.4833	−1.3723	19.3922	−1.5629
17.5	17.6257	−1.3836	18.4074	−1.6546	19.3281	−1.8862
18.0	17.5238	−1.6129	18.3188	−1.9330	19.2546	−2.2052
18.5	17.4084	−1.8401	18.2184	−2.2086	19.1721	−2.5211
19.0	17.2804	−2.0656	18.1070	−2.4821	19.0809	−2.8351
19.5	17.1407	−2.2899	17.9853	−2.7541	18.9812	−3.1479
20.0	16.9899	−2.5134	17.8537	−3.0253	18.8733	−3.4602
20.5	16.8286	−2.7363	17.7126	−3.2959	18.7575	−3.7725
21.0	16.6573	−2.9590	17.5625	−3.5664	18.6337	−4.0852
21.5	16.4765	−3.1815	17.4037	−3.8371	18.5023	−4.3986
22.0	16.2866	−3.4042	17.2364	−4.1081	18.3634	−4.7129
22.5	16.0878	−3.6271	17.0610	−4.3797	18.2170	−5.0283
23.0	15.8806	−3.8503	16.8778	−4.6519	18.0635	−5.3449
23.5	15.6653	−4.0741	16.6869	−4.9250	17.9028	−5.6629
24.0	15.4421	−4.2984	16.4885	−5.1989	17.7352	−5.9823
24.5	15.2113	−4.5233	16.2830	−5.4738	17.5608	−6.3031
25.0	14.9732	−4.7489	16.0704	−5.7497	17.3797	−6.6254

TABLE I. $a_r(q) = U + iV$, $q = \rho e^{i\phi}$ $r = 3$

ρ	$\phi = 35°$		$\phi = 40°$		$\phi = 45°$	
	U	V	U	V	U	V
0.0	9.0000	0.0000	9.0000	0.0000	9.0000	0.0000
0.5	9.0048	0.0166	9.0017	0.0171	8.9986	0.0170
1.0	9.0172	0.0742	9.0028	0.0755	8.9885	0.0739
1.5	9.0352	0.1854	8.9977	0.1869	8.9612	0.1806
2.0	9.0604	0.3637	8.9840	0.3662	8.9088	0.3515
2.5	9.1026	0.6231	8.9664	0.6327	8.8281	0.6094
3.0	9.1845	0.9722	8.9668	1.0089	8.7306	0.9921
3.5	9.3399	1.4017	9.0340	1.5022	8.6742	1.5423
4.0	9.5941	1.8762	9.2228	2.0732	8.7700	2.2321
4.5	9.9447	2.3522	9.5405	2.6523	9.0520	2.9372
5.0	10.3702	2.8024	9.9538	3.1971	9.4562	3.5870
5.5	10.8494	3.2164	10.4305	3.6974	9.9300	4.1775
6.0	11.3676	3.5927	10.9513	4.1553	10.4489	4.7194
6.5	11.9163	3.9319	11.5064	4.5754	11.0022	5.2226
7.0	12.4912	4.2351	12.0916	4.9614	11.5857	5.6945
7.5	13.0905	4.5024	12.7057	5.3162	12.1985	6.1407
8.0	13.7147	4.7333	13.3501	5.6420	12.8416	6.5660
8.5	14.3660	4.9260	14.0280	5.9405	13.5173	6.9749
9.0	15.0485	5.0773	14.7447	6.2133	14.2288	7.3727
9.5	15.7686	5.1820	15.5083	6.4627	14.9802	7.7660
10.0	16.5366	5.2313	16.3308	6.6929	15.7752	8.1640
10.5	17.3695	5.2097	17.2299	6.9131	16.6160	8.5795
11.0	18.2977	5.0843	18.2313	7.1464	17.4998	9.0296
11.5	19.3830	4.7616	19.3594	7.4517	18.4138	9.5324
12.0	20.5775	3.7860	20.5731	7.9390	19.3333	10.0984
12.5	20.7670	2.5088	21.7042	8.6311	20.2306	10.7210
13.0	20.7191	1.7245	22.6752	9.3886	21.0889	11.3799
13.5	20.6714	1.1284	23.5358	10.1253	21.9062	12.0536
14.0	20.6309	0.6251	24.3344	10.8236	22.6891	12.7274
14.5	20.5948	0.1763	25.0984	11.4853	23.4463	13.3937
15.0	20.5603	-0.2376	25.8431	12.1154	24.1852	14.0491
15.5	20.5252	-0.6280	26.5774	12.7190	24.9121	14.6928
16.0	20.4880	-1.0024	27.3070	13.3002	25.6314	15.3252
16.5	20.4477	-1.3656	28.0359	13.8627	26.3467	15.9473
17.0	20.4033	-1.7212	28.7668	14.4092	27.0604	16.5602
17.5	20.3543	-2.0717	29.5016	14.9423	27.7745	17.1652
18.0	20.3000	-2.4190	30.2419	15.4642	28.4904	17.7637
18.5	20.2402	-2.7645	30.9890	15.9769	29.2092	18.3569
19.0	20.1745	-3.1092	31.7437	16.4823	29.9317	18.9461
19.5	20.1027	-3.4540	32.5068	16.9824	30.6582	19.5325
20.0	20.0245	-3.7995	33.2788	17.4787	31.3892	20.1172
20.5	19.9399	-4.1461	34.0599	17.9732	32.1247	20.7013
21.0	19.8488	-4.4941	34.8501	18.4675	32.8646	21.2858
21.5	19.7511	-4.8439	35.6492	18.9634	33.6087	21.8715
22.0	19.6468	-5.1956	36.4566	19.4626	34.3565	22.4593
22.5	19.5358	-5.5493	37.2716	19.9665	35.1076	23.0498
23.0	19.4183	-5.9050	38.0930	20.4764	35.8615	23.6435
23.5	19.2942	-6.2629	38.9193	20.9935	36.6174	24.2409
24.0	19.1636	-6.6230	39.7491	21.5183	37.3746	24.8420
24.5	19.0266	-6.9852	40.5808	22.0513	38.1327	25.4470
25.0	18.8832	-7.3495	41.4126	22.5922	38.8908	26.0558

TABLE I. $a_r(q) = U + iV$, $q = \rho e^{i\phi}$ $r = 3$

ρ	$\phi = 50°$		$\phi = 55°$		$\phi = 60°$	
	U	V	U	V	U	V
0.0	9.0000	0.0000	9.0000	0.0000	9.0000	0.0000
0.5	8.9956	0.0164	8.9927	0.0152	8.9902	0.0135
1.0	8.9751	0.0695	8.9629	0.0627	8.9526	0.0538
1.5	8.9272	0.1668	8.8974	0.1466	8.8731	0.1210
2.0	8.8392	0.3200	8.7796	0.2738	8.7335	0.2160
2.5	8.6973	0.5510	8.5858	0.4595	8.5048	0.3425
3.0	8.4907	0.9069	8.2759	0.7423	8.1290	0.5090
3.5	8.2547	1.4886	7.7826	1.2640	7.4227	0.7305
4.0	8.2067	2.3447	7.4614	2.4217	6.0710	-0.0645
4.5	8.4656	3.2143	7.7728	3.5096	5.8801	-1.0487
5.0	8.8740	3.9759	8.2121	4.3726	5.7866	-1.7794
5.5	9.3478	4.6549	8.6899	5.1287	5.7169	-2.4256
6.0	9.8607	5.2780	9.1923	5.8242	5.6558	-3.0348
6.5	10.4035	5.8618	9.7160	6.4813	5.5973	-3.6275
7.0	10.9731	6.4171	10.2601	7.1128	5.5383	-4.2143
7.5	11.5686	6.9516	10.8246	7.7275	5.4767	-4.8012
8.0	12.1904	7.4717	11.4094	8.3322	5.4112	-5.3915
8.5	12.8393	7.9833	12.0144	8.9326	5.3406	-5.9873
9.0	13.5160	8.4922	12.6390	9.5340	5.2640	-6.5898
9.5	14.2205	9.0049	13.2816	10.1411	5.1810	-7.1993
10.0	14.9519	9.5286	13.9400	10.7583	5.0911	-7.8161
10.5	15.7068	10.0705	14.6108	11.3892	4.9940	-8.4399
11.0	16.4794	10.6371	15.2897	12.0362	4.8895	-9.0705
11.5	17.2612	11.2328	15.9721	12.7001	4.7776	-9.7075
12.0	18.0423	11.8577	16.6536	13.3804	4.6584	-10.3505
12.5	18.8141	12.5081	17.3304	14.0748	4.5319	-10.9990
13.0	19.5709	13.1775	18.0000	14.7806	4.3985	-11.6528
13.5	20.3106	13.8586	18.6613	15.4945	4.2583	-12.3112
14.0	21.0338	14.5454	19.3142	16.2139	4.1115	-12.9741
14.5	21.7427	15.2332	19.9592	16.9362	3.9584	-13.6411
15.0	22.4401	15.9193	20.5973	17.6598	3.7992	-14.3118
15.5	23.1287	16.6018	21.2296	18.3835	3.6343	-14.9861
16.0	23.8109	17.2802	21.8575	19.1065	3.4638	-15.6637
16.5	24.4890	17.9542	22.4819	19.8284	3.2881	-16.3443
17.0	25.1644	18.6240	23.1038	20.5491	3.1074	-17.0279
17.5	25.8386	19.2901	23.7241	21.2686	2.9218	-17.7142
18.0	26.5127	19.9531	24.3434	21.9871	2.7317	-18.4030
18.5	27.1873	20.6136	24.9621	22.7048	2.5371	-19.0944
19.0	27.8631	21.2721	25.5807	23.4220	2.3384	-19.7881
19.5	28.5404	21.9295	26.1995	24.1390	2.1356	-20.4840
20.0	29.2195	22.5862	26.8187	24.8561	1.9290	-21.1821
20.5	29.9004	23.2430	27.4383	25.5735	1.7186	-21.8823
21.0	30.5833	23.9001	28.0585	26.2916	1.5046	-22.5844
21.5	31.2678	24.5583	28.6791	27.0104	1.2873	-23.2885
22.0	31.9540	25.2177	29.3002	27.7303	1.0666	-23.9944
22.5	32.6415	25.8788	29.9217	28.4514	0.8427	-24.7021
23.0	33.3300	26.5418	30.5434	29.1737	0.6157	-25.4115
23.5	34.0194	27.2068	31.1654	29.8974	0.3857	-26.1226
24.0	34.7094	27.8739	31.7873	30.6225	0.1529	-26.8353
24.5	35.3995	28.5431	32.4092	31.3490	-0.0827	-27.5496
25.0	36.0897	29.2145	33.0309	32.0769	-0.3211	-28.2653

TABLE I. $a_r(q) = U + iV$, $q = \rho e^{i\phi}$ $r = 3$

ρ	$\phi=65°$		$\phi=70°$		$\phi=75°$	
	U	V	U	V	U	V
0.0	9.0000	0.0000	9.0000	0.0000	9.0000	0.0000
0.5	8.9881	0.0114	8.9863	0.0090	8.9851	0.0064
1.0	8.9443	0.0433	8.9384	0.0317	8.9349	0.0195
1.5	8.8553	0.0917	8.8444	0.0603	8.8404	0.0286
2.0	8.7034	0.1512	8.6897	0.0840	8.6916	0.0190
2.5	8.4609	0.2127	8.4539	0.0839	8.4780	−0.0330
3.0	8.0783	0.2516	8.1113	0.0190	8.1966	−0.1676
3.5	7.4656	0.1606	7.6608	−0.2055	7.8787	−0.4414
4.0	6.7778	−0.4047	7.2413	−0.6862	7.6128	−0.8731
4.5	6.4835	−1.1677	7.0088	−1.2976	7.4625	−1.3944
5.0	6.3668	−1.8486	6.9121	−1.9079	7.4119	−1.9384
5.5	6.3107	−2.4760	6.8847	−2.4983	7.4263	−2.4831
6.0	6.2814	−3.0772	6.8948	−3.0767	7.4825	−3.0274
6.5	6.2658	−3.6674	6.9269	−3.6515	7.5667	−3.5752
7.0	6.2572	−4.2554	6.9726	−4.2290	7.6704	−4.1304
7.5	6.2515	−4.8465	7.0266	−4.8133	7.7877	−4.6963
8.0	6.2458	−5.4438	7.0850	−5.4071	7.9141	−5.2755
8.5	6.2383	−6.0491	7.1449	−6.0121	8.0457	−5.8695
9.0	6.2272	−6.6634	7.2038	−6.6291	8.1796	−6.4792
9.5	6.2113	−7.2870	7.2599	−7.2582	8.3128	−7.1047
10.0	6.1897	−7.9199	7.3116	−7.8993	8.4431	−7.7456
10.5	6.1618	−8.5616	7.3576	−8.5517	8.5685	−8.4011
11.0	6.1270	−9.2118	7.3972	−9.2147	8.6875	−9.0700
11.5	6.0851	−9.8698	7.4297	−9.8873	8.7992	−9.7509
12.0	6.0359	−10.5351	7.4549	−10.5686	8.9029	−10.4426
12.5	5.9796	−11.2069	7.4725	−11.2578	8.9984	−11.1436
13.0	5.9161	−11.8847	7.4827	−11.9539	9.0856	−11.8527
13.5	5.8458	−12.5679	7.4856	−12.6562	9.1647	−12.5688
14.0	5.7687	−13.2562	7.4815	−13.3640	9.2361	−13.2910
14.5	5.6853	−13.9489	7.4707	−14.0768	9.3002	−14.0184
15.0	5.5957	−14.6459	7.4535	−14.7941	9.3574	−14.7505
15.5	5.5002	−15.3466	7.4302	−15.5155	9.4082	−15.4867
16.0	5.3992	−16.0509	7.4012	−16.2405	9.4529	−16.2266
16.5	5.2929	−16.7585	7.3668	−16.9690	9.4922	−16.9699
17.0	5.1815	−17.4692	7.3273	−17.7007	9.5262	−17.7163
17.5	5.0654	−18.1827	7.2830	−18.4354	9.5555	−18.4657
18.0	4.9447	−18.8991	7.2342	−19.1729	9.5802	−19.2179
18.5	4.8196	−19.6180	7.1811	−19.9130	9.6006	−19.9727
19.0	4.6904	−20.3394	7.1238	−20.6558	9.6171	−20.7301
19.5	4.5572	−21.0632	7.0627	−21.4009	9.6298	−21.4900
20.0	4.4202	−21.7892	6.9979	−22.1485	9.6390	−22.2522
20.5	4.2795	−22.5175	6.9296	−22.8982	9.6447	−23.0167
21.0	4.1354	−23.2478	6.8578	−23.6502	9.6472	−23.7835
21.5	3.9879	−23.9802	6.7828	−24.4043	9.6466	−24.5525
22.0	3.8372	−24.7145	6.7047	−25.1605	9.6431	−25.3236
22.5	3.6834	−25.4507	6.6236	−25.9187	9.6366	−26.0968
23.0	3.5266	−26.1888	6.5395	−26.6788	9.6274	−26.8720
23.5	3.3669	−26.9286	6.4527	−27.4407	9.6155	−27.6492
24.0	3.2044	−27.6702	6.3632	−28.2045	9.6010	−28.4284
24.5	3.0391	−28.4134	6.2711	−28.9701	9.5841	−29.2094
25.0	2.8713	−29.1583	6.1764	−29.7374	9.5647	−29.9922

TABLE I. $a_r(q) = U + iV$, $q = \rho e^{i\phi}$ $r = 3$

ρ	$\phi = 80°$		$\phi = 85°$		$\phi = 90°$	
	U	V	U	V	U	V
0.0	9.0000	0.0000	9.0000	0.0000	9.0000	0.0000
0.5	8.9844	0.0036	8.9841	0.0008	8.9844	−0.0020
1.0	8.9338	0.0072	8.9350	−0.0048	8.9382	−0.0159
1.5	8.8428	−0.0020	8.8508	−0.0301	8.8636	−0.0549
2.0	8.7068	−0.0404	8.7326	−0.0917	8.7660	−0.1336
2.5	8.5250	−0.1316	8.5868	−0.2096	8.6568	−0.2670
3.0	8.3086	−0.3069	8.4315	−0.4044	8.5556	−0.4665
3.5	8.0939	−0.5937	8.2982	−0.6860	8.4873	−0.7323
4.0	7.9346	−0.9866	8.2197	−1.0423	8.4725	−1.0514
4.5	7.8603	−1.4441	8.2112	−1.4461	8.5191	−1.4051
5.0	7.8640	−1.9285	8.2686	−1.8746	8.6247	−1.7783
5.5	7.9270	−2.4233	8.3809	−2.3161	8.7826	−2.1631
6.0	8.0334	−2.9249	8.5377	−2.7674	8.9861	−2.5571
6.5	8.1724	−3.4348	8.7311	−3.2294	9.2299	−2.9611
7.0	8.3362	−3.9560	8.9548	−3.7044	9.5100	−3.3775
7.5	8.5193	−4.4914	9.2042	−4.1958	9.8228	−3.8099
8.0	8.7168	−5.0435	9.4747	−4.7066	10.1653	−4.2626
8.5	8.9245	−5.6144	9.7619	−5.2400	10.5338	−4.7402
9.0	9.1383	−6.2053	10.0612	−5.7983	10.9238	−5.2473
9.5	9.3546	−6.8168	10.3677	−6.3830	11.3295	−5.7880
10.0	9.5699	−7.4484	10.6764	−6.9946	11.7439	−6.3652
10.5	9.7811	−8.0991	10.9823	−7.6322	12.1587	−6.9796
11.0	9.9858	−8.7674	11.2813	−8.2936	12.5659	−7.6289
11.5	10.1823	−9.4511	11.5701	−8.9760	12.9590	−8.3087
12.0	10.3694	−10.1483	11.8466	−9.6758	13.3337	−9.0126
12.5	10.5466	−10.8568	12.1099	−10.3895	13.6883	−9.7342
13.0	10.7139	−11.5746	12.3601	−11.1140	14.0233	−10.4678
13.5	10.8716	−12.3002	12.5978	−11.8467	14.3405	−11.2088
14.0	11.0203	−13.0322	12.8242	−12.5855	14.6422	−11.9541
14.5	11.1606	−13.7694	13.0404	−13.3290	14.9311	−12.7019
15.0	11.2931	−14.5112	13.2476	−14.0760	15.2093	−13.4509
15.5	11.4187	−15.2567	13.4469	−14.8260	15.4788	−14.2006
16.0	11.5379	−16.0057	13.6395	−15.5785	15.7412	−14.9508
16.5	11.6513	−16.7578	13.8261	−16.3332	15.9978	−15.7017
17.0	11.7594	−17.5127	14.0074	−17.0901	16.2495	−16.4534
17.5	11.8627	−18.2703	14.1841	−17.8490	16.4973	−17.2060
18.0	11.9616	−19.0304	14.3567	−18.6100	16.7416	−17.9600
18.5	12.0565	−19.7931	14.5256	−19.3732	16.9829	−18.7156
19.0	12.1475	−20.5582	14.6910	−20.1385	17.2215	−19.4729
19.5	12.2350	−21.3256	14.8532	−20.9061	17.4577	−20.2322
20.0	12.3191	−22.0954	15.0125	−21.6759	17.6917	−20.9937
20.5	12.4000	−22.8676	15.1690	−22.4480	17.9234	−21.7575
21.0	12.4780	−23.6420	15.3229	−23.2224	18.1531	−22.5237
21.5	12.5530	−24.4186	15.4742	−23.9991	18.3808	−23.2924
22.0	12.6253	−25.1975	15.6230	−24.7781	18.6064	−24.0635
22.5	12.6948	−25.9785	15.7694	−25.5594	18.8300	−24.8372
23.0	12.7619	−26.7617	15.9135	−26.3430	19.0517	−25.6134
23.5	12.8264	−27.5469	16.0553	−27.1289	19.2713	−26.3921
24.0	12.8884	−28.3342	16.1949	−27.9169	19.4889	−27.1733
24.5	12.9482	−29.1235	16.3323	−28.7071	19.7046	−27.9569
25.0	13.0056	−29.9148	16.4675	−29.4995	19.9183	−28.7428

322-566 O - 69 - 4

TABLE I. $a_r(q) = U + iV$, $q = \rho e^{i\phi}$ $r = 4$

ρ	$\phi=5°$		$\phi=10°$		$\phi=15°$	
	U	V	U	V	U	V
0.0	16.0000	0.0000	16.0000	0.0000	16.0000	0.0000
0.5	16.0082	0.0015	16.0079	0.0029	16.0072	0.0042
1.0	16.0333	0.0060	16.0317	0.0117	16.0291	0.0171
1.5	16.0762	0.0139	16.0724	0.0273	16.0662	0.0397
2.0	16.1387	0.0258	16.1314	0.0506	16.1195	0.0735
2.5	16.2231	0.0426	16.2105	0.0833	16.1902	0.1205
3.0	16.3320	0.0650	16.3122	0.1270	16.2803	0.1833
3.5	16.4686	0.0940	16.4391	0.1835	16.3918	0.2644
4.0	16.6358	0.1302	16.5944	0.2543	16.5275	0.3662
4.5	16.8365	0.1740	16.7810	0.3401	16.6906	0.4905
5.0	17.0727	0.2251	17.0016	0.4410	16.8848	0.6380
5.5	17.3455	0.2828	17.2584	0.5556	17.1139	0.8077
6.0	17.6548	0.3457	17.5525	0.6816	17.3810	0.9967
6.5	17.9989	0.4121	17.8835	0.8155	17.6881	1.2000
7.0	18.3752	0.4800	18.2494	0.9532	18.0351	1.4116
7.5	18.7797	0.5476	18.6472	1.0909	18.4200	1.6248
8.0	19.2082	0.6131	19.0724	1.2250	18.8387	1.8337
8.5	19.6558	0.6752	19.5204	1.3526	19.2862	2.0333
9.0	20.1179	0.7328	19.9861	1.4713	19.7571	2.2201
9.5	20.5899	0.7851	20.4648	1.5794	20.2461	2.3913
10.0	21.0673	0.8313	20.9519	1.6758	20.7482	2.5453
10.5	21.5463	0.8711	21.4434	1.7594	21.2592	2.6806
11.0	22.0232	0.9040	21.9355	1.8295	21.7753	2.7964
11.5	22.4945	0.9297	22.4247	1.8854	22.2930	2.8915
12.0	22.9573	0.9480	22.9080	1.9267	22.8092	2.9653
12.5	23.4087	0.9587	23.3825	1.9527	23.3212	3.0167
13.0	23.8462	0.9618	23.8453	1.9633	23.8260	3.0451
13.5	24.2674	0.9572	24.2938	1.9583	24.3209	3.0494
14.0	24.6703	0.9450	24.7257	1.9375	24.8031	3.0292
14.5	25.0531	0.9254	25.1386	1.9013	25.2694	2.9840
15.0	25.4143	0.8989	25.5304	1.8501	25.7168	2.9136
15.5	25.7525	0.8659	25.8991	1.7846	26.1421	2.8187
16.0	26.0669	0.8269	26.2430	1.7061	26.5419	2.7002
16.5	26.3567	0.7826	26.5610	1.6157	26.9133	2.5601
17.0	26.6217	0.7337	26.8520	1.5151	27.2537	2.4010
17.5	26.8618	0.6809	27.1156	1.4060	27.5613	2.2261
18.0	27.0771	0.6250	27.3517	1.2900	27.8353	2.0390
18.5	27.2682	0.5667	27.5608	1.1690	28.0757	1.8433
19.0	27.4357	0.5066	27.7435	1.0443	28.2835	1.6425
19.5	27.5803	0.4452	27.9010	0.9174	28.4604	1.4394
20.0	27.7030	0.3831	28.0342	0.7893	28.6085	1.2361
20.5	27.8047	0.3205	28.1447	0.6610	28.7300	1.0344
21.0	27.8864	0.2579	28.2336	0.5331	28.8273	0.8353
21.5	27.9491	0.1955	28.3024	0.4061	28.9025	0.6395
22.0	27.9938	0.1333	28.3523	0.2803	28.9575	0.4472
22.5	28.0214	0.0717	28.3845	0.1559	28.9943	0.2585
23.0	28.0329	0.0105	28.4002	0.0329	29.0142	0.0732
23.5	28.0290	−0.0502	28.4004	−0.0885	29.0187	−0.1088
24.0	28.0107	−0.1102	28.3861	−0.2086	29.0089	−0.2878
24.5	27.9786	−0.1698	28.3580	−0.3272	28.9859	−0.4642
25.0	27.9335	−0.2288	28.3171	−0.4447	28.9504	−0.6382

TABLE I. $a_r(q) = U+iV$, $q = \rho e^{i\phi}$ $\qquad\qquad r=4$

ρ	$\phi=20°$		$\phi=25°$		$\phi=30°$	
	U	V	U	V	U	V
0.0	16.0000	0.0000	16.0000	0.0000	16.0000	0.0000
0.5	16.0064	0.0054	16.0054	0.0064	16.0042	0.0072
1.0	16.0256	0.0219	16.0213	0.0260	16.0164	0.0293
1.5	16.0579	0.0507	16.0478	0.0599	16.0363	0.0672
2.0	16.1036	0.0935	16.0844	0.1100	16.0628	0.1224
2.5	16.1633	0.1527	16.1310	0.1786	16.0949	0.1974
3.0	16.2380	0.2314	16.1875	0.2691	16.1314	0.2953
3.5	16.3289	0.3327	16.2539	0.3853	16.1711	0.4198
4.0	16.4382	0.4603	16.3314	0.5314	16.2132	0.5759
4.5	16.5690	0.6172	16.4220	0.7125	16.2580	0.7698
5.0	16.7257	0.8057	16.5299	0.9332	16.3076	1.0090
5.5	16.9137	1.0265	16.6619	1.1973	16.3675	1.3024
6.0	17.1394	1.2774	16.8276	1.5062	16.4495	1.6585
6.5	17.4085	1.5529	17.0390	1.8561	16.5729	2.0814
7.0	17.7247	1.8445	17.3066	2.2364	16.7628	2.5629
7.5	18.0881	2.1419	17.6360	2.6315	17.0382	3.0786
8.0	18.4953	2.4355	18.0249	3.0251	17.4009	3.5969
8.5	18.9406	2.7175	18.4657	3.4041	17.8374	4.0938
9.0	19.4173	2.9825	18.9487	3.7608	18.3298	4.5580
9.5	19.9190	3.2271	19.4648	4.0910	18.8635	4.9865
10.0	20.4400	3.4491	20.0069	4.3932	19.4282	5.3801
10.5	20.9756	3.6473	20.5695	4.6669	20.0174	5.7407
11.0	21.5219	3.8207	21.1485	4.9120	20.6271	6.0701
11.5	22.0757	3.9685	21.7413	5.1283	21.2552	6.3698
12.0	22.6344	4.0895	22.3459	5.3151	21.9005	6.6406
12.5	23.1955	4.1825	22.9610	5.4714	22.5631	6.8829
13.0	23.7568	4.2461	23.5858	5.5958	23.2438	7.0962
13.5	24.3160	4.2785	24.2196	5.6860	23.9441	7.2798
14.0	24.8705	4.2777	24.8621	5.7388	24.6666	7.4320
14.5	25.4172	4.2415	25.5124	5.7501	25.4151	7.5503
15.0	25.9523	4.1677	26.1696	5.7142	26.1948	7.6309
15.5	26.4710	4.0544	26.8312	5.6237	27.0137	7.6680
16.0	26.9673	3.9005	27.4919	5.4688	27.8842	7.6524
16.5	27.4341	3.7066	28.1415	5.2381	28.8272	7.5676
17.0	27.8640	3.4755	28.7605	4.9207	29.8833	7.3794
17.5	28.2500	3.2129	29.3184	4.5151	31.1558	6.9834
18.0	28.5875	2.9269	29.7806	4.0411	32.5936	5.5175
18.5	28.8750	2.6269	30.1308	3.5396	32.4478	4.1622
19.0	29.1146	2.3216	30.3810	3.0500	32.3331	3.3988
19.5	29.3105	2.0180	30.5569	2.5926	32.2674	2.8177
20.0	29.4681	1.7206	30.6820	2.1713	32.2287	2.3304
20.5	29.5931	1.4319	30.7722	1.7827	32.2057	1.9006
21.0	29.6902	1.1527	30.8377	1.4216	32.1921	1.5094
21.5	29.7635	0.8830	30.8846	1.0827	32.1838	1.1455
22.0	29.8165	0.6222	30.9168	0.7617	32.1782	0.8016
22.5	29.8516	0.3695	30.9367	0.4550	32.1734	0.4726
23.0	29.8710	0.1239	30.9461	0.1598	32.1679	0.1547
23.5	29.8764	−0.1156	30.9458	−0.1262	32.1608	−0.1549
24.0	29.8689	−0.3498	30.9368	−0.4050	32.1512	−0.4581
24.5	29.8497	−0.5795	30.9196	−0.6778	32.1386	−0.7565
25.0	29.8196	−0.8055	30.8945	−0.9461	32.1223	−1.0516

TABLE I. $a_r(q) = U + iV$, $q = \rho e^{i\phi}$ $\qquad r = 4$

ρ	$\phi=35°$		$\phi=40°$		$\phi=45°$	
	U	V	U	V	U	V
0.0	16.0000	0.0000	16.0000	0.0000	16.0000	0.0000
0.5	16.0028	0.0079	16.0014	0.0082	16.0000	0.0083
1.0	16.0110	0.0316	16.0053	0.0330	15.9995	0.0333
1.5	16.0237	0.0721	16.0107	0.0747	15.9975	0.0750
2.0	16.0396	0.1305	16.0157	0.1342	15.9920	0.1335
2.5	16.0567	0.2087	16.0180	0.2124	15.9803	0.2088
3.0	16.0728	0.3091	16.0144	0.3109	15.9590	0.3015
3.5	16.0853	0.4352	16.0012	0.4321	15.9235	0.4123
4.0	16.0913	0.5916	15.9737	0.5792	15.8678	0.5422
4.5	16.0882	0.7848	15.9260	0.7575	15.7843	0.6934
5.0	16.0741	1.0239	15.8510	0.9746	15.6619	0.8690
5.5	16.0491	1.3225	15.7396	1.2441	15.4842	1.0745
6.0	16.0196	1.7000	15.5809	1.5904	15.2229	1.3193
6.5	16.0073	2.1809	15.3674	2.0642	14.8190	1.6221
7.0	16.0617	2.7795	15.1405	2.7725	14.0779	2.0277
7.5	16.2473	3.4626	15.1419	3.7650	12.5119	1.3897
8.0	16.5813	4.1529	15.4967	4.7356	12.2387	0.4258
8.5	17.0261	4.7972	16.0065	5.5545	12.1093	-0.2470
9.0	17.5404	5.3842	16.5737	6.2637	12.0197	-0.8113
9.5	18.0990	5.9192	17.1701	6.8990	11.9463	-1.3201
10.0	18.6885	6.4100	17.7865	7.4816	11.8795	-1.7976
10.5	19.3020	6.8633	18.4196	8.0240	11.8145	-2.2566
11.0	19.9362	7.2842	19.0685	8.5348	11.7483	-2.7050
11.5	20.5896	7.6765	19.7332	9.0198	11.6791	-3.1478
12.0	21.2620	8.0431	20.4144	9.4834	11.6055	-3.5883
12.5	21.9542	8.3861	21.1132	9.9293	11.5267	-4.0288
13.0	22.6677	8.7075	21.8308	10.3608	11.4420	-4.4708
13.5	23.4047	9.0089	22.5687	10.7811	11.3508	-4.9153
14.0	24.1684	9.2920	23.3284	11.1936	11.2528	-5.3630
14.5	24.9630	9.5590	24.1114	11.6021	11.1477	-5.8144
15.0	25.7936	9.8129	24.9190	12.0111	11.0354	-6.2697
15.5	26.6670	10.0585	25.7517	12.4261	10.9157	-6.7290
16.0	27.5913	10.3041	26.6087	12.8531	10.7885	-7.1925
16.5	28.5750	10.5639	27.4873	13.2987	10.6540	-7.6599
17.0	29.6228	10.8620	28.3821	13.7690	10.5121	-8.1313
17.5	30.7240	11.2321	29.2853	14.2682	10.3629	-8.6065
18.0	31.8399	11.7023	30.1876	14.7969	10.2066	-9.0854
18.5	32.9165	12.2652	31.0804	15.3521	10.0431	-9.5679
19.0	33.9234	12.8803	31.9574	15.9275	9.8728	-10.0537
19.5	34.8630	13.5094	32.8160	16.5163	9.6958	-10.5428
20.0	35.7507	14.1310	33.6559	17.1119	9.5122	-11.0349
20.5	36.6015	14.7364	34.4788	17.7092	9.3222	-11.5299
21.0	37.4268	15.3230	35.2874	18.3046	9.1260	-12.0278
21.5	38.2348	15.8908	36.0844	18.8959	8.9237	-12.5283
22.0	39.0315	16.4410	36.8724	19.4818	8.7156	-13.0314
22.5	39.8210	16.9751	37.6537	20.0617	8.5018	-13.5369
23.0	40.6066	17.4944	38.4303	20.6354	8.2825	-14.0448
23.5	41.3906	18.0005	39.2038	21.2031	8.0578	-14.5549
24.0	42.1750	18.4949	39.9758	21.7651	7.8279	-15.0671
24.5	42.9614	18.9787	40.7473	22.3220	7.5931	-15.5814
25.0	43.7508	19.4532	41.5193	22.8742	7.3533	-16.0977

TABLE I. $a_r(q) = U + iV$, $q = \rho e^{i\phi}$ $r = 4$

ρ	$\phi = 50°$		$\phi = 55°$		$\phi = 60°$	
	U	V	U	V	U	V
0.0	16.0000	0.0000	16.0000	0.0000	16.0000	0.0000
0.5	15.9985	0.0082	15.9971	0.0078	15.9958	0.0072
1.0	15.9937	0.0327	15.9882	0.0310	15.9831	0.0284
1.5	15.9846	0.0730	15.9724	0.0689	15.9612	0.0628
2.0	15.9692	0.1287	15.9481	0.1202	15.9292	0.1085
2.5	15.9451	0.1989	15.9133	0.1834	15.8856	0.1634
3.0	15.9087	0.2827	15.8649	0.2562	15.8284	0.2243
3.5	15.8555	0.3789	15.7991	0.3360	15.7550	0.2873
4.0	15.7794	0.4864	15.7111	0.4192	15.6625	0.3474
4.5	15.6726	0.6034	15.5945	0.5008	15.5474	0.3977
5.0	15.5242	0.7269	15.4419	0.5735	15.4065	0.4294
5.5	15.3184	0.8517	15.2442	0.6259	15.2381	0.4305
6.0	15.0314	0.9653	14.9935	0.6388	15.0441	0.3861
6.5	14.6286	1.0341	14.6890	0.5816	14.8342	0.2795
7.0	14.0848	0.9626	14.3540	0.4166	14.6277	0.0995
7.5	13.5236	0.6105	14.0435	0.1288	14.4486	-0.1520
8.0	13.1566	0.0823	13.8065	-0.2479	14.3140	-0.4598
8.5	12.9507	-0.4514	13.6488	-0.6650	14.2281	-0.8048
9.0	12.8274	-0.9558	13.5520	-1.0946	14.1855	-1.1726
9.5	12.7469	-1.4357	13.4969	-1.5267	14.1779	-1.5551
10.0	12.6898	-1.8997	13.4699	-1.9595	14.1973	-1.9489
10.5	12.6459	-2.3544	13.4613	-2.3940	14.2372	-2.3529
11.0	12.6091	-2.8047	13.4650	-2.8320	14.2921	-2.7672
11.5	12.5753	-3.2540	13.4762	-3.2750	14.3579	-3.1923
12.0	12.5420	-3.7048	13.4916	-3.7243	14.4312	-3.6289
12.5	12.5070	-4.1588	13.5087	-4.1810	14.5090	-4.0773
13.0	12.4691	-4.6170	13.5255	-4.6457	14.5890	-4.5381
13.5	12.4270	-5.0804	13.5402	-5.1188	14.6691	-5.0113
14.0	12.3799	-5.5493	13.5515	-5.6004	14.7475	-5.4968
14.5	12.3272	-6.0239	13.5585	-6.0905	14.8226	-5.9943
15.0	12.2682	-6.5044	13.5602	-6.5889	14.8932	-6.5034
15.5	12.2027	-6.9906	13.5560	-7.0954	14.9583	-7.0235
16.0	12.1304	-7.4824	13.5453	-7.6095	15.0169	-7.5538
16.5	12.0511	-7.9797	13.5278	-8.1308	15.0685	-8.0937
17.0	11.9648	-8.4821	13.5033	-8.6588	15.1126	-8.6424
17.5	11.8713	-8.9895	13.4716	-9.1931	15.1490	-9.1991
18.0	11.7708	-9.5015	13.4327	-9.7333	15.1776	-9.7630
18.5	11.6632	-10.0180	13.3865	-10.2789	15.1983	-10.3334
19.0	11.5488	-10.5385	13.3332	-10.8294	15.2113	-10.9098
19.5	11.4276	-11.0630	13.2730	-11.3846	15.2166	-11.4914
20.0	11.2999	-11.5911	13.2059	-11.9440	15.2146	-12.0780
20.5	11.1657	-12.1226	13.1322	-12.5074	15.2054	-12.6688
21.0	11.0252	-12.6574	13.0520	-13.0745	15.1894	-13.2637
21.5	10.8787	-13.1953	12.9656	-13.6450	15.1667	-13.8623
22.0	10.7262	-13.7361	12.8731	-14.2187	15.1378	-14.4643
22.5	10.5681	-14.2796	12.7748	-14.7954	15.1028	-15.0694
23.0	10.4045	-14.8258	12.6709	-15.3750	15.0620	-15.6774
23.5	10.2354	-15.3744	12.5616	-15.9573	15.0156	-16.2883
24.0	10.0612	-15.9255	12.4471	-16.5421	14.9640	-16.9018
24.5	9.8820	-16.4788	12.3275	-17.1294	14.9073	-17.5177
25.0	9.6980	-17.0344	12.2031	-17.7191	14.8458	-18.1361

TABLE I. $a_r(q) = U + iV,\ q = \rho e^{i\phi}$ $\qquad\qquad$ $r = 4$

ρ	$\phi = 65°$		$\phi = 70°$		$\phi = 75°$	
	U	V	U	V	U	V
0.0	16.0000	0.0000	16.0000	0.0000	16.0000	0.0000
0.5	15.9946	0.0064	15.9936	0.0053	15.9928	0.0041
1.0	15.9785	0.0250	15.9746	0.0209	15.9714	0.0162
1.5	15.9513	0.0549	15.9430	0.0457	15.9363	0.0353
2.0	15.9128	0.0942	15.8992	0.0777	15.8885	0.0596
2.5	15.8623	0.1400	15.8436	0.1142	15.8294	0.0868
3.0	15.7991	0.1889	15.7768	0.1517	15.7607	0.1136
3.5	15.7224	0.2363	15.6996	0.1855	15.6846	0.1363
4.0	15.6311	0.2766	15.6130	0.2104	15.6042	0.1503
4.5	15.5249	0.3026	15.5192	0.2200	15.5229	0.1507
5.0	15.4043	0.3062	15.4211	0.2077	15.4455	0.1327
5.5	15.2719	0.2777	15.3235	0.1669	15.3772	0.0922
6.0	15.1337	0.2077	15.2328	0.0921	15.3241	0.0261
6.5	14.9992	0.0886	15.1569	-0.0199	15.2923	-0.0669
7.0	14.8810	-0.0821	15.1036	-0.1692	15.2869	-0.1862
7.5	14.7907	-0.3012	15.0791	-0.3530	15.3120	-0.3301
8.0	14.7357	-0.5604	15.0873	-0.5669	15.3696	-0.4962
8.5	14.7179	-0.8508	15.1291	-0.8063	15.4605	-0.6821
9.0	14.7353	-1.1650	15.2034	-1.0675	15.5841	-0.8861
9.5	14.7837	-1.4981	15.3078	-1.3479	15.7393	-1.1072
10.0	14.8583	-1.8477	15.4396	-1.6463	15.9245	-1.3452
10.5	14.9548	-2.2125	15.5957	-1.9623	16.1378	-1.6005
11.0	15.0690	-2.5927	15.7732	-2.2964	16.3775	-1.8741
11.5	15.1974	-2.9884	15.9691	-2.6494	16.6416	-2.1677
12.0	15.3366	-3.4002	16.1805	-3.0222	16.9280	-2.4830
12.5	15.4838	-3.8286	16.4047	-3.4159	17.2344	-2.8223
13.0	15.6361	-4.2740	16.6385	-3.8316	17.5580	-3.1879
13.5	15.7911	-4.7365	16.8790	-4.2699	17.8958	-3.5821
14.0	15.9463	-5.2161	17.1229	-4.7312	18.2436	-4.0069
14.5	16.0996	-5.7123	17.3672	-5.2156	18.5971	-4.4639
15.0	16.2490	-6.2245	17.6088	-5.7223	18.9512	-4.9536
15.5	16.3930	-6.7517	17.8449	-6.2504	19.3004	-5.4752
16.0	16.5301	-7.2929	18.0731	-6.7980	19.6399	-6.0269
16.5	16.6594	-7.8469	18.2914	-7.3634	19.9653	-6.6053
17.0	16.7800	-8.4123	18.4984	-7.9442	20.2736	-7.2062
17.5	16.8916	-8.9879	18.6934	-8.5383	20.5630	-7.8251
18.0	16.9938	-9.5725	18.8761	-9.1434	20.8333	-8.4576
18.5	17.0868	-10.1649	19.0466	-9.7577	21.0852	-9.0999
19.0	17.1707	-10.7641	19.2052	-10.3794	21.3199	-9.7491
19.5	17.2457	-11.3692	19.3527	-11.0072	21.5393	-10.4028
20.0	17.3123	-11.9795	19.4898	-11.6398	21.7450	-11.0594
20.5	17.3708	-12.5944	19.6173	-12.2766	21.9388	-11.7178
21.0	17.4217	-13.2133	19.7360	-12.9167	22.1222	-12.3774
21.5	17.4654	-13.8358	19.8466	-13.5597	22.2967	-13.0379
22.0	17.5023	-14.4616	19.9498	-14.2053	22.4634	-13.6991
22.5	17.5329	-15.0904	20.0463	-14.8532	22.6232	-14.3611
23.0	17.5574	-15.7220	20.1365	-15.5033	22.7769	-15.0238
23.5	17.5762	-16.3563	20.2210	-16.1554	22.9253	-15.6875
24.0	17.5897	-16.9930	20.3002	-16.8096	23.0689	-16.3523
24.5	17.5980	-17.6321	20.3745	-17.4658	23.2081	-17.0184
25.0	17.6016	-18.2736	20.4441	-18.1240	23.3433	-17.6859

TABLE I. $a_r(q) = U + iV$, $q = \rho e^{i\phi}$ $\qquad\qquad$ $r = 4$

ρ	$\phi = 80°$		$\phi = 85°$		$\phi = 90°$	
	U	V	U	V	U	V
0.0	16.0000	0.0000	16.0000	0.0000	16.0000	0.0000
0.5	15.9922	0.0028	15.9918	0.0014	15.9917	0.0000
1.0	15.9691	0.0111	15.9676	0.0056	15.9672	0.0000
1.5	15.9315	0.0240	15.9285	0.0121	15.9276	0.0000
2.0	15.8809	0.0403	15.8763	0.0204	15.8748	0.0000
2.5	15.8195	0.0583	15.8136	0.0293	15.8117	0.0000
3.0	15.7499	0.0756	15.7437	0.0377	15.7417	0.0000
3.5	15.6756	0.0893	15.6709	0.0441	15.6694	0.0000
4.0	15.6007	0.0962	15.5999	0.0469	15.5998	0.0000
4.5	15.5300	0.0932	15.5360	0.0443	15.5383	0.0000
5.0	15.4687	0.0771	15.4849	0.0351	15.4907	0.0000
5.5	15.4223	0.0455	15.4520	0.0180	15.4624	0.0000
6.0	15.3963	−0.0030	15.4424	−0.0076	15.4581	0.0000
6.5	15.3955	−0.0691	15.4601	−0.0419	15.4821	0.0000
7.0	15.4238	−0.1522	15.5085	−0.0846	15.5372	0.0000
7.5	15.4840	−0.2514	15.5899	−0.1352	15.6257	0.0000
8.0	15.5778	−0.3655	15.7058	−0.1933	15.7490	0.0000
8.5	15.7057	−0.4932	15.8568	−0.2586	15.9080	0.0000
9.0	15.8678	−0.6341	16.0436	−0.3307	16.1032	0.0000
9.5	16.0638	−0.7879	16.2662	−0.4098	16.3351	0.0000
10.0	16.2931	−0.9549	16.5249	−0.4962	16.6042	0.0000
10.5	16.5551	−1.1360	16.8202	−0.5906	16.9114	0.0000
11.0	16.8492	−1.3326	17.1527	−0.6941	17.2579	0.0000
11.5	17.1751	−1.5466	17.5235	−0.8081	17.6454	0.0000
12.0	17.5321	−1.7808	17.9341	−0.9347	18.0765	0.0000
12.5	17.9196	−2.0382	18.3866	−1.0768	18.5550	0.0000
13.0	18.3366	−2.3231	18.8836	−1.2384	19.0857	0.0000
13.5	18.7814	−2.6402	19.4284	−1.4253	19.6763	0.0000
14.0	19.2509	−2.9953	20.0247	−1.6457	20.3373	0.0000
14.5	19.7403	−3.3944	20.6758	−1.9125	21.0859	0.0000
15.0	20.2420	−3.8432	21.3821	−2.2445	21.9506	0.0000
15.5	20.7457	−4.3455	22.1354	−2.6690	22.9879	0.0000
16.0	21.2386	−4.9015	22.9070	−3.2169	24.3458	0.0000
16.5	21.7083	−5.5059	23.6397	−3.9002	27.3308	−0.6974
17.0	22.1452	−6.1488	24.2746	−4.6835	27.5373	−3.0201
17.5	22.5449	−6.8182	24.7959	−5.5038	27.7532	−4.2599
18.0	22.9080	−7.5027	25.2260	−6.3164	27.9782	−5.2517
18.5	23.2385	−8.1937	25.5943	−7.1039	28.2121	−6.1188
19.0	23.5414	−8.8855	25.9227	−7.8638	28.4546	−6.9098
19.5	23.8219	−9.5749	26.2257	−8.5989	28.7057	−7.6497
20.0	24.0846	−10.2603	26.5123	−9.3131	28.9650	−8.3536
20.5	24.3333	−10.9415	26.7885	−10.0107	29.2322	−9.0313
21.0	24.5709	−11.6185	27.0579	−10.6949	29.5071	−9.6897
21.5	24.7997	−12.2920	27.3232	−11.3689	29.7894	−10.3339
22.0	25.0216	−12.9626	27.5859	−12.0351	30.0786	−10.9677
22.5	25.2378	−13.6310	27.8473	−12.6955	30.3744	−11.5943
23.0	25.4494	−14.2979	28.1079	−13.3520	30.6763	−12.2160
23.5	25.6571	−14.9641	28.3682	−14.0059	30.9840	−12.8350
24.0	25.8615	−15.6300	28.6285	−14.6585	31.2968	−13.4528
24.5	26.0629	−16.2962	28.8889	−15.3108	31.6144	−14.0708
25.0	26.2618	−16.9633	29.1493	−15.9636	31.9361	−14.6903

TABLE I. $\quad a_r(q) = U + iV, \; q = \rho e^{i\phi}$ $\qquad\qquad r=5$

ρ	$\phi=5°$		$\phi=10°$		$\phi=15°$	
	U	V	U	V	U	V
0.0	25.0000	0.0000	25.0000	0.0000	25.0000	0.0000
0.5	25.0051	0.0009	25.0049	0.0018	25.0045	0.0026
1.0	25.0205	0.0036	25.0196	0.0071	25.0181	0.0104
1.5	25.0463	0.0082	25.0441	0.0161	25.0406	0.0235
2.0	25.0825	0.0146	25.0786	0.0288	25.0723	0.0421
2.5	25.1294	0.0231	25.1232	0.0454	25.1132	0.0662
3.0	25.1872	0.0336	25.1781	0.0661	25.1634	0.0963
3.5	25.2565	0.0465	25.2437	0.0913	25.2230	0.1328
4.0	25.3379	0.0620	25.3205	0.1215	25.2924	0.1764
4.5	25.4320	0.0803	25.4089	0.1572	25.3717	0.2277
5.0	25.5397	0.1018	25.5097	0.1992	25.4614	0.2877
5.5	25.6623	0.1271	25.6237	0.2481	25.5620	0.3575
6.0	25.8007	0.1564	25.7519	0.3049	25.6741	0.4384
6.5	25.9564	0.1903	25.8956	0.3706	25.7985	0.5316
7.0	26.1307	0.2291	26.0559	0.4459	25.9363	0.6386
7.5	26.3251	0.2732	26.2343	0.5316	26.0887	0.7607
8.0	26.5410	0.3228	26.4325	0.6285	26.2573	0.8994
8.5	26.7798	0.3780	26.6520	0.7366	26.4442	1.0556
9.0	27.0423	0.4385	26.8945	0.8560	26.6518	1.2298
9.5	27.3295	0.5038	27.1614	0.9861	26.8825	1.4221
10.0	27.6416	0.5734	27.4541	1.1255	27.1393	1.6314
10.5	27.9785	0.6462	27.7732	1.2728	27.4247	1.8556
11.0	28.3396	0.7213	28.1190	1.4256	27.7408	2.0915
11.5	28.7238	0.7974	28.4911	1.5816	28.0888	2.3353
12.0	29.1294	0.8734	28.8882	1.7381	28.4686	2.5822
12.5	29.5545	0.9481	29.3087	1.8928	28.8790	2.8279
13.0	29.9968	1.0206	29.7503	2.0432	29.3177	3.0681
13.5	30.4540	1.0899	30.2104	2.1876	29.7816	3.2992
14.0	30.9234	1.1553	30.6863	2.3242	30.2675	3.5187
14.5	31.4025	1.2162	31.1751	2.4517	30.7718	3.7245
15.0	31.8889	1.2721	31.6743	2.5693	31.2913	3.9151
15.5	32.3800	1.3225	32.1810	2.6759	31.8230	4.0894
16.0	32.8735	1.3671	32.6929	2.7711	32.3641	4.2468
16.5	33.3672	1.4056	33.2076	2.8543	32.9121	4.3865
17.0	33.8590	1.4378	33.7229	2.9250	33.4648	4.5080
17.5	34.3469	1.4636	34.2367	2.9828	34.0202	4.6109
18.0	34.8290	1.4828	34.7471	3.0274	34.5764	4.6944
18.5	35.3035	1.4952	35.2522	3.0585	35.1317	4.7581
19.0	35.7686	1.5009	35.7501	3.0759	35.6842	4.8012
19.5	36.2230	1.4998	36.2391	3.0793	36.2321	4.8230
20.0	36.6650	1.4921	36.7174	3.0687	36.7736	4.8229
20.5	37.0933	1.4777	37.1833	3.0440	37.3067	4.8001
21.0	37.5067	1.4569	37.6351	3.0055	37.8290	4.7540
21.5	37.9042	1.4299	38.0713	2.9534	38.3382	4.6843
22.0	38.2847	1.3971	38.4902	2.8882	38.8316	4.5909
22.5	38.6474	1.3589	38.8906	2.8106	39.3064	4.4739
23.0	38.9918	1.3157	39.2710	2.7216	39.7595	4.3344
23.5	39.3173	1.2680	39.6305	2.6221	40.1881	4.1739
24.0	39.6235	1.2164	39.9682	2.5135	40.5896	3.9945
24.5	39.9104	1.1614	40.2836	2.3971	40.9618	3.7991
25.0	40.1780	1.1035	40.5765	2.2743	41.3035	3.5911

ρ	$\phi = 20°$		$\phi = 25°$		$\phi = 30°$	
	U	V	U	V	U	V
0.0	25.0000	0.0000	25.0000	0.0000	25.0000	0.0000
0.5	25.0040	0.0033	25.0033	0.0040	25.0026	0.0045
1.0	25.0160	0.0134	25.0134	0.0160	25.0104	0.0181
1.5	25.0359	0.0303	25.0301	0.0360	25.0234	0.0407
2.0	25.0638	0.0540	25.0534	0.0642	25.0414	0.0725
2.5	25.0997	0.0849	25.0832	0.1008	25.0643	0.1136
3.0	25.1436	0.1233	25.1194	0.1461	25.0918	0.1642
3.5	25.1953	0.1696	25.1617	0.2005	25.1235	0.2247
4.0	25.2549	0.2246	25.2098	0.2647	25.1589	0.2955
4.5	25.3224	0.2891	25.2634	0.3393	25.1975	0.3770
5.0	25.3977	0.3640	25.3221	0.4253	25.2383	0.4701
5.5	25.4809	0.4506	25.3852	0.5240	25.2804	0.5757
6.0	25.5721	0.5505	25.4525	0.6367	25.3227	0.6948
6.5	25.6715	0.6651	25.5233	0.7653	25.3638	0.8290
7.0	25.7796	0.7966	25.5972	0.9118	25.4025	0.9802
7.5	25.8972	0.9469	25.6739	1.0789	25.4369	1.1507
8.0	26.0255	1.1183	25.7537	1.2697	25.4654	1.3438
8.5	26.1664	1.3131	25.8370	1.4878	25.4863	1.5636
9.0	26.3226	1.5336	25.9257	1.7379	25.4977	1.8160
9.5	26.4977	1.7814	26.0227	2.0248	25.4986	2.1089
10.0	26.6965	2.0571	26.1339	2.3540	25.4895	2.4541
10.5	26.9249	2.3599	26.2683	2.7298	25.4752	2.8679
11.0	27.1886	2.6865	26.4388	3.1535	25.4710	3.3723
11.5	27.4927	3.0312	26.6609	3.6198	25.5141	3.9874
12.0	27.8403	3.3860	26.9478	4.1154	25.6663	4.7029
12.5	28.2314	3.7425	27.3051	4.6207	25.9713	5.4550
13.0	28.6634	4.0927	27.7284	5.1169	26.4101	6.1726
13.5	29.1320	4.4301	28.2076	5.5911	26.9363	6.8275
14.0	29.6317	4.7505	28.7309	6.0366	27.5154	7.4207
14.5	30.1574	5.0511	29.2883	6.4513	28.1281	7.9610
15.0	30.7046	5.3304	29.8722	6.8358	28.7640	8.4570
15.5	31.2691	5.5878	30.4772	7.1911	29.4175	8.9155
16.0	31.8479	5.8228	31.0995	7.5188	30.0858	9.3418
16.5	32.4384	6.0354	31.7366	7.8201	30.7674	9.7399
17.0	33.0385	6.2252	32.3869	8.0962	31.4617	10.1126
17.5	33.6465	6.3920	33.0492	8.3477	32.1687	10.4622
18.0	34.2610	6.5354	33.7233	8.5749	32.8888	10.7905
18.5	34.8809	6.6545	34.4089	8.7779	33.6227	11.0987
19.0	35.5051	6.7484	35.1065	8.9563	34.3718	11.3881
19.5	36.1327	6.8158	35.8166	9.1092	35.1375	11.6596
20.0	36.7626	6.8551	36.5404	9.2355	35.9218	11.9142
20.5	37.3935	6.8643	37.2793	9.3334	36.7271	12.1528
21.0	38.0240	6.8409	38.0353	9.4003	37.5566	12.3768
21.5	38.6519	6.7821	38.8110	9.4326	38.4142	12.5877
22.0	39.2742	6.6847	39.6099	9.4252	39.3046	12.7884
22.5	39.8868	6.5453	40.4367	9.3705	40.2338	12.9830
23.0	40.4836	6.3605	41.2977	9.2565	41.2087	13.1786
23.5	41.0565	6.1283	42.2008	9.0631	42.2363	13.3870
24.0	41.5952	5.8490	43.1543	8.7518	43.3208	13.6275
24.5	42.0885	5.5272	44.1500	8.2411	44.4562	13.9269
25.0	42.5266	5.1725	45.0496	7.3889	45.6165	14.3114

ρ	$\phi = 35°$		$\phi = 40°$		$\phi = 45°$	
	U	V	U	V	U	V
0.0	25.0000	0.0000	25.0000	0.0000	25.0000	0.0000
0.5	25.0018	0.0049	25.0009	0.0051	25.0000	0.0052
1.0	25.0071	0.0196	25.0036	0.0205	25.0000	0.0208
1.5	25.0159	0.0441	25.0080	0.0462	24.9999	0.0468
2.0	25.0281	0.0785	25.0141	0.0821	24.9996	0.0832
2.5	25.0434	0.1228	25.0215	0.1282	24.9990	0.1297
3.0	25.0616	0.1771	25.0299	0.1845	24.9977	0.1863
3.5	25.0821	0.2416	25.0389	0.2509	24.9953	0.2527
4.0	25.1043	0.3164	25.0478	0.3273	24.9912	0.3285
4.5	25.1274	0.4018	25.0557	0.4136	24.9848	0.4132
5.0	25.1503	0.4980	25.0616	0.5096	24.9751	0.5062
5.5	25.1717	0.6056	25.0640	0.6152	24.9609	0.6069
6.0	25.1901	0.7251	25.0613	0.7302	24.9407	0.7142
6.5	25.2036	0.8573	25.0513	0.8544	24.9127	0.8271
7.0	25.2099	1.0032	25.0315	0.9877	24.8747	0.9443
7.5	25.2061	1.1642	24.9988	1.1298	24.8242	1.0640
8.0	25.1890	1.3422	24.9490	1.2806	24.7578	1.1840
8.5	25.1539	1.5399	24.8770	1.4395	24.6719	1.3013
9.0	25.0954	1.7611	24.7762	1.6058	24.5622	1.4118
9.5	25.0056	2.0113	24.6374	1.7777	24.4240	1.5095
10.0	24.8734	2.2996	24.4478	1.9514	24.2526	1.5856
10.5	24.6809	2.6419	24.1888	2.1179	24.0454	1.6274
11.0	24.3972	3.0709	23.8344	2.2542	23.8047	1.6181
11.5	23.9599	3.6803	23.3596	2.3017	23.5428	1.5396
12.0	23.4166	4.9258	22.8051	2.1504	23.2840	1.3816
12.5	23.8810	6.4563	22.3386	1.7778	23.0554	1.1507
13.0	24.5855	7.4771	22.0374	1.3232	22.8734	0.8675
13.5	25.2922	8.2933	21.8515	0.8731	22.7397	0.5534
14.0	25.9941	9.0002	21.7323	0.4454	22.6471	0.2234
14.5	26.6941	9.6363	21.6522	0.0387	22.5868	-0.1145
15.0	27.3950	10.2215	21.5959	-0.3518	22.5506	-0.4566
15.5	28.0991	10.7676	21.5542	-0.7308	22.5321	-0.8017
16.0	28.8083	11.2821	21.5213	-1.1018	22.5262	-1.1497
16.5	29.5240	11.7705	21.4935	-1.4676	22.5291	-1.5009
17.0	30.2475	12.2368	21.4679	-1.8306	22.5378	-1.8558
17.5	30.9800	12.6839	21.4427	-2.1924	22.5500	-2.2150
18.0	31.7227	13.1146	21.4162	-2.5543	22.5638	-2.5789
18.5	32.4768	13.5311	21.3874	-2.9173	22.5775	-2.9479
19.0	33.2433	13.9354	21.3554	-3.2820	22.5900	-3.3224
19.5	34.0235	14.3295	21.3194	-3.6491	22.6002	-3.7023
20.0	34.8185	14.7155	21.2789	-4.0190	22.6073	-4.0880
20.5	35.6295	15.0957	21.2334	-4.3919	22.6104	-4.4792
21.0	36.4573	15.4726	21.1825	-4.7679	22.6091	-4.8760
21.5	37.3029	15.8491	21.1261	-5.1473	22.6028	-5.2783
22.0	38.1665	16.2284	21.0638	-5.5300	22.5911	-5.6860
22.5	39.0481	16.6141	20.9955	-5.9161	22.5738	-6.0987
23.0	39.9464	17.0102	20.9211	-6.3055	22.5506	-6.5163
23.5	40.8593	17.4207	20.8406	-6.6981	22.5213	-6.9387
24.0	41.7832	17.8488	20.7538	-7.0939	22.4859	-7.3654
24.5	42.7135	18.2970	20.6609	-7.4927	22.4442	-7.7964
25.0	43.6449	18.7660	20.5618	-7.8945	22.3962	-8.2314

ρ	$\phi = 50°$		$\phi = 55°$		$\phi = 60°$	
	U	V	U	V	U	V
0.0	25.0000	0.0000	25.0000	0.0000	25.0000	0.0000
0.5	24.9991	0.0051	24.9982	0.0049	24.9974	0.0045
1.0	24.9964	0.0205	24.9929	0.0196	24.9896	0.0180
1.5	24.9918	0.0461	24.9839	0.0440	24.9766	0.0405
2.0	24.9852	0.0818	24.9713	0.0779	24.9583	0.0718
2.5	24.9756	0.1274	24.9551	0.1213	24.9350	0.1117
3.0	24.9658	0.1827	24.9351	0.1738	24.9065	0.1599
3.5	24.9524	0.2472	24.9113	0.2348	24.8731	0.2160
4.0	24.9361	0.3204	24.8837	0.3038	24.8350	0.2792
4.5	24.9165	0.4016	24.8520	0.3798	24.7924	0.3489
5.0	24.8929	0.4897	24.8161	0.4617	24.7456	0.4238
5.5	24.8646	0.5836	24.7759	0.5482	24.6951	0.5027
6.0	24.8306	0.6819	24.7312	0.6376	24.6413	0.5839
6.5	24.7898	0.7828	24.6816	0.7277	24.5850	0.6655
7.0	24.7410	0.8842	24.6270	0.8162	24.5269	0.7453
7.5	24.6826	0.9833	24.5671	0.9002	24.4678	0.8206
8.0	24.6130	1.0771	24.5020	0.9764	24.4091	0.8887
8.5	24.5307	1.1615	24.4318	1.0412	24.3522	0.9467
9.0	24.4345	1.2318	24.3575	1.0905	24.2987	0.9915
9.5	24.3237	1.2821	24.2803	1.1201	24.2510	1.0203
10.0	24.1991	1.3058	24.2026	1.1260	24.2114	1.0305
10.5	24.0635	1.2958	24.1277	1.1045	24.1827	1.0201
11.0	23.9224	1.2455	24.0594	1.0531	24.1675	0.9879
11.5	23.7838	1.1507	24.0022	0.9708	24.1684	0.9333
12.0	23.6572	1.0110	23.9602	0.8579	24.1874	0.8563
12.5	23.5507	0.8302	23.9366	0.7163	24.2262	0.7576
13.0	23.4694	0.6148	23.9334	0.5486	24.2855	0.6381
13.5	23.4149	0.3719	23.9511	0.3575	24.3655	0.4986
14.0	23.3861	0.1079	23.9892	0.1458	24.4658	0.3402
14.5	23.3800	−0.1727	24.0465	−0.0844	24.5856	0.1634
15.0	23.3933	−0.4668	24.1211	−0.3316	24.7238	−0.0312
15.5	23.4225	−0.7725	24.2110	−0.5947	24.8791	−0.2435
16.0	23.4645	−1.0887	24.3140	−0.8729	25.0497	−0.4736
16.5	23.5164	−1.4150	24.4281	−1.1659	25.2342	−0.7215
17.0	23.5756	−1.7511	24.5512	−1.4735	25.4308	−0.9876
17.5	23.6401	−2.0969	24.6813	−1.7956	25.6377	−1.2724
18.0	23.7078	−2.4523	24.8166	−2.1321	25.8530	−1.5761
18.5	23.7773	−2.8174	24.9553	−2.4829	26.0748	−1.8991
19.0	23.8469	−3.1920	25.0956	−2.8479	26.3010	−2.2417
19.5	23.9154	−3.5761	25.2361	−3.2270	26.5297	−2.6040
20.0	23.9817	−3.9693	25.3752	−3.6196	26.7587	−2.9858
20.5	24.0448	−4.3715	25.5117	−4.0254	26.9860	−3.3867
21.0	24.1038	−4.7824	25.6443	−4.4440	27.2097	−3.8063
21.5	24.1581	−5.2015	25.7719	−4.8745	27.4278	−4.2435
22.0	24.2072	−5.6284	25.8937	−5.3163	27.6389	−4.6973
22.5	24.2504	−6.0628	26.0089	−5.7686	27.8414	−5.1664
23.0	24.2874	−6.5041	26.1170	−6.2307	28.0344	−5.6493
23.5	24.3180	−6.9520	26.2174	−6.7016	28.2171	−6.1445
24.0	24.3420	−7.4059	26.3099	−7.1806	28.3890	−6.6505
24.5	24.3592	−7.8654	26.3944	−7.6668	28.5499	−7.1658
25.0	24.3697	−8.3301	26.4707	−8.1596	28.6998	−7.6890

TABLE I. $a_r(q) = U + iV$, $q = \rho e^{i\phi}$ $r = 5$

ρ	$\phi = 65°$		$\phi = 70°$		$\phi = 75°$	
	U	V	U	V	U	V
0.0	25.0000	0.0000	25.0000	0.0000	25.0000	0.0000
0.5	24.9967	0.0040	24.9960	0.0033	24.9955	0.0026
1.0	24.9866	0.0159	24.9840	0.0134	24.9820	0.0104
1.5	24.9699	0.0358	24.9642	0.0301	24.9595	0.0234
2.0	24.9466	0.0635	24.9364	0.0533	24.9282	0.0415
2.5	24.9168	0.0988	24.9010	0.0830	24.8882	0.0648
3.0	24.8807	0.1415	24.8582	0.1191	24.8398	0.0932
3.5	24.8386	0.1913	24.8085	0.1613	24.7836	0.1267
4.0	24.7909	0.2475	24.7524	0.2094	24.7202	0.1654
4.5	24.7384	0.3097	24.6907	0.2630	24.6503	0.2092
5.0	24.6816	0.3769	24.6246	0.3217	24.5753	0.2583
5.5	24.6216	0.4482	24.5552	0.3850	24.4963	0.3127
6.0	24.5594	0.5222	24.4841	0.4522	24.4153	0.3724
6.5	24.4965	0.5975	24.4133	0.5224	24.3342	0.4375
7.0	24.4345	0.6723	24.3449	0.5948	24.2555	0.5079
7.5	24.3750	0.7447	24.2812	0.6682	24.1820	0.5835
8.0	24.3203	0.8127	24.2248	0.7413	24.1164	0.6640
8.5	24.2724	0.8740	24.1785	0.8128	24.0621	0.7490
9.0	24.2336	0.9265	24.1450	0.8813	24.0223	0.8376
9.5	24.2065	0.9683	24.1270	0.9453	23.9999	0.9292
10.0	24.1933	0.9975	24.1270	1.0035	23.9980	1.0224
10.5	24.1965	1.0129	24.1472	1.0546	24.0190	1.1161
11.0	24.2180	1.0133	24.1894	1.0976	24.0651	1.2090
11.5	24.2595	0.9980	24.2553	1.1314	24.1379	1.2997
12.0	24.3225	0.9667	24.3459	1.1553	24.2386	1.3870
12.5	24.4078	0.9191	24.4621	1.1684	24.3680	1.4697
13.0	24.5160	0.8553	24.6042	1.1702	24.5267	1.5468
13.5	24.6471	0.7752	24.7727	1.1601	24.7150	1.6172
14.0	24.8011	0.6787	24.9674	1.1375	24.9331	1.6802
14.5	24.9773	0.5655	25.1884	1.1016	25.1811	1.7351
15.0	25.1753	0.4354	25.4355	1.0518	25.4593	1.7812
15.5	25.3940	0.2878	25.7085	0.9872	25.7679	1.8176
16.0	25.6327	0.1219	26.0073	0.9066	26.1074	1.8438
16.5	25.8902	−0.0630	26.3316	0.8088	26.4786	1.8588
17.0	26.1653	−0.2682	26.6813	0.6922	26.8824	1.8615
17.5	26.4566	−0.4947	27.0561	0.5549	27.3203	1.8508
18.0	26.7626	−0.7440	27.4557	0.3947	27.7939	1.8249
18.5	27.0813	−1.0173	27.8795	0.2086	28.3057	1.7817
19.0	27.4106	−1.3163	28.3267	−0.0065	28.8588	1.7180
19.5	27.7479	−1.6420	28.7958	−0.2548	29.4570	1.6297
20.0	28.0904	−1.9956	29.2844	−0.5405	30.1051	1.5104
20.5	28.4346	−2.3779	29.7884	−0.8687	30.8093	1.3505
21.0	28.7771	−2.7887	30.3022	−1.2442	31.5763	1.1346
21.5	29.1140	−3.2277	30.8175	−1.6707	32.4109	0.8371
22.0	29.4417	−3.6933	31.3242	−2.1496	33.3076	0.4158
22.5	29.7570	−4.1833	31.8107	−2.6786	34.2240	−0.1872
23.0	30.0572	−4.6949	32.2668	−3.2510	35.0511	−0.9936
23.5	30.3405	−5.2248	32.6854	−3.8567	35.6878	−1.9127
24.0	30.6060	−5.7697	33.0638	−4.4843	36.1490	−2.8250
24.5	30.8534	−6.3261	33.4037	−5.1235	36.4997	−3.6827
25.0	31.0833	−6.8914	33.7091	−5.7666	36.7878	−4.4831

TABLE I. $a_r(q) = U + iV, \; q = \rho e^{i\phi}$ $r = 5$

ρ	$\phi=80°$		$\phi=85°$		$\phi=90°$	
	U	V	U	V	U	V
0.0	25.0000	0.0000	25.0000	0.0000	25.0000	0.0000
0.5	24.9951	0.0018	24.9949	0.0009	24.9948	0.0000
1.0	24.9804	0.0071	24.9795	0.0036	24.9792	0.0000
1.5	24.9560	0.0160	24.9539	0.0082	24.9532	0.0001
2.0	24.9220	0.0285	24.9182	0.0146	24.9169	0.0002
2.5	24.8786	0.0446	24.8726	0.0230	24.8703	0.0007
3.0	24.8260	0.0645	24.8171	0.0337	24.8136	0.0017
3.5	24.7646	0.0883	24.7522	0.0470	24.7469	0.0037
4.0	24.6951	0.1164	24.6782	0.0633	24.6702	0.0073
4.5	24.6182	0.1491	24.5955	0.0833	24.5837	0.0133
5.0	24.5348	0.1869	24.5049	0.1081	24.4876	0.0228
5.5	24.4463	0.2306	24.4072	0.1387	24.3822	0.0373
6.0	24.3541	0.2810	24.3035	0.1765	24.2677	0.0585
6.5	24.2603	0.3389	24.1951	0.2234	24.1447	0.0887
7.0	24.1671	0.4054	24.0839	0.2813	24.0138	0.1308
7.5	24.0773	0.4815	23.9720	0.3524	23.8762	0.1880
8.0	23.9940	0.5679	23.8624	0.4390	23.7335	0.2641
8.5	23.9207	0.6655	23.7586	0.5434	23.5886	0.3635
9.0	23.8611	0.7744	23.6646	0.6675	23.4452	0.4904
9.5	23.8191	0.8945	23.5853	0.8124	23.3088	0.6490
10.0	23.7982	1.0252	23.5256	0.9784	23.1864	0.8420
10.5	23.8018	1.1650	23.4904	1.1646	23.0857	1.0701
11.0	23.8327	1.3126	23.4842	1.3690	23.0148	1.3315
11.5	23.8930	1.4660	23.5102	1.5889	22.9801	1.6218
12.0	23.9844	1.6232	23.5707	1.8211	22.9859	1.9350
12.5	24.1075	1.7825	23.6668	2.0625	23.0336	2.2652
13.0	24.2630	1.9423	23.7986	2.3105	23.1227	2.6070
13.5	24.4510	2.1013	23.9656	2.5630	23.2513	2.9566
14.0	24.6714	2.2586	24.1671	2.8185	23.4167	3.3116
14.5	24.9242	2.4135	24.4020	3.0764	23.6164	3.6706
15.0	25.2093	2.5655	24.6696	3.3365	23.8479	4.0336
15.5	25.5271	2.7147	24.9690	3.5989	24.1090	4.4009
16.0	25.8778	2.8609	25.2998	3.8645	24.3977	4.7734
16.5	26.2622	3.0046	25.6616	4.1343	24.7123	5.1526
17.0	26.6815	3.1461	26.0543	4.4099	25.0514	5.5401
17.5	27.1372	3.2861	26.4779	4.6930	25.4135	5.9377
18.0	27.6315	3.4255	26.9327	4.9863	25.7971	6.3475
18.5	28.1673	3.5658	27.4188	5.2925	26.2006	6.7717
19.0	28.7485	3.7088	27.9362	5.6154	26.6220	7.2125
19.5	29.3803	3.8574	28.4847	5.9594	27.0593	7.6724
20.0	30.0696	4.0158	29.0634	6.3300	27.5097	8.1533
20.5	30.8258	4.1912	29.6698	6.7333	27.9702	8.6572
21.0	31.6616	4.3960	30.2997	7.1764	28.4371	9.1853
21.5	32.5933	4.6536	30.9458	7.6660	28.9065	9.7382
22.0	33.6354	5.0109	31.5977	8.2069	29.3743	10.3158
22.5	34.7704	5.5560	32.2425	8.8002	29.8366	10.9166
23.0	35.8678	6.3735	32.8667	9.4414	30.2902	11.5385
23.5	36.7487	7.3685	33.4602	10.1212	30.7323	12.1787
24.0	37.4178	8.3655	34.0176	10.8274	31.1612	12.8340
24.5	37.9619	9.3014	34.5388	11.5485	31.5762	13.5013
25.0	38.4384	10.1746	35.0271	12.2753	31.9774	14.1776

TABLE I. $a_r(q) = U + iV$, $q = \rho e^{i\phi}$ $r = 6$

ρ	$\phi = 5°$		$\phi = 10°$		$\phi = 15°$	
	U	V	U	V	U	V
0.0	36.0000	0.0000	36.0000	0.0000	36.0000	0.0000
0.5	36.0035	0.0006	36.0034	0.0012	36.0031	0.0018
1.0	36.0141	0.0025	36.0134	0.0049	36.0124	0.0071
1.5	36.0317	0.0056	36.0302	0.0110	36.0278	0.0161
2.0	36.0563	0.0099	36.0538	0.0196	36.0495	0.0286
2.5	36.0881	0.0156	36.0840	0.0307	36.0774	0.0448
3.0	36.1270	0.0225	36.1211	0.0442	36.1115	0.0646
3.5	36.1731	0.0307	36.1650	0.0604	36.1519	0.0882
4.0	36.2264	0.0402	36.2158	0.0791	36.1985	0.1155
4.5	36.2870	0.0511	36.2735	0.1006	36.2514	0.1467
5.0	36.3552	0.0635	36.3382	0.1248	36.3106	0.1820
5.5	36.4309	0.0773	36.4101	0.1520	36.3762	0.2214
6.0	36.5145	0.0928	36.4892	0.1822	36.4482	0.2652
6.5	36.6060	0.1099	36.5757	0.2158	36.5267	0.3136
7.0	36.7059	0.1290	36.6698	0.2528	36.6116	0.3669
7.5	36.8145	0.1500	36.7717	0.2937	36.7031	0.4255
8.0	36.9320	0.1732	36.8817	0.3388	36.8014	0.4898
8.5	37.0590	0.1988	37.0002	0.3883	36.9063	0.5604
9.0	37.1959	0.2270	37.1274	0.4429	37.0183	0.6377
9.5	37.3434	0.2581	37.2637	0.5029	37.1373	0.7224
10.0	37.5021	0.2923	37.4098	0.5689	37.2637	0.8153
10.5	37.6726	0.3300	37.5661	0.6414	37.3977	0.9171
11.0	37.8556	0.3713	37.7333	0.7210	37.5398	1.0288
11.5	38.0521	0.4166	37.9121	0.8083	37.6904	1.1512
12.0	38.2627	0.4661	38.1033	0.9038	37.8502	1.2853
12.5	38.4884	0.5198	38.3079	1.0079	38.0199	1.4323
13.0	38.7299	0.5780	38.5268	1.1211	38.2007	1.5929
13.5	38.9880	0.6406	38.7611	1.2436	38.3938	1.7683
14.0	39.2634	0.7075	39.0119	1.3755	38.6008	1.9590
14.5	39.5567	0.7785	39.2803	1.5164	38.8235	2.1657
15.0	39.8683	0.8531	39.5675	1.6659	39.0642	2.3883
15.5	40.1986	0.9310	39.8744	1.8233	39.3252	2.6264
16.0	40.5475	1.0115	40.2019	1.9872	39.6090	2.8788
16.5	40.9148	1.0938	40.5504	2.1565	39.9180	3.1437
17.0	41.3001	1.1773	40.9201	2.3293	40.2539	3.4181
17.5	41.7028	1.2612	41.3109	2.5038	40.6181	3.6989
18.0	42.1219	1.3445	41.7222	2.6782	41.0109	3.9822
18.5	42.5563	1.4265	42.1529	2.8507	41.4318	4.2643
19.0	43.0047	1.5066	42.6019	3.0195	41.8794	4.5415
19.5	43.4658	1.5839	43.0675	3.1831	42.3516	4.8107
20.0	43.9381	1.6580	43.5482	3.3401	42.8460	5.0695
20.5	44.4199	1.7283	44.0420	3.4895	43.3600	5.3160
21.0	44.9098	1.7943	44.5472	3.6302	43.8909	5.5486
21.5	45.4061	1.8558	45.0620	3.7616	44.4363	5.7665
22.0	45.9073	1.9123	45.5845	3.8830	44.9938	5.9689
22.5	46.4119	1.9636	46.1131	3.9940	45.5616	6.1554
23.0	46.9183	2.0095	46.6462	4.0941	46.1376	6.3257
23.5	47.4251	2.0498	47.1821	4.1830	46.7204	6.4794
24.0	47.9310	2.0843	47.7195	4.2604	47.3084	6.6162
24.5	48.4345	2.1129	48.2569	4.3259	47.9002	6.7358
25.0	48.9344	2.1356	48.7930	4.3794	48.4947	6.8380

TABLE I. $a_r(q) = U + iV$, $q = \rho e^{i\phi}$ $r = 6$

ρ	$\phi=20°$		$\phi=25°$		$\phi=30°$	
	U	V	U	V	U	V
0.0	36.0000	0.0000	36.0000	0.0000	36.0000	0.0000
0.5	36.0027	0.0023	36.0023	0.0027	36.0018	0.0031
1.0	36.0109	0.0092	36.0092	0.0109	36.0071	0.0124
1.5	36.0246	0.0207	36.0207	0.0246	36.0161	0.0279
2.0	36.0438	0.0368	36.0367	0.0438	36.0285	0.0495
2.5	36.0684	0.0576	36.0573	0.0686	36.0445	0.0775
3.0	36.0985	0.0830	36.0825	0.0989	36.0641	0.1116
3.5	36.1341	0.1132	36.1123	0.1348	36.0870	0.1521
4.0	36.1751	0.1483	36.1465	0.1763	36.1134	0.1989
4.5	36.2216	0.1882	36.1851	0.2236	36.1432	0.2521
5.0	36.2735	0.2332	36.2282	0.2768	36.1761	0.3116
5.5	36.3308	0.2833	36.2754	0.3359	36.2122	0.3777
6.0	36.3934	0.3389	36.3268	0.4012	36.2511	0.4503
6.5	36.4612	0.4001	36.3822	0.4727	36.2927	0.5296
7.0	36.5343	0.4672	36.4413	0.5508	36.3366	0.6156
7.5	36.6124	0.5406	36.5039	0.6356	36.3826	0.7084
8.0	36.6954	0.6208	36.5697	0.7276	36.4302	0.8083
8.5	36.7834	0.7082	36.6384	0.8272	36.4789	0.9154
9.0	36.8760	0.8033	36.7094	0.9347	36.5281	1.0299
9.5	36.9731	0.9070	36.7825	1.0508	36.5770	1.1521
10.0	37.0747	1.0200	36.8569	1.1762	36.6249	1.2823
10.5	37.1807	1.1433	36.9322	1.3116	36.6708	1.4210
11.0	37.2909	1.2778	37.0077	1.4580	36.7135	1.5686
11.5	37.4053	1.4249	37.0826	1.6167	36.7518	1.7258
12.0	37.5241	1.5859	37.1563	1.7890	36.7840	1.8935
12.5	37.6475	1.7625	37.2278	1.9767	36.8082	2.0725
13.0	37.7761	1.9564	37.2964	2.1820	36.8223	2.2642
13.5	37.9107	2.1697	37.3613	2.4076	36.8234	2.4703
14.0	38.0526	2.4046	37.4220	2.6570	36.8082	2.6929
14.5	38.2039	2.6635	37.4779	2.9347	36.7720	2.9350
15.0	38.3675	2.9485	37.5297	3.2465	36.7090	3.2007
15.5	38.5475	3.2618	37.5790	3.6000	36.6106	3.4959
16.0	38.7492	3.6043	37.6304	4.0050	36.4640	3.8302
16.5	38.9790	3.9755	37.6938	4.4731	36.2479	4.2200
17.0	39.2439	4.3725	37.7881	5.0151	35.9211	4.6997
17.5	39.5504	4.7895	37.9437	5.6325	35.3804	5.3737
18.0	39.9027	5.2183	38.1945	6.3056	34.6763	7.1042
18.5	40.3020	5.6494	38.5570	6.9933	35.5577	8.7108
19.0	40.7459	6.0737	39.0188	7.6561	36.4096	9.7121
19.5	41.2300	6.4843	39.5540	8.2737	37.2141	10.5178
20.0	41.7486	6.8764	40.1391	8.8420	37.9930	11.2165
20.5	42.2960	7.2472	40.7581	9.3644	38.7576	11.8446
21.0	42.8672	7.5956	41.4010	9.8461	39.5143	12.4209
21.5	43.4580	7.9213	42.0616	10.2920	40.2671	12.9569
22.0	44.0652	8.2246	42.7361	10.7064	41.0189	13.4601
22.5	44.6860	8.5059	43.4224	11.0927	41.7718	13.9358
23.0	45.3185	8.7657	44.1191	11.4536	42.5273	14.3877
23.5	45.9610	9.0045	44.8254	11.7912	43.2867	14.8189
24.0	46.6124	9.2226	45.5410	12.1072	44.0512	15.2317
24.5	47.2718	9.4202	46.2658	12.4028	44.8220	15.6279
25.0	47.9386	9.5973	47.0002	12.6789	45.5999	16.0093

TABLE I. $a_r(q) = U + iV$, $q = \rho e^{i\phi}$ $r = 6$

ρ	$\phi=35°$		$\phi=40°$		$\phi=45°$	
	U	V	U	V	U	V
0.0	36.0000	0.0000	36.0000	0.0000	36.0000	0.0000
0.5	36.0012	0.0034	36.0006	0.0035	36.0000	0.0036
1.0	36.0049	0.0134	36.0025	0.0141	36.0000	0.0143
1.5	36.0110	0.0302	36.0056	0.0317	36.0000	0.0321
2.0	36.0195	0.0537	36.0099	0.0563	35.9999	0.0571
2.5	36.0304	0.0840	36.0153	0.0880	35.9998	0.0893
3.0	36.0437	0.1210	36.0220	0.1267	35.9997	0.1285
3.5	36.0592	0.1648	36.0297	0.1724	35.9994	0.1749
4.0	36.0771	0.2153	36.0385	0.2252	35.9989	0.2283
4.5	36.0971	0.2727	36.0483	0.2850	35.9982	0.2887
5.0	36.1191	0.3368	36.0589	0.3517	35.9973	0.3560
5.5	36.1431	0.4077	36.0703	0.4252	35.9960	0.4301
6.0	36.1687	0.4853	36.0823	0.5055	35.9943	0.5109
6.5	36.1958	0.5696	36.0947	0.5925	35.9921	0.5981
7.0	36.2241	0.6606	36.1073	0.6858	35.9892	0.6915
7.5	36.2532	0.7583	36.1197	0.7854	35.9855	0.7907
8.0	36.2826	0.8624	36.1317	0.8910	35.9809	0.8953
8.5	36.3119	0.9731	36.1427	1.0021	35.9752	1.0049
9.0	36.3403	1.0900	36.1524	1.1184	35.9680	1.1188
9.5	36.3671	1.2133	36.1600	1.2394	35.9592	1.2363
10.0	36.3915	1.3426	36.1649	1.3646	35.9483	1.3565
10.5	36.4123	1.4779	36.1663	1.4932	35.9351	1.4785
11.0	36.4283	1.6189	36.1631	1.6245	35.9190	1.6012
11.5	36.4379	1.7655	36.1542	1.7575	35.8997	1.7231
12.0	36.4395	1.9175	36.1384	1.8911	35.8766	1.8428
12.5	36.4309	2.0744	36.1143	2.0239	35.8493	1.9584
13.0	36.4096	2.2359	36.0801	2.1541	35.8173	2.0681
13.5	36.3726	2.4012	36.0342	2.2797	35.7804	2.1695
14.0	36.3160	2.5694	35.9749	2.3981	35.7383	2.2602
14.5	36.2352	2.7389	35.9002	2.5060	35.6913	2.3374
15.0	36.1244	2.9069	35.8089	2.5991	35.6399	2.3983
15.5	35.9766	3.0689	35.7001	2.6724	35.5853	2.4400
16.0	35.7833	3.2169	35.5744	2.7200	35.5291	2.4599
16.5	35.5355	3.3367	35.4343	2.7352	35.4737	2.4556
17.0	35.2284	3.4046	35.2847	2.7122	35.4218	2.4257
17.5	34.8724	3.3867	35.1333	2.6467	35.3764	2.3694
18.0	34.5057	3.2551	34.9891	2.5382	35.3405	2.2872
18.5	34.1823	3.0174	34.8604	2.3899	35.3164	2.1803
19.0	33.9324	2.7140	34.7532	2.2078	35.3058	2.0504
19.5	33.7532	2.3834	34.6699	1.9992	35.3096	1.8998
20.0	33.6293	2.0472	34.6105	1.7706	35.3280	1.7306
20.5	33.5456	1.7141	34.5727	1.5273	35.3603	1.5449
21.0	33.4904	1.3871	34.5539	1.2731	35.4057	1.3442
21.5	33.4556	1.0664	34.5508	1.0103	35.4629	1.1301
22.0	33.4351	0.7510	34.5608	0.7407	35.5306	0.9035
22.5	33.4246	0.4399	34.5810	0.4651	35.6071	0.6654
23.0	33.4210	0.1318	34.6093	0.1840	35.6911	0.4162
23.5	33.4218	-0.1741	34.6435	-0.1023	35.7812	0.1566
24.0	33.4252	-0.4789	34.6821	-0.3936	35.8759	-0.1133
24.5	33.4297	-0.7834	34.7235	-0.6900	35.9742	-0.3931
25.0	33.4340	-1.0882	34.7665	-0.9915	36.0746	-0.6826

TABLE I. $a_r(q) = U + iV$, $q = \rho e^{i\phi}$ $\qquad r = 6$

ρ	$\phi = 50°$		$\phi = 55°$		$\phi = 60°$	
	U	V	U	V	U	V
0.0	36.0000	0.0000	36.0000	0.0000	36.0000	0.0000
0.5	35.9994	0.0035	35.9988	0.0034	35.9982	0.0031
1.0	35.9975	0.0141	35.9951	0.0134	35.9929	0.0124
1.5	35.9944	0.0316	35.9890	0.0302	35.9839	0.0278
2.0	35.9900	0.0562	35.9804	0.0537	35.9714	0.0494
2.5	35.9843	0.0879	35.9694	0.0838	35.9553	0.0772
3.0	35.9774	0.1265	35.9558	0.1206	35.9356	0.1110
3.5	35.9691	0.1720	35.9398	0.1640	35.9123	0.1510
4.0	35.9594	0.2245	35.9212	0.2139	35.8855	0.1970
4.5	35.9484	0.2838	35.9002	0.2704	35.8551	0.2490
5.0	35.9360	0.3498	35.8768	0.3333	35.8212	0.3070
5.5	35.9222	0.4225	35.8509	0.4025	35.7840	0.3708
6.0	35.9071	0.5015	35.8228	0.4779	35.7436	0.4405
6.5	35.8905	0.5869	35.7924	0.5592	35.7000	0.5158
7.0	35.8727	0.6781	35.7600	0.6464	35.6537	0.5968
7.5	35.8535	0.7750	35.7258	0.7390	35.6048	0.6833
8.0	35.8330	0.8770	35.6900	0.8368	35.5539	0.7752
8.5	35.8115	0.9836	35.6530	0.9393	35.5013	0.8721
9.0	35.7888	1.0942	35.6151	1.0461	35.4478	0.9740
9.5	35.7651	1.2080	35.5769	1.1564	35.3939	1.0805
10.0	35.7406	1.3242	35.5389	1.2697	35.3407	1.1912
10.5	35.7154	1.4416	35.5017	1.3850	35.2889	1.3057
11.0	35.6897	1.5592	35.4660	1.5015	35.2398	1.4236
11.5	35.6637	1.6755	35.4326	1.6179	35.1946	1.5440
12.0	35.6378	1.7891	35.4025	1.7332	35.1546	1.6665
12.5	35.6121	1.8984	35.3765	1.8461	35.1213	1.7900
13.0	35.5873	2.0015	35.3558	1.9551	35.0961	1.9138
13.5	35.5637	2.0966	35.3413	2.0588	35.0807	2.0366
14.0	35.5423	2.1818	35.3343	2.1558	35.0765	2.1576
14.5	35.5238	2.2552	35.3360	2.2447	35.0850	2.2755
15.0	35.5093	2.3150	35.3474	2.3240	35.1077	2.3891
15.5	35.4999	2.3594	35.3698	2.3927	35.1457	2.4973
16.0	35.4972	2.3871	35.4043	2.4495	35.2002	2.5989
16.5	35.5025	2.3969	35.4518	2.4935	35.2723	2.6929
17.0	35.5172	2.3882	35.5133	2.5240	35.3625	2.7782
17.5	35.5427	2.3605	35.5894	2.5403	35.4716	2.8538
18.0	35.5800	2.3138	35.6807	2.5420	35.6000	2.9190
18.5	35.6301	2.2484	35.7876	2.5288	35.7479	2.9730
19.0	35.6933	2.1647	35.9101	2.5005	35.9153	3.0149
19.5	35.7700	2.0634	36.0484	2.4567	36.1024	3.0442
20.0	35.8600	1.9450	36.2022	2.3974	36.3089	3.0603
20.5	35.9629	1.8102	36.3711	2.3224	36.5348	3.0624
21.0	36.0781	1.6595	36.5546	2.2315	36.7796	3.0499
21.5	36.2046	1.4934	36.7522	2.1244	37.0431	3.0222
22.0	36.3417	1.3121	36.9630	2.0008	37.3250	2.9784
22.5	36.4882	1.1160	37.1863	1.8605	37.6247	2.9178
23.0	36.6429	0.9053	37.4211	1.7030	37.9418	2.8394
23.5	36.8048	0.6801	37.6664	1.5278	38.2758	2.7421
24.0	36.9726	0.4404	37.9211	1.3346	38.6260	2.6249
24.5	37.1451	0.1865	38.1838	1.1229	38.9916	2.4863
25.0	37.3210	-0.0817	38.4534	0.8923	39.3717	2.3250

-41-

322-566 O - 69 - 5

TABLE I. $a_r(q) = U + iV$, $q = \rho e^{i\phi}$ $r = 6$

ρ	$\phi = 65°$		$\phi = 70°$		$\phi = 75°$	
	U	V	U	V	U	V
0.0	36.0000	0.0000	36.0000	0.0000	36.0000	0.0000
0.5	35.9977	0.0027	35.9973	0.0023	35.9969	0.0018
1.0	35.9908	0.0109	35.9891	0.0092	35.9876	0.0071
1.5	35.9793	0.0246	35.9754	0.0206	35.9722	0.0161
2.0	35.9633	0.0437	35.9562	0.0367	35.9505	0.0285
2.5	35.9426	0.0682	35.9316	0.0572	35.9228	0.0445
3.0	35.9173	0.0982	35.9016	0.0824	35.8888	0.0640
3.5	35.8875	0.1335	35.8661	0.1120	35.8488	0.0871
4.0	35.8532	0.1742	35.8252	0.1461	35.8026	0.1136
4.5	35.8143	0.2202	35.7790	0.1848	35.7504	0.1437
5.0	35.7710	0.2715	35.7275	0.2279	35.6921	0.1774
5.5	35.7234	0.3282	35.6707	0.2757	35.6277	0.2148
6.0	35.6716	0.3902	35.6088	0.3281	35.5575	0.2559
6.5	35.6158	0.4575	35.5420	0.3853	35.4813	0.3010
7.0	35.5562	0.5302	35.4704	0.4475	35.3992	0.3502
7.5	35.4933	0.6084	35.3942	0.5147	35.3114	0.4039
8.0	35.4273	0.6920	35.3138	0.5875	35.2179	0.4625
8.5	35.3589	0.7813	35.2296	0.6660	35.1189	0.5266
9.0	35.2887	0.8763	35.1421	0.7508	35.0145	0.5968
9.5	35.2175	0.9771	35.0519	0.8424	34.9051	0.6738
10.0	35.1461	1.0838	34.9598	0.9413	34.7908	0.7588
10.5	35.0759	1.1966	34.8667	1.0484	34.6723	0.8530
11.0	35.0079	1.3156	34.7739	1.1644	34.5501	0.9577
11.5	34.9438	1.4406	34.6827	1.2902	34.4251	1.0746
12.0	34.8851	1.5718	34.5949	1.4265	34.2984	1.2057
12.5	34.8337	1.7089	34.5125	1.5741	34.1717	1.3530
13.0	34.7916	1.8515	34.4377	1.7337	34.0471	1.5188
13.5	34.7608	1.9993	34.3732	1.9058	33.9275	1.7051
14.0	34.7432	2.1514	34.3217	2.0903	33.8163	1.9140
14.5	34.7411	2.3071	34.2863	2.2871	33.7179	2.1469
15.0	34.7562	2.4651	34.2698	2.4952	33.6371	2.4042
15.5	34.7903	2.6244	34.2751	2.7135	33.5791	2.6853
16.0	34.8449	2.7834	34.3045	2.9403	33.5489	2.9882
16.5	34.9213	2.9409	34.3602	3.1734	33.5508	3.3096
17.0	35.0203	3.0954	34.4436	3.4107	33.5877	3.6454
17.5	35.1427	3.2454	34.5556	3.6500	33.6614	3.9913
18.0	35.2888	3.3898	34.6968	3.8892	33.7722	4.3432
18.5	35.4590	3.5272	34.8672	4.1264	33.9195	4.6974
19.0	35.6534	3.6567	35.0667	4.3600	34.1022	5.0512
19.5	35.8720	3.7772	35.2949	4.5888	34.3185	5.4026
20.0	36.1146	3.8879	35.5515	4.8117	34.5670	5.7505
20.5	36.3812	3.9880	35.8360	5.0280	34.8461	6.0941
21.0	36.6718	4.0766	36.1483	5.2372	35.1545	6.4333
21.5	36.9864	4.1532	36.4881	5.4389	35.4912	6.7684
22.0	37.3249	4.2169	36.8555	5.6330	35.8553	7.0999
22.5	37.6876	4.2669	37.2507	5.8195	36.2463	7.4286
23.0	38.0747	4.3024	37.6742	5.9983	36.6637	7.7556
23.5	38.4866	4.3224	38.1268	6.1697	37.1076	8.0820
24.0	38.9238	4.3256	38.6096	6.3337	37.5778	8.4093
24.5	39.3871	4.3104	39.1240	6.4907	38.0746	8.7392
25.0	39.8772	4.2752	39.6720	6.6410	38.5982	9.0739

TABLE I. $a_r(q) = U+iV$, $q = \rho e^{i\phi}$ $\qquad r=6$

ρ	$\phi=80°$		$\phi=85°$		$\phi=90°$	
	U	V	U	V	U	V
0.0	36.0000	0.0000	36.0000	0.0000	36.0000	0.0000
0.5	35.9966	0.0012	35.9965	0.0006	35.9964	0.0000
1.0	35.9866	0.0049	35.9859	0.0025	35.9857	0.0000
1.5	35.9698	0.0110	35.9684	0.0056	35.9679	0.0000
2.0	35.9464	0.0195	35.9438	0.0099	35.9429	0.0000
2.5	35.9162	0.0304	35.9122	0.0155	35.9109	0.0000
3.0	35.8794	0.0438	35.8737	0.0222	35.8717	0.0000
3.5	35.8360	0.0596	35.8281	0.0302	35.8255	0.0000
4.0	35.7859	0.0777	35.7757	0.0395	35.7722	0.0000
4.5	35.7292	0.0984	35.7162	0.0499	35.7118	0.0000
5.0	35.6659	0.1215	35.6498	0.0617	35.6443	0.0000
5.5	35.5959	0.1471	35.5763	0.0748	35.5697	0.0000
6.0	35.5192	0.1755	35.4956	0.0892	35.4877	0.0000
6.5	35.4359	0.2066	35.4077	0.1052	35.3982	0.0000
7.0	35.3457	0.2408	35.3124	0.1227	35.3011	0.0000
7.5	35.2486	0.2784	35.2093	0.1421	35.1959	0.0000
8.0	35.1445	0.3198	35.0982	0.1635	35.0823	0.0000
8.5	35.0331	0.3654	34.9785	0.1873	34.9597	0.0000
9.0	34.9142	0.4159	34.8497	0.2139	34.8274	0.0000
9.5	34.7876	0.4723	34.7111	0.2438	34.6844	0.0000
10.0	34.6530	0.5355	34.5617	0.2778	34.5296	0.0000
10.5	34.5099	0.6070	34.4003	0.3167	34.3614	0.0000
11.0	34.3581	0.6884	34.2256	0.3618	34.1780	0.0000
11.5	34.1971	0.7818	34.0358	0.4146	33.9769	0.0000
12.0	34.0269	0.8899	33.8287	0.4773	33.7549	0.0000
12.5	33.8474	1.0159	33.6017	0.5527	33.5078	0.0000
13.0	33.6592	1.1640	33.3516	0.6448	33.2300	0.0000
13.5	33.4635	1.3388	33.0747	0.7594	32.9138	0.0000
14.0	33.2629	1.5461	32.7669	0.9049	32.5478	0.0000
14.5	33.0621	1.7920	32.4247	1.0939	32.1149	0.0000
15.0	32.8683	2.0821	32.0472	1.3455	31.5859	0.0000
15.5	32.6917	2.4204	31.6423	1.6870	30.9042	0.0000
16.0	32.5448	2.8070	31.2386	2.1493	29.9214	0.0000
16.5	32.4400	3.2368	30.8929	2.7444	27.3308	0.6974
17.0	32.3866	3.7001	30.6639	3.4371	27.5373	3.0201
17.5	32.3888	4.1850	30.5670	4.1646	27.7532	4.2599
18.0	32.4459	4.6803	30.5795	4.8822	27.9782	5.2517
18.5	32.5539	5.1778	30.6719	5.5728	28.2121	6.1188
19.0	32.7076	5.6720	30.8217	6.2340	28.4546	6.9098
19.5	32.9015	6.1601	31.0143	6.8689	28.7057	7.6497
20.0	33.1311	6.6411	31.2401	7.4817	28.9650	8.3536
20.5	33.3923	7.1150	31.4927	8.0769	29.2322	9.0313
21.0	33.6821	7.5825	31.7680	8.6582	29.5071	9.6897
21.5	33.9979	8.0449	32.0628	9.2290	29.7894	10.3339
22.0	34.3377	8.5036	32.3749	9.7921	30.0786	10.9677
22.5	34.7000	8.9600	32.7026	10.3502	30.3744	11.5943
23.0	35.0835	9.4158	33.0445	10.9054	30.6763	12.2160
23.5	35.4869	9.8727	33.3991	11.4596	30.9840	12.8350
24.0	35.9092	10.3323	33.7656	12.0147	31.2968	13.4528
24.5	36.3496	10.7964	34.1426	12.5721	31.6144	14.0708
25.0	36.8069	11.2667	34.5293	13.1334	31.9361	14.6903

TABLE I. $a_r(q) = U + iV$, $q = \rho e^{i\phi}$　　　　　　$r = 7$

ρ	$\phi=5°$		$\phi=10°$		$\phi=15°$	
	U	V	U	V	U	V
0.0	49.0000	0.0000	49.0000	0.0000	49.0000	0.0000
0.5	49.0026	0.0005	49.0024	0.0009	49.0023	0.0013
1.0	49.0103	0.0018	49.0098	0.0036	49.0090	0.0052
1.5	49.0231	0.0041	49.0220	0.0080	49.0203	0.0117
2.0	49.0411	0.0072	49.0392	0.0143	49.0361	0.0209
2.5	49.0642	0.0113	49.0612	0.0223	49.0564	0.0326
3.0	49.0924	0.0163	49.0882	0.0321	49.0813	0.0470
3.5	49.1259	0.0222	49.1201	0.0438	49.1106	0.0640
4.0	49.1645	0.0291	49.1569	0.0573	49.1445	0.0837
4.5	49.2084	0.0369	49.1987	0.0726	49.1830	0.1061
5.0	49.2574	0.0456	49.2455	0.0897	49.2260	0.1311
5.5	49.3118	0.0553	49.2972	0.1088	49.2736	0.1589
6.0	49.3714	0.0659	49.3540	0.1297	49.3258	0.1894
6.5	49.4363	0.0775	49.4158	0.1526	49.3825	0.2228
7.0	49.5066	0.0902	49.4827	0.1775	49.4438	0.2590
7.5	49.5824	0.1039	49.5547	0.2043	49.5098	0.2980
8.0	49.6636	0.1186	49.6319	0.2333	49.5804	0.3401
8.5	49.7504	0.1345	49.7142	0.2643	49.6556	0.3852
9.0	49.8428	0.1515	49.8018	0.2976	49.7354	0.4334
9.5	49.9410	0.1697	49.8947	0.3332	49.8199	0.4848
10.0	50.0450	0.1892	49.9930	0.3712	49.9091	0.5397
10.5	50.1551	0.2100	50.0968	0.4118	50.0029	0.5980
11.0	50.2712	0.2322	50.2060	0.4550	50.1014	0.6600
11.5	50.3937	0.2559	50.3210	0.5011	50.2046	0.7259
12.0	50.5227	0.2812	50.4417	0.5502	50.3125	0.7959
12.5	50.6584	0.3083	50.5684	0.6026	50.4251	0.8702
13.0	50.8010	0.3373	50.7011	0.6584	50.5424	0.9492
13.5	50.9510	0.3682	50.8400	0.7180	50.6645	1.0331
14.0	51.1084	0.4013	50.9854	0.7816	50.7914	1.1224
14.5	51.2737	0.4368	51.1375	0.8496	50.9231	1.2174
15.0	51.4473	0.4747	51.2965	0.9223	51.0597	1.3186
15.5	51.6295	0.5153	51.4627	1.0000	51.2013	1.4264
16.0	51.8207	0.5588	51.6364	1.0831	51.3479	1.5416
16.5	52.0215	0.6054	51.8181	1.1721	51.4998	1.6646
17.0	52.2323	0.6552	52.0081	1.2673	51.6572	1.7961
17.5	52.4536	0.7084	52.2070	1.3692	51.8204	1.9368
18.0	52.6859	0.7651	52.4153	1.4781	51.9896	2.0876
18.5	52.9298	0.8255	52.6335	1.5945	52.1654	2.2492
19.0	53.1858	0.8895	52.8624	1.7185	52.3484	2.4226
19.5	53.4545	0.9574	53.1027	1.8506	52.5393	2.6084
20.0	53.7363	1.0289	53.3553	1.9907	52.7392	2.8077
20.5	54.0317	1.1039	53.6208	2.1390	52.9493	3.0213
21.0	54.3411	1.1824	53.9004	2.2954	53.1710	3.2497
21.5	54.6649	1.2640	54.1947	2.4595	53.4063	3.4935
22.0	55.0033	1.3484	54.5049	2.6308	53.6570	3.7527
22.5	55.3564	1.4352	54.8315	2.8086	53.9256	4.0272
23.0	55.7244	1.5239	55.1754	2.9919	54.2146	4.3161
23.5	56.1070	1.6139	55.5370	3.1798	54.5263	4.6177
24.0	56.5041	1.7048	55.9167	3.3707	54.8630	4.9298
24.5	56.9153	1.7958	56.3144	3.5634	55.2265	5.2494
25.0	57.3400	1.8864	56.7302	3.7563	55.6177	5.5733

ρ	$\phi=20°$		$\phi=25°$		$\phi=30°$	
	U	V	U	V	U	V
0.0	49.0000	0.0000	49.0000	0.0000	49.0000	0.0000
0.5	49.0020	0.0017	49.0017	0.0020	49.0013	0.0023
1.0	49.0080	0.0067	49.0067	0.0080	49.0052	0.0090
1.5	49.0180	0.0151	49.0151	0.0180	49.0117	0.0203
2.0	49.0319	0.0268	49.0268	0.0319	49.0208	0.0361
2.5	49.0499	0.0419	49.0418	0.0499	49.0325	0.0564
3.0	49.0718	0.0604	49.0602	0.0719	49.0468	0.0813
3.5	49.0978	0.0823	49.0820	0.0980	49.0637	0.1107
4.0	49.1277	0.1075	49.1070	0.1281	49.0831	0.1447
4.5	49.1617	0.1362	49.1355	0.1622	49.1051	0.1832
5.0	49.1996	0.1684	49.1672	0.2005	49.1297	0.2264
5.5	49.2416	0.2040	49.2022	0.2428	49.1567	0.2741
6.0	49.2875	0.2432	49.2405	0.2893	49.1863	0.3265
6.5	49.3374	0.2859	49.2821	0.3400	49.2184	0.3835
7.0	49.3913	0.3322	49.3270	0.3948	49.2529	0.4451
7.5	49.4492	0.3821	49.3750	0.4539	49.2898	0.5115
8.0	49.5110	0.4357	49.4263	0.5173	49.3290	0.5825
8.5	49.5767	0.4931	49.4806	0.5850	49.3705	0.6583
9.0	49.6463	0.5544	49.5380	0.6571	49.4143	0.7387
9.5	49.7198	0.6196	49.5984	0.7336	49.4601	0.8239
10.0	49.7971	0.6889	49.6617	0.8147	49.5080	0.9138
10.5	49.8780	0.7624	49.7277	0.9003	49.5577	1.0085
11.0	49.9627	0.8402	49.7963	0.9905	49.6092	1.1079
11.5	50.0509	0.9225	49.8674	1.0856	49.6621	1.2121
12.0	50.1425	1.0096	49.9408	1.1855	49.7164	1.3210
12.5	50.2375	1.1015	50.0163	1.2905	49.7718	1.4346
13.0	50.3357	1.1987	50.0935	1.4006	49.8279	1.5529
13.5	50.4370	1.3014	50.1723	1.5160	49.8844	1.6760
14.0	50.5412	1.4099	50.2522	1.6370	49.9410	1.8037
14.5	50.6480	1.5246	50.3329	1.7638	49.9971	1.9361
15.0	50.7574	1.6460	50.4140	1.8966	50.0523	2.0732
15.5	50.8690	1.7746	50.4949	2.0358	50.1059	2.2148
16.0	50.9828	1.9109	50.5752	2.1817	50.1573	2.3611
16.5	51.0983	2.0558	50.6541	2.3349	50.2057	2.5120
17.0	51.2155	2.2098	50.7310	2.4957	50.2501	2.6674
17.5	51.3341	2.3740	50.8050	2.6650	50.2895	2.8273
18.0	51.4539	2.5493	50.8753	2.8433	50.3227	2.9917
18.5	51.5747	2.7370	50.9407	3.0317	50.3483	3.1604
19.0	51.6965	2.9385	51.0000	3.2311	50.3646	3.3334
19.5	51.8194	3.1554	51.0519	3.4431	50.3697	3.5105
20.0	51.9435	3.3895	51.0945	3.6692	50.3612	3.6912
20.5	52.0693	3.6433	51.1258	3.9117	50.3363	3.8751
21.0	52.1979	3.9192	51.1434	4.1735	50.2917	4.0613
21.5	52.3306	4.2203	51.1443	4.4583	50.2232	4.2484
22.0	52.4701	4.5499	51.1244	4.7714	50.1258	4.4338
22.5	52.6201	4.9116	51.0789	5.1207	49.9932	4.6136
23.0	52.7861	5.3086	51.0012	5.5181	49.8185	4.7808
23.5	52.9760	5.7430	50.8829	5.9840	49.5942	4.9236
24.0	53.1997	6.2145	50.7157	6.5567	49.3162	5.0230
24.5	53.4681	6.7185	50.5075	7.3180	48.9902	5.0522
25.0	53.7909	7.2454	50.3963	8.4098	48.6420	4.9850

TABLE I. $a_r(q) = U + iV$, $q = \rho e^{i\phi}$ $r = 7$

ρ	$\phi = 35°$		$\phi = 40°$		$\phi = 45°$	
	U	V	U	V	U	V
0.0	49.0000	0.0000	49.0000	0.0000	49.0000	0.0000
0.5	49.0009	0.0024	49.0005	0.0026	49.0000	0.0026
1.0	49.0036	0.0098	49.0018	0.0103	49.0000	0.0104
1.5	49.0080	0.0220	49.0041	0.0231	49.0000	0.0234
2.0	49.0142	0.0392	49.0072	0.0410	49.0000	0.0417
2.5	49.0222	0.0612	49.0112	0.0641	48.9999	0.0651
3.0	49.0320	0.0882	49.0162	0.0924	48.9999	0.0937
3.5	49.0435	0.1201	49.0219	0.1257	48.9998	0.1276
4.0	49.0567	0.1569	49.0286	0.1643	48.9996	0.1667
4.5	49.0716	0.1986	49.0360	0.2079	48.9994	0.2109
5.0	49.0883	0.2453	49.0443	0.2568	48.9990	0.2604
5.5	49.1066	0.2970	49.0534	0.3107	48.9986	0.3150
6.0	49.1266	0.3536	49.0632	0.3698	48.9980	0.3749
6.5	49.1482	0.4151	49.0738	0.4341	48.9973	0.4399
7.0	49.1714	0.4817	49.0851	0.5035	48.9965	0.5100
7.5	49.1962	0.5532	49.0970	0.5780	48.9954	0.5853
8.0	49.2224	0.6297	49.1097	0.6576	48.9942	0.6657
8.5	49.2501	0.7111	49.1229	0.7422	48.9928	0.7512
9.0	49.2792	0.7974	49.1368	0.8319	48.9911	0.8416
9.5	49.3096	0.8886	49.1512	0.9264	48.9893	0.9370
10.0	49.3411	0.9846	49.1660	1.0259	48.9873	1.0372
10.5	49.3738	1.0854	49.1813	1.1300	48.9850	1.1422
11.0	49.4075	1.1908	49.1970	1.2388	48.9827	1.2517
11.5	49.4420	1.3009	49.2130	1.3521	48.9802	1.3658
12.0	49.4772	1.4154	49.2293	1.4696	48.9777	1.4841
12.5	49.5127	1.5343	49.2457	1.5911	48.9752	1.6064
13.0	49.5486	1.6573	49.2622	1.7165	48.9728	1.7325
13.5	49.5843	1.7843	49.2787	1.8452	48.9705	1.8620
14.0	49.6197	1.9149	49.2949	1.9771	48.9685	1.9946
14.5	49.6543	2.0491	49.3109	2.1116	48.9668	2.1298
15.0	49.6878	2.1863	49.3263	2.2483	48.9657	2.2671
15.5	49.7197	2.3263	49.3411	2.3867	48.9653	2.4061
16.0	49.7493	2.4687	49.3550	2.5259	48.9657	2.5459
16.5	49.7762	2.6130	49.3679	2.6655	48.9672	2.6860
17.0	49.7996	2.7586	49.3793	2.8045	48.9699	2.8255
17.5	49.8188	2.9048	49.3892	2.9421	48.9741	2.9636
18.0	49.8329	3.0510	49.3972	3.0772	48.9801	3.0993
18.5	49.8409	3.1962	49.4031	3.2088	48.9881	3.2317
19.0	49.8419	3.3393	49.4068	3.3355	48.9985	3.3596
19.5	49.8347	3.4792	49.4079	3.4561	49.0117	3.4819
20.0	49.8183	3.6143	49.4065	3.5692	49.0281	3.5976
20.5	49.7915	3.7427	49.4026	3.6731	49.0482	3.7055
21.0	49.7532	3.8623	49.3964	3.7662	49.0725	3.8045
21.5	49.7027	3.9704	49.3883	3.8470	49.1016	3.8934
22.0	49.6394	4.0640	49.3788	3.9137	49.1360	3.9714
22.5	49.5634	4.1395	49.3688	3.9649	49.1766	4.0374
23.0	49.4757	4.1931	49.3595	3.9991	49.2239	4.0907
23.5	49.3784	4.2208	49.3520	4.0153	49.2785	4.1306
24.0	49.2748	4.2195	49.3479	4.0127	49.3411	4.1566
24.5	49.1694	4.1867	49.3486	3.9908	49.4123	4.1684
25.0	49.0675	4.1219	49.3556	3.9499	49.4925	4.1658

TABLE I. $a_r(q) = U + iV,\ q = \rho e^{i\phi}$ $r = 7$

ρ	$\phi=50°$		$\phi=55°$		$\phi=60°$	
	U	V	U	V	U	V
0.0	49.0000	0.0000	49.0000	0.0000	49.0000	0.0000
0.5	48.9995	0.0026	48.9991	0.0024	48.9987	0.0023
1.0	48.9982	0.0103	48.9964	0.0098	48.9948	0.0090
1.5	48.9959	0.0231	48.9920	0.0220	48.9883	0.0203
2.0	48.9927	0.0410	48.9857	0.0391	48.9792	0.0361
2.5	48.9886	0.0641	48.9777	0.0611	48.9674	0.0563
3.0	48.9836	0.0923	48.9678	0.0880	48.9531	0.0811
3.5	48.9776	0.1256	48.9562	0.1198	48.9361	0.1103
4.0	48.9707	0.1640	48.9427	0.1564	48.9165	0.1440
4.5	48.9628	0.2075	48.9274	0.1978	48.8942	0.1821
5.0	48.9539	0.2561	48.9102	0.2441	48.8693	0.2247
5.5	48.9440	0.3098	48.8912	0.2952	48.8418	0.2717
6.0	48.9331	0.3685	48.8703	0.3511	48.8116	0.3231
6.5	48.9212	0.4323	48.8476	0.4118	48.7787	0.3789
7.0	48.9082	0.5012	48.8230	0.4773	48.7432	0.4391
7.5	48.8942	0.5751	48.7965	0.5476	48.7050	0.5037
8.0	48.8792	0.6539	48.7681	0.6226	48.6642	0.5726
8.5	48.8632	0.7377	48.7380	0.7023	48.6207	0.6459
9.0	48.8462	0.8265	48.7060	0.7868	48.5747	0.7237
9.5	48.8282	0.9201	48.6723	0.8760	48.5260	0.8059
10.0	48.8093	1.0185	48.6369	0.9700	48.4749	0.8925
10.5	48.7896	1.1217	48.5999	1.0686	48.4213	0.9837
11.0	48.7692	1.2295	48.5615	1.1720	48.3653	1.0795
11.5	48.7482	1.3419	48.5218	1.2801	48.3071	1.1800
12.0	48.7266	1.4588	48.4809	1.3929	48.2468	1.2854
12.5	48.7048	1.5799	48.4391	1.5103	48.1846	1.3957
13.0	48.6830	1.7052	48.3968	1.6325	48.1207	1.5111
13.5	48.6614	1.8344	48.3542	1.7594	48.0554	1.6320
14.0	48.6402	1.9673	48.3117	1.8909	47.9891	1.7584
14.5	48.6199	2.1036	48.2699	2.0271	47.9222	1.8907
15.0	48.6009	2.2429	48.2292	2.1678	47.8552	2.0293
15.5	48.5836	2.3848	48.1903	2.3131	47.7887	2.1743
16.0	48.5684	2.5289	48.1539	2.4627	47.7235	2.3263
16.5	48.5560	2.6747	48.1209	2.6166	47.6604	2.4855
17.0	48.5470	2.8215	48.0921	2.7744	47.6003	2.6523
17.5	48.5420	2.9688	48.0684	2.9360	47.5445	2.8271
18.0	48.5416	3.1159	48.0509	3.1010	47.4943	3.0101
18.5	48.5466	3.2618	48.0407	3.2690	47.4510	3.2015
19.0	48.5577	3.4059	48.0389	3.4394	47.4163	3.4013
19.5	48.5757	3.5472	48.0467	3.6115	47.3919	3.6096
20.0	48.6012	3.6848	48.0653	3.7848	47.3795	3.8258
20.5	48.6351	3.8179	48.0957	3.9584	47.3812	4.0496
21.0	48.6780	3.9454	48.1389	4.1313	47.3985	4.2801
21.5	48.7307	4.0664	48.1961	4.3027	47.4334	4.5163
22.0	48.7937	4.1802	48.2680	4.4715	47.4873	4.7570
22.5	48.8677	4.2857	48.3555	4.6366	47.5615	5.0006
23.0	48.9531	4.3822	48.4590	4.7972	47.6572	5.2457
23.5	49.0505	4.4690	48.5792	4.9521	47.7752	5.4906
24.0	49.1600	4.5454	48.7163	5.1003	47.9160	5.7338
24.5	49.2821	4.6108	48.8707	5.2409	48.0799	5.9736
25.0	49.4168	4.6646	49.0425	5.3731	48.2670	6.2087

TABLE I. $a_r(q) = U + iV$, $q = \rho e^{i\phi}$ $\qquad r=7$

ρ	$\phi=65°$ U	$\phi=65°$ V	$\phi=70°$ U	$\phi=70°$ V	$\phi=75°$ U	$\phi=75°$ V
0.0	49.0000	0.0000	49.0000	0.0000	49.0000	0.0000
0.5	48.9983	0.0020	48.9980	0.0017	48.9977	0.0013
1.0	48.9933	0.0080	48.9920	0.0067	48.9910	0.0052
1.5	48.9849	0.0179	48.9820	0.0151	48.9797	0.0117
2.0	48.9732	0.0319	48.9681	0.0268	48.9639	0.0208
2.5	48.9581	0.0498	48.9501	0.0418	48.9436	0.0325
3.0	48.9397	0.0717	48.9282	0.0601	48.9189	0.0468
3.5	48.9179	0.0975	48.9023	0.0818	48.8896	0.0636
4.0	48.8928	0.1273	48.8724	0.1067	48.8559	0.0830
4.5	48.8643	0.1610	48.8385	0.1350	48.8176	0.1049
5.0	48.8324	0.1986	48.8007	0.1665	48.7749	0.1294
5.5	48.7972	0.2400	48.7588	0.2012	48.7278	0.1563
6.0	48.7586	0.2854	48.7130	0.2392	48.6761	0.1858
6.5	48.7167	0.3346	48.6632	0.2804	48.6200	0.2177
7.0	48.6713	0.3877	48.6095	0.3247	48.5595	0.2521
7.5	48.6226	0.4447	48.5517	0.3723	48.4944	0.2890
8.0	48.5705	0.5055	48.4899	0.4231	48.4249	0.3282
8.5	48.5150	0.5701	48.4241	0.4772	48.3508	0.3699
9.0	48.4561	0.6387	48.3542	0.5344	48.2722	0.4140
9.5	48.3939	0.7113	48.2802	0.5949	48.1889	0.4605
10.0	48.3283	0.7878	48.2021	0.6588	48.1009	0.5095
10.5	48.2593	0.8685	48.1198	0.7260	48.0081	0.5608
11.0	48.1869	0.9534	48.0332	0.7967	47.9103	0.6147
11.5	48.1113	1.0427	47.9423	0.8711	47.8074	0.6710
12.0	48.0323	1.1366	47.8468	0.9493	47.6992	0.7300
12.5	47.9501	1.2352	47.7468	1.0316	47.5854	0.7916
13.0	47.8648	1.3391	47.6420	1.1181	47.4656	0.8560
13.5	47.7763	1.4484	47.5322	1.2094	47.3395	0.9233
14.0	47.6849	1.5636	47.4173	1.3059	47.2066	0.9939
14.5	47.5907	1.6853	47.2971	1.4080	47.0663	1.0679
15.0	47.4939	1.8141	47.1711	1.5165	46.9179	1.1456
15.5	47.3949	1.9507	47.0392	1.6323	46.7605	1.2276
16.0	47.2941	2.0960	46.9011	1.7563	46.5932	1.3144
16.5	47.1919	2.2509	46.7565	1.8898	46.4146	1.4066
17.0	47.0891	2.4164	46.6050	2.0343	46.2232	1.5054
17.5	46.9865	2.5938	46.4466	2.1917	46.0173	1.6118
18.0	46.8853	2.7844	46.2810	2.3642	45.7946	1.7275
18.5	46.7870	2.9895	46.1085	2.5546	45.5523	1.8547
19.0	46.6934	3.2103	45.9296	2.7663	45.2870	1.9964
19.5	46.6067	3.4482	45.7455	3.0030	44.9945	2.1569
20.0	46.5297	3.7041	45.5584	3.2694	44.6696	2.3425
20.5	46.4654	3.9787	45.3720	3.5702	44.3060	2.5629
21.0	46.4173	4.2719	45.1919	3.9103	43.8968	2.8334
21.5	46.3890	4.5831	45.0259	4.2936	43.4368	3.1797
22.0	46.3840	4.9109	44.8844	4.7214	42.9313	3.6441
22.5	46.4055	5.2530	44.7784	5.1915	42.4226	4.2845
23.0	46.4561	5.6067	44.7183	5.6972	42.0193	5.1227
23.5	46.5377	5.9685	44.7111	6.2285	41.8225	6.0680
24.0	46.6511	6.3353	44.7591	6.7741	41.8171	7.0011
24.5	46.7967	6.7037	44.8609	7.3240	41.9377	7.8742
25.0	46.9740	7.0710	45.0122	7.8703	42.1364	8.6850

TABLE I. $a_r(q) = U + iV$, $q = \rho e^{i\phi}$ $r = 7$

ρ	$\phi=80°$		$\phi=85°$		$\phi=90°$	
	U	V	U	V	U	V
0.0	49.0000	0.0000	49.0000	0.0000	49.0000	0.0000
0.5	48.9976	0.0009	48.9974	0.0005	48.9974	-0.0000
1.0	48.9902	0.0036	48.9897	0.0018	48.9896	-0.0000
1.5	48.9780	0.0080	48.9769	0.0041	48.9766	-0.0000
2.0	48.9609	0.0142	48.9590	0.0072	48.9584	-0.0000
2.5	48.9389	0.0222	48.9359	0.0113	48.9350	-0.0000
3.0	48.9120	0.0320	48.9078	0.0162	48.9064	-0.0000
3.5	48.8803	0.0435	48.8746	0.0221	48.8726	-0.0000
4.0	48.8437	0.0567	48.8362	0.0288	48.8337	-0.0000
4.5	48.8023	0.0717	48.7929	0.0364	48.7897	-0.0000
5.0	48.7560	0.0884	48.7444	0.0449	48.7406	-0.0000
5.5	48.7049	0.1068	48.6910	0.0542	48.6863	-0.0001
6.0	48.6490	0.1269	48.6325	0.0643	48.6270	-0.0001
6.5	48.5883	0.1487	48.5690	0.0753	48.5627	-0.0002
7.0	48.5228	0.1721	48.5006	0.0870	48.4933	-0.0004
7.5	48.4525	0.1971	48.4272	0.0996	48.4189	-0.0007
8.0	48.3774	0.2237	48.3488	0.1128	48.3396	-0.0011
8.5	48.2974	0.2518	48.2654	0.1267	48.2554	-0.0016
9.0	48.2126	0.2815	48.1770	0.1412	48.1662	-0.0024
9.5	48.1228	0.3126	48.0837	0.1562	48.0722	-0.0036
10.0	48.0280	0.3451	47.9853	0.1717	47.9734	-0.0052
10.5	47.9281	0.3790	47.8819	0.1874	47.8698	-0.0074
11.0	47.8229	0.4142	47.7733	0.2033	47.7614	-0.0103
11.5	47.7123	0.4506	47.6595	0.2191	47.6484	-0.0142
12.0	47.5961	0.4880	47.5403	0.2347	47.5307	-0.0193
12.5	47.4739	0.5265	47.4156	0.2498	47.4084	-0.0260
13.0	47.3455	0.5658	47.2853	0.2640	47.2815	-0.0346
13.5	47.2104	0.6059	47.1490	0.2769	47.1501	-0.0456
14.0	47.0681	0.6465	47.0065	0.2881	47.0144	-0.0595
14.5	46.9180	0.6875	46.8574	0.2970	46.8743	-0.0770
15.0	46.7592	0.7285	46.7014	0.3029	46.7301	-0.0989
15.5	46.5909	0.7694	46.5380	0.3049	46.5819	-0.1260
16.0	46.4118	0.8097	46.3665	0.3021	46.4299	-0.1594
16.5	46.2206	0.8491	46.1865	0.2931	46.2745	-0.2003
17.0	46.0155	0.8868	45.9971	0.2765	46.1160	-0.2502
17.5	45.7944	0.9223	45.7976	0.2503	45.9552	-0.3105
18.0	45.5546	0.9545	45.5874	0.2122	45.7927	-0.3830
18.5	45.2928	0.9821	45.3656	0.1595	45.6298	-0.4697
19.0	45.0046	1.0032	45.1318	0.0884	45.4678	-0.5725
19.5	44.6846	1.0150	44.8860	-0.0054	45.3087	-0.6935
20.0	44.3254	1.0131	44.6288	-0.1272	45.1549	-0.8347
20.5	43.9174	0.9906	44.3622	-0.2832	45.0094	-0.9979
21.0	43.4476	0.9350	44.0905	-0.4805	44.8756	-1.1841
21.5	42.8996	0.8229	43.8204	-0.7256	44.7572	-1.3940
22.0	42.2585	0.6076	43.5624	-1.0234	44.6584	-1.6274
22.5	41.5415	0.2007	43.3292	-1.3751	44.5830	-1.8828
23.0	40.8790	-0.4822	43.1339	-1.7763	44.5342	-2.1584
23.5	40.4496	-1.3462	42.9866	-2.2177	44.5145	-2.4514
24.0	40.2484	-2.2158	42.8924	-2.6871	44.5257	-2.7587
24.5	40.1883	-3.0279	42.8512	-3.1733	44.5685	-3.0774
25.0	40.2115	-3.7809	42.8595	-3.6671	44.6427	-3.4048

TABLE I. $a_r(q) = U + iV,\ q = \rho e^{i\phi}$ $r = 8$

ρ	$\phi = 5°$		$\phi = 10°$		$\phi = 15°$	
	U	V	U	V	U	V
0.0	64.0000	0.0000	64.0000	0.0000	64.0000	0.0000
0.5	64.0020	0.0003	64.0019	0.0007	64.0017	0.0010
1.0	64.0078	0.0014	64.0075	0.0027	64.0069	0.0040
1.5	64.0176	0.0031	64.0168	0.0061	64.0155	0.0089
2.0	64.0313	0.0055	64.0298	0.0109	64.0275	0.0159
2.5	64.0489	0.0086	64.0466	0.0170	64.0430	0.0248
3.0	64.0704	0.0124	64.0672	0.0245	64.0619	0.0358
3.5	64.0958	0.0169	64.0914	0.0333	64.0842	0.0487
4.0	64.1252	0.0221	64.1195	0.0435	64.1101	0.0636
4.5	64.1585	0.0280	64.1512	0.0551	64.1393	0.0806
5.0	64.1958	0.0346	64.1868	0.0681	64.1720	0.0996
5.5	64.2370	0.0419	64.2261	0.0825	64.2082	0.1206
6.0	64.2822	0.0499	64.2692	0.0983	64.2479	0.1436
6.5	64.3314	0.0587	64.3160	0.1155	64.2910	0.1687
7.0	64.3845	0.0681	64.3667	0.1341	64.3376	0.1959
7.5	64.4417	0.0783	64.4212	0.1541	64.3877	0.2251
8.0	64.5029	0.0892	64.4795	0.1756	64.4413	0.2565
8.5	64.5682	0.1009	64.5416	0.1985	64.4983	0.2899
9.0	64.6375	0.1133	64.6076	0.2229	64.5589	0.3255
9.5	64.7108	0.1264	64.6774	0.2488	64.6230	0.3632
10.0	64.7883	0.1404	64.7511	0.2762	64.6906	0.4031
10.5	64.8700	0.1551	64.8288	0.3052	64.7617	0.4452
11.0	64.9558	0.1707	64.9103	0.3356	64.8364	0.4896
11.5	65.0458	0.1870	64.9958	0.3677	64.9146	0.5362
12.0	65.1400	0.2042	65.0852	0.4014	64.9963	0.5851
12.5	65.2386	0.2223	65.1787	0.4368	65.0816	0.6364
13.0	65.3414	0.2412	65.2761	0.4739	65.1704	0.6901
13.5	65.4487	0.2610	65.3776	0.5127	65.2628	0.7462
14.0	65.5603	0.2819	65.4832	0.5533	65.3587	0.8049
14.5	65.6765	0.3037	65.5929	0.5959	65.4582	0.8661
15.0	65.7973	0.3265	65.7068	0.6403	65.5612	0.9300
15.5	65.9227	0.3504	65.8248	0.6868	65.6677	0.9967
16.0	66.0529	0.3754	65.9471	0.7355	65.7778	1.0663
16.5	66.1879	0.4017	66.0737	0.7863	65.8914	1.1388
17.0	66.3278	0.4292	66.2047	0.8395	66.0085	1.2144
17.5	66.4729	0.4580	66.3401	0.8951	66.1291	1.2933
18.0	66.6231	0.4882	66.4800	0.9534	66.2531	1.3755
18.5	66.7788	0.5199	66.6244	1.0144	66.3806	1.4613
19.0	66.9399	0.5533	66.7736	1.0783	66.5116	1.5509
19.5	67.1067	0.5883	66.9274	1.1454	66.6459	1.6445
20.0	67.2794	0.6251	67.0862	1.2157	66.7837	1.7422
20.5	67.4582	0.6639	67.2500	1.2896	66.9249	1.8445
21.0	67.6433	0.7047	67.4189	1.3673	67.0694	1.9515
21.5	67.8350	0.7477	67.5930	1.4489	67.2173	2.0637
22.0	68.0335	0.7930	67.7727	1.5349	67.3685	2.1812
22.5	68.2391	0.8407	67.9580	1.6254	67.5232	2.3047
23.0	68.4521	0.8910	68.1492	1.7207	67.6812	2.4344
23.5	68.6729	0.9440	68.3466	1.8212	67.8427	2.5708
24.0	68.9016	0.9999	68.5504	1.9272	68.0076	2.7145
24.5	69.1388	1.0587	68.7610	2.0390	68.1763	2.8661
25.0	69.3847	1.1206	68.9787	2.1570	68.3486	3.0260

TABLE I. $a_r(q) = U + iV$, $q = \rho e^{i\phi}$ $\qquad\qquad r = 8$

ρ	$\phi = 20°$		$\phi = 25°$		$\phi = 30°$	
	U	V	U	V	U	V
0.0	64.0000	0.0000	64.0000	0.0000	64.0000	0.0000
0.5	64.0015	0.0013	64.0013	0.0015	64.0010	0.0017
1.0	64.0061	0.0051	64.0051	0.0061	64.0040	0.0069
1.5	64.0137	0.0115	64.0115	0.0137	64.0089	0.0155
2.0	64.0243	0.0204	64.0204	0.0243	64.0159	0.0275
2.5	64.0380	0.0319	64.0319	0.0380	64.0248	0.0430
3.0	64.0547	0.0460	64.0459	0.0548	64.0357	0.0619
3.5	64.0745	0.0626	64.0625	0.0746	64.0486	0.0843
4.0	64.0973	0.0818	64.0816	0.0974	64.0634	0.1101
4.5	64.1232	0.1036	64.1033	0.1234	64.0802	0.1394
5.0	64.1521	0.1280	64.1275	0.1524	64.0990	0.1722
5.5	64.1840	0.1549	64.1542	0.1845	64.1197	0.2085
6.0	64.2190	0.1845	64.1835	0.2197	64.1424	0.2482
6.5	64.2571	0.2168	64.2153	0.2581	64.1670	0.2914
7.0	64.2982	0.2516	64.2497	0.2995	64.1936	0.3382
7.5	64.3423	0.2891	64.2865	0.3441	64.2221	0.3885
8.0	64.3895	0.3293	64.3259	0.3919	64.2525	0.4423
8.5	64.4398	0.3722	64.3678	0.4428	64.2848	0.4996
9.0	64.4931	0.4177	64.4123	0.4969	64.3190	0.5605
9.5	64.5494	0.4661	64.4592	0.5542	64.3551	0.6250
10.0	64.6088	0.5171	64.5086	0.6147	64.3931	0.6930
10.5	64.6713	0.5710	64.5604	0.6785	64.4329	0.7646
11.0	64.7367	0.6276	64.6148	0.7455	64.4745	0.8399
11.5	64.8052	0.6871	64.6715	0.8158	64.5180	0.9187
12.0	64.8767	0.7494	64.7307	0.8894	64.5632	1.0011
12.5	64.9512	0.8147	64.7922	0.9663	64.6102	1.0872
13.0	65.0287	0.8829	64.8561	1.0466	64.6589	1.1768
13.5	65.1091	0.9541	64.9223	1.1302	64.7092	1.2701
14.0	65.1924	1.0283	64.9908	1.2172	64.7612	1.3670
14.5	65.2786	1.1056	65.0614	1.3077	64.8148	1.4675
15.0	65.3676	1.1861	65.1342	1.4016	64.8698	1.5715
15.5	65.4594	1.2699	65.2091	1.4989	64.9264	1.6791
16.0	65.5539	1.3569	65.2859	1.5997	64.9842	1.7903
16.5	65.6511	1.4473	65.3646	1.7041	65.0434	1.9049
17.0	65.7509	1.5412	65.4451	1.8120	65.1037	2.0231
17.5	65.8531	1.6387	65.5272	1.9235	65.1651	2.1446
18.0	65.9578	1.7399	65.6108	2.0387	65.2274	2.2695
18.5	66.0647	1.8450	65.6957	2.1575	65.2905	2.3976
19.0	66.1737	1.9540	65.7817	2.2800	65.3541	2.5289
19.5	66.2848	2.0672	65.8687	2.4062	65.4182	2.6634
20.0	66.3977	2.1848	65.9563	2.5363	65.4824	2.8008
20.5	66.5123	2.3069	66.0443	2.6702	65.5465	2.9412
21.0	66.6283	2.4339	66.1323	2.8081	65.6103	3.0842
21.5	66.7456	2.5659	66.2201	2.9500	65.6734	3.2298
22.0	66.8640	2.7033	66.3073	3.0960	65.7354	3.3778
22.5	66.9831	2.8464	66.3933	3.2463	65.7961	3.5281
23.0	67.1027	2.9957	66.4778	3.4009	65.8548	3.6802
23.5	67.2225	3.1515	66.5601	3.5599	65.9112	3.8341
24.0	67.3421	3.3144	66.6396	3.7236	65.9646	3.9894
24.5	67.4613	3.4850	66.7157	3.8920	66.0145	4.1457
25.0	67.5796	3.6640	66.7875	4.0655	66.0602	4.3027

TABLE I. $a_r(q) = U + iV$, $q = \rho e^{i\phi}$ $r = 8$

ρ	$\phi=35°$		$\phi=40°$		$\phi=45°$	
	U	V	U	V	U	V
0.0	64.0000	0.0000	64.0000	0.0000	64.0000	0.0000
0.5	64.0007	0.0019	64.0003	0.0020	64.0000	0.0020
1.0	64.0027	0.0075	64.0014	0.0078	64.0000	0.0079
1.5	64.0061	0.0168	64.0031	0.0176	64.0000	0.0179
2.0	64.0108	0.0298	64.0055	0.0313	64.0000	0.0317
2.5	64.0169	0.0466	64.0086	0.0489	64.0000	0.0496
3.0	64.0244	0.0672	64.0124	0.0704	63.9999	0.0714
3.5	64.0332	0.0914	64.0168	0.0958	63.9999	0.0972
4.0	64.0433	0.1194	64.0219	0.1251	63.9998	0.1270
4.5	64.0548	0.1512	64.0276	0.1584	63.9997	0.1607
5.0	64.0675	0.1867	64.0341	0.1955	63.9996	0.1984
5.5	64.0816	0.2260	64.0411	0.2366	63.9994	0.2401
6.0	64.0970	0.2690	64.0488	0.2817	63.9991	0.2857
6.5	64.1137	0.3159	64.0571	0.3306	63.9988	0.3353
7.0	64.1317	0.3665	64.0660	0.3835	63.9984	0.3889
7.5	64.1510	0.4208	64.0755	0.4403	63.9979	0.4464
8.0	64.1715	0.4790	64.0856	0.5011	63.9973	0.5079
8.5	64.1933	0.5410	64.0962	0.5658	63.9965	0.5733
9.0	64.2164	0.6068	64.1075	0.6345	63.9956	0.6427
9.5	64.2406	0.6764	64.1192	0.7071	63.9946	0.7161
10.0	64.2661	0.7498	64.1315	0.7836	63.9934	0.7934
10.5	64.2927	0.8271	64.1443	0.8641	63.9921	0.8747
11.0	64.3206	0.9081	64.1576	0.9485	63.9906	0.9599
11.5	64.3495	0.9930	64.1714	1.0368	63.9888	1.0491
12.0	64.3797	1.0817	64.1856	1.1291	63.9869	1.1422
12.5	64.4109	1.1742	64.2004	1.2252	63.9849	1.2392
13.0	64.4432	1.2705	64.2156	1.3253	63.9826	1.3401
13.5	64.4766	1.3705	64.2312	1.4292	63.9801	1.4450
14.0	64.5110	1.4743	64.2473	1.5370	63.9775	1.5537
14.5	64.5464	1.5818	64.2638	1.6485	63.9747	1.6663
15.0	64.5827	1.6930	64.2808	1.7639	63.9719	1.7827
15.5	64.6200	1.8077	64.2983	1.8829	63.9689	1.9029
16.0	64.6582	1.9261	64.3162	2.0055	63.9660	2.0269
16.5	64.6973	2.0479	64.3346	2.1317	63.9631	2.1546
17.0	64.7371	2.1731	64.3535	2.2613	63.9603	2.2861
17.5	64.7777	2.3015	64.3729	2.3943	63.9578	2.4211
18.0	64.8189	2.4332	64.3930	2.5305	63.9556	2.5597
18.5	64.8608	2.5678	64.4136	2.6697	63.9538	2.7017
19.0	64.9031	2.7052	64.4349	2.8118	63.9527	2.8471
19.5	64.9459	2.8453	64.4568	2.9566	63.9525	2.9957
20.0	64.9890	2.9878	64.4796	3.1038	63.9532	3.1474
20.5	65.0324	3.1325	64.5032	3.2532	63.9552	3.3021
21.0	65.0758	3.2790	64.5277	3.4044	63.9586	3.4594
21.5	65.1191	3.4271	64.5532	3.5572	63.9639	3.6193
22.0	65.1622	3.5765	64.5798	3.7111	63.9713	3.7814
22.5	65.2049	3.7266	64.6076	3.8657	63.9812	3.9455
23.0	65.2470	3.8772	64.6366	4.0206	63.9938	4.1112
23.5	65.2883	4.0276	64.6671	4.1753	64.0097	4.2782
24.0	65.3286	4.1774	64.6991	4.3291	64.0293	4.4460
24.5	65.3676	4.3259	64.7328	4.4816	64.0529	4.6142
25.0	65.4051	4.4725	64.7683	4.6321	64.0811	4.7824

TABLE I. $a_r(q) = U + iV$, $q = \rho e^{i\phi}$ $r = 8$

ρ	$\phi = 50°$ U	$\phi = 50°$ V	$\phi = 55°$ U	$\phi = 55°$ V	$\phi = 60°$ U	$\phi = 60°$ V
0.0	64.0000	0.0000	64.0000	0.0000	64.0000	0.0000
0.5	63.9997	0.0020	63.9993	0.0019	63.9990	0.0017
1.0	63.9986	0.0078	63.9973	0.0075	63.9960	0.0069
1.5	63.9969	0.0176	63.9939	0.0168	63.9911	0.0155
2.0	63.9945	0.0313	63.9891	0.0298	63.9841	0.0275
2.5	63.9914	0.0488	63.9830	0.0466	63.9752	0.0429
3.0	63.9875	0.0703	63.9755	0.0671	63.9643	0.0618
3.5	63.9830	0.0957	63.9667	0.0913	63.9513	0.0841
4.0	63.9778	0.1250	63.9564	0.1192	63.9364	0.1098
4.5	63.9718	0.1582	63.9448	0.1508	63.9195	0.1389
5.0	63.9651	0.1953	63.9318	0.1862	63.9006	0.1715
5.5	63.9577	0.2362	63.9174	0.2252	63.8797	0.2074
6.0	63.9496	0.2811	63.9016	0.2679	63.8567	0.2467
6.5	63.9406	0.3298	63.8844	0.3143	63.8317	0.2893
7.0	63.9310	0.3824	63.8658	0.3644	63.8048	0.3354
7.5	63.9205	0.4389	63.8457	0.4181	63.7757	0.3848
8.0	63.9092	0.4992	63.8242	0.4755	63.7447	0.4375
8.5	63.8972	0.5635	63.8012	0.5366	63.7116	0.4936
9.0	63.8843	0.6315	63.7768	0.6013	63.6764	0.5530
9.5	63.8706	0.7035	63.7509	0.6696	63.6392	0.6157
10.0	63.8561	0.7792	63.7236	0.7416	63.5998	0.6817
10.5	63.8407	0.8589	63.6947	0.8171	63.5584	0.7509
11.0	63.8245	0.9423	63.6643	0.8964	63.5150	0.8235
11.5	63.8074	1.0296	63.6325	0.9792	63.4693	0.8994
12.0	63.7895	1.1208	63.5991	1.0656	63.4216	0.9785
12.5	63.7706	1.2158	63.5642	1.1557	63.3717	1.0609
13.0	63.7510	1.3146	63.5277	1.2494	63.3197	1.1467
13.5	63.7305	1.4173	63.4897	1.3468	63.2654	1.2357
14.0	63.7092	1.5238	63.4503	1.4479	63.2090	1.3280
14.5	63.6870	1.6342	63.4092	1.5526	63.1503	1.4238
15.0	63.6641	1.7484	63.3667	1.6612	63.0894	1.5229
15.5	63.6405	1.8665	63.3227	1.7735	63.0261	1.6255
16.0	63.6163	1.9886	63.2772	1.8897	62.9606	1.7316
16.5	63.5914	2.1145	63.2303	2.0098	62.8927	1.8413
17.0	63.5661	2.2444	63.1820	2.1339	62.8224	1.9547
17.5	63.5404	2.3783	63.1324	2.2622	62.7496	2.0721
18.0	63.5144	2.5162	63.0816	2.3947	62.6744	2.1934
18.5	63.4884	2.6581	63.0296	2.5317	62.5966	2.3190
19.0	63.4625	2.8040	62.9767	2.6733	62.5163	2.4490
19.5	63.4370	2.9541	62.9229	2.8196	62.4333	2.5838
20.0	63.4121	3.1083	62.8684	2.9710	62.3477	2.7237
20.5	63.3881	3.2667	62.8134	3.1277	62.2594	2.8690
21.0	63.3653	3.4292	62.7583	3.2900	62.1685	3.0203
21.5	63.3443	3.5960	62.7034	3.4582	62.0748	3.1780
22.0	63.3254	3.7669	62.6491	3.6326	61.9785	3.3429
22.5	63.3091	3.9420	62.5958	3.8136	61.8796	3.5156
23.0	63.2960	4.1213	62.5440	4.0017	61.7782	3.6970
23.5	63.2867	4.3046	62.4946	4.1972	61.6746	3.8881
24.0	63.2819	4.4918	62.4481	4.4006	61.5690	4.0899
24.5	63.2824	4.6829	62.4055	4.6123	61.4620	4.3038
25.0	63.2888	4.8774	62.3679	4.8325	61.3542	4.5311

TABLE I. $a_r(q) = U + iV$, $q = \rho e^{i\phi}$ $r = 8$

ρ	$\phi=65°$		$\phi=70°$		$\phi=75°$	
	U	V	U	V	U	V
0.0	64.0000	0.0000	64.0000	0.0000	64.0000	0.0000
0.5	63.9987	0.0015	63.9985	0.0013	63.9983	0.0010
1.0	63.9949	0.0061	63.9939	0.0051	63.9931	0.0040
1.5	63.9885	0.0137	63.9863	0.0115	63.9845	0.0089
2.0	63.9796	0.0243	63.9757	0.0204	63.9725	0.0159
2.5	63.9681	0.0380	63.9620	0.0319	63.9571	0.0248
3.0	63.9541	0.0547	63.9453	0.0459	63.9382	0.0357
3.5	63.9375	0.0744	63.9255	0.0624	63.9159	0.0485
4.0	63.9183	0.0971	63.9028	0.0815	63.8901	0.0633
4.5	63.8966	0.1228	63.8769	0.1030	63.8610	0.0801
5.0	63.8724	0.1516	63.8481	0.1271	63.8284	0.0988
5.5	63.8456	0.1833	63.8162	0.1537	63.7924	0.1195
6.0	63.8162	0.2180	63.7813	0.1828	63.7530	0.1421
6.5	63.7843	0.2557	63.7433	0.2144	63.7102	0.1666
7.0	63.7497	0.2963	63.7024	0.2484	63.6640	0.1930
7.5	63.7127	0.3399	63.6584	0.2849	63.6144	0.2214
8.0	63.6730	0.3864	63.6114	0.3238	63.5615	0.2516
8.5	63.6308	0.4358	63.5613	0.3651	63.5052	0.2836
9.0	63.5860	0.4881	63.5083	0.4089	63.4454	0.3176
9.5	63.5386	0.5434	63.4522	0.4550	63.3824	0.3533
10.0	63.4886	0.6015	63.3931	0.5035	63.3159	0.3909
10.5	63.4360	0.6624	63.3309	0.5544	63.2462	0.4303
11.0	63.3808	0.7262	63.2657	0.6076	63.1730	0.4714
11.5	63.3229	0.7929	63.1975	0.6631	63.0965	0.5142
12.0	63.2624	0.8623	63.1262	0.7209	63.0167	0.5588
12.5	63.1992	0.9346	63.0518	0.7809	62.9335	0.6050
13.0	63.1333	1.0097	62.9743	0.8432	62.8470	0.6529
13.5	63.0647	1.0876	62.8936	0.9076	62.7570	0.7023
14.0	62.9932	1.1683	62.8098	0.9743	62.6637	0.7532
14.5	62.9190	1.2518	62.7227	1.0430	62.5670	0.8055
15.0	62.8418	1.3381	62.6323	1.1139	62.4668	0.8592
15.5	62.7617	1.4273	62.5386	1.1868	62.3632	0.9142
16.0	62.6785	1.5193	62.4413	1.2618	62.2560	0.9704
16.5	62.5921	1.6143	62.3405	1.3387	62.1452	1.0276
17.0	62.5025	1.7122	62.2359	1.4175	62.0307	1.0856
17.5	62.4095	1.8132	62.1275	1.4982	61.9125	1.1445
18.0	62.3129	1.9174	62.0149	1.5807	61.7904	1.2038
18.5	62.2124	2.0248	61.8980	1.6650	61.6642	1.2635
19.0	62.1080	2.1356	61.7764	1.7510	61.5338	1.3233
19.5	61.9994	2.2499	61.6499	1.8386	61.3991	1.3828
20.0	61.8861	2.3682	61.5180	1.9277	61.2597	1.4418
20.5	61.7680	2.4905	61.3802	2.0184	61.1154	1.4997
21.0	61.6445	2.6172	61.2361	2.1104	60.9658	1.5562
21.5	61.5153	2.7488	61.0849	2.2038	60.8107	1.6108
22.0	61.3798	2.8857	60.9258	2.2983	60.6495	1.6626
22.5	61.2373	3.0286	60.7580	2.3939	60.4819	1.7110
23.0	61.0872	3.1782	60.5804	2.4905	60.3073	1.7552
23.5	60.9287	3.3354	60.3915	2.5878	60.1250	1.7939
24.0	60.7609	3.5015	60.1900	2.6857	59.9345	1.8259
24.5	60.5827	3.6778	59.9737	2.7838	59.7350	1.8498
25.0	60.3930	3.8663	59.7404	2.8819	59.5259	1.8636

TABLE I. $a_r(q) = U + iV$, $q = \rho e^{i\phi}$ $r = 8$

ρ	$\phi = 80°$		$\phi = 85°$		$\phi = 90°$	
	U	V	U	V	U	V
0.0	64.0000	0.0000	64.0000	0.0000	64.0000	0.0000
0.5	63.9981	0.0007	63.9980	0.0003	63.9980	0.0000
1.0	63.9925	0.0027	63.9922	0.0014	63.9921	0.0000
1.5	63.9832	0.0061	63.9824	0.0031	63.9821	0.0000
2.0	63.9702	0.0109	63.9687	0.0055	63.9683	0.0000
2.5	63.9534	0.0169	63.9512	0.0086	63.9504	0.0000
3.0	63.9329	0.0244	63.9297	0.0124	63.9286	0.0000
3.5	63.9087	0.0332	63.9044	0.0168	63.9029	0.0000
4.0	63.8808	0.0433	63.8751	0.0220	63.8732	0.0000
4.5	63.8492	0.0548	63.8420	0.0278	63.8396	0.0000
5.0	63.8139	0.0676	63.8050	0.0343	63.8020	0.0000
5.5	63.7749	0.0817	63.7642	0.0415	63.7605	0.0000
6.0	63.7322	0.0972	63.7195	0.0493	63.7152	0.0000
6.5	63.6858	0.1139	63.6709	0.0578	63.6659	0.0000
7.0	63.6358	0.1320	63.6185	0.0670	63.6127	0.0000
7.5	63.5821	0.1513	63.5624	0.0768	63.5557	0.0000
8.0	63.5248	0.1719	63.5024	0.0872	63.4948	0.0000
8.5	63.4639	0.1938	63.4386	0.0983	63.4301	0.0000
9.0	63.3993	0.2170	63.3711	0.1101	63.3616	0.0000
9.5	63.3311	0.2414	63.2998	0.1224	63.2893	0.0000
10.0	63.2594	0.2670	63.2248	0.1354	63.2132	0.0000
10.5	63.1840	0.2938	63.1461	0.1490	63.1334	0.0000
11.0	63.1052	0.3218	63.0638	0.1631	63.0499	0.0000
11.5	63.0227	0.3509	62.9778	0.1779	62.9627	0.0000
12.0	62.9368	0.3812	62.8882	0.1932	62.8719	0.0000
12.5	62.8473	0.4125	62.7950	0.2090	62.7774	0.0000
13.0	62.7544	0.4448	62.6983	0.2253	62.6795	0.0000
13.5	62.6580	0.4782	62.5981	0.2420	62.5781	0.0000
14.0	62.5581	0.5124	62.4945	0.2592	62.4733	0.0000
14.5	62.4549	0.5475	62.3876	0.2768	62.3651	0.0000
15.0	62.3482	0.5833	62.2774	0.2946	62.2538	0.0000
15.5	62.2382	0.6198	62.1640	0.3127	62.1394	0.0000
16.0	62.1249	0.6568	62.0475	0.3310	62.0220	0.0000
16.5	62.0083	0.6942	61.9281	0.3494	61.9018	0.0000
17.0	61.8884	0.7318	61.8059	0.3677	61.7790	0.0000
17.5	61.7653	0.7694	61.6810	0.3858	61.6537	0.0000
18.0	61.6390	0.8068	61.5536	0.4036	61.5263	0.0000
18.5	61.5096	0.8437	61.4240	0.4209	61.3970	0.0000
19.0	61.3770	0.8799	61.2924	0.4375	61.2660	0.0000
19.5	61.2415	0.9148	61.1590	0.4532	61.1339	0.0000
20.0	61.1030	0.9482	61.0242	0.4677	61.0009	0.0000
20.5	60.9616	0.9796	60.8883	0.4807	60.8676	0.0000
21.0	60.8174	1.0084	60.7518	0.4919	60.7344	0.0000
21.5	60.6705	1.0340	60.6151	0.5008	60.6019	0.0000
22.0	60.5212	1.0557	60.4788	0.5072	60.4709	0.0000
22.5	60.3695	1.0727	60.3434	0.5105	60.3420	0.0000
23.0	60.2157	1.0841	60.2096	0.5103	60.2160	0.0000
23.5	60.0602	1.0889	60.0782	0.5061	60.0937	0.0000
24.0	59.9032	1.0861	59.9500	0.4973	59.9762	0.0000
24.5	59.7455	1.0743	59.8259	0.4833	59.8643	0.0000
25.0	59.5875	1.0524	59.7069	0.4637	59.7592	0.0000

ρ	$\phi = 5°$		$\phi = 10°$		$\phi = 15°$	
	U	V	U	V	U	V
0.0	81.0000	0.0000	81.0000	0.0000	81.0000	0.0000
0.5	81.0015	0.0003	81.0015	0.0005	81.0014	0.0008
1.0	81.0062	0.0011	81.0059	0.0021	81.0054	0.0031
1.5	81.0139	0.0024	81.0132	0.0048	81.0122	0.0070
2.0	81.0246	0.0043	81.0235	0.0086	81.0217	0.0125
2.5	81.0385	0.0068	81.0367	0.0134	81.0338	0.0195
3.0	81.0554	0.0098	81.0529	0.0193	81.0487	0.0281
3.5	81.0754	0.0133	81.0720	0.0262	81.0663	0.0383
4.0	81.0986	0.0174	81.0940	0.0343	81.0866	0.0501
4.5	81.1248	0.0220	81.1190	0.0434	81.1097	0.0634
5.0	81.1541	0.0272	81.1470	0.0536	81.1354	0.0783
5.5	81.1865	0.0329	81.1779	0.0649	81.1639	0.0948
6.0	81.2220	0.0392	81.2118	0.0772	81.1951	0.1129
6.5	81.2606	0.0461	81.2486	0.0907	81.2290	0.1325
7.0	81.3023	0.0535	81.2884	0.1053	81.2656	0.1538
7.5	81.3472	0.0614	81.3312	0.1209	81.3050	0.1767
8.0	81.3952	0.0699	81.3769	0.1377	81.3471	0.2012
8.5	81.4463	0.0790	81.4256	0.1556	81.3919	0.2273
9.0	81.5006	0.0887	81.4774	0.1746	81.4395	0.2550
9.5	81.5580	0.0989	81.5321	0.1947	81.4898	0.2844
10.0	81.6186	0.1097	81.5898	0.2159	81.5429	0.3154
10.5	81.6824	0.1211	81.6506	0.2383	81.5987	0.3481
11.0	81.7494	0.1330	81.7144	0.2618	81.6573	0.3824
11.5	81.8195	0.1456	81.7812	0.2865	81.7187	0.4184
12.0	81.8929	0.1587	81.8510	0.3124	81.7828	0.4561
12.5	81.9695	0.1725	81.9239	0.3394	81.8497	0.4955
13.0	82.0493	0.1868	81.9998	0.3676	81.9193	0.5365
13.5	82.1323	0.2018	82.0788	0.3970	81.9918	0.5794
14.0	82.2187	0.2174	82.1609	0.4276	82.0670	0.6239
14.5	82.3083	0.2336	82.2461	0.4594	82.1450	0.6703
15.0	82.4012	0.2504	82.3344	0.4925	82.2259	0.7183
15.5	82.4975	0.2679	82.4259	0.5268	82.3095	0.7682
16.0	82.5971	0.2861	82.5204	0.5624	82.3959	0.8200
16.5	82.7000	0.3049	82.6181	0.5993	82.4851	0.8735
17.0	82.8064	0.3244	82.7189	0.6376	82.5772	0.9289
17.5	82.9162	0.3446	82.8230	0.6771	82.6720	0.9862
18.0	83.0294	0.3655	82.9302	0.7181	82.7697	1.0455
18.5	83.1461	0.3872	83.0406	0.7604	82.8701	1.1066
19.0	83.2663	0.4096	83.1543	0.8042	82.9734	1.1698
19.5	83.3901	0.4328	83.2712	0.8494	83.0794	1.2350
20.0	83.5174	0.4568	83.3913	0.8962	83.1883	1.3023
20.5	83.6484	0.4816	83.5148	0.9445	83.2999	1.3717
21.0	83.7831	0.5073	83.6415	0.9944	83.4144	1.4433
21.5	83.9216	0.5339	83.7716	1.0460	83.5316	1.5170
22.0	84.0638	0.5614	83.9051	1.0994	83.6515	1.5931
22.5	84.2099	0.5899	84.0420	1.1545	83.7742	1.6716
23.0	84.3599	0.6194	84.1822	1.2115	83.8997	1.7524
23.5	84.5138	0.6500	84.3260	1.2704	84.0278	1.8358
24.0	84.6719	0.6817	84.4732	1.3314	84.1586	1.9218
24.5	84.8342	0.7146	84.6239	1.3945	84.2921	2.0105
25.0	85.0006	0.7487	84.7782	1.4598	84.4282	2.1019

ρ	$\phi = 20°$		$\phi = 25°$		$\phi = 30°$	
	U	V	U	V	U	V
0.0	81.0000	0.0000	81.0000	0.0000	81.0000	0.0000
0.5	81.0012	0.0010	81.0010	0.0012	81.0008	0.0014
1.0	81.0048	0.0040	81.0040	0.0048	81.0031	0.0054
1.5	81.0108	0.0090	81.0090	0.0108	81.0070	0.0122
2.0	81.0192	0.0161	81.0161	0.0192	81.0125	0.0217
2.5	81.0299	0.0251	81.0251	0.0299	81.0195	0.0338
3.0	81.0431	0.0362	81.0362	0.0431	81.0281	0.0487
3.5	81.0587	0.0493	81.0492	0.0587	81.0383	0.0663
4.0	81.0766	0.0644	81.0643	0.0767	81.0500	0.0867
4.5	81.0970	0.0815	81.0813	0.0971	81.0632	0.1097
5.0	81.1197	0.1006	81.1004	0.1199	81.0780	0.1355
5.5	81.1449	0.1218	81.1215	0.1451	81.0944	0.1640
6.0	81.1724	0.1450	81.1446	0.1728	81.1123	0.1952
6.5	81.2024	0.1703	81.1696	0.2029	81.1317	0.2292
7.0	81.2347	0.1976	81.1967	0.2354	81.1527	0.2659
7.5	81.2695	0.2270	81.2258	0.2703	81.1753	0.3054
8.0	81.3066	0.2584	81.2569	0.3077	81.1993	0.3476
8.5	81.3462	0.2920	81.2899	0.3476	81.2249	0.3925
9.0	81.3882	0.3275	81.3250	0.3899	81.2520	0.4403
9.5	81.4325	0.3652	81.3621	0.4347	81.2807	0.4908
10.0	81.4793	0.4050	81.4011	0.4820	81.3108	0.5441
10.5	81.5285	0.4469	81.4422	0.5318	81.3425	0.6002
11.0	81.5801	0.4909	81.4852	0.5841	81.3756	0.6590
11.5	81.6341	0.5370	81.5302	0.6388	81.4103	0.7207
12.0	81.6905	0.5853	81.5772	0.6962	81.4464	0.7852
12.5	81.7493	0.6358	81.6261	0.7560	81.4841	0.8526
13.0	81.8105	0.6884	81.6770	0.8184	81.5232	0.9227
13.5	81.8741	0.7432	81.7299	0.8833	81.5638	0.9957
14.0	81.9402	0.8001	81.7847	0.9508	81.6058	1.0715
14.5	82.0086	0.8593	81.8415	1.0209	81.6493	1.1502
15.0	82.0794	0.9208	81.9002	1.0936	81.6942	1.2318
15.5	82.1527	0.9845	81.9609	1.1689	81.7405	1.3162
16.0	82.2283	1.0504	82.0234	1.2468	81.7883	1.4035
16.5	82.3063	1.1186	82.0879	1.3273	81.8375	1.4937
17.0	82.3866	1.1892	82.1543	1.4105	81.8880	1.5867
17.5	82.4693	1.2620	82.2225	1.4963	81.9399	1.6827
18.0	82.5544	1.3372	82.2926	1.5848	81.9932	1.7815
18.5	82.6418	1.4148	82.3645	1.6759	82.0478	1.8832
19.0	82.7315	1.4948	82.4383	1.7698	82.1038	1.9878
19.5	82.8236	1.5772	82.5138	1.8663	82.1610	2.0953
20.0	82.9178	1.6621	82.5910	1.9655	82.2195	2.2056
20.5	83.0143	1.7494	82.6700	2.0675	82.2793	2.3187
21.0	83.1131	1.8393	82.7507	2.1721	82.3403	2.4347
21.5	83.2140	1.9317	82.8330	2.2795	82.4025	2.5535
22.0	83.3170	2.0267	82.9169	2.3895	82.4658	2.6751
22.5	83.4221	2.1244	83.0022	2.5023	82.5303	2.7994
23.0	83.5292	2.2247	83.0891	2.6178	82.5958	2.9264
23.5	83.6383	2.3278	83.1773	2.7361	82.6624	3.0560
24.0	83.7492	2.4337	83.2668	2.8570	82.7299	3.1883
24.5	83.8620	2.5424	83.3575	2.9807	82.7984	3.3231
25.0	83.9765	2.6540	83.4493	3.1070	82.8677	3.4603

322-566 O - 69 - 6

TABLE I. $a_r(q) = U + iV$, $q = \rho e^{i\phi}$ $r = 9$

ρ	$\phi=35°$		$\phi=40°$		$\phi=45°$	
	U	V	U	V	U	V
0.0	81.0000	0.0000	81.0000	0.0000	81.0000	0.0000
0.5	81.0005	0.0015	81.0003	0.0015	81.0000	0.0016
1.0	81.0021	0.0059	81.0011	0.0062	81.0000	0.0062
1.5	81.0048	0.0132	81.0024	0.0138	81.0000	0.0141
2.0	81.0085	0.0235	81.0043	0.0246	81.0000	0.0250
2.5	81.0133	0.0367	81.0068	0.0385	81.0000	0.0391
3.0	81.0192	0.0529	81.0097	0.0554	81.0000	0.0562
3.5	81.0261	0.0720	81.0132	0.0754	81.0000	0.0766
4.0	81.0341	0.0940	81.0173	0.0985	80.9999	0.1000
4.5	81.0432	0.1190	81.0219	0.1247	80.9999	0.1266
5.0	81.0533	0.1470	81.0269	0.1539	80.9998	0.1562
5.5	81.0644	0.1779	81.0325	0.1863	80.9997	0.1891
6.0	81.0766	0.2117	81.0387	0.2217	80.9996	0.2250
6.5	81.0899	0.2485	81.0453	0.2602	80.9994	0.2641
7.0	81.1041	0.2883	81.0524	0.3019	80.9992	0.3062
7.5	81.1194	0.3310	81.0601	0.3466	80.9990	0.3516
8.0	81.1358	0.3767	81.0682	0.3944	80.9987	0.4000
8.5	81.1531	0.4254	81.0768	0.4453	80.9983	0.4515
9.0	81.1715	0.4771	81.0859	0.4993	80.9979	0.5062
9.5	81.1909	0.5317	81.0954	0.5564	80.9973	0.5640
10.0	81.2112	0.5894	81.1054	0.6166	80.9967	0.6250
10.5	81.2326	0.6500	81.1159	0.6799	80.9960	0.6890
11.0	81.2549	0.7136	81.1268	0.7463	80.9952	0.7562
11.5	81.2782	0.7803	81.1381	0.8158	80.9943	0.8265
12.0	81.3025	0.8500	81.1499	0.8885	80.9933	0.8999
12.5	81.3278	0.9226	81.1621	0.9643	80.9921	0.9764
13.0	81.3540	0.9983	81.1746	1.0431	80.9908	1.0561
13.5	81.3811	1.0771	81.1876	1.1252	80.9893	1.1388
14.0	81.4091	1.1588	81.2009	1.2103	80.9876	1.2247
14.5	81.4381	1.2436	81.2146	1.2986	80.9858	1.3137
15.0	81.4680	1.3315	81.2287	1.3899	80.9838	1.4059
15.5	81.4988	1.4223	81.2432	1.4845	80.9816	1.5011
16.0	81.5304	1.5163	81.2579	1.5821	80.9792	1.5995
16.5	81.5630	1.6132	81.2731	1.6829	80.9765	1.7010
17.0	81.5964	1.7132	81.2885	1.7868	80.9737	1.8056
17.5	81.6307	1.8163	81.3043	1.8938	80.9706	1.9134
18.0	81.6658	1.9224	81.3204	2.0040	80.9674	2.0243
18.5	81.7018	2.0315	81.3369	2.1173	80.9639	2.1383
19.0	81.7386	2.1437	81.3537	2.2337	80.9601	2.2555
19.5	81.7763	2.2588	81.3708	2.3532	80.9562	2.3758
20.0	81.8148	2.3770	81.3882	2.4759	80.9521	2.4993
20.5	81.8540	2.4981	81.4060	2.6016	80.9477	2.6260
21.0	81.8941	2.6222	81.4242	2.7304	80.9432	2.7558
21.5	81.9351	2.7491	81.4428	2.8622	80.9386	2.8889
22.0	81.9768	2.8790	81.4618	2.9971	80.9339	3.0252
22.5	82.0193	3.0117	81.4812	3.1351	80.9290	3.1646
23.0	82.0627	3.1471	81.5012	3.2760	80.9242	3.3074
23.5	82.1068	3.2853	81.5217	3.4199	80.9194	3.4534
24.0	82.1518	3.4261	81.5428	3.5667	80.9148	3.6027
24.5	82.1976	3.5694	81.5646	3.7163	80.9103	3.7553
25.0	82.2442	3.7153	81.5871	3.8688	80.9061	3.9112

TABLE I. $a_r(q) = U + iV$, $q = \rho e^{i\phi}$ $\qquad r = 9$

ρ	$\phi = 50°$		$\phi = 55°$		$\phi = 60°$	
	U	V	U	V	U	V
0.0	81.0000	0.0000	81.0000	0.0000	81.0000	0.0000
0.5	80.9997	0.0015	80.9995	0.0015	80.9992	0.0014
1.0	80.9989	0.0062	80.9979	0.0059	80.9969	0.0054
1.5	80.9976	0.0138	80.9952	0.0132	80.9930	0.0122
2.0	80.9957	0.0246	80.9914	0.0235	80.9875	0.0216
2.5	80.9932	0.0385	80.9866	0.0367	80.9805	0.0338
3.0	80.9902	0.0554	80.9807	0.0528	80.9719	0.0487
3.5	80.9867	0.0754	80.9738	0.0719	80.9617	0.0663
4.0	80.9826	0.0985	80.9657	0.0939	80.9500	0.0865
4.5	80.9779	0.1246	80.9566	0.1188	80.9367	0.1095
5.0	80.9727	0.1538	80.9464	0.1467	80.9218	0.1351
5.5	80.9669	0.1861	80.9351	0.1775	80.9053	0.1635
6.0	80.9605	0.2214	80.9227	0.2112	80.8873	0.1945
6.5	80.9536	0.2598	80.9092	0.2478	80.8677	0.2282
7.0	80.9461	0.3013	80.8947	0.2873	80.8465	0.2645
7.5	80.9380	0.3459	80.8790	0.3297	80.8237	0.3036
8.0	80.9293	0.3935	80.8622	0.3750	80.7993	0.3453
8.5	80.9200	0.4441	80.8443	0.4232	80.7734	0.3896
9.0	80.9101	0.4978	80.8252	0.4743	80.7458	0.4366
9.5	80.8996	0.5546	80.8051	0.5283	80.7167	0.4862
10.0	80.8884	0.6144	80.7838	0.5852	80.6859	0.5384
10.5	80.8767	0.6772	80.7613	0.6449	80.6535	0.5933
11.0	80.8642	0.7431	80.7378	0.7075	80.6196	0.6508
11.5	80.8512	0.8120	80.7130	0.7730	80.5840	0.7109
12.0	80.8374	0.8839	80.6871	0.8413	80.5467	0.7736
12.5	80.8230	0.9589	80.6600	0.9125	80.5079	0.8388
13.0	80.8080	1.0369	80.6318	0.9865	80.4674	0.9067
13.5	80.7922	1.1179	80.6023	1.0634	80.4252	0.9771
14.0	80.7757	1.2020	80.5716	1.1430	80.3814	1.0500
14.5	80.7585	1.2890	80.5398	1.2255	80.3360	1.1256
15.0	80.7406	1.3791	80.5067	1.3108	80.2888	1.2036
15.5	80.7220	1.4722	80.4723	1.3989	80.2400	1.2842
16.0	80.7026	1.5683	80.4368	1.4899	80.1895	1.3672
16.5	80.6825	1.6674	80.3999	1.5836	80.1373	1.4528
17.0	80.6616	1.7695	80.3618	1.6801	80.0833	1.5408
17.5	80.6399	1.8747	80.3223	1.7795	80.0276	1.6314
18.0	80.6174	1.9829	80.2816	1.8816	79.9701	1.7244
18.5	80.5942	2.0942	80.2395	1.9866	79.9109	1.8198
19.0	80.5701	2.2085	80.1960	2.0943	79.8498	1.9177
19.5	80.5453	2.3258	80.1512	2.2049	79.7868	2.0181
20.0	80.5196	2.4463	80.1050	2.3184	79.7220	2.1208
20.5	80.4931	2.5699	80.0573	2.4347	79.6552	2.2260
21.0	80.4658	2.6966	80.0081	2.5539	79.5864	2.3337
21.5	80.4377	2.8265	79.9575	2.6761	79.5155	2.4437
22.0	80.4088	2.9597	79.9053	2.8012	79.4426	2.5562
22.5	80.3791	3.0961	79.8515	2.9293	79.3674	2.6711
23.0	80.3487	3.2359	79.7961	3.0606	79.2899	2.7885
23.5	80.3174	3.3791	79.7391	3.1950	79.2100	2.9083
24.0	80.2855	3.5258	79.6803	3.3326	79.1276	3.0307
24.5	80.2529	3.6761	79.6197	3.4737	79.0426	3.1555
25.0	80.2197	3.8301	79.5573	3.6182	78.9547	3.2829

TABLE I. $a_r(q) = U + iV$, $q = \rho e^{i\phi}$ $\qquad r = 9$

ρ	$\phi=65°$		$\phi=70°$		$\phi=75°$	
	U	V	U	V	U	V
0.0	81.0000	0.0000	81.0000	0.0000	81.0000	0.0000
0.5	80.9990	0.0012	80.9988	0.0010	80.9986	0.0008
1.0	80.9960	0.0048	80.9952	0.0040	80.9946	0.0031
1.5	80.9910	0.0108	80.9892	0.0090	80.9878	0.0070
2.0	80.9839	0.0191	80.9808	0.0161	80.9784	0.0125
2.5	80.9749	0.0299	80.9701	0.0251	80.9662	0.0195
3.0	80.9638	0.0431	80.9569	0.0361	80.9513	0.0281
3.5	80.9508	0.0586	80.9414	0.0492	80.9337	0.0382
4.0	80.9357	0.0765	80.9234	0.0642	80.9134	0.0499
4.5	80.9186	0.0968	80.9031	0.0812	80.8905	0.0632
5.0	80.8995	0.1195	80.8803	0.1002	80.8648	0.0779
5.5	80.8784	0.1445	80.8552	0.1212	80.8364	0.0943
6.0	80.8553	0.1719	80.8277	0.1442	80.8054	0.1121
6.5	80.8302	0.2017	80.7978	0.1692	80.7716	0.1315
7.0	80.8030	0.2338	80.7655	0.1961	80.7352	0.1525
7.5	80.7738	0.2683	80.7309	0.2250	80.6961	0.1749
8.0	80.7427	0.3051	80.6938	0.2558	80.6543	0.1989
8.5	80.7095	0.3442	80.6544	0.2886	80.6098	0.2243
9.0	80.6742	0.3857	80.6126	0.3233	80.5626	0.2513
9.5	80.6370	0.4295	80.5684	0.3600	80.5128	0.2798
10.0	80.5977	0.4756	80.5218	0.3986	80.4604	0.3097
10.5	80.5564	0.5240	80.4729	0.4391	80.4052	0.3412
11.0	80.5131	0.5746	80.4216	0.4815	80.3475	0.3741
11.5	80.4678	0.6276	80.3679	0.5258	80.2871	0.4084
12.0	80.4204	0.6828	80.3118	0.5719	80.2240	0.4443
12.5	80.3710	0.7403	80.2534	0.6200	80.1583	0.4815
13.0	80.3196	0.8000	80.1926	0.6699	80.0900	0.5202
13.5	80.2661	0.8620	80.1295	0.7216	80.0191	0.5603
14.0	80.2106	0.9261	80.0640	0.7752	79.9455	0.6019
14.5	80.1530	0.9925	79.9961	0.8306	79.8694	0.6448
15.0	80.0934	1.0610	79.9259	0.8878	79.7907	0.6891
15.5	80.0318	1.1318	79.8533	0.9467	79.7094	0.7348
16.0	79.9680	1.2046	79.7784	1.0075	79.6255	0.7818
16.5	79.9022	1.2796	79.7011	1.0699	79.5391	0.8302
17.0	79.8344	1.3567	79.6215	1.1341	79.4502	0.8798
17.5	79.7644	1.4359	79.5396	1.1999	79.3587	0.9308
18.0	79.6923	1.5172	79.4553	1.2674	79.2648	0.9830
18.5	79.6181	1.6004	79.3687	1.3365	79.1683	1.0364
19.0	79.5417	1.6857	79.2798	1.4071	79.0695	1.0910
19.5	79.4632	1.7730	79.1885	1.4793	78.9682	1.1468
20.0	79.3824	1.8622	79.0948	1.5530	78.8645	1.2037
20.5	79.2994	1.9533	78.9989	1.6280	78.7585	1.2617
21.0	79.2142	2.0462	78.9006	1.7044	78.6502	1.3207
21.5	79.1265	2.1410	78.7999	1.7821	78.5396	1.3806
22.0	79.0365	2.2375	78.6968	1.8610	78.4268	1.4414
22.5	78.9441	2.3357	78.5914	1.9410	78.3119	1.5031
23.0	78.8490	2.4355	78.4836	2.0219	78.1949	1.5654
23.5	78.7514	2.5369	78.3734	2.1037	78.0758	1.6283
24.0	78.6509	2.6398	78.2608	2.1862	77.9549	1.6917
24.5	78.5476	2.7441	78.1457	2.2693	77.8322	1.7554
25.0	78.4413	2.8497	78.0282	2.3527	77.7077	1.8193

TABLE I. $a_r(q) = U + iV$, $q = \rho e^{i\phi}$ $\qquad\qquad$ $r = 9$

ρ	$\phi = 80°$		$\phi = 85°$		$\phi = 90°$	
	U	V	U	V	U	V
0.0	81.0000	0.0000	81.0000	0.0000	81.0000	0.0000
0.5	80.9985	0.0005	80.9985	0.0003	80.9984	0.0000
1.0	80.9941	0.0021	80.9938	0.0011	80.9937	0.0000
1.5	80.9868	0.0048	80.9862	0.0024	80.9859	0.0000
2.0	80.9765	0.0085	80.9754	0.0043	80.9750	0.0000
2.5	80.9633	0.0134	80.9615	0.0068	80.9609	0.0000
3.0	80.9472	0.0192	80.9446	0.0098	80.9438	0.0000
3.5	80.9281	0.0262	80.9246	0.0133	80.9235	0.0000
4.0	80.9061	0.0341	80.9016	0.0173	80.9001	0.0000
4.5	80.8812	0.0432	80.8755	0.0219	80.8736	0.0000
5.0	80.8533	0.0533	80.8463	0.0271	80.8440	0.0000
5.5	80.8226	0.0645	80.8141	0.0327	80.8112	0.0000
6.0	80.7889	0.0767	80.7788	0.0389	80.7754	0.0000
6.5	80.7523	0.0899	80.7405	0.0457	80.7365	0.0000
7.0	80.7128	0.1042	80.6991	0.0529	80.6945	0.0000
7.5	80.6704	0.1196	80.6547	0.0607	80.6495	0.0000
8.0	80.6251	0.1360	80.6073	0.0690	80.6013	0.0000
8.5	80.5770	0.1534	80.5569	0.0778	80.5501	0.0000
9.0	80.5259	0.1718	80.5034	0.0872	80.4959	0.0000
9.5	80.4720	0.1912	80.4470	0.0971	80.4386	0.0000
10.0	80.4152	0.2117	80.3875	0.1074	80.3782	0.0000
10.5	80.3555	0.2332	80.3251	0.1183	80.3148	0.0000
11.0	80.2930	0.2557	80.2597	0.1297	80.2484	0.0000
11.5	80.2276	0.2791	80.1913	0.1417	80.1790	0.0000
12.0	80.1594	0.3036	80.1199	0.1541	80.1066	0.0001
12.5	80.0884	0.3291	80.0456	0.1670	80.0312	0.0001
13.0	80.0146	0.3555	79.9684	0.1804	79.9528	0.0001
13.5	79.9379	0.3829	79.8883	0.1943	79.8715	0.0002
14.0	79.8585	0.4112	79.8052	0.2088	79.7872	0.0002
14.5	79.7763	0.4406	79.7193	0.2237	79.6999	0.0003
15.0	79.6913	0.4708	79.6304	0.2391	79.6097	0.0004
15.5	79.6036	0.5020	79.5387	0.2550	79.5166	0.0005
16.0	79.5132	0.5342	79.4442	0.2714	79.4205	0.0007
16.5	79.4200	0.5673	79.3468	0.2884	79.3216	0.0010
17.0	79.3242	0.6012	79.2467	0.3058	79.2198	0.0013
17.5	79.2257	0.6361	79.1437	0.3237	79.1151	0.0016
18.0	79.1246	0.6719	79.0380	0.3422	79.0076	0.0021
18.5	79.0209	0.7086	78.9296	0.3612	78.8972	0.0027
19.0	78.9147	0.7462	78.8185	0.3808	78.7840	0.0035
19.5	78.8059	0.7846	78.7048	0.4009	78.6679	0.0045
20.0	78.6947	0.8239	78.5884	0.4217	78.5491	0.0057
20.5	78.5811	0.8640	78.4695	0.4430	78.4275	0.0071
21.0	78.4652	0.9049	78.3481	0.4650	78.3031	0.0089
21.5	78.3470	0.9467	78.2243	0.4877	78.1759	0.0111
22.0	78.2267	0.9892	78.0981	0.5112	78.0460	0.0138
22.5	78.1043	1.0326	77.9696	0.5354	77.9134	0.0171
23.0	77.9799	1.0767	77.8389	0.5605	77.7781	0.0210
23.5	77.8538	1.1215	77.7062	0.5865	77.6400	0.0257
24.0	77.7259	1.1670	77.5714	0.6136	77.4994	0.0314
24.5	77.5966	1.2132	77.4349	0.6417	77.3560	0.0381
25.0	77.4659	1.2601	77.2967	0.6711	77.2101	0.0461

TABLE I. $a_r(q) = U + iV$, $q = \rho e^{i\phi}$ $r = 10$

ρ	$\phi = 5°$		$\phi = 10°$		$\phi = 15°$	
	U	V	U	V	U	V
0.0	100.0000	0.0000	100.0000	0.0000	100.0000	0.0000
0.5	100.0012	0.0002	100.0012	0.0004	100.0011	0.0006
1.0	100.0050	0.0009	100.0047	0.0017	100.0044	0.0025
1.5	100.0112	0.0020	100.0107	0.0039	100.0098	0.0057
2.0	100.0199	0.0035	100.0190	0.0069	100.0175	0.0101
2.5	100.0311	0.0055	100.0297	0.0108	100.0273	0.0158
3.0	100.0448	0.0079	100.0427	0.0156	100.0394	0.0227
3.5	100.0610	0.0108	100.0582	0.0212	100.0536	0.0310
4.0	100.0796	0.0140	100.0760	0.0277	100.0700	0.0404
4.5	100.1008	0.0178	100.0962	0.0350	100.0886	0.0512
5.0	100.1244	0.0220	100.1187	0.0433	100.1094	0.0632
5.5	100.1506	0.0266	100.1437	0.0524	100.1324	0.0765
6.0	100.1793	0.0316	100.1710	0.0623	100.1576	0.0911
6.5	100.2104	0.0372	100.2007	0.0732	100.1849	0.1070
7.0	100.2441	0.0431	100.2329	0.0849	100.2145	0.1241
7.5	100.2803	0.0495	100.2674	0.0975	100.2463	0.1425
8.0	100.3190	0.0564	100.3043	0.1110	100.2803	0.1622
8.5	100.3602	0.0637	100.3436	0.1254	100.3165	0.1832
9.0	100.4039	0.0714	100.3853	0.1406	100.3548	0.2055
9.5	100.4502	0.0796	100.4294	0.1568	100.3954	0.2291
10.0	100.4990	0.0883	100.4759	0.1738	100.4382	0.2540
10.5	100.5503	0.0974	100.5248	0.1918	100.4833	0.2802
11.0	100.6042	0.1070	100.5762	0.2106	100.5305	0.3077
11.5	100.6606	0.1170	100.6299	0.2304	100.5799	0.3366
12.0	100.7196	0.1275	100.6861	0.2511	100.6316	0.3667
12.5	100.7811	0.1385	100.7448	0.2726	100.6855	0.3982
13.0	100.8452	0.1499	100.8058	0.2951	100.7416	0.4311
13.5	100.9119	0.1618	100.8693	0.3185	100.8000	0.4652
14.0	100.9811	0.1742	100.9353	0.3429	100.8605	0.5008
14.5	101.0530	0.1871	101.0037	0.3682	100.9234	0.5376
15.0	101.1274	0.2004	101.0745	0.3944	100.9884	0.5759
15.5	101.2044	0.2142	101.1479	0.4216	101.0557	0.6155
16.0	101.2841	0.2285	101.2236	0.4497	101.1253	0.6564
16.5	101.3663	0.2433	101.3019	0.4788	101.1970	0.6988
17.0	101.4512	0.2586	101.3827	0.5088	101.2711	0.7426
17.5	101.5387	0.2744	101.4659	0.5398	101.3474	0.7878
18.0	101.6289	0.2907	101.5517	0.5718	101.4260	0.8343
18.5	101.7217	0.3075	101.6399	0.6048	101.5068	0.8823
19.0	101.8172	0.3248	101.7307	0.6388	101.5899	0.9318
19.5	101.9154	0.3426	101.8240	0.6738	101.6752	0.9827
20.0	102.0163	0.3609	101.9198	0.7098	101.7629	1.0350
20.5	102.1199	0.3798	102.0181	0.7468	101.8528	1.0889
21.0	102.2262	0.3992	102.1190	0.7849	101.9450	1.1442
21.5	102.3353	0.4192	102.2225	0.8241	102.0395	1.2010
22.0	102.4471	0.4397	102.3285	0.8643	102.1362	1.2593
22.5	102.5617	0.4608	102.4371	0.9056	102.2353	1.3192
23.0	102.6790	0.4825	102.5483	0.9480	102.3366	1.3806
23.5	102.7992	0.5047	102.6621	0.9915	102.4402	1.4435
24.0	102.9222	0.5276	102.7785	1.0361	102.5461	1.5081
24.5	103.0481	0.5510	102.8975	1.0819	102.6542	1.5742
25.0	103.1768	0.5751	103.0191	1.1289	102.7647	1.6420

TABLE I. $a_r(q) = U + iV$, $q = \rho e^{i\phi}$ $\qquad\qquad$ $r = 10$

ρ	$\phi = 20°$		$\phi = 25°$		$\phi = 30°$	
	U	V	U	V	U	V
0.0	100.0000	0.0000	100.0000	0.0000	100.0000	0.0000
0.5	100.0010	0.0008	100.0008	0.0010	100.0006	0.0011
1.0	100.0039	0.0032	100.0032	0.0039	100.0025	0.0044
1.5	100.0087	0.0073	100.0073	0.0087	100.0057	0.0098
2.0	100.0155	0.0130	100.0130	0.0155	100.0101	0.0175
2.5	100.0242	0.0203	100.0203	0.0242	100.0158	0.0273
3.0	100.0348	0.0292	100.0292	0.0348	100.0227	0.0394
3.5	100.0474	0.0398	100.0398	0.0474	100.0309	0.0536
4.0	100.0619	0.0520	100.0519	0.0619	100.0404	0.0700
4.5	100.0784	0.0658	100.0657	0.0784	100.0511	0.0886
5.0	100.0967	0.0813	100.0811	0.0968	100.0631	0.1094
5.5	100.1171	0.0984	100.0982	0.1172	100.0763	0.1324
6.0	100.1393	0.1171	100.1168	0.1395	100.0908	0.1577
6.5	100.1635	0.1375	100.1371	0.1638	100.1065	0.1851
7.0	100.1896	0.1595	100.1590	0.1900	100.1235	0.2147
7.5	100.2177	0.1831	100.1825	0.2182	100.1418	0.2465
8.0	100.2477	0.2085	100.2076	0.2483	100.1613	0.2805
8.5	100.2797	0.2354	100.2344	0.2804	100.1820	0.3168
9.0	100.3136	0.2641	100.2628	0.3145	100.2040	0.3552
9.5	100.3494	0.2944	100.2927	0.3505	100.2272	0.3959
10.0	100.3872	0.3263	100.3243	0.3886	100.2517	0.4389
10.5	100.4269	0.3600	100.3575	0.4286	100.2774	0.4840
11.0	100.4686	0.3953	100.3924	0.4706	100.3043	0.5314
11.5	100.5122	0.4323	100.4288	0.5146	100.3324	0.5810
12.0	100.5577	0.4710	100.4668	0.5606	100.3618	0.6329
12.5	100.6052	0.5114	100.5065	0.6086	100.3924	0.6870
13.0	100.6546	0.5535	100.5477	0.6587	100.4243	0.7434
13.5	100.7060	0.5973	100.5906	0.7107	100.4573	0.8020
14.0	100.7594	0.6428	100.6350	0.7648	100.4915	0.8629
14.5	100.8146	0.6901	100.6811	0.8209	100.5270	0.9261
15.0	100.8719	0.7391	100.7288	0.8791	100.5637	0.9916
15.5	100.9311	0.7898	100.7780	0.9393	100.6015	1.0593
16.0	100.9922	0.8423	100.8289	1.0015	100.6406	1.1293
16.5	101.0553	0.8966	100.8813	1.0659	100.6808	1.2017
17.0	101.1203	0.9526	100.9353	1.1323	100.7223	1.2763
17.5	101.1873	1.0104	100.9909	1.2007	100.7649	1.3532
18.0	101.2562	1.0699	101.0481	1.2713	100.8087	1.4325
18.5	101.3271	1.1313	101.1069	1.3440	100.8536	1.5141
19.0	101.3999	1.1945	101.1672	1.4188	100.8997	1.5980
19.5	101.4747	1.2595	101.2292	1.4956	100.9470	1.6842
20.0	101.5514	1.3263	101.2926	1.5747	100.9954	1.7728
20.5	101.6300	1.3950	101.3577	1.6558	101.0450	1.8637
21.0	101.7106	1.4655	101.4243	1.7391	101.0957	1.9570
21.5	101.7932	1.5379	101.4924	1.8245	101.1475	2.0526
22.0	101.8776	1.6121	101.5621	1.9121	101.2005	2.1506
22.5	101.9640	1.6883	101.6333	2.0019	101.2545	2.2510
23.0	102.0523	1.7663	101.7060	2.0938	101.3097	2.3537
23.5	102.1425	1.8463	101.7803	2.1879	101.3660	2.4588
24.0	102.2347	1.9282	101.8561	2.2842	101.4234	2.5663
24.5	102.3287	2.0121	101.9333	2.3827	101.4818	2.6762
25.0	102.4246	2.0979	102.0120	2.4833	101.5413	2.7884

TABLE I. $a_r(q) = U + iV$, $q = \rho e^{i\phi}$ $r = 10$

ρ	$\phi = 35°$		$\phi = 40°$		$\phi = 45°$	
	U	V	U	V	U	V
0.0	100.0000	0.0000	100.0000	0.0000	100.0000	0.0000
0.5	100.0004	0.0012	100.0002	0.0012	100.0000	0.0013
1.0	100.0017	0.0047	100.0009	0.0050	100.0000	0.0051
1.5	100.0039	0.0107	100.0020	0.0112	100.0000	0.0114
2.0	100.0069	0.0190	100.0035	0.0199	100.0000	0.0202
2.5	100.0108	0.0297	100.0055	0.0311	100.0000	0.0316
3.0	100.0155	0.0427	100.0079	0.0448	100.0000	0.0455
3.5	100.0211	0.0582	100.0107	0.0609	100.0000	0.0619
4.0	100.0276	0.0760	100.0140	0.0796	100.0000	0.0808
4.5	100.0349	0.0961	100.0177	0.1007	99.9999	0.1023
5.0	100.0431	0.1187	100.0218	0.1244	99.9999	0.1263
5.5	100.0521	0.1437	100.0264	0.1505	99.9998	0.1528
6.0	100.0620	0.1710	100.0314	0.1791	99.9998	0.1818
6.5	100.0727	0.2007	100.0368	0.2102	99.9997	0.2134
7.0	100.0843	0.2328	100.0426	0.2439	99.9996	0.2475
7.5	100.0967	0.2673	100.0488	0.2800	99.9995	0.2841
8.0	100.1100	0.3042	100.0555	0.3186	99.9993	0.3232
8.5	100.1241	0.3435	100.0625	0.3597	99.9991	0.3649
9.0	100.1391	0.3851	100.0700	0.4032	99.9989	0.4091
9.5	100.1548	0.4292	100.0778	0.4493	99.9986	0.4558
10.0	100.1714	0.4757	100.0861	0.4979	99.9983	0.5050
10.5	100.1888	0.5246	100.0947	0.5490	99.9979	0.5568
11.0	100.2071	0.5758	100.1038	0.6027	99.9975	0.6111
11.5	100.2261	0.6295	100.1132	0.6588	99.9970	0.6679
12.0	100.2460	0.6857	100.1230	0.7174	99.9965	0.7272
12.5	100.2667	0.7442	100.1331	0.7785	99.9958	0.7891
13.0	100.2881	0.8051	100.1436	0.8422	99.9951	0.8535
13.5	100.3104	0.8685	100.1545	0.9083	99.9944	0.9204
14.0	100.3335	0.9343	100.1657	0.9770	99.9935	0.9898
14.5	100.3573	1.0026	100.1773	1.0482	99.9925	1.0617
15.0	100.3819	1.0733	100.1892	1.1219	99.9914	1.1362
15.5	100.4073	1.1464	100.2014	1.1981	99.9902	1.2132
16.0	100.4334	1.2219	100.2139	1.2768	99.9889	1.2927
16.5	100.4603	1.3000	100.2268	1.3581	99.9874	1.3747
17.0	100.4880	1.3805	100.2400	1.4419	99.9858	1.4592
17.5	100.5164	1.4634	100.2534	1.5283	99.9841	1.5463
18.0	100.5456	1.5488	100.2672	1.6171	99.9822	1.6359
18.5	100.5754	1.6367	100.2812	1.7085	99.9801	1.7280
19.0	100.6060	1.7270	100.2955	1.8024	99.9779	1.8226
19.5	100.6374	1.8198	100.3101	1.8989	99.9755	1.9197
20.0	100.6694	1.9151	100.3250	1.9979	99.9729	2.0194
20.5	100.7021	2.0129	100.3401	2.0995	99.9701	2.1215
21.0	100.7356	2.1132	100.3554	2.2036	99.9671	2.2262
21.5	100.7697	2.2160	100.3710	2.3103	99.9639	2.3334
22.0	100.8045	2.3212	100.3868	2.4195	99.9604	2.4432
22.5	100.8400	2.4290	100.4028	2.5312	99.9567	2.5555
23.0	100.8762	2.5393	100.4191	2.6456	99.9528	2.6703
23.5	100.9130	2.6520	100.4356	2.7625	99.9487	2.7876
24.0	100.9505	2.7673	100.4522	2.8819	99.9442	2.9075
24.5	100.9887	2.8851	100.4691	3.0040	99.9395	3.0300
25.0	101.0275	3.0053	100.4862	3.1286	99.9345	3.1550

TABLE I. $a_r(q) = U + iV$, $q = \rho e^{i\phi}$ $r = 10$

ρ	$\phi=50°$		$\phi=55°$		$\phi=60°$	
	U	V	U	V	U	V
0.0	100.0000	0.0000	100.0000	0.0000	100.0000	0.0000
0.5	99.9998	0.0012	99.9996	0.0012	99.9994	0.0011
1.0	99.9991	0.0050	99.9983	0.0047	99.9975	0.0044
1.5	99.9980	0.0112	99.9961	0.0107	99.9943	0.0098
2.0	99.9965	0.0199	99.9931	0.0190	99.9899	0.0175
2.5	99.9945	0.0311	99.9892	0.0297	99.9842	0.0273
3.0	99.9921	0.0448	99.9844	0.0427	99.9773	0.0394
3.5	99.9892	0.0609	99.9788	0.0581	99.9691	0.0536
4.0	99.9859	0.0796	99.9723	0.0759	99.9596	0.0699
4.5	99.9822	0.1007	99.9650	0.0961	99.9488	0.0885
5.0	99.9780	0.1243	99.9567	0.1186	99.9368	0.1093
5.5	99.9733	0.1504	99.9476	0.1435	99.9235	0.1322
6.0	99.9682	0.1790	99.9376	0.1707	99.9090	0.1573
6.5	99.9627	0.2100	99.9268	0.2003	99.8932	0.1845
7.0	99.9566	0.2436	99.9150	0.2323	99.8761	0.2140
7.5	99.9502	0.2796	99.9024	0.2666	99.8577	0.2456
8.0	99.9432	0.3181	99.8889	0.3033	99.8380	0.2793
8.5	99.9358	0.3590	99.8745	0.3423	99.8171	0.3152
9.0	99.9279	0.4025	99.8592	0.3837	99.7949	0.3533
9.5	99.9196	0.4484	99.8431	0.4274	99.7714	0.3935
10.0	99.9107	0.4968	99.8260	0.4735	99.7466	0.4359
10.5	99.9014	0.5476	99.8080	0.5219	99.7206	0.4804
11.0	99.8916	0.6009	99.7891	0.5726	99.6932	0.5271
11.5	99.8812	0.6567	99.7693	0.6257	99.6646	0.5759
12.0	99.8704	0.7150	99.7486	0.6811	99.6347	0.6268
12.5	99.8591	0.7757	99.7270	0.7388	99.6034	0.6798
13.0	99.8473	0.8388	99.7044	0.7989	99.5709	0.7350
13.5	99.8349	0.9045	99.6809	0.8613	99.5371	0.7922
14.0	99.8220	0.9725	99.6565	0.9259	99.5019	0.8516
14.5	99.8086	1.0430	99.6312	0.9929	99.4655	0.9131
15.0	99.7947	1.1160	99.6049	1.0622	99.4277	0.9767
15.5	99.7802	1.1914	99.5777	1.1338	99.3886	1.0423
16.0	99.7651	1.2692	99.5495	1.2076	99.3482	1.1100
16.5	99.7495	1.3495	99.5203	1.2838	99.3065	1.1798
17.0	99.7334	1.4322	99.4902	1.3622	99.2635	1.2517
17.5	99.7166	1.5174	99.4591	1.4429	99.2191	1.3256
18.0	99.6993	1.6050	99.4271	1.5259	99.1734	1.4016
18.5	99.6814	1.6950	99.3940	1.6112	99.1264	1.4796
19.0	99.6629	1.7874	99.3600	1.6986	99.0780	1.5597
19.5	99.6438	1.8822	99.3250	1.7884	99.0283	1.6417
20.0	99.6240	1.9795	99.2889	1.8804	98.9772	1.7258
20.5	99.6037	2.0791	99.2518	1.9746	98.9248	1.8118
21.0	99.5827	2.1812	99.2137	2.0710	98.8710	1.8999
21.5	99.5610	2.2857	99.1746	2.1697	98.8158	1.9899
22.0	99.5387	2.3926	99.1344	2.2705	98.7593	2.0819
22.5	99.5157	2.5019	99.0931	2.3736	98.7014	2.1758
23.0	99.4920	2.6136	99.0508	2.4789	98.6421	2.2717
23.5	99.4676	2.7278	99.0074	2.5863	98.5814	2.3695
24.0	99.4425	2.8443	98.9628	2.6959	98.5193	2.4691
24.5	99.4167	2.9633	98.9172	2.8077	98.4557	2.5707
25.0	99.3901	3.0846	98.8704	2.9217	98.3907	2.6741

TABLE I. $a_r(q) = U + iV$, $q = \rho e^{i\phi}$ $r = 10$

ρ	$\phi = 65°$		$\phi = 70°$		$\phi = 75°$	
	U	V	U	V	U	V
0.0	100.0000	0.0000	100.0000	0.0000	100.0000	0.0000
0.5	99.9992	0.0010	99.9990	0.0008	99.9989	0.0006
1.0	99.9968	0.0039	99.9961	0.0032	99.9956	0.0025
1.5	99.9927	0.0087	99.9913	0.0073	99.9902	0.0057
2.0	99.9870	0.0155	99.9845	0.0130	99.9825	0.0101
2.5	99.9797	0.0242	99.9758	0.0203	99.9727	0.0158
3.0	99.9708	0.0348	99.9652	0.0292	99.9606	0.0227
3.5	99.9602	0.0474	99.9526	0.0397	99.9464	0.0309
4.0	99.9480	0.0619	99.9381	0.0519	99.9300	0.0404
4.5	99.9342	0.0783	99.9217	0.0657	99.9115	0.0511
5.0	99.9188	0.0966	99.9033	0.0811	99.8907	0.0630
5.5	99.9018	0.1169	99.8830	0.0981	99.8678	0.0763
6.0	99.8831	0.1391	99.8608	0.1167	99.8427	0.0907
6.5	99.8628	0.1632	99.8366	0.1369	99.8154	0.1064
7.0	99.8409	0.1892	99.8105	0.1587	99.7859	0.1234
7.5	99.8173	0.2171	99.7825	0.1821	99.7542	0.1416
8.0	99.7921	0.2469	99.7525	0.2071	99.7204	0.1610
8.5	99.7653	0.2787	99.7206	0.2337	99.6844	0.1817
9.0	99.7369	0.3123	99.6868	0.2619	99.6463	0.2036
9.5	99.7068	0.3478	99.6511	0.2916	99.6060	0.2267
10.0	99.6751	0.3852	99.6134	0.3230	99.5635	0.2511
10.5	99.6417	0.4245	99.5738	0.3559	99.5188	0.2766
11.0	99.6068	0.4657	99.5323	0.3904	99.4720	0.3034
11.5	99.5702	0.5088	99.4889	0.4264	99.4230	0.3314
12.0	99.5320	0.5537	99.4435	0.4641	99.3719	0.3606
12.5	99.4921	0.6005	99.3962	0.5032	99.3187	0.3910
13.0	99.4506	0.6491	99.3470	0.5439	99.2632	0.4226
13.5	99.4075	0.6996	99.2959	0.5862	99.2057	0.4554
14.0	99.3627	0.7519	99.2429	0.6300	99.1460	0.4894
14.5	99.3163	0.8061	99.1880	0.6753	99.0842	0.5246
15.0	99.2682	0.8621	99.1311	0.7221	99.0202	0.5609
15.5	99.2186	0.9199	99.0723	0.7705	98.9541	0.5984
16.0	99.1672	0.9796	99.0117	0.8203	98.8859	0.6371
16.5	99.1143	1.0410	98.9491	0.8717	98.8156	0.6770
17.0	99.0597	1.1043	98.8846	0.9246	98.7431	0.7179
17.5	99.0035	1.1693	98.8182	0.9789	98.6685	0.7601
18.0	98.9456	1.2362	98.7500	1.0347	98.5919	0.8034
18.5	98.8861	1.3047	98.6798	1.0920	98.5131	0.8478
19.0	98.8249	1.3751	98.6077	1.1508	98.4323	0.8933
19.5	98.7622	1.4472	98.5338	1.2110	98.3493	0.9400
20.0	98.6977	1.5210	98.4580	1.2726	98.2643	0.9878
20.5	98.6317	1.5966	98.3803	1.3357	98.1772	1.0367
21.0	98.5640	1.6739	98.3007	1.4002	98.0881	1.0867
21.5	98.4946	1.7529	98.2193	1.4661	97.9969	1.1378
22.0	98.4236	1.8336	98.1360	1.5334	97.9037	1.1900
22.5	98.3510	1.9159	98.0509	1.6020	97.8084	1.2433
23.0	98.2768	1.9999	97.9640	1.6721	97.7112	1.2977
23.5	98.2009	2.0855	97.8752	1.7435	97.6119	1.3532
24.0	98.1234	2.1727	97.7846	1.8163	97.5107	1.4098
24.5	98.0443	2.2615	97.6923	1.8904	97.4075	1.4674
25.0	97.9635	2.3519	97.5981	1.9658	97.3023	1.5261

TABLE I. $a_r(q) = U + iV$, $q = \rho e^{i\phi}$　　　　　　$r = 10$

ρ	$\phi = 80°$		$\phi = 85°$		$\phi = 90°$	
	U	V	U	V	U	V
0.0	100.0000	0.0000	100.0000	0.0000	100.0000	0.0000
0.5	99.9988	0.0004	99.9988	0.0002	99.9987	0.0000
1.0	99.9953	0.0017	99.9950	0.0009	99.9949	0.0000
1.5	99.9893	0.0039	99.9888	0.0020	99.9886	0.0000
2.0	99.9810	0.0069	99.9801	0.0035	99.9798	0.0000
2.5	99.9703	0.0108	99.9689	0.0055	99.9684	0.0000
3.0	99.9573	0.0155	99.9552	0.0079	99.9546	0.0000
3.5	99.9419	0.0211	99.9391	0.0107	99.9382	0.0000
4.0	99.9241	0.0276	99.9205	0.0140	99.9192	0.0000
4.5	99.9039	0.0349	99.8993	0.0177	99.8978	0.0000
5.0	99.8814	0.0431	99.8758	0.0219	99.8738	0.0000
5.5	99.8566	0.0522	99.8497	0.0265	99.8474	0.0000
6.0	99.8293	0.0620	99.8211	0.0315	99.8184	0.0000
6.5	99.7997	0.0728	99.7901	0.0370	99.7869	0.0000
7.0	99.7678	0.0844	99.7567	0.0428	99.7529	0.0000
7.5	99.7335	0.0968	99.7207	0.0491	99.7164	0.0000
8.0	99.6968	0.1101	99.6823	0.0559	99.6775	0.0000
8.5	99.6578	0.1242	99.6415	0.0631	99.6360	0.0000
9.0	99.6164	0.1392	99.5982	0.0707	99.5920	0.0000
9.5	99.5727	0.1550	99.5524	0.0787	99.5456	0.0000
10.0	99.5267	0.1717	99.5042	0.0871	99.4966	0.0000
10.5	99.4783	0.1891	99.4536	0.0960	99.4452	0.0000
11.0	99.4276	0.2074	99.4005	0.1053	99.3913	0.0000
11.5	99.3746	0.2266	99.3450	0.1150	99.3350	0.0000
12.0	99.3193	0.2465	99.2870	0.1251	99.2762	0.0000
12.5	99.2616	0.2673	99.2267	0.1356	99.2149	0.0000
13.0	99.2016	0.2889	99.1639	0.1466	99.1512	0.0000
13.5	99.1393	0.3113	99.0987	0.1580	99.0851	0.0000
14.0	99.0747	0.3345	99.0312	0.1697	99.0165	0.0000
14.5	99.0078	0.3585	98.9612	0.1819	98.9455	0.0000
15.0	98.9387	0.3833	98.8888	0.1945	98.8720	0.0000
15.5	98.8672	0.4089	98.8141	0.2075	98.7962	0.0000
16.0	98.7934	0.4353	98.7369	0.2209	98.7179	0.0000
16.5	98.7174	0.4625	98.6574	0.2347	98.6372	0.0000
17.0	98.6391	0.4905	98.5755	0.2489	98.5541	0.0000
17.5	98.5585	0.5193	98.4913	0.2634	98.4687	0.0000
18.0	98.4757	0.5488	98.4047	0.2784	98.3808	0.0000
18.5	98.3906	0.5791	98.3158	0.2938	98.2906	0.0000
19.0	98.3033	0.6102	98.2245	0.3096	98.1979	0.0000
19.5	98.2138	0.6421	98.1309	0.3257	98.1029	0.0000
20.0	98.1220	0.6747	98.0349	0.3423	98.0056	0.0000
20.5	98.0280	0.7081	97.9366	0.3592	97.9059	0.0000
21.0	97.9318	0.7423	97.8360	0.3766	97.8038	0.0000
21.5	97.8333	0.7772	97.7331	0.3943	97.6994	0.0000
22.0	97.7327	0.8129	97.6279	0.4125	97.5926	0.0000
22.5	97.6299	0.8494	97.5204	0.4310	97.4835	0.0000
23.0	97.5249	0.8866	97.4106	0.4500	97.3720	0.0000
23.5	97.4177	0.9247	97.2985	0.4693	97.2582	0.0000
24.0	97.3084	0.9635	97.1840	0.4891	97.1420	0.0000
24.5	97.1969	1.0031	97.0673	0.5093	97.0235	0.0000
25.0	97.0834	1.0435	96.9483	0.5300	96.9026	0.0000

TABLE I. $a_r(q) = U + iV$, $q = \rho e^{i\phi}$ $\qquad\qquad r = 11$

ρ	$\phi = 5°$		$\phi = 10°$		$\phi = 15°$	
	U	V	U	V	U	V
0.0	121.0000	0.0000	121.0000	0.0000	121.0000	0.0000
0.5	121.0010	0.0002	121.0010	0.0004	121.0009	0.0005
1.0	121.0041	0.0007	121.0039	0.0014	121.0036	0.0021
1.5	121.0092	0.0016	121.0088	0.0032	121.0081	0.0047
2.0	121.0164	0.0029	121.0157	0.0057	121.0144	0.0083
2.5	121.0256	0.0045	121.0245	0.0089	121.0226	0.0130
3.0	121.0369	0.0065	121.0352	0.0128	121.0325	0.0188
3.5	121.0503	0.0089	121.0480	0.0175	121.0442	0.0255
4.0	121.0657	0.0116	121.0627	0.0228	121.0577	0.0334
4.5	121.0831	0.0147	121.0793	0.0289	121.0731	0.0422
5.0	121.1026	0.0181	121.0979	0.0357	121.0902	0.0521
5.5	121.1242	0.0219	121.1185	0.0432	121.1092	0.0631
6.0	121.1478	0.0261	121.1410	0.0514	121.1300	0.0751
6.5	121.1735	0.0306	121.1656	0.0603	121.1525	0.0882
7.0	121.2013	0.0355	121.1920	0.0700	121.1769	0.1023
7.5	121.2311	0.0408	121.2205	0.0804	121.2031	0.1174
8.0	121.2630	0.0464	121.2509	0.0915	121.2311	0.1337
8.5	121.2969	0.0524	121.2833	0.1033	121.2610	0.1510
9.0	121.3330	0.0588	121.3176	0.1158	121.2926	0.1693
9.5	121.3711	0.0656	121.3540	0.1291	121.3260	0.1887
10.0	121.4112	0.0727	121.3923	0.1431	121.3613	0.2092
10.5	121.4535	0.0802	121.4326	0.1579	121.3984	0.2307
11.0	121.4978	0.0880	121.4748	0.1733	121.4373	0.2533
11.5	121.5442	0.0963	121.5191	0.1895	121.4780	0.2770
12.0	121.5927	0.1049	121.5653	0.2065	121.5206	0.3017
12.5	121.6433	0.1139	121.6136	0.2242	121.5650	0.3275
13.0	121.6960	0.1232	121.6638	0.2426	121.6112	0.3545
13.5	121.7508	0.1330	121.7160	0.2618	121.6592	0.3824
14.0	121.8077	0.1431	121.7702	0.2817	121.7091	0.4115
14.5	121.8667	0.1536	121.8264	0.3024	121.7608	0.4417
15.0	121.9278	0.1645	121.8847	0.3238	121.8143	0.4730
15.5	121.9910	0.1757	121.9449	0.3460	121.8697	0.5053
16.0	122.0564	0.1874	122.0071	0.3689	121.9269	0.5388
16.5	122.1238	0.1995	122.0714	0.3926	121.9859	0.5734
17.0	122.1934	0.2119	122.1377	0.4171	122.0468	0.6091
17.5	122.2652	0.2247	122.2060	0.4423	122.1095	0.6459
18.0	122.3390	0.2379	122.2763	0.4683	122.1741	0.6838
18.5	122.4150	0.2516	122.3487	0.4951	122.2405	0.7229
19.0	122.4932	0.2656	122.4231	0.5227	122.3088	0.7631
19.5	122.5735	0.2800	122.4995	0.5510	122.3789	0.8044
20.0	122.6560	0.2948	122.5780	0.5802	122.4509	0.8469
20.5	122.7406	0.3101	122.6585	0.6101	122.5248	0.8905
21.0	122.8274	0.3257	122.7411	0.6408	122.6005	0.9353
21.5	122.9164	0.3417	122.8257	0.6724	122.6781	0.9812
22.0	123.0076	0.3582	122.9124	0.7047	122.7575	1.0283
22.5	123.1009	0.3751	123.0012	0.7379	122.8388	1.0766
23.0	123.1965	0.3924	123.0920	0.7719	122.9220	1.1261
23.5	123.2943	0.4101	123.1849	0.8067	123.0071	1.1767
24.0	123.3943	0.4283	123.2799	0.8423	123.0940	1.2286
24.5	123.4965	0.4468	123.3770	0.8788	123.1828	1.2816
25.0	123.6009	0.4659	123.4762	0.9161	123.2735	1.3359

TABLE I. $a_r(q) = U + iV$, $q = \rho e^{i\phi}$ $r=11$

ρ	$\phi=20°$		$\phi=25°$		$\phi=30°$	
	U	V	U	V	U	V
0.0	121.0000	0.0000	121.0000	0.0000	121.0000	0.0000
0.5	121.0008	0.0007	121.0007	0.0008	121.0005	0.0009
1.0	121.0032	0.0027	121.0027	0.0032	121.0021	0.0036
1.5	121.0072	0.0060	121.0060	0.0072	121.0047	0.0081
2.0	121.0128	0.0107	121.0107	0.0128	121.0083	0.0144
2.5	121.0199	0.0167	121.0167	0.0200	121.0130	0.0226
3.0	121.0287	0.0241	121.0241	0.0287	121.0187	0.0325
3.5	121.0391	0.0328	121.0328	0.0391	121.0255	0.0442
4.0	121.0511	0.0429	121.0428	0.0511	121.0333	0.0578
4.5	121.0646	0.0543	121.0542	0.0647	121.0422	0.0731
5.0	121.0798	0.0670	121.0669	0.0799	121.0521	0.0903
5.5	121.0966	0.0811	121.0810	0.0966	121.0630	0.1092
6.0	121.1149	0.0965	121.0964	0.1150	121.0749	0.1300
6.5	121.1349	0.1133	121.1131	0.1350	121.0879	0.1526
7.0	121.1564	0.1315	121.1312	0.1566	121.1020	0.1770
7.5	121.1796	0.1509	121.1506	0.1798	121.1170	0.2032
8.0	121.2043	0.1718	121.1713	0.2047	121.1331	0.2313
8.5	121.2307	0.1940	121.1934	0.2311	121.1503	0.2611
9.0	121.2586	0.2176	121.2168	0.2592	121.1684	0.2928
9.5	121.2882	0.2425	121.2416	0.2888	121.1876	0.3263
10.0	121.3193	0.2688	121.2677	0.3201	121.2079	0.3617
10.5	121.3521	0.2964	121.2951	0.3530	121.2291	0.3988
11.0	121.3864	0.3254	121.3238	0.3876	121.2514	0.4378
11.5	121.4224	0.3558	121.3539	0.4238	121.2747	0.4786
12.0	121.4600	0.3876	121.3853	0.4616	121.2990	0.5213
12.5	121.4991	0.4208	121.4181	0.5010	121.3243	0.5658
13.0	121.5399	0.4553	121.4521	0.5421	121.3507	0.6122
13.5	121.5822	0.4912	121.4875	0.5848	121.3781	0.6604
14.0	121.6262	0.5286	121.5243	0.6292	121.4065	0.7104
14.5	121.6718	0.5673	121.5623	0.6752	121.4359	0.7623
15.0	121.7190	0.6074	121.6017	0.7229	121.4663	0.8160
15.5	121.7677	0.6489	121.6424	0.7723	121.4977	0.8717
16.0	121.8181	0.6918	121.6845	0.8233	121.5301	0.9291
16.5	121.8701	0.7362	121.7278	0.8760	121.5635	0.9885
17.0	121.9237	0.7819	121.7725	0.9303	121.5980	1.0497
17.5	121.9789	0.8291	121.8185	0.9863	121.6334	1.1128
18.0	122.0358	0.8777	121.8658	1.0440	121.6698	1.1777
18.5	122.0942	0.9278	121.9145	1.1034	121.7072	1.2446
19.0	122.1542	0.9793	121.9644	1.1645	121.7456	1.3133
19.5	122.2159	1.0322	122.0157	1.2273	121.7850	1.3839
20.0	122.2791	1.0866	122.0683	1.2918	121.8253	1.4565
20.5	122.3440	1.1424	122.1222	1.3580	121.8667	1.5309
21.0	122.4105	1.1997	122.1774	1.4260	121.9090	1.6072
21.5	122.4786	1.2585	122.2339	1.4956	121.9523	1.6855
22.0	122.5483	1.3188	122.2917	1.5670	121.9965	1.7656
22.5	122.6196	1.3805	122.3509	1.6401	122.0417	1.8477
23.0	122.6925	1.4437	122.4113	1.7150	122.0879	1.9317
23.5	122.7670	1.5084	122.4730	1.7916	122.1350	2.0176
24.0	122.8432	1.5747	122.5361	1.8699	122.1831	2.1055
24.5	122.9209	1.6424	122.6004	1.9500	122.2321	2.1953
25.0	123.0003	1.7117	122.6660	2.0319	122.2821	2.2871

TABLE I. $a_r(q) = U+iV,\ q = \rho e^{i\phi}$ $r=11$

ρ	$\phi=35°$ U	$\phi=35°$ V	$\phi=40°$ U	$\phi=40°$ V	$\phi=45°$ U	$\phi=45°$ V
0.0	121.0000	0.0000	121.0000	0.0000	121.0000	0.0000
0.5	121.0004	0.0010	121.0002	0.0010	121.0000	0.0010
1.0	121.0014	0.0039	121.0007	0.0041	121.0000	0.0042
1.5	121.0032	0.0088	121.0016	0.0092	121.0000	0.0094
2.0	121.0057	0.0157	121.0029	0.0164	121.0000	0.0167
2.5	121.0089	0.0245	121.0045	0.0256	121.0000	0.0260
3.0	121.0128	0.0352	121.0065	0.0369	121.0000	0.0375
3.5	121.0174	0.0480	121.0088	0.0503	121.0000	0.0510
4.0	121.0228	0.0627	121.0116	0.0657	121.0000	0.0667
4.5	121.0288	0.0793	121.0146	0.0831	121.0000	0.0844
5.0	121.0356	0.0979	121.0180	0.1026	120.9999	0.1042
5.5	121.0430	0.1185	121.0218	0.1242	120.9999	0.1260
6.0	121.0512	0.1410	121.0259	0.1478	120.9999	0.1500
6.5	121.0601	0.1655	121.0304	0.1734	120.9998	0.1760
7.0	121.0697	0.1920	121.0352	0.2011	120.9998	0.2042
7.5	121.0799	0.2204	121.0404	0.2309	120.9997	0.2344
8.0	121.0909	0.2508	121.0459	0.2627	120.9996	0.2667
8.5	121.1026	0.2832	121.0518	0.2966	120.9995	0.3010
9.0	121.1150	0.3175	121.0580	0.3326	120.9994	0.3375
9.5	121.1280	0.3539	121.0646	0.3706	120.9992	0.3760
10.0	121.1418	0.3921	121.0715	0.4107	120.9991	0.4167
10.5	121.1562	0.4324	121.0787	0.4528	120.9988	0.4594
11.0	121.1714	0.4746	121.0862	0.4970	120.9986	0.5042
11.5	121.1872	0.5189	121.0941	0.5432	120.9983	0.5510
12.0	121.2037	0.5651	121.1023	0.5915	120.9980	0.6000
12.5	121.2209	0.6133	121.1109	0.6419	120.9977	0.6510
13.0	121.2387	0.6634	121.1197	0.6944	120.9973	0.7041
13.5	121.2573	0.7156	121.1289	0.7489	120.9969	0.7593
14.0	121.2765	0.7697	121.1384	0.8055	120.9964	0.8166
14.5	121.2964	0.8259	121.1482	0.8641	120.9958	0.8760
15.0	121.3169	0.8840	121.1583	0.9248	120.9952	0.9374
15.5	121.3381	0.9441	121.1687	0.9876	120.9945	1.0010
16.0	121.3600	1.0063	121.1793	1.0525	120.9938	1.0666
16.5	121.3825	1.0704	121.1903	1.1194	120.9930	1.1342
17.0	121.4057	1.1365	121.2016	1.1884	120.9921	1.2040
17.5	121.4295	1.2047	121.2132	1.2595	120.9911	1.2759
18.0	121.4539	1.2748	121.2250	1.3327	120.9901	1.3498
18.5	121.4790	1.3470	121.2371	1.4079	120.9889	1.4258
19.0	121.5048	1.4212	121.2495	1.4853	120.9877	1.5039
19.5	121.5311	1.4974	121.2621	1.5647	120.9863	1.5840
20.0	121.5581	1.5757	121.2750	1.6462	120.9849	1.6663
20.5	121.5857	1.6559	121.2881	1.7297	120.9833	1.7506
21.0	121.6139	1.7382	121.3015	1.8154	120.9816	1.8370
21.5	121.6427	1.8225	121.3152	1.9031	120.9798	1.9254
22.0	121.6722	1.9089	121.3290	1.9930	120.9779	2.0159
22.5	121.7022	1.9973	121.3431	2.0849	120.9758	2.1086
23.0	121.7328	2.0877	121.3574	2.1789	120.9735	2.2032
23.5	121.7640	2.1802	121.3720	2.2750	120.9712	2.3000
24.0	121.7958	2.2748	121.3867	2.3732	120.9686	2.3988
24.5	121.8282	2.3713	121.4017	2.4735	120.9659	2.4997
25.0	121.8612	2.4700	121.4168	2.5759	120.9631	2.6027

TABLE I. $a_r(q) = U + iV$, $q = \rho e^{i\phi}$ $r = 11$

ρ	$\phi = 50°$		$\phi = 55°$		$\phi = 60°$	
	U	V	U	V	U	V
0.0	121.0000	0.0000	121.0000	0.0000	121.0000	0.0000
0.5	120.9998	0.0010	120.9996	0.0010	120.9995	0.0009
1.0	120.9993	0.0041	120.9986	0.0039	120.9979	0.0036
1.5	120.9984	0.0092	120.9968	0.0088	120.9953	0.0081
2.0	120.9971	0.0164	120.9943	0.0157	120.9917	0.0144
2.5	120.9955	0.0256	120.9911	0.0245	120.9870	0.0225
3.0	120.9935	0.0369	120.9872	0.0352	120.9812	0.0325
3.5	120.9911	0.0503	120.9825	0.0480	120.9745	0.0442
4.0	120.9884	0.0656	120.9772	0.0626	120.9667	0.0577
4.5	120.9853	0.0831	120.9711	0.0793	120.9578	0.0730
5.0	120.9819	0.1026	120.9643	0.0978	120.9479	0.0902
5.5	120.9780	0.1241	120.9568	0.1184	120.9369	0.1091
6.0	120.9738	0.1477	120.9486	0.1409	120.9249	0.1298
6.5	120.9693	0.1733	120.9397	0.1653	120.9119	0.1523
7.0	120.9643	0.2010	120.9300	0.1917	120.8978	0.1766
7.5	120.9590	0.2307	120.9196	0.2200	120.8827	0.2027
8.0	120.9533	0.2625	120.9085	0.2503	120.8665	0.2306
8.5	120.9473	0.2963	120.8967	0.2826	120.8492	0.2603
9.0	120.9408	0.3322	120.8841	0.3167	120.8309	0.2917
9.5	120.9340	0.3701	120.8708	0.3529	120.8116	0.3250
10.0	120.9268	0.4100	120.8568	0.3909	120.7912	0.3600
10.5	120.9192	0.4520	120.8420	0.4309	120.7697	0.3968
11.0	120.9112	0.4960	120.8265	0.4729	120.7472	0.4354
11.5	120.9028	0.5421	120.8103	0.5167	120.7237	0.4758
12.0	120.8940	0.5902	120.7933	0.5625	120.6990	0.5179
12.5	120.8848	0.6403	120.7756	0.6103	120.6733	0.5618
13.0	120.8752	0.6925	120.7571	0.6599	120.6466	0.6075
13.5	120.8652	0.7467	120.7379	0.7115	120.6188	0.6549
14.0	120.8548	0.8030	120.7179	0.7651	120.5899	0.7041
14.5	120.8440	0.8612	120.6972	0.8205	120.5599	0.7551
15.0	120.8327	0.9216	120.6758	0.8778	120.5289	0.8078
15.5	120.8211	0.9839	120.6535	0.9371	120.4968	0.8622
16.0	120.8090	1.0482	120.6305	0.9983	120.4637	0.9184
16.5	120.7965	1.1146	120.6068	1.0614	120.4294	0.9763
17.0	120.7836	1.1830	120.5822	1.1264	120.3941	1.0360
17.5	120.7702	1.2535	120.5569	1.1933	120.3577	1.0974
18.0	120.7564	1.3259	120.5309	1.2621	120.3203	1.1605
18.5	120.7421	1.4004	120.5040	1.3328	120.2817	1.2254
19.0	120.7274	1.4768	120.4764	1.4054	120.2421	1.2920
19.5	120.7122	1.5553	120.4479	1.4799	120.2013	1.3603
20.0	120.6966	1.6358	120.4187	1.5562	120.1595	1.4303
20.5	120.6805	1.7183	120.3887	1.6345	120.1166	1.5020
21.0	120.6639	1.8028	120.3579	1.7146	120.0726	1.5754
21.5	120.6469	1.8893	120.3263	1.7966	120.0275	1.6505
22.0	120.6293	1.9778	120.2939	1.8804	119.9813	1.7273
22.5	120.6113	2.0683	120.2607	1.9661	119.9341	1.8058
23.0	120.5928	2.1608	120.2267	2.0537	119.8857	1.8859
23.5	120.5738	2.2553	120.1918	2.1432	119.8362	1.9677
24.0	120.5543	2.3518	120.1562	2.2344	119.7856	2.0512
24.5	120.5343	2.4502	120.1197	2.3276	119.7339	2.1364
25.0	120.5138	2.5506	120.0823	2.4225	119.6811	2.2232

ρ	$\phi = 65°$		$\phi = 70°$		$\phi = 75°$	
	U	V	U	V	U	V
0.0	121.0000	0.0000	121.0000	0.0000	121.0000	0.0000
0.5	120.9993	0.0008	120.9992	0.0007	120.9991	0.0005
1.0	120.9973	0.0032	120.9968	0.0027	120.9964	0.0021
1.5	120.9940	0.0072	120.9928	0.0060	120.9919	0.0047
2.0	120.9893	0.0128	120.9872	0.0107	120.9856	0.0083
2.5	120.9833	0.0199	120.9801	0.0167	120.9774	0.0130
3.0	120.9759	0.0287	120.9713	0.0241	120.9675	0.0187
3.5	120.9672	0.0391	120.9609	0.0328	120.9558	0.0255
4.0	120.9571	0.0510	120.9489	0.0428	120.9423	0.0333
4.5	120.9458	0.0646	120.9354	0.0542	120.9269	0.0422
5.0	120.9330	0.0797	120.9202	0.0669	120.9098	0.0520
5.5	120.9190	0.0965	120.9035	0.0809	120.8909	0.0629
6.0	120.9036	0.1148	120.8851	0.0963	120.8702	0.0749
6.5	120.8868	0.1347	120.8652	0.1130	120.8476	0.0879
7.0	120.8687	0.1562	120.8436	0.1310	120.8233	0.1019
7.5	120.8493	0.1792	120.8205	0.1504	120.7972	0.1169
8.0	120.8285	0.2039	120.7958	0.1710	120.7693	0.1330
8.5	120.8064	0.2301	120.7695	0.1930	120.7395	0.1501
9.0	120.7830	0.2579	120.7416	0.2163	120.7080	0.1682
9.5	120.7582	0.2873	120.7121	0.2410	120.6747	0.1874
10.0	120.7320	0.3183	120.6810	0.2669	120.6396	0.2075
10.5	120.7045	0.3508	120.6483	0.2942	120.6027	0.2287
11.0	120.6757	0.3849	120.6140	0.3227	120.5641	0.2509
11.5	120.6455	0.4205	120.5782	0.3526	120.5236	0.2741
12.0	120.6140	0.4577	120.5407	0.3838	120.4814	0.2983
12.5	120.5811	0.4965	120.5017	0.4162	120.4373	0.3235
13.0	120.5469	0.5368	120.4611	0.4500	120.3915	0.3498
13.5	120.5114	0.5786	120.4188	0.4851	120.3439	0.3770
14.0	120.4745	0.6220	120.3751	0.5214	120.2946	0.4052
14.5	120.4362	0.6670	120.3297	0.5590	120.2434	0.4345
15.0	120.3966	0.7135	120.2827	0.5980	120.1905	0.4647
15.5	120.3557	0.7615	120.2341	0.6382	120.1358	0.4959
16.0	120.3134	0.8111	120.1840	0.6796	120.0793	0.5281
16.5	120.2697	0.8621	120.1323	0.7224	120.0211	0.5612
17.0	120.2247	0.9147	120.0790	0.7664	119.9611	0.5954
17.5	120.1784	0.9689	120.0241	0.8117	119.8993	0.6305
18.0	120.1307	1.0245	119.9677	0.8582	119.8358	0.6666
18.5	120.0817	1.0816	119.9096	0.9060	119.7705	0.7037
19.0	120.0313	1.1403	119.8500	0.9550	119.7035	0.7417
19.5	119.9795	1.2004	119.7889	1.0053	119.6347	0.7807
20.0	119.9264	1.2621	119.7261	1.0568	119.5642	0.8207
20.5	119.8720	1.3252	119.6618	1.1095	119.4919	0.8615
21.0	119.8162	1.3898	119.5959	1.1635	119.4179	0.9034
21.5	119.7590	1.4559	119.5284	1.2187	119.3421	0.9462
22.0	119.7005	1.5234	119.4594	1.2751	119.2646	0.9899
22.5	119.6407	1.5924	119.3888	1.3328	119.1853	1.0346
23.0	119.5795	1.6629	119.3166	1.3916	119.1043	1.0802
23.5	119.5169	1.7349	119.2429	1.4517	119.0216	1.1267
24.0	119.4530	1.8082	119.1676	1.5129	118.9372	1.1741
24.5	119.3878	1.8831	119.0908	1.5754	118.8510	1.2225
25.0	119.3211	1.9593	119.0124	1.6390	118.7631	1.2718

TABLE I. $a_r(q) = U + iV$, $q = \rho e^{i\phi}$ $\qquad$ $r = 11$

ρ	$\phi=80°$		$\phi=85°$		$\phi=90°$	
	U	V	U	V	U	V
0.0	121.0000	0.0000	121.0000	0.0000	121.0000	0.0000
0.5	120.9990	0.0004	120.9990	0.0002	120.9990	-0.0000
1.0	120.9961	0.0014	120.9959	0.0007	120.9958	-0.0000
1.5	120.9912	0.0032	120.9908	0.0016	120.9906	-0.0000
2.0	120.9843	0.0057	120.9836	0.0029	120.9833	-0.0000
2.5	120.9755	0.0089	120.9744	0.0045	120.9740	-0.0000
3.0	120.9648	0.0128	120.9631	0.0065	120.9625	-0.0000
3.5	120.9520	0.0174	120.9497	0.0089	120.9490	-0.0000
4.0	120.9374	0.0228	120.9344	0.0116	120.9334	-0.0000
4.5	120.9207	0.0288	120.9169	0.0146	120.9157	-0.0000
5.0	120.9022	0.0356	120.8975	0.0181	120.8959	-0.0000
5.5	120.8816	0.0431	120.8760	0.0219	120.8740	-0.0000
6.0	120.8591	0.0512	120.8524	0.0260	120.8501	-0.0000
6.5	120.8347	0.0601	120.8268	0.0305	120.8241	-0.0000
7.0	120.8083	0.0697	120.7991	0.0354	120.7961	-0.0000
7.5	120.7800	0.0800	120.7695	0.0406	120.7659	-0.0000
8.0	120.7497	0.0910	120.7377	0.0462	120.7337	-0.0000
8.5	120.7175	0.1026	120.7040	0.0521	120.6994	-0.0000
9.0	120.6833	0.1150	120.6682	0.0584	120.6631	-0.0000
9.5	120.6472	0.1281	120.6304	0.0650	120.6247	-0.0000
10.0	120.6092	0.1419	120.5905	0.0720	120.5843	-0.0000
10.5	120.5692	0.1564	120.5487	0.0794	120.5418	-0.0000
11.0	120.5273	0.1716	120.5048	0.0871	120.4972	-0.0000
11.5	120.4834	0.1874	120.4589	0.0951	120.4506	-0.0000
12.0	120.4377	0.2040	120.4109	0.1035	120.4019	-0.0000
12.5	120.3900	0.2212	120.3610	0.1123	120.3512	-0.0000
13.0	120.3404	0.2391	120.3090	0.1214	120.2985	-0.0000
13.5	120.2888	0.2577	120.2551	0.1308	120.2437	-0.0000
14.0	120.2353	0.2770	120.1991	0.1406	120.1869	-0.0000
14.5	120.1800	0.2970	120.1411	0.1507	120.1281	-0.0000
15.0	120.1227	0.3176	120.0812	0.1612	120.0672	-0.0000
15.5	120.0635	0.3389	120.0192	0.1720	120.0043	-0.0000
16.0	120.0024	0.3609	119.9553	0.1832	119.9394	-0.0000
16.5	119.9393	0.3836	119.8893	0.1946	119.8725	-0.0000
17.0	119.8744	0.4069	119.8214	0.2065	119.8036	-0.0000
17.5	119.8076	0.4309	119.7515	0.2186	119.7326	-0.0000
18.0	119.7389	0.4555	119.6796	0.2311	119.6597	-0.0000
18.5	119.6683	0.4808	119.6058	0.2440	119.5848	-0.0000
19.0	119.5958	0.5068	119.5300	0.2571	119.5079	-0.0000
19.5	119.5215	0.5334	119.4522	0.2706	119.4290	-0.0000
20.0	119.4452	0.5607	119.3725	0.2844	119.3481	-0.0000
20.5	119.3671	0.5886	119.2908	0.2986	119.2652	-0.0000
21.0	119.2871	0.6171	119.2072	0.3130	119.1804	-0.0000
21.5	119.2052	0.6463	119.1216	0.3278	119.0935	-0.0000
22.0	119.1215	0.6761	119.0341	0.3429	119.0048	-0.0000
22.5	119.0359	0.7066	118.9447	0.3584	118.9141	-0.0001
23.0	118.9485	0.7377	118.8533	0.3741	118.8214	-0.0001
23.5	118.8592	0.7694	118.7600	0.3902	118.7267	-0.0001
24.0	118.7680	0.8018	118.6648	0.4065	118.6302	-0.0001
24.5	118.6751	0.8347	118.5677	0.4232	118.5317	-0.0002
25.0	118.5802	0.8683	118.4686	0.4402	118.4313	-0.0002

322-566 O - 69 - 7

TABLE I. $a_r(q) = U + iV$, $q = \rho e^{i\phi}$ $r = 12$

ρ	$\phi = 5°$		$\phi = 10°$		$\phi = 15°$	
	U	V	U	V	U	V
0.0	144.0000	0.0000	144.0000	0.0000	144.0000	0.0000
0.5	144.0009	0.0002	144.0008	0.0003	144.0008	0.0004
1.0	144.0034	0.0006	144.0033	0.0012	144.0030	0.0017
1.5	144.0077	0.0014	144.0074	0.0027	144.0068	0.0039
2.0	144.0138	0.0024	144.0131	0.0048	144.0121	0.0070
2.5	144.0215	0.0038	144.0205	0.0075	144.0189	0.0109
3.0	144.0310	0.0055	144.0296	0.0108	144.0273	0.0157
3.5	144.0422	0.0074	144.0403	0.0147	144.0371	0.0214
4.0	144.0551	0.0097	144.0526	0.0191	144.0485	0.0280
4.5	144.0697	0.0123	144.0666	0.0242	144.0613	0.0354
5.0	144.0861	0.0152	144.0822	0.0299	144.0757	0.0437
5.5	144.1042	0.0184	144.0994	0.0362	144.0916	0.0529
6.0	144.1240	0.0219	144.1183	0.0431	144.1090	0.0630
6.5	144.1456	0.0257	144.1389	0.0506	144.1280	0.0739
7.0	144.1688	0.0298	144.1611	0.0587	144.1484	0.0858
7.5	144.1939	0.0342	144.1850	0.0674	144.1704	0.0985
8.0	144.2206	0.0389	144.2105	0.0767	144.1939	0.1121
8.5	144.2491	0.0440	144.2376	0.0866	144.2189	0.1266
9.0	144.2793	0.0493	144.2664	0.0971	144.2455	0.1419
9.5	144.3112	0.0550	144.2969	0.1082	144.2735	0.1582
10.0	144.3449	0.0609	144.3290	0.1199	144.3031	0.1753
10.5	144.3803	0.0672	144.3628	0.1323	144.3342	0.1933
11.0	144.4174	0.0737	144.3982	0.1452	144.3668	0.2122
11.5	144.4563	0.0806	144.4353	0.1588	144.4009	0.2321
12.0	144.4969	0.0878	144.4740	0.1730	144.4366	0.2528
12.5	144.5393	0.0953	144.5144	0.1877	144.4738	0.2743
13.0	144.5834	0.1032	144.5565	0.2031	144.5125	0.2968
13.5	144.6293	0.1113	144.6002	0.2191	144.5528	0.3202
14.0	144.6769	0.1197	144.6456	0.2358	144.5946	0.3445
14.5	144.7263	0.1285	144.6927	0.2530	144.6379	0.3697
15.0	144.7774	0.1376	144.7414	0.2709	144.6827	0.3958
15.5	144.8303	0.1470	144.7918	0.2894	144.7291	0.4228
16.0	144.8850	0.1567	144.8439	0.3085	144.7770	0.4507
16.5	144.9414	0.1667	144.8977	0.3283	144.8264	0.4796
17.0	144.9995	0.1771	144.9531	0.3486	144.8774	0.5093
17.5	145.0595	0.1878	145.0103	0.3697	144.9299	0.5400
18.0	145.1212	0.1988	145.0691	0.3913	144.9840	0.5716
18.5	145.1847	0.2101	145.1295	0.4136	145.0396	0.6041
19.0	145.2500	0.2217	145.1917	0.4365	145.0967	0.6375
19.5	145.3170	0.2337	145.2556	0.4600	145.1554	0.6719
20.0	145.3859	0.2460	145.3211	0.4842	145.2157	0.7072
20.5	145.4565	0.2586	145.3884	0.5090	145.2774	0.7434
21.0	145.5289	0.2716	145.4573	0.5345	145.3408	0.7806
21.5	145.6031	0.2849	145.5280	0.5607	145.4056	0.8187
22.0	145.6791	0.2985	145.6004	0.5874	145.4721	0.8577
22.5	145.7569	0.3124	145.6744	0.6149	145.5401	0.8977
23.0	145.8365	0.3267	145.7502	0.6430	145.6096	0.9387
23.5	145.9179	0.3413	145.8277	0.6717	145.6807	0.9806
24.0	146.0012	0.3563	145.9069	0.7011	145.7534	1.0235
24.5	146.0862	0.3716	145.9878	0.7312	145.8276	1.0673
25.0	146.1731	0.3872	146.0705	0.7620	145.9034	1.1121

TABLE I. $a_r(q) = U + iV$, $q = \rho e^{i\phi}$ $\qquad\qquad r = 12$

ρ	$\phi = 20°$ U	$\phi = 20°$ V	$\phi = 25°$ U	$\phi = 25°$ V	$\phi = 30°$ U	$\phi = 30°$ V
0.0	144.0000	0.0000	144.0000	0.0000	144.0000	0.0000
0.5	144.0007	0.0006	144.0006	0.0007	144.0004	0.0008
1.0	144.0027	0.0022	144.0022	0.0027	144.0017	0.0030
1.5	144.0060	0.0051	144.0051	0.0060	144.0039	0.0068
2.0	144.0107	0.0090	144.0090	0.0107	144.0070	0.0121
2.5	144.0167	0.0140	144.0140	0.0167	144.0109	0.0189
3.0	144.0241	0.0202	144.0202	0.0241	144.0157	0.0273
3.5	144.0328	0.0275	144.0275	0.0328	144.0214	0.0371
4.0	144.0429	0.0360	144.0360	0.0429	144.0280	0.0485
4.5	144.0542	0.0455	144.0455	0.0543	144.0354	0.0613
5.0	144.0670	0.0562	144.0562	0.0670	144.0437	0.0757
5.5	144.0810	0.0680	144.0680	0.0811	144.0529	0.0916
6.0	144.0964	0.0810	144.0809	0.0965	144.0629	0.1091
6.5	144.1132	0.0951	144.0949	0.1133	144.0738	0.1280
7.0	144.1313	0.1103	144.1101	0.1314	144.0856	0.1485
7.5	144.1507	0.1266	144.1264	0.1508	144.0982	0.1705
8.0	144.1715	0.1441	144.1438	0.1716	144.1118	0.1940
8.5	144.1936	0.1627	144.1623	0.1938	144.1262	0.2190
9.0	144.2170	0.1824	144.1820	0.2173	144.1414	0.2456
9.5	144.2418	0.2033	144.2028	0.2422	144.1576	0.2737
10.0	144.2679	0.2253	144.2247	0.2684	144.1745	0.3033
10.5	144.2954	0.2485	144.2477	0.2960	144.1924	0.3344
11.0	144.3242	0.2728	144.2718	0.3249	144.2111	0.3671
11.5	144.3544	0.2982	144.2971	0.3552	144.2307	0.4013
12.0	144.3859	0.3248	144.3234	0.3868	144.2512	0.4370
12.5	144.4187	0.3525	144.3509	0.4199	144.2725	0.4743
13.0	144.4529	0.3814	144.3795	0.4542	144.2946	0.5131
13.5	144.4885	0.4114	144.4093	0.4900	144.3177	0.5535
14.0	144.5253	0.4426	144.4401	0.5271	144.3416	0.5953
14.5	144.5636	0.4750	144.4721	0.5656	144.3663	0.6388
15.0	144.6031	0.5085	144.5052	0.6054	144.3919	0.6837
15.5	144.6440	0.5432	144.5394	0.6467	144.4184	0.7303
16.0	144.6863	0.5790	144.5747	0.6893	144.4457	0.7783
16.5	144.7299	0.6160	144.6111	0.7333	144.4738	0.8280
17.0	144.7748	0.6542	144.6487	0.7787	144.5029	0.8791
17.5	144.8211	0.6935	144.6873	0.8254	144.5327	0.9318
18.0	144.8688	0.7340	144.7271	0.8736	144.5634	0.9861
18.5	144.9178	0.7757	144.7680	0.9232	144.5950	1.0420
19.0	144.9681	0.8186	144.8100	0.9741	144.6274	1.0994
19.5	145.0198	0.8626	144.8531	1.0265	144.6606	1.1584
20.0	145.0728	0.9079	144.8973	1.0802	144.6947	1.2189
20.5	145.1272	0.9543	144.9426	1.1354	144.7296	1.2810
21.0	145.1830	1.0020	144.9891	1.1919	144.7653	1.3447
21.5	145.2400	1.0508	145.0366	1.2499	144.8019	1.4100
22.0	145.2985	1.1009	145.0853	1.3093	144.8393	1.4768
22.5	145.3583	1.1521	145.1350	1.3702	144.8776	1.5453
23.0	145.4194	1.2046	145.1859	1.4324	144.9167	1.6153
23.5	145.4819	1.2583	145.2378	1.4961	144.9566	1.6869
24.0	145.5457	1.3131	145.2909	1.5612	144.9973	1.7601
24.5	145.6109	1.3693	145.3451	1.6277	145.0388	1.8349
25.0	145.6774	1.4266	145.4003	1.6957	145.0812	1.9113

ρ	$\phi = 35°$		$\phi = 40°$		$\phi = 45°$	
	U	V	U	V	U	V
0.0	144.0000	0.0000	144.0000	0.0000	144.0000	0.0000
0.5	144.0003	0.0008	144.0002	0.0009	144.0000	0.0009
1.0	144.0012	0.0033	144.0006	0.0034	144.0000	0.0035
1.5	144.0027	0.0074	144.0014	0.0077	144.0000	0.0079
2.0	144.0048	0.0131	144.0024	0.0138	144.0000	0.0140
2.5	144.0075	0.0205	144.0038	0.0215	144.0000	0.0219
3.0	144.0108	0.0296	144.0055	0.0310	144.0000	0.0315
3.5	144.0146	0.0403	144.0074	0.0422	144.0000	0.0428
4.0	144.0191	0.0526	144.0097	0.0551	144.0000	0.0559
4.5	144.0242	0.0665	144.0123	0.0697	144.0000	0.0708
5.0	144.0299	0.0822	144.0151	0.0861	144.0000	0.0874
5.5	144.0361	0.0994	144.0183	0.1042	143.9999	0.1058
6.0	144.0430	0.1183	144.0218	0.1240	143.9999	0.1259
6.5	144.0504	0.1389	144.0256	0.1455	143.9999	0.1477
7.0	144.0585	0.1611	144.0296	0.1688	143.9999	0.1713
7.5	144.0671	0.1849	144.0340	0.1937	143.9998	0.1967
8.0	144.0764	0.2104	144.0386	0.2205	143.9998	0.2238
8.5	144.0862	0.2376	144.0436	0.2489	143.9997	0.2526
9.0	144.0966	0.2664	144.0488	0.2790	143.9996	0.2832
9.5	144.1076	0.2968	144.0544	0.3109	143.9995	0.3156
10.0	144.1192	0.3289	144.0602	0.3445	143.9994	0.3496
10.5	144.1313	0.3627	144.0663	0.3799	143.9993	0.3855
11.0	144.1441	0.3981	144.0727	0.4169	143.9992	0.4231
11.5	144.1574	0.4351	144.0794	0.4557	143.9990	0.4624
12.0	144.1713	0.4739	144.0863	0.4962	143.9988	0.5035
12.5	144.1858	0.5142	144.0936	0.5385	143.9986	0.5463
13.0	144.2009	0.5563	144.1011	0.5825	143.9984	0.5909
13.5	144.2165	0.6000	144.1089	0.6282	143.9982	0.6372
14.0	144.2327	0.6453	144.1170	0.6756	143.9979	0.6853
14.5	144.2495	0.6924	144.1253	0.7248	143.9975	0.7351
15.0	144.2669	0.7411	144.1340	0.7757	143.9972	0.7867
15.5	144.2848	0.7914	144.1428	0.8283	143.9968	0.8400
16.0	144.3033	0.8434	144.1520	0.8827	143.9964	0.8951
16.5	144.3224	0.8971	144.1614	0.9388	143.9959	0.9519
17.0	144.3420	0.9525	144.1711	0.9967	143.9954	1.0104
17.5	144.3622	1.0095	144.1810	1.0562	143.9948	1.0707
18.0	144.3829	1.0682	144.1912	1.1176	143.9942	1.1328
18.5	144.4042	1.1286	144.2016	1.1806	143.9935	1.1966
19.0	144.4261	1.1907	144.2123	1.2454	143.9928	1.2621
19.5	144.4485	1.2544	144.2233	1.3120	143.9920	1.3294
20.0	144.4714	1.3199	144.2344	1.3802	143.9911	1.3984
20.5	144.4949	1.3870	144.2459	1.4503	143.9902	1.4692
21.0	144.5189	1.4558	144.2575	1.5220	143.9892	1.5417
21.5	144.5435	1.5263	144.2694	1.5955	143.9881	1.6160
22.0	144.5686	1.5984	144.2815	1.6708	143.9870	1.6920
22.5	144.5942	1.6723	144.2938	1.7478	143.9858	1.7698
23.0	144.6204	1.7479	144.3064	1.8265	143.9845	1.8493
23.5	144.6471	1.8251	144.3192	1.9070	143.9831	1.9305
24.0	144.6743	1.9041	144.3322	1.9892	143.9816	2.0135
24.5	144.7020	1.9847	144.3454	2.0732	143.9800	2.0982
25.0	144.7303	2.0671	144.3588	2.1589	143.9783	2.1847

TABLE I. $a_r(q) = U + iV$, $q = \rho e^{i\phi}$ $r = 12$

ρ	$\phi = 50°$		$\phi = 55°$		$\phi = 60°$	
	U	V	U	V	U	V
0.0	144.0000	0.0000	144.0000	0.0000	144.0000	0.0000
0.5	143.9998	0.0009	143.9997	0.0008	143.9996	0.0008
1.0	143.9994	0.0034	143.9988	0.0033	143.9983	0.0030
1.5	143.9986	0.0077	143.9973	0.0074	143.9961	0.0068
2.0	143.9976	0.0138	143.9952	0.0131	143.9930	0.0121
2.5	143.9962	0.0215	143.9925	0.0205	143.9891	0.0189
3.0	143.9945	0.0310	143.9892	0.0296	143.9843	0.0272
3.5	143.9926	0.0422	143.9853	0.0402	143.9786	0.0371
4.0	143.9903	0.0551	143.9809	0.0526	143.9720	0.0484
4.5	143.9877	0.0697	143.9758	0.0665	143.9646	0.0613
5.0	143.9848	0.0861	143.9701	0.0821	143.9563	0.0757
5.5	143.9816	0.1041	143.9638	0.0994	143.9471	0.0916
6.0	143.9781	0.1239	143.9569	0.1182	143.9370	0.1089
6.5	143.9743	0.1454	143.9494	0.1388	143.9261	0.1278
7.0	143.9701	0.1687	143.9413	0.1609	143.9143	0.1483
7.5	143.9657	0.1936	143.9326	0.1847	143.9016	0.1702
8.0	143.9609	0.2203	143.9233	0.2101	143.8880	0.1936
8.5	143.9559	0.2487	143.9134	0.2372	143.8735	0.2185
9.0	143.9505	0.2788	143.9029	0.2659	143.8582	0.2450
9.5	143.9448	0.3106	143.8917	0.2962	143.8420	0.2729
10.0	143.9388	0.3441	143.8800	0.3282	143.8249	0.3023
10.5	143.9324	0.3794	143.8676	0.3618	143.8069	0.3333
11.0	143.9258	0.4164	143.8547	0.3970	143.7881	0.3657
11.5	143.9188	0.4551	143.8411	0.4339	143.7683	0.3996
12.0	143.9115	0.4954	143.8269	0.4724	143.7477	0.4350
12.5	143.9039	0.5376	143.8121	0.5125	143.7262	0.4720
13.0	143.8959	0.5814	143.7967	0.5542	143.7038	0.5104
13.5	143.8876	0.6269	143.7807	0.5976	143.6805	0.5503
14.0	143.8790	0.6742	143.7640	0.6426	143.6563	0.5917
14.5	143.8701	0.7231	143.7467	0.6892	143.6312	0.6345
15.0	143.8608	0.7738	143.7288	0.7374	143.6053	0.6789
15.5	143.8511	0.8261	143.7103	0.7873	143.5784	0.7247
16.0	143.8412	0.8802	143.6911	0.8388	143.5507	0.7720
16.5	143.8309	0.9360	143.6713	0.8918	143.5220	0.8208
17.0	143.8202	0.9935	143.6509	0.9465	143.4925	0.8711
17.5	143.8092	1.0527	143.6298	1.0028	143.4621	0.9228
18.0	143.7979	1.1136	143.6082	1.0608	143.4307	0.9760
18.5	143.7861	1.1762	143.5858	1.1203	143.3985	1.0307
19.0	143.7741	1.2405	143.5629	1.1814	143.3654	1.0869
19.5	143.7617	1.3065	143.5392	1.2441	143.3314	1.1445
20.0	143.7489	1.3742	143.5150	1.3085	143.2964	1.2035
20.5	143.7357	1.4436	143.4901	1.3744	143.2606	1.2641
21.0	143.7222	1.5146	143.4646	1.4419	143.2239	1.3260
21.5	143.7083	1.5874	143.4384	1.5110	143.1862	1.3895
22.0	143.6941	1.6619	143.4115	1.5817	143.1476	1.4543
22.5	143.6794	1.7381	143.3840	1.6540	143.1082	1.5206
23.0	143.6644	1.8159	143.3558	1.7279	143.0678	1.5884
23.5	143.6490	1.8954	143.3270	1.8034	143.0265	1.6576
24.0	143.6332	1.9767	143.2975	1.8805	142.9843	1.7282
24.5	143.6171	2.0596	143.2674	1.9591	142.9412	1.8003
25.0	143.6005	2.1441	143.2365	2.0393	142.8972	1.8738

TABLE I. $a_r(q) = U + iV$, $q = \rho e^{i\phi}$ $r = 12$

ρ	$\phi = 65°$		$\phi = 70°$		$\phi = 75°$	
	U	V	U	V	U	V
0.0	144.0000	0.0000	144.0000	0.0000	144.0000	0.0000
0.5	143.9994	0.0007	143.9993	0.0006	143.9992	0.0004
1.0	143.9978	0.0027	143.9973	0.0022	143.9970	0.0017
1.5	143.9949	0.0060	143.9940	0.0051	143.9932	0.0039
2.0	143.9910	0.0107	143.9893	0.0090	143.9879	0.0070
2.5	143.9860	0.0167	143.9833	0.0140	143.9811	0.0109
3.0	143.9798	0.0241	143.9759	0.0202	143.9727	0.0157
3.5	143.9725	0.0328	143.9672	0.0275	143.9629	0.0214
4.0	143.9640	0.0428	143.9571	0.0359	143.9516	0.0280
4.5	143.9545	0.0542	143.9458	0.0455	143.9387	0.0354
5.0	143.9438	0.0669	143.9330	0.0562	143.9243	0.0437
5.5	143.9320	0.0810	143.9190	0.0679	143.9084	0.0528
6.0	143.9191	0.0964	143.9036	0.0808	143.8910	0.0629
6.5	143.9050	0.1131	143.8869	0.0949	143.8721	0.0738
7.0	143.8898	0.1311	143.8688	0.1100	143.8517	0.0855
7.5	143.8735	0.1505	143.8494	0.1262	143.8298	0.0982
8.0	143.8561	0.1712	143.8286	0.1436	143.8063	0.1117
8.5	143.8376	0.1932	143.8065	0.1621	143.7814	0.1261
9.0	143.8179	0.2166	143.7831	0.1817	143.7549	0.1413
9.5	143.7971	0.2413	143.7583	0.2024	143.7269	0.1574
10.0	143.7752	0.2673	143.7322	0.2242	143.6975	0.1743
10.5	143.7521	0.2946	143.7048	0.2471	143.6665	0.1922
11.0	143.7279	0.3233	143.6760	0.2712	143.6340	0.2108
11.5	143.7026	0.3533	143.6459	0.2963	143.6000	0.2304
12.0	143.6762	0.3846	143.6145	0.3225	143.5645	0.2508
12.5	143.6486	0.4172	143.5817	0.3498	143.5275	0.2720
13.0	143.6199	0.4511	143.5476	0.3783	143.4890	0.2941
13.5	143.5901	0.4863	143.5122	0.4078	143.4491	0.3170
14.0	143.5591	0.5229	143.4754	0.4384	143.4076	0.3408
14.5	143.5271	0.5607	143.4373	0.4701	143.3646	0.3655
15.0	143.4938	0.5999	143.3978	0.5029	143.3201	0.3910
15.5	143.4595	0.6404	143.3571	0.5368	143.2741	0.4173
16.0	143.4240	0.6821	143.3150	0.5718	143.2266	0.4444
16.5	143.3874	0.7252	143.2715	0.6079	143.1777	0.4725
17.0	143.3497	0.7695	143.2268	0.6450	143.1272	0.5013
17.5	143.3109	0.8152	143.1807	0.6832	143.0753	0.5310
18.0	143.2709	0.8621	143.1332	0.7225	143.0218	0.5615
18.5	143.2298	0.9104	143.0845	0.7629	142.9669	0.5928
19.0	143.1875	0.9599	143.0344	0.8043	142.9105	0.6250
19.5	143.1441	1.0107	142.9830	0.8468	142.8526	0.6580
20.0	143.0996	1.0627	142.9302	0.8904	142.7932	0.6918
20.5	143.0539	1.1161	142.8762	0.9350	142.7324	0.7264
21.0	143.0072	1.1707	142.8208	0.9807	142.6700	0.7619
21.5	142.9593	1.2266	142.7641	1.0275	142.6062	0.7981
22.0	142.9102	1.2837	142.7060	1.0753	142.5409	0.8352
22.5	142.8600	1.3422	142.6467	1.1241	142.4741	0.8731
23.0	142.8087	1.4018	142.5860	1.1740	142.4059	0.9118
23.5	142.7563	1.4628	142.5240	1.2249	142.3362	0.9513
24.0	142.7027	1.5249	142.4606	1.2769	142.2650	0.9915
24.5	142.6479	1.5884	142.3960	1.3299	142.1924	1.0326
25.0	142.5921	1.6530	142.3300	1.3839	142.1183	1.0745

TABLE I. $a_r(q) = U + iV$, $q = \rho e^{i\phi}$ $r = 12$

ρ	$\phi = 80°$		$\phi = 85°$		$\phi = 90°$	
	U	V	U	V	U	V
0.0	144.0000	0.0000	144.0000	0.0000	144.0000	0.0000
0.5	143.9992	0.0003	143.9991	0.0002	143.9991	0.0000
1.0	143.9967	0.0012	143.9966	0.0006	143.9965	0.0000
1.5	143.9926	0.0027	143.9923	0.0014	143.9921	0.0000
2.0	143.9869	0.0048	143.9862	0.0024	143.9860	0.0000
2.5	143.9795	0.0075	143.9785	0.0038	143.9781	0.0000
3.0	143.9704	0.0108	143.9690	0.0055	143.9685	0.0000
3.5	143.9598	0.0146	143.9578	0.0074	143.9572	0.0000
4.0	143.9474	0.0191	143.9449	0.0097	143.9441	0.0000
4.5	143.9335	0.0242	143.9303	0.0123	143.9292	0.0000
5.0	143.9179	0.0299	143.9139	0.0152	143.9126	0.0000
5.5	143.9006	0.0361	143.8959	0.0183	143.8943	0.0000
6.0	143.8818	0.0430	143.8761	0.0218	143.8742	0.0000
6.5	143.8613	0.0505	143.8546	0.0256	143.8524	0.0000
7.0	143.8391	0.0585	143.8314	0.0297	143.8288	0.0000
7.5	143.8153	0.0672	143.8065	0.0341	143.8035	0.0000
8.0	143.7899	0.0764	143.7798	0.0388	143.7764	0.0000
8.5	143.7628	0.0862	143.7515	0.0438	143.7477	0.0000
9.0	143.7341	0.0966	143.7214	0.0491	143.7171	0.0000
9.5	143.7038	0.1076	143.6897	0.0546	143.6849	0.0000
10.0	143.6719	0.1192	143.6562	0.0605	143.6509	0.0000
10.5	143.6383	0.1314	143.6210	0.0667	143.6152	0.0000
11.0	143.6031	0.1442	143.5841	0.0732	143.5777	0.0000
11.5	143.5662	0.1575	143.5455	0.0800	143.5386	0.0000
12.0	143.5277	0.1715	143.5052	0.0870	143.4976	0.0000
12.5	143.4876	0.1860	143.4632	0.0944	143.4550	0.0000
13.0	143.4459	0.2011	143.4195	0.1021	143.4107	0.0000
13.5	143.4026	0.2168	143.3742	0.1100	143.3646	0.0000
14.0	143.3576	0.2330	143.3271	0.1183	143.3168	0.0000
14.5	143.3111	0.2499	143.2783	0.1268	143.2673	0.0000
15.0	143.2629	0.2673	143.2279	0.1357	143.2161	0.0000
15.5	143.2131	0.2853	143.1757	0.1448	143.1631	0.0000
16.0	143.1616	0.3038	143.1219	0.1542	143.1085	0.0000
16.5	143.1086	0.3230	143.0664	0.1639	143.0521	0.0000
17.0	143.0540	0.3427	143.0092	0.1739	142.9941	0.0000
17.5	142.9977	0.3630	142.9503	0.1842	142.9343	0.0000
18.0	142.9399	0.3838	142.8897	0.1948	142.8729	0.0000
18.5	142.8804	0.4052	142.8275	0.2056	142.8097	0.0000
19.0	142.8194	0.4272	142.7636	0.2168	142.7449	0.0000
19.5	142.7567	0.4497	142.6981	0.2282	142.6783	0.0000
20.0	142.6925	0.4728	142.6308	0.2399	142.6101	0.0000
20.5	142.6266	0.4964	142.5620	0.2519	142.5402	0.0000
21.0	142.5592	0.5206	142.4914	0.2642	142.4686	0.0000
21.5	142.4902	0.5454	142.4192	0.2767	142.3953	0.0000
22.0	142.4196	0.5707	142.3454	0.2896	142.3204	0.0000
22.5	142.3474	0.5966	142.2699	0.3027	142.2438	0.0000
23.0	142.2736	0.6230	142.1927	0.3161	142.1655	0.0000
23.5	142.1982	0.6499	142.1139	0.3297	142.0855	0.0000
24.0	142.1213	0.6774	142.0335	0.3437	142.0039	0.0000
24.5	142.0428	0.7054	141.9514	0.3579	141.9207	0.0000
25.0	141.9628	0.7340	141.8677	0.3724	141.8357	0.0000

TABLE I. $a_r(q) = U + iV$, $q = \rho e^{i\phi}$ $\quad\quad\quad\quad r = 13$

ρ	$\phi = 5°$		$\phi = 10°$		$\phi = 15°$	
	U	V	U	V	U	V
0.0	169.0000	0.0000	169.0000	0.0000	169.0000	0.0000
0.5	169.0007	0.0001	169.0007	0.0003	169.0006	0.0004
1.0	169.0029	0.0005	169.0028	0.0010	169.0026	0.0015
1.5	169.0066	0.0012	169.0063	0.0023	169.0058	0.0033
2.0	169.0117	0.0021	169.0112	0.0041	169.0103	0.0060
2.5	169.0183	0.0032	169.0175	0.0064	169.0161	0.0093
3.0	169.0264	0.0047	169.0252	0.0092	169.0232	0.0134
3.5	169.0359	0.0063	169.0343	0.0125	169.0316	0.0182
4.0	169.0469	0.0083	169.0448	0.0163	169.0412	0.0238
4.5	169.0594	0.0105	169.0566	0.0206	169.0522	0.0301
5.0	169.0733	0.0129	169.0699	0.0255	169.0644	0.0372
5.5	169.0887	0.0156	169.0846	0.0308	169.0780	0.0450
6.0	169.1056	0.0186	169.1007	0.0367	169.0928	0.0536
6.5	169.1239	0.0219	169.1182	0.0430	169.1089	0.0629
7.0	169.1437	0.0254	169.1371	0.0499	169.1263	0.0730
7.5	169.1650	0.0291	169.1574	0.0573	169.1450	0.0838
8.0	169.1877	0.0331	169.1791	0.0652	169.1650	0.0954
8.5	169.2119	0.0374	169.2022	0.0737	169.1863	0.1077
9.0	169.2376	0.0419	169.2267	0.0826	169.2089	0.1207
9.5	169.2648	0.0467	169.2526	0.0920	169.2328	0.1345
10.0	169.2934	0.0518	169.2799	0.1020	169.2579	0.1491
10.5	169.3235	0.0571	169.3087	0.1125	169.2844	0.1644
11.0	169.3551	0.0627	169.3388	0.1235	169.3121	0.1805
11.5	169.3882	0.0686	169.3703	0.1350	169.3412	0.1973
12.0	169.4227	0.0747	169.4033	0.1470	169.3715	0.2149
12.5	169.4587	0.0810	169.4376	0.1596	169.4031	0.2332
13.0	169.4963	0.0877	169.4734	0.1727	169.4361	0.2523
13.5	169.5352	0.0946	169.5106	0.1862	169.4703	0.2722
14.0	169.5757	0.1017	169.5492	0.2004	169.5058	0.2928
14.5	169.6177	0.1092	169.5892	0.2150	169.5427	0.3142
15.0	169.6611	0.1169	169.6306	0.2302	169.5808	0.3363
15.5	169.7060	0.1248	169.6734	0.2458	169.6202	0.3592
16.0	169.7524	0.1331	169.7177	0.2620	169.6609	0.3829
16.5	169.8003	0.1416	169.7633	0.2788	169.7030	0.4073
17.0	169.8497	0.1503	169.8104	0.2960	169.7463	0.4325
17.5	169.9006	0.1594	169.8590	0.3138	169.7909	0.4585
18.0	169.9530	0.1687	169.9089	0.3321	169.8369	0.4853
18.5	170.0069	0.1783	169.9602	0.3510	169.8841	0.5128
19.0	170.0623	0.1881	170.0130	0.3704	169.9327	0.5411
19.5	170.1192	0.1982	170.0672	0.3903	169.9825	0.5702
20.0	170.1776	0.2086	170.1229	0.4107	170.0337	0.6000
20.5	170.2375	0.2193	170.1800	0.4317	170.0862	0.6307
21.0	170.2989	0.2302	170.2385	0.4532	170.1400	0.6621
21.5	170.3618	0.2414	170.2984	0.4753	170.1951	0.6943
22.0	170.4262	0.2529	170.3598	0.4979	170.2515	0.7273
22.5	170.4921	0.2647	170.4226	0.5211	170.3092	0.7611
23.0	170.5596	0.2767	170.4868	0.5448	170.3682	0.7956
23.5	170.6286	0.2891	170.5525	0.5690	170.4286	0.8310
24.0	170.6991	0.3017	170.6197	0.5938	170.4903	0.8672
24.5	170.7711	0.3145	170.6882	0.6191	170.5532	0.9041
25.0	170.8446	0.3277	170.7583	0.6450	170.6175	0.9419

ρ	$\phi=20°$		$\phi=25°$		$\phi=30°$	
	U	V	U	V	U	V
0.0	169.0000	0.0000	169.0000	0.0000	169.0000	0.0000
0.5	169.0006	0.0005	169.0005	0.0006	169.0004	0.0006
1.0	169.0023	0.0019	169.0019	0.0023	169.0015	0.0026
1.5	169.0051	0.0043	169.0043	0.0051	169.0033	0.0058
2.0	169.0091	0.0077	169.0077	0.0091	169.0060	0.0103
2.5	169.0142	0.0120	169.0120	0.0143	169.0093	0.0161
3.0	169.0205	0.0172	169.0172	0.0205	169.0134	0.0232
3.5	169.0279	0.0234	169.0234	0.0279	169.0182	0.0316
4.0	169.0365	0.0306	169.0306	0.0365	169.0238	0.0412
4.5	169.0462	0.0388	169.0387	0.0462	169.0301	0.0522
5.0	169.0570	0.0478	169.0478	0.0570	169.0372	0.0645
5.5	169.0690	0.0579	169.0579	0.0690	169.0450	0.0780
6.0	169.0821	0.0689	169.0689	0.0821	169.0535	0.0928
6.5	169.0963	0.0809	169.0808	0.0964	169.0628	0.1090
7.0	169.1117	0.0938	169.0937	0.1118	169.0729	0.1264
7.5	169.1283	0.1077	169.1076	0.1284	169.0837	0.1451
8.0	169.1459	0.1226	169.1224	0.1461	169.0952	0.1651
8.5	169.1648	0.1384	169.1382	0.1649	169.1074	0.1864
9.0	169.1847	0.1552	169.1549	0.1849	169.1204	0.2090
9.5	169.2058	0.1729	169.1726	0.2060	169.1342	0.2329
10.0	169.2280	0.1916	169.1912	0.2283	169.1486	0.2580
10.5	169.2514	0.2113	169.2108	0.2518	169.1639	0.2845
11.0	169.2760	0.2320	169.2314	0.2764	169.1798	0.3123
11.5	169.3016	0.2536	169.2529	0.3021	169.1965	0.3414
12.0	169.3284	0.2762	169.2754	0.3290	169.2139	0.3718
12.5	169.3564	0.2997	169.2988	0.3571	169.2321	0.4034
13.0	169.3855	0.3243	169.3231	0.3863	169.2510	0.4364
13.5	169.4157	0.3498	169.3485	0.4166	169.2706	0.4707
14.0	169.4471	0.3763	169.3747	0.4482	169.2910	0.5063
14.5	169.4796	0.4037	169.4019	0.4808	169.3121	0.5432
15.0	169.5133	0.4321	169.4301	0.5147	169.3339	0.5814
15.5	169.5481	0.4616	169.4593	0.5497	169.3565	0.6209
16.0	169.5840	0.4920	169.4893	0.5859	169.3798	0.6618
16.5	169.6211	0.5233	169.5204	0.6232	169.4038	0.7039
17.0	169.6594	0.5557	169.5524	0.6617	169.4286	0.7473
17.5	169.6988	0.5890	169.5853	0.7014	169.4541	0.7921
18.0	169.7393	0.6234	169.6192	0.7422	169.4803	0.8382
18.5	169.7810	0.6587	169.6540	0.7842	169.5073	0.8856
19.0	169.8238	0.6950	169.6898	0.8274	169.5349	0.9343
19.5	169.8678	0.7323	169.7265	0.8718	169.5633	0.9843
20.0	169.9129	0.7707	169.7642	0.9174	169.5924	1.0357
20.5	169.9591	0.8100	169.8028	0.9641	169.6223	1.0884
21.0	170.0065	0.8503	169.8424	1.0120	169.6528	1.1424
21.5	170.0551	0.8916	169.8829	1.0611	169.6841	1.1977
22.0	170.1048	0.9339	169.9244	1.1114	169.7161	1.2544
22.5	170.1556	0.9772	169.9668	1.1629	169.7488	1.3124
23.0	170.2076	1.0215	170.0102	1.2155	169.7823	1.3717
23.5	170.2608	1.0669	170.0545	1.2694	169.8164	1.4324
24.0	170.3151	1.1132	170.0998	1.3244	169.8513	1.4944
24.5	170.3705	1.1606	170.1460	1.3807	169.8868	1.5577
25.0	170.4271	1.2090	170.1931	1.4382	169.9231	1.6224

TABLE I. $a_r(q) = U + iV$, $q = \rho e^{i\phi}$ $r = 13$

ρ	$\phi=35°$		$\phi=40°$		$\phi=45°$	
	U	V	U	V	U	V
0.0	169.0000	0.0000	169.0000	0.0000	169.0000	0.0000
0.5	169.0003	0.0007	169.0001	0.0007	169.0000	0.0007
1.0	169.0010	0.0028	169.0005	0.0029	169.0000	0.0030
1.5	169.0023	0.0063	169.0012	0.0066	169.0000	0.0067
2.0	169.0041	0.0112	169.0021	0.0117	169.0000	0.0119
2.5	169.0064	0.0175	169.0032	0.0183	169.0000	0.0186
3.0	169.0092	0.0252	169.0046	0.0264	169.0000	0.0268
3.5	169.0125	0.0343	169.0063	0.0359	169.0000	0.0365
4.0	169.0163	0.0448	169.0083	0.0469	169.0000	0.0476
4.5	169.0206	0.0566	169.0105	0.0594	169.0000	0.0603
5.0	169.0254	0.0699	169.0129	0.0733	169.0000	0.0744
5.5	169.0308	0.0846	169.0156	0.0887	169.0000	0.0900
6.0	169.0366	0.1007	169.0186	0.1055	169.0000	0.1071
6.5	169.0430	0.1182	169.0218	0.1239	168.9999	0.1257
7.0	169.0498	0.1371	169.0252	0.1436	168.9999	0.1458
7.5	169.0572	0.1574	169.0290	0.1649	168.9999	0.1674
8.0	169.0650	0.1791	169.0329	0.1876	168.9999	0.1905
8.5	169.0734	0.2022	169.0372	0.2118	168.9998	0.2150
9.0	169.0823	0.2267	169.0417	0.2375	168.9998	0.2411
9.5	169.0917	0.2526	169.0464	0.2646	168.9997	0.2686
10.0	169.1015	0.2799	169.0514	0.2932	168.9997	0.2976
10.5	169.1119	0.3086	169.0566	0.3233	168.9996	0.3281
11.0	169.1228	0.3387	169.0621	0.3548	168.9995	0.3601
11.5	169.1342	0.3702	169.0678	0.3878	168.9994	0.3936
12.0	169.1460	0.4032	169.0738	0.4223	168.9993	0.4286
12.5	169.1584	0.4375	169.0800	0.4582	168.9992	0.4650
13.0	169.1713	0.4733	169.0864	0.4957	168.9990	0.5030
13.5	169.1846	0.5104	169.0931	0.5346	168.9989	0.5424
14.0	169.1985	0.5490	169.1001	0.5749	168.9987	0.5833
14.5	169.2129	0.5890	169.1072	0.6167	168.9985	0.6257
15.0	169.2277	0.6304	169.1147	0.6600	168.9983	0.6696
15.5	169.2430	0.6732	169.1223	0.7048	168.9980	0.7150
16.0	169.2589	0.7174	169.1302	0.7511	168.9978	0.7619
16.5	169.2752	0.7630	169.1383	0.7988	168.9975	0.8102
17.0	169.2920	0.8101	169.1467	0.8480	168.9972	0.8601
17.5	169.3093	0.8585	169.1553	0.8987	168.9968	0.9114
18.0	169.3270	0.9084	169.1641	0.9508	168.9964	0.9642
18.5	169.3453	0.9597	169.1731	1.0044	168.9960	1.0186
19.0	169.3640	1.0124	169.1824	1.0596	168.9956	1.0743
19.5	169.3832	1.0666	169.1919	1.1161	168.9951	1.1316
20.0	169.4029	1.1221	169.2016	1.1742	168.9946	1.1904
20.5	169.4231	1.1791	169.2115	1.2337	168.9940	1.2507
21.0	169.4437	1.2375	169.2216	1.2947	168.9934	1.3124
21.5	169.4649	1.2974	169.2320	1.3572	168.9927	1.3756
22.0	169.4864	1.3587	169.2426	1.4212	168.9920	1.4403
22.5	169.5085	1.4214	169.2534	1.4867	168.9913	1.5065
23.0	169.5310	1.4855	169.2644	1.5536	168.9905	1.5742
23.5	169.5540	1.5510	169.2756	1.6220	168.9896	1.6434
24.0	169.5775	1.6180	169.2870	1.6919	168.9887	1.7141
24.5	169.6014	1.6865	169.2986	1.7633	168.9877	1.7862
25.0	169.6258	1.7563	169.3104	1.8362	168.9867	1.8598

TABLE I. $a_r(q) = U + iV$, $q = \rho e^{i\phi}$ $\qquad\qquad$ $r = 13$

ρ	$\phi=50°$		$\phi=55°$		$\phi=60°$	
	U	V	U	V	U	V
0.0	169.0000	0.0000	169.0000	0.0000	169.0000	0.0000
0.5	168.9999	0.0007	168.9997	0.0007	168.9996	0.0006
1.0	168.9995	0.0029	168.9990	0.0028	168.9985	0.0026
1.5	168.9988	0.0066	168.9977	0.0063	168.9967	0.0058
2.0	168.9979	0.0117	168.9959	0.0112	168.9940	0.0103
2.5	168.9968	0.0183	168.9936	0.0175	168.9907	0.0161
3.0	168.9953	0.0264	168.9908	0.0252	168.9866	0.0232
3.5	168.9937	0.0359	168.9875	0.0343	168.9818	0.0316
4.0	168.9917	0.0469	168.9837	0.0447	168.9762	0.0412
4.5	168.9895	0.0593	168.9794	0.0566	168.9699	0.0522
5.0	168.9871	0.0733	168.9745	0.0699	168.9628	0.0644
5.5	168.9843	0.0887	168.9692	0.0846	168.9550	0.0779
6.0	168.9814	0.1055	168.9633	0.1007	168.9464	0.0928
6.5	168.9781	0.1238	168.9569	0.1181	168.9371	0.1088
7.0	168.9746	0.1436	168.9501	0.1370	168.9270	0.1262
7.5	168.9708	0.1648	168.9427	0.1572	168.9162	0.1449
8.0	168.9668	0.1875	168.9347	0.1789	168.9047	0.1648
8.5	168.9625	0.2117	168.9263	0.2019	168.8924	0.1861
9.0	168.9579	0.2373	168.9174	0.2264	168.8794	0.2086
9.5	168.9531	0.2644	168.9079	0.2522	168.8656	0.2324
10.0	168.9480	0.2930	168.8979	0.2795	168.8510	0.2575
10.5	168.9426	0.3230	168.8875	0.3081	168.8357	0.2838
11.0	168.9370	0.3545	168.8765	0.3381	168.8197	0.3114
11.5	168.9311	0.3874	168.8649	0.3695	168.8029	0.3404
12.0	168.9249	0.4218	168.8529	0.4023	168.7854	0.3705
12.5	168.9185	0.4577	168.8403	0.4364	168.7671	0.4020
13.0	168.9117	0.4950	168.8272	0.4720	168.7480	0.4347
13.5	168.9048	0.5338	168.8136	0.5090	168.7282	0.4688
14.0	168.8975	0.5740	168.7995	0.5473	168.7077	0.5040
14.5	168.8899	0.6157	168.7848	0.5870	168.6864	0.5406
15.0	168.8821	0.6589	168.7697	0.6281	168.6643	0.5784
15.5	168.8740	0.7035	168.7540	0.6706	168.6415	0.6175
16.0	168.8656	0.7496	168.7377	0.7145	168.6180	0.6579
16.5	168.8569	0.7971	168.7210	0.7598	168.5936	0.6995
17.0	168.8480	0.8461	168.7037	0.8064	168.5685	0.7424
17.5	168.8387	0.8965	168.6858	0.8544	168.5427	0.7866
18.0	168.8292	0.9484	168.6675	0.9038	168.5161	0.8320
18.5	168.8194	1.0017	168.6486	0.9546	168.4888	0.8787
19.0	168.8093	1.0565	168.6292	1.0067	168.4606	0.9266
19.5	168.7989	1.1128	168.6092	1.0603	168.4318	0.9758
20.0	168.7882	1.1705	168.5887	1.1151	168.4021	1.0263
20.5	168.7772	1.2296	168.5677	1.1714	168.3717	1.0780
21.0	168.7659	1.2902	168.5461	1.2290	168.3405	1.1309
21.5	168.7543	1.3523	168.5240	1.2880	168.3086	1.1851
22.0	168.7424	1.4158	168.5013	1.3484	168.2759	1.2406
22.5	168.7302	1.4807	168.4781	1.4102	168.2424	1.2973
23.0	168.7177	1.5471	168.4544	1.4733	168.2082	1.3552
23.5	168.7049	1.6149	168.4301	1.5377	168.1732	1.4144
24.0	168.6918	1.6842	168.4052	1.6035	168.1374	1.4748
24.5	168.6784	1.7549	168.3798	1.6707	168.1009	1.5365
25.0	168.6647	1.8271	168.3539	1.7393	168.0636	1.5994

TABLE I. $a_r(q) = U + iV$, $q = \rho e^{i\phi}$ $r = 13$

ρ	$\phi = 65°$		$\phi = 70°$		$\phi = 75°$	
	U	V	U	V	U	V
0.0	169.0000	0.0000	169.0000	0.0000	169.0000	0.0000
0.5	168.9995	0.0006	168.9994	0.0005	168.9994	0.0004
1.0	168.9981	0.0023	168.9977	0.0019	168.9974	0.0015
1.5	168.9957	0.0051	168.9949	0.0043	168.9942	0.0033
2.0	168.9923	0.0091	168.9909	0.0077	168.9897	0.0060
2.5	168.9880	0.0142	168.9858	0.0120	168.9839	0.0093
3.0	168.9828	0.0205	168.9795	0.0172	168.9768	0.0134
3.5	168.9766	0.0279	168.9721	0.0234	168.9684	0.0182
4.0	168.9694	0.0365	168.9635	0.0306	168.9588	0.0238
4.5	168.9613	0.0462	168.9538	0.0387	168.9478	0.0301
5.0	168.9522	0.0570	168.9430	0.0478	168.9356	0.0372
5.5	168.9421	0.0689	168.9310	0.0578	168.9220	0.0450
6.0	168.9311	0.0820	168.9179	0.0688	168.9072	0.0535
6.5	168.9192	0.0963	168.9037	0.0808	168.8911	0.0628
7.0	168.9062	0.1116	168.8883	0.0937	168.8737	0.0728
7.5	168.8924	0.1281	168.8718	0.1075	168.8551	0.0836
8.0	168.8775	0.1458	168.8541	0.1223	168.8351	0.0951
8.5	168.8617	0.1645	168.8353	0.1380	168.8139	0.1074
9.0	168.8450	0.1845	168.8154	0.1547	168.7913	0.1203
9.5	168.8273	0.2055	168.7943	0.1724	168.7675	0.1341
10.0	168.8086	0.2277	168.7721	0.1910	168.7424	0.1485
10.5	168.7890	0.2510	168.7487	0.2105	168.7160	0.1637
11.0	168.7684	0.2754	168.7242	0.2310	168.6884	0.1796
11.5	168.7469	0.3009	168.6986	0.2524	168.6594	0.1963
12.0	168.7244	0.3276	168.6718	0.2748	168.6292	0.2137
12.5	168.7009	0.3554	168.6439	0.2981	168.5977	0.2318
13.0	168.6765	0.3843	168.6149	0.3224	168.5649	0.2507
13.5	168.6512	0.4144	168.5847	0.3475	168.5308	0.2702
14.0	168.6248	0.4456	168.5534	0.3737	168.4955	0.2905
14.5	168.5975	0.4779	168.5209	0.4007	168.4588	0.3116
15.0	168.5693	0.5113	168.4873	0.4288	168.4209	0.3333
15.5	168.5401	0.5458	168.4526	0.4577	168.3817	0.3558
16.0	168.5099	0.5815	168.4167	0.4876	168.3413	0.3790
16.5	168.4788	0.6182	168.3797	0.5184	168.2995	0.4030
17.0	168.4467	0.6561	168.3416	0.5501	168.2565	0.4276
17.5	168.4136	0.6951	168.3024	0.5828	168.2122	0.4530
18.0	168.3796	0.7352	168.2620	0.6163	168.1667	0.4791
18.5	168.3446	0.7764	168.2204	0.6509	168.1199	0.5059
19.0	168.3087	0.8187	168.1778	0.6863	168.0718	0.5334
19.5	168.2718	0.8621	168.1340	0.7227	168.0224	0.5617
20.0	168.2339	0.9066	168.0890	0.7599	167.9717	0.5906
20.5	168.1951	0.9523	168.0430	0.7981	167.9198	0.6203
21.0	168.1553	0.9990	167.9958	0.8372	167.8666	0.6506
21.5	168.1145	1.0468	167.9474	0.8773	167.8122	0.6817
22.0	168.0728	1.0957	167.8980	0.9182	167.7565	0.7135
22.5	168.0301	1.1457	167.8474	0.9600	167.6995	0.7459
23.0	167.9865	1.1968	167.7957	1.0028	167.6413	0.7791
23.5	167.9419	1.2490	167.7428	1.0464	167.5818	0.8130
24.0	167.8963	1.3022	167.6888	1.0910	167.5210	0.8476
24.5	167.8498	1.3566	167.6337	1.1365	167.4590	0.8829
25.0	167.8023	1.4120	167.5775	1.1828	167.3957	0.9188

TABLE I. $a_r(q) = U + iV$, $q = \rho e^{i\phi}$ $r = 13$

ρ	$\phi=80°$		$\phi=85°$		$\phi=90°$	
	U	V	U	V	U	V
0.0	169.0000	0.0000	169.0000	0.0000	169.0000	0.0000
0.5	168.9993	0.0003	168.9993	0.0001	168.9993	0.0000
1.0	168.9972	0.0010	168.9971	0.0005	168.9970	0.0000
1.5	168.9937	0.0023	168.9934	0.0012	168.9933	0.0000
2.0	168.9888	0.0041	168.9883	0.0021	168.9881	0.0000
2.5	168.9825	0.0064	168.9817	0.0032	168.9814	0.0000
3.0	168.9748	0.0092	168.9736	0.0047	168.9732	0.0000
3.5	168.9657	0.0125	168.9641	0.0063	168.9635	0.0000
4.0	168.9553	0.0163	168.9531	0.0083	168.9524	0.0000
4.5	168.9434	0.0206	168.9407	0.0105	168.9397	0.0000
5.0	168.9301	0.0254	168.9267	0.0129	168.9256	0.0000
5.5	168.9154	0.0308	168.9114	0.0156	168.9100	0.0000
6.0	168.8994	0.0366	168.8945	0.0186	168.8929	0.0000
6.5	168.8819	0.0430	168.8762	0.0218	168.8743	0.0000
7.0	168.8630	0.0498	168.8565	0.0253	168.8542	0.0000
7.5	168.8428	0.0572	168.8352	0.0290	168.8327	0.0000
8.0	168.8211	0.0651	168.8125	0.0330	168.8097	0.0000
8.5	168.7981	0.0734	168.7884	0.0373	168.7851	0.0000
9.0	168.7736	0.0823	168.7628	0.0418	168.7591	0.0000
9.5	168.7478	0.0917	168.7357	0.0465	168.7317	0.0000
10.0	168.7206	0.1016	168.7072	0.0516	168.7027	0.0000
10.5	168.6920	0.1120	168.6772	0.0568	168.6723	0.0000
11.0	168.6620	0.1228	158.6458	0.0624	168.6404	0.0000
11.5	168.6306	0.1342	168.6129	0.0681	168.6070	0.0000
12.0	168.5978	0.1461	168.5786	0.0742	168.5721	0.0000
12.5	168.5636	0.1585	168.5428	0.0805	168.5358	0.0000
13.0	168.5281	0.1714	168.5056	0.0870	168.4980	0.0000
13.5	168.4912	0.1848	168.4669	0.0938	168.4587	0.0000
14.0	168.4528	0.1987	168.4267	0.1009	168.4180	0.0000
14.5	168.4131	0.2131	168.3852	0.1082	168.3757	0.0000
15.0	168.3721	0.2279	168.3421	0.1157	168.3321	0.0000
15.5	168.3296	0.2433	168.2977	0.1235	168.2869	0.0000
16.0	168.2857	0.2592	168.2517	0.1316	168.2403	0.0000
16.5	168.2405	0.2755	168.2044	0.1399	168.1922	0.0000
17.0	168.1939	0.2924	168.1556	0.1484	168.1427	0.0000
17.5	168.1459	0.3097	168.1054	0.1572	168.0917	0.0000
18.0	168.0966	0.3275	168.0537	0.1662	168.0392	0.0000
18.5	168.0459	0.3459	168.0006	0.1755	167.9853	0.0000
19.0	167.9938	0.3647	167.9460	0.1851	167.9300	0.0000
19.5	167.9403	0.3840	167.8901	0.1949	167.8732	0.0000
20.0	167.8855	0.4037	167.8327	0.2049	167.8149	0.0000
20.5	167.8292	0.4240	167.7738	0.2152	167.7552	0.0000
21.0	167.7717	0.4447	167.7136	0.2257	167.6940	0.0000
21.5	167.7127	0.4660	167.6519	0.2365	167.6314	0.0000
22.0	167.6524	0.4877	167.5888	0.2475	167.5674	0.0000
22.5	167.5908	0.5098	167.5243	0.2587	167.5019	0.0000
23.0	167.5278	0.5325	167.4583	0.2702	167.4349	0.0000
23.5	167.4634	0.5556	167.3910	0.2820	167.3666	0.0000
24.0	167.3976	0.5793	167.3222	0.2939	167.2968	0.0000
24.5	167.3305	0.6033	167.2520	0.3061	167.2256	0.0000
25.0	167.2621	0.6279	167.1804	0.3186	167.1529	0.0000

TABLE I. $a_r(q) = U + iV, \; q = \rho e^{i\phi}$ $r = 14$

ρ	$\phi = 5°$		$\phi = 10°$		$\phi = 15°$	
	U	V	U	V	U	V
0.0	196.0000	0.0000	196.0000	0.0000	196.0000	0.0000
0.5	196.0006	0.0001	196.0006	0.0002	196.0006	0.0003
1.0	196.0025	0.0004	196.0024	0.0009	196.0022	0.0013
1.5	196.0057	0.0010	196.0054	0.0020	196.0050	0.0029
2.0	196.0101	0.0018	196.0096	0.0035	196.0089	0.0051
2.5	196.0158	0.0028	196.0151	0.0055	196.0139	0.0080
3.0	196.0227	0.0040	196.0217	0.0079	196.0200	0.0115
3.5	196.0309	0.0055	196.0295	0.0107	196.0272	0.0157
4.0	196.0404	0.0071	196.0386	0.0140	196.0355	0.0205
4.5	196.0511	0.0090	196.0488	0.0178	196.0450	0.0260
5.0	196.0631	0.0111	196.0602	0.0219	196.0555	0.0321
5.5	196.0764	0.0135	196.0729	0.0265	196.0672	0.0388
6.0	196.0909	0.0160	196.0868	0.0316	196.0800	0.0462
6.5	196.1067	0.0188	196.1018	0.0371	196.0938	0.0542
7.0	196.1238	0.0218	196.1181	0.0430	196.1088	0.0629
7.5	196.1421	0.0251	196.1356	0.0494	196.1249	0.0722
8.0	196.1617	0.0285	196.1543	0.0562	196.1422	0.0821
8.5	196.1825	0.0322	196.1742	0.0634	196.1605	0.0927
9.0	196.2047	0.0361	196.1953	0.0711	196.1799	0.1040
9.5	196.2281	0.0402	196.2176	0.0793	196.2005	0.1159
10.0	196.2527	0.0446	196.2411	0.0878	196.2222	0.1284
10.5	196.2786	0.0492	196.2658	0.0969	196.2449	0.1416
11.0	196.3058	0.0540	196.2918	0.1063	196.2688	0.1554
11.5	196.3343	0.0590	196.3189	0.1162	196.2939	0.1699
12.0	196.3640	0.0643	196.3473	0.1266	196.3200	0.1850
12.5	196.3951	0.0698	196.3769	0.1374	196.3472	0.2008
13.0	196.4273	0.0755	196.4077	0.1486	196.3756	0.2172
13.5	196.4609	0.0814	196.4397	0.1603	196.4051	0.2343
14.0	196.4957	0.0876	196.4729	0.1724	196.4356	0.2520
14.5	196.5318	0.0939	196.5073	0.1850	196.4674	0.2704
15.0	196.5692	0.1006	196.5430	0.1980	196.5002	0.2894
15.5	196.6078	0.1074	196.5798	0.2115	196.5341	0.3091
16.0	196.6478	0.1145	196.6179	0.2254	196.5692	0.3294
16.5	196.6890	0.1218	196.6572	0.2398	196.6054	0.3504
17.0	196.7315	0.1293	196.6977	0.2546	196.6427	0.3721
17.5	196.7752	0.1371	196.7395	0.2699	196.6811	0.3944
18.0	196.8203	0.1450	196.7824	0.2856	196.7206	0.4174
18.5	196.8666	0.1533	196.8266	0.3018	196.7613	0.4410
19.0	196.9143	0.1617	196.8720	0.3184	196.8030	0.4653
19.5	196.9632	0.1704	196.9186	0.3355	196.8459	0.4902
20.0	197.0133	0.1793	196.9665	0.3530	196.8900	0.5159
20.5	197.0648	0.1884	197.0155	0.3710	196.9351	0.5421
21.0	197.1176	0.1978	197.0658	0.3895	196.9814	0.5691
21.5	197.1716	0.2074	197.1173	0.4084	197.0288	0.5967
22.0	197.2270	0.2173	197.1701	0.4278	197.0773	0.6250
22.5	197.2836	0.2273	197.2241	0.4476	197.1269	0.6539
23.0	197.3416	0.2377	197.2793	0.4679	197.1777	0.6835
23.5	197.4008	0.2482	197.3357	0.4886	197.2296	0.7138
24.0	197.4613	0.2590	197.3934	0.5099	197.2826	0.7448
24.5	197.5232	0.2700	197.4523	0.5315	197.3368	0.7764
25.0	197.5863	0.2812	197.5125	0.5537	197.3921	0.8087

TABLE I. $a_r(q) = U + iV$, $q = \rho e^{i\phi}$ $r = 14$

ρ	$\phi=20°$			$\phi=25°$			$\phi=30°$		
	U	V		U	V		U	V	
0.0	196.0000	0.0000		196.0000	0.0000		196.0000	0.0000	
0.5	196.0005	0.0004		196.0004	0.0005		196.0003	0.0006	
1.0	196.0020	0.0016		196.0016	0.0020		196.0013	0.0022	
1.5	196.0044	0.0037		196.0037	0.0044		196.0029	0.0050	
2.0	196.0079	0.0066		196.0066	0.0079		196.0051	0.0089	
2.5	196.0123	0.0103		196.0103	0.0123		196.0080	0.0139	
3.0	196.0177	0.0148		196.0148	0.0177		196.0115	0.0200	
3.5	196.0241	0.0202		196.0202	0.0241		196.0157	0.0272	
4.0	196.0314	0.0264		196.0264	0.0314		196.0205	0.0355	
4.5	196.0398	0.0334		196.0334	0.0398		196.0260	0.0450	
5.0	196.0491	0.0412		196.0412	0.0491		196.0320	0.0555	
5.5	196.0594	0.0499		196.0499	0.0594		196.0388	0.0672	
6.0	196.0707	0.0594		196.0593	0.0707		196.0461	0.0800	
6.5	196.0830	0.0697		196.0696	0.0830		196.0541	0.0939	
7.0	196.0963	0.0808		196.0807	0.0963		196.0628	0.1089	
7.5	196.1105	0.0928		196.0927	0.1106		196.0721	0.1250	
8.0	196.1257	0.1056		196.1055	0.1258		196.0820	0.1422	
8.5	196.1419	0.1192		196.1191	0.1420		196.0926	0.1605	
9.0	196.1591	0.1336		196.1335	0.1592		196.1038	0.1800	
9.5	196.1773	0.1489		196.1487	0.1774		196.1156	0.2006	
10.0	196.1965	0.1650		196.1648	0.1966		196.1281	0.2222	
10.5	196.2166	0.1820		196.1817	0.2168		196.1412	0.2450	
11.0	196.2377	0.1997		196.1994	0.2380		196.1550	0.2690	
11.5	196.2598	0.2183		196.2179	0.2601		196.1694	0.2940	
12.0	196.2829	0.2378		196.2373	0.2833		196.1844	0.3202	
12.5	196.3070	0.2580		196.2574	0.3074		196.2001	0.3474	
13.0	196.3321	0.2792		196.2784	0.3326		196.2164	0.3758	
13.5	196.3581	0.3011		196.3003	0.3587		196.2333	0.4053	
14.0	196.3851	0.3239		196.3229	0.3858		196.2509	0.4360	
14.5	196.4131	0.3475		196.3464	0.4139		196.2691	0.4677	
15.0	196.4421	0.3719		196.3706	0.4430		196.2879	0.5006	
15.5	196.4721	0.3972		196.3957	0.4731		196.3074	0.5346	
16.0	196.5031	0.4233		196.4217	0.5042		196.3275	0.5697	
16.5	196.5350	0.4503		196.4484	0.5363		196.3482	0.6059	
17.0	196.5680	0.4781		196.4760	0.5694		196.3696	0.6433	
17.5	196.6019	0.5068		196.5044	0.6036		196.3916	0.6818	
18.0	196.6368	0.5363		196.5336	0.6387		196.4142	0.7214	
18.5	196.6727	0.5666		196.5636	0.6748		196.4375	0.7622	
19.0	196.7096	0.5978		196.5945	0.7119		196.4614	0.8041	
19.5	196.7474	0.6298		196.6261	0.7500		196.4859	0.8471	
20.0	196.7863	0.6627		196.6586	0.7891		196.5111	0.8912	
20.5	196.8261	0.6964		196.6919	0.8293		196.5368	0.9365	
21.0	196.8669	0.7310		196.7261	0.8704		196.5632	0.9829	
21.5	196.9087	0.7665		196.7610	0.9125		196.5903	1.0305	
22.0	196.9515	0.8028		196.7968	0.9557		196.6179	1.0792	
22.5	196.9953	0.8399		196.8334	0.9999		196.6462	1.1290	
23.0	197.0401	0.8779		196.8708	1.0451		196.6751	1.1799	
23.5	197.0858	0.9168		196.9090	1.0913		196.7046	1.2320	
24.0	197.1326	0.9565		196.9480	1.1385		196.7348	1.2853	
24.5	197.1803	0.9971		196.9879	1.1868		196.7655	1.3397	
25.0	197.2290	1.0386		197.0285	1.2360		196.7969	1.3952	

TABLE I. $a_r(q) = U + iV$, $q = \rho e^{i\phi}$ $r = 14$

ρ	$\phi=35°$		$\phi=40°$		$\phi=45°$	
	U	V	U	V	U	V
0.0	196.0000	0.0000	196.0000	0.0000	196.0000	0.0000
0.5	196.0002	0.0006	196.0001	0.0006	196.0000	0.0006
1.0	196.0009	0.0024	196.0004	0.0025	196.0000	0.0026
1.5	196.0020	0.0054	196.0010	0.0057	196.0000	0.0058
2.0	196.0035	0.0096	196.0018	0.0101	196.0000	0.0103
2.5	196.0055	0.0151	196.0028	0.0158	196.0000	0.0160
3.0	196.0079	0.0217	196.0040	0.0227	196.0000	0.0231
3.5	196.0107	0.0295	196.0055	0.0309	196.0000	0.0314
4.0	196.0140	0.0386	196.0071	0.0404	196.0000	0.0410
4.5	196.0178	0.0488	196.0090	0.0511	196.0000	0.0519
5.0	196.0219	0.0602	196.0111	0.0631	196.0000	0.0641
5.5	196.0265	0.0729	196.0134	0.0764	196.0000	0.0776
6.0	196.0315	0.0868	196.0160	0.0909	196.0000	0.0923
6.5	196.0370	0.1018	196.0188	0.1067	196.0000	0.1083
7.0	196.0429	0.1181	196.0218	0.1237	195.9999	0.1256
7.5	196.0493	0.1356	196.0250	0.1421	195.9999	0.1442
8.0	196.0561	0.1543	196.0284	0.1616	195.9999	0.1641
8.5	196.0633	0.1742	196.0321	0.1825	195.9999	0.1853
9.0	196.0709	0.1953	196.0359	0.2046	195.9999	0.2077
9.5	196.0790	0.2176	196.0400	0.2280	195.9998	0.2314
10.0	196.0875	0.2411	196.0443	0.2526	195.9998	0.2564
10.5	196.0965	0.2658	196.0488	0.2785	195.9997	0.2827
11.0	196.1059	0.2917	196.0536	0.3057	195.9997	0.3103
11.5	196.1157	0.3189	196.0585	0.3341	195.9996	0.3391
12.0	196.1259	0.3473	196.0637	0.3638	195.9995	0.3692
12.5	196.1366	0.3768	196.0691	0.3947	195.9995	0.4006
13.0	196.1477	0.4076	196.0747	0.4270	195.9994	0.4333
13.5	196.1593	0.4396	196.0805	0.4605	195.9993	0.4673
14.0	196.1712	0.4728	196.0865	0.4952	195.9992	0.5026
14.5	196.1836	0.5072	196.0927	0.5312	195.9990	0.5391
15.0	196.1965	0.5428	196.0991	0.5685	195.9989	0.5769
15.5	196.2097	0.5797	196.1058	0.6071	195.9987	0.6160
16.0	196.2234	0.6177	196.1126	0.6469	195.9986	0.6564
16.5	196.2375	0.6570	196.1197	0.6880	195.9984	0.6981
17.0	196.2520	0.6975	196.1270	0.7304	195.9982	0.7410
17.5	196.2670	0.7392	196.1344	0.7740	195.9980	0.7852
18.0	196.2824	0.7821	196.1421	0.8189	195.9977	0.8308
18.5	196.2982	0.8263	196.1500	0.8651	195.9975	0.8775
19.0	196.3144	0.8716	196.1581	0.9125	195.9972	0.9256
19.5	196.3310	0.9182	196.1663	0.9612	195.9969	0.9750
20.0	196.3481	0.9660	196.1748	1.0112	195.9965	1.0256
20.5	196.3656	1.0150	196.1835	1.0625	195.9962	1.0775
21.0	196.3835	1.0653	196.1924	1.1150	195.9958	1.1307
21.5	196.4018	1.1167	196.2014	1.1688	195.9954	1.1852
22.0	196.4205	1.1694	196.2107	1.2239	195.9949	1.2410
22.5	196.4397	1.2233	196.2202	1.2802	195.9944	1.2980
23.0	196.4592	1.2785	196.2298	1.3378	195.9939	1.3563
23.5	196.4792	1.3348	196.2396	1.3967	195.9934	1.4159
24.0	196.4995	1.3924	196.2497	1.4569	195.9928	1.4768
24.5	196.5203	1.4512	196.2599	1.5183	195.9922	1.5390
25.0	196.5415	1.5113	196.2703	1.5810	195.9915	1.6024

TABLE I. $a_r(q) = U + iV$, $q = \rho e^{i\phi}$ $r = 14$

ρ	$\phi = 50°$		$\phi = 55°$		$\phi = 60°$	
	U	V	U	V	U	V
0.0	196.0000	0.0000	196.0000	0.0000	196.0000	0.0000
0.5	195.9999	0.0006	195.9998	0.0006	195.9997	0.0006
1.0	195.9996	0.0025	195.9991	0.0024	195.9987	0.0022
1.5	195.9990	0.0057	195.9980	0.0054	195.9971	0.0050
2.0	195.9982	0.0101	195.9965	0.0096	195.9949	0.0089
2.5	195.9972	0.0158	195.9945	0.0151	195.9920	0.0139
3.0	195.9960	0.0227	195.9921	0.0217	195.9885	0.0200
3.5	195.9945	0.0309	195.9893	0.0295	195.9843	0.0272
4.0	195.9929	0.0404	195.9860	0.0385	195.9795	0.0355
4.5	195.9910	0.0511	195.9822	0.0488	195.9740	0.0450
5.0	195.9889	0.0631	195.9781	0.0602	195.9679	0.0555
5.5	195.9865	0.0764	195.9735	0.0729	195.9612	0.0672
6.0	195.9839	0.0909	195.9684	0.0867	195.9538	0.0799
6.5	195.9812	0.1067	195.9629	0.1018	195.9458	0.0938
7.0	195.9781	0.1237	195.9570	0.1180	195.9372	0.1088
7.5	195.9749	0.1420	195.9506	0.1355	195.9278	0.1248
8.0	195.9714	0.1616	195.9438	0.1541	195.9179	0.1420
8.5	195.9677	0.1824	195.9366	0.1740	195.9073	0.1603
9.0	195.9638	0.2045	195.9289	0.1951	195.8961	0.1797
9.5	195.9597	0.2278	195.9207	0.2173	195.8842	0.2003
10.0	195.9553	0.2524	195.9121	0.2408	195.8717	0.2219
10.5	195.9507	0.2783	195.9031	0.2655	195.8585	0.2446
11.0	195.9458	0.3054	195.8936	0.2913	195.8447	0.2684
11.5	195.9408	0.3338	195.8837	0.3184	195.8303	0.2933
12.0	195.9355	0.3635	195.8734	0.3467	195.8152	0.3194
12.5	195.9299	0.3944	195.8626	0.3761	195.7994	0.3465
13.0	195.9242	0.4265	195.8513	0.4068	195.7830	0.3747
13.5	195.9182	0.4600	195.8396	0.4387	195.7660	0.4041
14.0	195.9119	0.4946	195.8275	0.4717	195.7483	0.4345
14.5	195.9055	0.5306	195.8149	0.5060	195.7300	0.4660
15.0	195.8988	0.5678	195.8018	0.5414	195.7110	0.4987
15.5	195.8919	0.6062	195.7884	0.5781	195.6914	0.5324
16.0	195.8847	0.6459	195.7744	0.6159	195.6711	0.5672
16.5	195.8773	0.6869	195.7600	0.6549	195.6502	0.6032
17.0	195.8696	0.7291	195.7452	0.6952	195.6286	0.6402
17.5	195.8617	0.7726	195.7299	0.7366	195.6064	0.6783
18.0	195.8536	0.8174	195.7141	0.7792	195.5835	0.7175
18.5	195.8452	0.8633	195.6979	0.8230	195.5600	0.7578
19.0	195.8366	0.9106	195.6813	0.8680	195.5358	0.7992
19.5	195.8278	0.9591	195.6642	0.9142	195.5110	0.8417
20.0	195.8187	1.0088	195.6466	0.9615	195.4855	0.8852
20.5	195.8093	1.0598	195.6286	1.0101	195.4593	0.9299
21.0	195.7997	1.1121	195.6101	1.0598	195.4326	0.9756
21.5	195.7899	1.1656	195.5911	1.1108	195.4051	1.0225
22.0	195.7798	1.2204	195.5717	1.1629	195.3770	1.0704
22.5	195.7694	1.2764	195.5518	1.2162	195.3483	1.1194
23.0	195.7588	1.3337	195.5315	1.2707	195.3188	1.1694
23.5	195.7479	1.3922	195.5107	1.3263	195.2888	1.2206
24.0	195.7368	1.4519	195.4894	1.3832	195.2580	1.2728
24.5	195.7255	1.5129	195.4677	1.4412	195.2267	1.3261
25.0	195.7138	1.5752	195.4455	1.5004	195.1946	1.3805

322-566 O - 69 - 8

TABLE I. $a_r(q) = U+iV$, $q=\rho e^{i\phi}$ $\qquad r=14$

ρ	$\phi=65°$		$\phi=70°$		$\phi=75°$	
	U	V	U	V	U	V
0.0	196.0000	0.0000	196.0000	0.0000	196.0000	0.0000
0.5	195.9996	0.0005	195.9995	0.0004	195.9994	0.0003
1.0	195.9984	0.0020	195.9980	0.0016	195.9978	0.0013
1.5	195.9963	0.0044	195.9956	0.0037	195.9950	0.0029
2.0	195.9934	0.0079	195.9921	0.0066	195.9911	0.0051
2.5	195.9897	0.0123	195.9877	0.0103	195.9861	0.0080
3.0	195.9852	0.0177	195.9823	0.0148	195.9800	0.0115
3.5	195.9798	0.0241	195.9759	0.0202	195.9728	0.0157
4.0	195.9736	0.0314	195.9686	0.0264	195.9645	0.0205
4.5	195.9666	0.0398	195.9602	0.0334	195.9550	0.0260
5.0	195.9588	0.0491	195.9509	0.0412	195.9445	0.0320
5.5	195.9501	0.0594	195.9406	0.0498	195.9328	0.0388
6.0	195.9407	0.0707	195.9293	0.0593	195.9201	0.0461
6.5	195.9304	0.0830	195.9170	0.0696	195.9062	0.0541
7.0	195.9192	0.0962	195.9038	0.0807	195.8912	0.0628
7.5	195.9073	0.1104	195.8895	0.0926	195.8751	0.0721
8.0	195.8945	0.1256	195.8743	0.1054	195.8579	0.0820
8.5	195.8809	0.1418	195.8581	0.1190	195.8396	0.0925
9.0	195.8665	0.1590	195.8409	0.1334	195.8202	0.1037
9.5	195.8512	0.1771	195.8228	0.1486	195.7997	0.1156
10.0	195.8351	0.1962	195.8036	0.1646	195.7780	0.1280
10.5	195.8182	0.2163	195.7835	0.1815	195.7553	0.1411
11.0	195.8005	0.2374	195.7624	0.1991	195.7315	0.1549
11.5	195.7820	0.2594	195.7403	0.2176	195.7065	0.1692
12.0	195.7626	0.2824	195.7172	0.2369	195.6805	0.1842
12.5	195.7424	0.3064	195.6932	0.2570	195.6533	0.1999
13.0	195.7214	0.3313	195.6682	0.2779	195.6250	0.2161
13.5	195.6995	0.3573	195.6421	0.2997	195.5957	0.2330
14.0	195.6768	0.3842	195.6152	0.3222	195.5652	0.2506
14.5	195.6533	0.4120	195.5872	0.3456	195.5336	0.2687
15.0	195.6290	0.4409	195.5582	0.3698	195.5009	0.2875
15.5	195.6038	0.4707	195.5283	0.3947	195.4671	0.3069
16.0	195.5778	0.5014	195.4974	0.4205	195.4322	0.3270
16.5	195.5510	0.5332	195.4655	0.4471	195.3962	0.3477
17.0	195.5234	0.5659	195.4327	0.4746	195.3592	0.3690
17.5	195.4949	0.5995	195.3988	0.5028	195.3210	0.3909
18.0	195.4656	0.6342	195.3640	0.5318	195.2817	0.4134
18.5	195.4355	0.6698	195.3282	0.5616	195.2413	0.4366
19.0	195.4045	0.7063	195.2914	0.5922	195.1998	0.4604
19.5	195.3728	0.7438	195.2537	0.6237	195.1572	0.4848
20.0	195.3402	0.7823	195.2149	0.6559	195.1135	0.5099
20.5	195.3067	0.8217	195.1752	0.6889	195.0687	0.5355
21.0	195.2725	0.8621	195.1345	0.7227	195.0228	0.5618
21.5	195.2374	0.9034	195.0929	0.7574	194.9759	0.5887
22.0	195.2015	0.9457	195.0502	0.7928	194.9278	0.6162
22.5	195.1647	0.9890	195.0066	0.8290	194.8786	0.6443
23.0	195.1271	1.0331	194.9620	0.8660	194.8283	0.6730
23.5	195.0887	1.0783	194.9165	0.9038	194.7770	0.7024
24.0	195.0495	1.1244	194.8699	0.9424	194.7245	0.7323
24.5	195.0094	1.1714	194.8224	0.9817	194.6710	0.7629
25.0	194.9685	1.2194	194.7739	1.0219	194.6164	0.7941

TABLE I. $a_r(q) = U + iV$, $q = \rho e^{i\phi}$ $r = 14$

ρ	$\phi = 80°$		$\phi = 85°$		$\phi = 90°$	
	U	V	U	V	U	V
0.0	196.0000	0.0000	196.0000	0.0000	196.0000	0.0000
0.5	195.9994	0.0002	195.9994	0.0001	195.9994	0.0000
1.0	195.9976	0.0009	195.9975	0.0004	195.9974	0.0000
1.5	195.9946	0.0020	195.9943	0.0010	195.9942	0.0000
2.0	195.9904	0.0035	195.9899	0.0018	195.9897	0.0000
2.5	195.9849	0.0055	195.9842	0.0028	195.9840	0.0000
3.0	195.9783	0.0079	195.9773	0.0040	195.9769	0.0000
3.5	195.9705	0.0107	195.9691	0.0055	195.9686	0.0000
4.0	195.9615	0.0140	195.9596	0.0071	195.9590	0.0000
4.5	195.9512	0.0178	195.9489	0.0090	195.9481	0.0000
5.0	195.9398	0.0219	195.9369	0.0111	195.9359	0.0000
5.5	195.9271	0.0265	195.9236	0.0135	195.9225	0.0000
6.0	195.9133	0.0316	195.9091	0.0160	195.9077	0.0000
6.5	195.8982	0.0370	195.8933	0.0188	195.8917	0.0000
7.0	195.8820	0.0429	195.8763	0.0218	195.8744	0.0000
7.5	195.8645	0.0493	195.8580	0.0250	195.8558	0.0000
8.0	195.8459	0.0561	195.8385	0.0285	195.8360	0.0000
8.5	195.8260	0.0633	195.8177	0.0321	195.8149	0.0000
9.0	195.8049	0.0709	195.7956	0.0360	195.7924	0.0000
9.5	195.7827	0.0790	195.7723	0.0401	195.7688	0.0000
10.0	195.7592	0.0876	195.7477	0.0445	195.7438	0.0000
10.5	195.7346	0.0965	195.7218	0.0490	195.7176	0.0000
11.0	195.7087	0.1059	195.6948	0.0538	195.6901	0.0000
11.5	195.6816	0.1157	195.6664	0.0588	195.6613	0.0000
12.0	195.6534	0.1260	195.6368	0.0640	195.6312	0.0000
12.5	195.6239	0.1367	195.6059	0.0694	195.5999	0.0000
13.0	195.5933	0.1478	195.5738	0.0750	195.5673	0.0000
13.5	195.5614	0.1594	195.5405	0.0809	195.5334	0.0000
14.0	195.5284	0.1714	195.5058	0.0870	195.4983	0.0000
14.5	195.4941	0.1838	195.4700	0.0933	195.4618	0.0000
15.0	195.4587	0.1966	195.4329	0.0998	195.4242	0.0000
15.5	195.4221	0.2099	195.3945	0.1065	195.3852	0.0000
16.0	195.3843	0.2236	195.3549	0.1135	195.3450	0.0000
16.5	195.3452	0.2377	195.3140	0.1207	195.3035	0.0000
17.0	195.3050	0.2523	195.2719	0.1281	195.2608	0.0000
17.5	195.2636	0.2673	195.2286	0.1357	195.2168	0.0000
18.0	195.2211	0.2827	195.1840	0.1435	195.1715	0.0000
18.5	195.1773	0.2985	195.1381	0.1515	195.1250	0.0000
19.0	195.1323	0.3148	195.0911	0.1598	195.0772	0.0000
19.5	195.0862	0.3315	195.0427	0.1683	195.0281	0.0000
20.0	195.0388	0.3486	194.9932	0.1769	194.9778	0.0000
20.5	194.9903	0.3661	194.9424	0.1858	194.9262	0.0000
21.0	194.9406	0.3841	194.8903	0.1949	194.8734	0.0000
21.5	194.8897	0.4025	194.8371	0.2043	194.8193	0.0000
22.0	194.8377	0.4212	194.7825	0.2138	194.7640	0.0000
22.5	194.7844	0.4405	194.7268	0.2235	194.7074	0.0000
23.0	194.7300	0.4601	194.6698	0.2335	194.6496	0.0000
23.5	194.6744	0.4801	194.6116	0.2437	194.5905	0.0000
24.0	194.6176	0.5006	194.5522	0.2541	194.5302	0.0000
24.5	194.5596	0.5215	194.4915	0.2647	194.4686	0.0000
25.0	194.5005	0.5428	194.4296	0.2755	194.4058	0.0000

TABLE I. $a_r(q) = U + iV$, $q = \rho e^{i\phi}$ $\qquad\qquad r = 15$

ρ	$\phi=5°$		$\phi=10°$		$\phi=15°$	
	U	V	U	V	U	V
0.0	225.0000	0.0000	225.0000	0.0000	225.0000	0.0000
0.5	225.0005	0.0001	225.0005	0.0002	225.0005	0.0003
1.0	225.0022	0.0004	225.0021	0.0008	225.0019	0.0011
1.5	225.0049	0.0009	225.0047	0.0017	225.0043	0.0025
2.0	225.0088	0.0016	225.0084	0.0031	225.0077	0.0045
2.5	225.0137	0.0024	225.0131	0.0048	225.0121	0.0070
3.0	225.0198	0.0035	225.0189	0.0069	225.0174	0.0100
3.5	225.0269	0.0047	225.0257	0.0094	225.0237	0.0137
4.0	225.0352	0.0062	225.0336	0.0122	225.0309	0.0179
4.5	225.0445	0.0079	225.0425	0.0155	225.0391	0.0226
5.0	225.0550	0.0097	225.0524	0.0191	225.0483	0.0279
5.5	225.0665	0.0117	225.0635	0.0231	225.0585	0.0338
6.0	225.0792	0.0140	225.0755	0.0275	225.0696	0.0402
6.5	225.0929	0.0164	225.0886	0.0323	225.0817	0.0472
7.0	225.1077	0.0190	225.1028	0.0374	225.0947	0.0547
7.5	225.1237	0.0218	225.1180	0.0430	225.1088	0.0628
8.0	225.1407	0.0248	225.1343	0.0489	225.1237	0.0715
8.5	225.1589	0.0280	225.1516	0.0552	225.1397	0.0807
9.0	225.1781	0.0314	225.1700	0.0619	225.1566	0.0905
9.5	225.1985	0.0350	225.1894	0.0690	225.1745	0.1008
10.0	225.2200	0.0388	225.2099	0.0764	225.1934	0.1117
10.5	225.2425	0.0428	225.2314	0.0843	225.2132	0.1232
11.0	225.2662	0.0470	225.2540	0.0925	225.2340	0.1352
11.5	225.2909	0.0513	225.2776	0.1011	225.2558	0.1478
12.0	225.3168	0.0559	225.3023	0.1101	225.2785	0.1610
12.5	225.3438	0.0607	225.3280	0.1195	225.3022	0.1747
13.0	225.3719	0.0656	225.3548	0.1293	225.3269	0.1890
13.5	225.4011	0.0708	225.3826	0.1394	225.3525	0.2038
14.0	225.4314	0.0762	225.4115	0.1500	225.3792	0.2192
14.5	225.4628	0.0817	225.4415	0.1609	225.4067	0.2352
15.0	225.4953	0.0875	225.4725	0.1722	225.4353	0.2517
15.5	225.5289	0.0934	225.5046	0.1839	225.4648	0.2689
16.0	225.5636	0.0995	225.5377	0.1960	225.4953	0.2865
16.5	225.5995	0.1059	225.5719	0.2085	225.5268	0.3048
17.0	225.6364	0.1124	225.6071	0.2214	225.5593	0.3236
17.5	225.6745	0.1192	225.6434	0.2347	225.5927	0.3430
18.0	225.7136	0.1261	225.6807	0.2483	225.6271	0.3629
18.5	225.7539	0.1332	225.7192	0.2624	225.6624	0.3834
19.0	225.7953	0.1406	225.7586	0.2768	225.6988	0.4045
19.5	225.8378	0.1481	225.7992	0.2916	225.7361	0.4262
20.0	225.8814	0.1558	225.8408	0.3069	225.7744	0.4484
20.5	225.9262	0.1638	225.8834	0.3225	225.8136	0.4712
21.0	225.9720	0.1719	225.9271	0.3385	225.8539	0.4946
21.5	226.0190	0.1802	225.9719	0.3549	225.8951	0.5186
22.0	226.0671	0.1888	226.0178	0.3717	225.9373	0.5431
22.5	226.1163	0.1975	226.0647	0.3889	225.9805	0.5682
23.0	226.1666	0.2064	226.1127	0.4065	226.0246	0.5939
23.5	226.2181	0.2156	226.1617	0.4244	226.0697	0.6202
24.0	226.2707	0.2249	226.2118	0.4428	226.1158	0.6470
24.5	226.3244	0.2344	226.2630	0.4616	226.1629	0.6744
25.0	226.3792	0.2442	226.3152	0.4808	226.2110	0.7024

TABLE I. $a_r(q) = U + iV$, $q = \rho e^{i\phi}$ $r = 15$

ρ	$\phi = 20°$		$\phi = 25°$		$\phi = 30°$	
	U	V	U	V	U	V
0.0	225.0000	0.0000	225.0000	0.0000	225.0000	0.0000
0.5	225.0004	0.0004	225.0004	0.0004	225.0003	0.0005
1.0	225.0017	0.0014	225.0014	0.0017	225.0011	0.0019
1.5	225.0038	0.0032	225.0032	0.0038	225.0025	0.0043
2.0	225.0068	0.0057	225.0057	0.0068	225.0045	0.0077
2.5	225.0107	0.0090	225.0090	0.0107	225.0070	0.0121
3.0	225.0154	0.0129	225.0129	0.0154	225.0100	0.0174
3.5	225.0209	0.0176	225.0176	0.0209	225.0137	0.0237
4.0	225.0274	0.0230	225.0230	0.0274	225.0179	0.0309
4.5	225.0346	0.0291	225.0291	0.0346	225.0226	0.0392
5.0	225.0427	0.0359	225.0359	0.0428	225.0279	0.0483
5.5	225.0517	0.0434	225.0434	0.0517	225.0338	0.0585
6.0	225.0616	0.0517	225.0516	0.0616	225.0402	0.0696
6.5	225.0722	0.0606	225.0606	0.0723	225.0471	0.0817
7.0	225.0838	0.0703	225.0703	0.0838	225.0547	0.0948
7.5	225.0962	0.0808	225.0807	0.0962	225.0628	0.1088
8.0	225.1094	0.0919	225.0918	0.1095	225.0714	0.1238
8.5	225.1236	0.1037	225.1036	0.1236	225.0806	0.1397
9.0	225.1385	0.1163	225.1162	0.1386	225.0904	0.1567
9.5	225.1543	0.1296	225.1295	0.1544	225.1007	0.1746
10.0	225.1710	0.1436	225.1435	0.1711	225.1115	0.1934
10.5	225.1885	0.1584	225.1582	0.1887	225.1230	0.2133
11.0	225.2069	0.1738	225.1736	0.2071	225.1349	0.2341
11.5	225.2262	0.1900	225.1897	0.2264	225.1475	0.2559
12.0	225.2463	0.2069	225.2066	0.2465	225.1606	0.2786
12.5	225.2672	0.2245	225.2241	0.2675	225.1742	0.3023
13.0	225.2890	0.2429	225.2424	0.2894	225.1884	0.3270
13.5	225.3117	0.2620	225.2614	0.3121	225.2032	0.3527
14.0	225.3352	0.2818	225.2811	0.3357	225.2185	0.3794
14.5	225.3596	0.3023	225.3016	0.3601	225.2343	0.4070
15.0	225.3849	0.3235	225.3227	0.3854	225.2508	0.4356
15.5	225.4109	0.3455	225.3446	0.4116	225.2677	0.4651
16.0	225.4379	0.3682	225.3671	0.4387	225.2852	0.4957
16.5	225.4657	0.3917	225.3904	0.4666	225.3033	0.5272
17.0	225.4944	0.4158	225.4144	0.4953	225.3219	0.5597
17.5	225.5239	0.4407	225.4392	0.5250	225.3411	0.5932
18.0	225.5543	0.4664	225.4646	0.5555	225.3608	0.6276
18.5	225.5855	0.4927	225.4908	0.5869	225.3811	0.6630
19.0	225.6176	0.5198	225.5176	0.6191	225.4020	0.6995
19.5	225.6505	0.5476	225.5452	0.6522	225.4233	0.7368
20.0	225.6844	0.5762	225.5735	0.6862	225.4453	0.7752
20.5	225.7190	0.6055	225.6025	0.7211	225.4678	0.8146
21.0	225.7545	0.6355	225.6322	0.7568	225.4908	0.8549
21.5	225.7909	0.6663	225.6627	0.7934	225.5144	0.8962
22.0	225.8282	0.6978	225.6938	0.8309	225.5385	0.9385
22.5	225.8663	0.7300	225.7257	0.8693	225.5632	0.9818
23.0	225.9052	0.7630	225.7583	0.9085	225.5884	1.0261
23.5	225.9450	0.7967	225.7916	0.9486	225.6141	1.0713
24.0	225.9857	0.8311	225.8256	0.9896	225.6404	1.1176
24.5	226.0272	0.8663	225.8603	1.0315	225.6673	1.1648
25.0	226.0696	0.9023	225.8957	1.0742	225.6947	1.2130

TABLE I. $a_r(q) = U + iV$, $q = \rho e^{i\phi}$ $\qquad r = 15$

ρ	$\phi=35°$		$\phi=40°$		$\phi=45°$	
	U	V	U	V	U	V
0.0	225.0000	0.0000	225.0000	0.0000	225.0000	0.0000
0.5	225.0002	0.0005	225.0001	0.0005	225.0000	0.0006
1.0	225.0008	0.0021	225.0004	0.0022	225.0000	0.0022
1.5	225.0017	0.0047	225.0009	0.0049	225.0000	0.0050
2.0	225.0031	0.0084	225.0015	0.0088	225.0000	0.0089
2.5	225.0048	0.0131	225.0024	0.0137	225.0000	0.0140
3.0	225.0069	0.0189	225.0035	0.0198	225.0000	0.0201
3.5	225.0093	0.0257	225.0047	0.0269	225.0000	0.0273
4.0	225.0122	0.0336	225.0062	0.0352	225.0000	0.0357
4.5	225.0155	0.0425	225.0078	0.0445	225.0000	0.0452
5.0	225.0191	0.0524	225.0097	0.0550	225.0000	0.0558
5.5	225.0231	0.0635	225.0117	0.0665	225.0000	0.0675
6.0	225.0275	0.0755	225.0139	0.0791	225.0000	0.0804
6.5	225.0322	0.0886	225.0164	0.0929	225.0000	0.0943
7.0	225.0374	0.1028	225.0190	0.1077	225.0000	0.1094
7.5	225.0429	0.1180	225.0218	0.1237	225.0000	0.1256
8.0	225.0488	0.1343	225.0248	0.1407	224.9999	0.1429
8.5	225.0551	0.1516	225.0279	0.1588	224.9999	0.1613
9.0	225.0618	0.1700	225.0313	0.1781	224.9999	0.1808
9.5	225.0688	0.1894	225.0349	0.1984	224.9999	0.2015
10.0	225.0762	0.2098	225.0386	0.2199	224.9999	0.2232
10.5	225.0840	0.2314	225.0426	0.2424	224.9998	0.2461
11.0	225.0922	0.2539	225.0467	0.2661	224.9998	0.2701
11.5	225.1008	0.2776	225.0510	0.2908	224.9998	0.2952
12.0	225.1097	0.3022	225.0555	0.3166	224.9997	0.3214
12.5	225.1190	0.3280	225.0602	0.3436	224.9997	0.3488
13.0	225.1287	0.3547	225.0651	0.3716	224.9996	0.3772
13.5	225.1388	0.3826	225.0702	0.4008	224.9995	0.4068
14.0	225.1492	0.4115	225.0755	0.4310	224.9995	0.4375
14.5	225.1600	0.4414	225.0809	0.4624	224.9994	0.4693
15.0	225.1712	0.4724	225.0865	0.4948	224.9993	0.5022
15.5	225.1828	0.5045	225.0923	0.5284	224.9992	0.5363
16.0	225.1947	0.5376	225.0983	0.5631	224.9991	0.5714
16.5	225.2070	0.5717	225.1045	0.5988	224.9989	0.6077
17.0	225.2197	0.6069	225.1109	0.6357	224.9988	0.6451
17.5	225.2328	0.6432	225.1174	0.6737	224.9987	0.6836
18.0	225.2462	0.6806	225.1242	0.7127	224.9985	0.7232
18.5	225.2600	0.7189	225.1311	0.7529	224.9983	0.7639
19.0	225.2742	0.7584	225.1382	0.7942	224.9981	0.8058
19.5	225.2887	0.7989	225.1454	0.8366	224.9979	0.8488
20.0	225.3036	0.8405	225.1529	0.8801	224.9977	0.8928
20.5	225.3189	0.8831	225.1605	0.9246	224.9975	0.9380
21.0	225.3345	0.9268	225.1683	0.9703	224.9972	0.9844
21.5	225.3505	0.9715	225.1763	1.0171	224.9970	1.0318
22.0	225.3669	1.0173	225.1845	1.0651	224.9967	1.0803
22.5	225.3837	1.0642	225.1928	1.1141	224.9963	1.1300
23.0	225.4008	1.1121	225.2013	1.1642	224.9960	1.1808
23.5	225.4182	1.1611	225.2100	1.2154	224.9957	1.2327
24.0	225.4361	1.2112	225.2188	1.2678	224.9953	1.2857
24.5	225.4543	1.2623	225.2278	1.3212	224.9949	1.3398
25.0	225.4728	1.3145	225.2370	1.3757	224.9944	1.3950

TABLE I. $a_r(q) = U+iV$, $q=\rho e^{i\phi}$ $r=15$

ρ	$\phi=50°$		$\phi=55°$		$\phi=60°$	
	U	V	U	V	U	V
0.0	225.0000	0.0000	225.0000	0.0000	225.0000	0.0000
0.5	224.9999	0.0005	224.9998	0.0005	224.9997	0.0005
1.0	224.9996	0.0022	224.9992	0.0021	224.9989	0.0019
1.5	224.9991	0.0049	224.9983	0.0047	224.9975	0.0043
2.0	224.9984	0.0088	224.9969	0.0084	224.9955	0.0077
2.5	224.9976	0.0137	224.9952	0.0131	224.9930	0.0121
3.0	224.9965	0.0198	224.9931	0.0189	224.9900	0.0174
3.5	224.9952	0.0269	224.9906	0.0257	224.9863	0.0237
4.0	224.9938	0.0352	224.9878	0.0336	224.9821	0.0309
4.5	224.9921	0.0445	224.9845	0.0425	224.9774	0.0391
5.0	224.9903	0.0550	224.9809	0.0524	224.9721	0.0483
5.5	224.9883	0.0665	224.9769	0.0634	224.9662	0.0585
6.0	224.9860	0.0791	224.9725	0.0755	224.9598	0.0696
6.5	224.9836	0.0929	224.9677	0.0886	224.9528	0.0817
7.0	224.9810	0.1077	224.9626	0.1028	224.9453	0.0947
7.5	224.9782	0.1236	224.9570	0.1180	224.9372	0.1087
8.0	224.9751	0.1407	224.9511	0.1342	224.9285	0.1237
8.5	224.9719	0.1588	224.9448	0.1515	224.9193	0.1396
9.0	224.9685	0.1780	224.9381	0.1698	224.9096	0.1565
9.5	224.9649	0.1984	224.9310	0.1892	224.8992	0.1744
10.0	224.9611	0.2198	224.9235	0.2097	224.8883	0.1932
10.5	224.9571	0.2423	224.9157	0.2311	224.8769	0.2130
11.0	224.9529	0.2659	224.9075	0.2537	224.8649	0.2337
11.5	224.9485	0.2906	224.8988	0.2772	224.8523	0.2554
12.0	224.9439	0.3164	224.8898	0.3019	224.8391	0.2781
12.5	224.9391	0.3434	224.8804	0.3275	224.8254	0.3017
13.0	224.9341	0.3714	224.8707	0.3542	224.8112	0.3263
13.5	224.9289	0.4005	224.8605	0.3820	224.7964	0.3519
14.0	224.9235	0.4307	224.8499	0.4108	224.7810	0.3784
14.5	224.9179	0.4620	224.8390	0.4406	224.7650	0.4059
15.0	224.9121	0.4944	224.8277	0.4715	224.7485	0.4343
15.5	224.9061	0.5278	224.8160	0.5034	224.7315	0.4637
16.0	224.8999	0.5624	224.8038	0.5364	224.7138	0.4941
16.5	224.8935	0.5981	224.7913	0.5704	224.6956	0.5254
17.0	224.8869	0.6349	224.7785	0.6054	224.6769	0.5576
17.5	224.8800	0.6727	224.7652	0.6415	224.6575	0.5909
18.0	224.8730	0.7117	224.7515	0.6786	224.6377	0.6250
18.5	224.8658	0.7518	224.7374	0.7168	224.6172	0.6602
19.0	224.8583	0.7929	224.7230	0.7560	224.5962	0.6962
19.5	224.8507	0.8352	224.7081	0.7963	224.5746	0.7333
20.0	224.8428	0.8785	224.6929	0.8375	224.5524	0.7713
20.5	224.8348	0.9229	224.6773	0.8799	224.5297	0.8102
21.0	224.8265	0.9685	224.6612	0.9232	224.5065	0.8501
21.5	224.8180	1.0151	224.6448	0.9676	224.4826	0.8909
22.0	224.8093	1.0628	224.6280	1.0130	224.4582	0.9327
22.5	224.8004	1.1116	224.6107	1.0595	224.4332	0.9755
23.0	224.7912	1.1615	224.5931	1.1070	224.4076	1.0192
23.5	224.7819	1.2124	224.5751	1.1555	224.3815	1.0638
24.0	224.7723	1.2645	224.5567	1.2051	224.3548	1.1094
24.5	224.7625	1.3177	224.5379	1.2557	224.3276	1.1559
25.0	224.7526	1.3719	224.5186	1.3073	224.2997	1.2034

TABLE I. $a_r(q) = U + iV$, $q = \rho e^{i\phi}$ $\qquad r = 15$

ρ	$\phi = 65°$		$\phi = 70°$		$\phi = 75°$	
	U	V	U	V	U	V
0.0	225.0000	0.0000	225.0000	0.0000	225.0000	0.0000
0.5	224.9996	0.0004	224.9996	0.0004	224.9995	0.0003
1.0	224.9986	0.0017	224.9983	0.0014	224.9981	0.0011
1.5	224.9968	0.0038	224.9962	0.0032	224.9956	0.0025
2.0	224.9943	0.0068	224.9932	0.0057	224.9923	0.0045
2.5	224.9910	0.0107	224.9893	0.0090	224.9879	0.0070
3.0	224.9871	0.0154	224.9846	0.0129	224.9826	0.0100
3.5	224.9824	0.0209	224.9791	0.0176	224.9763	0.0137
4.0	224.9770	0.0274	224.9726	0.0230	224.9691	0.0179
4.5	224.9709	0.0346	224.9654	0.0290	224.9609	0.0226
5.0	224.9641	0.0427	224.9573	0.0359	224.9517	0.0279
5.5	224.9566	0.0517	224.9483	0.0434	224.9415	0.0337
6.0	224.9483	0.0615	224.9384	0.0516	224.9304	0.0402
6.5	224.9394	0.0722	224.9278	0.0606	224.9183	0.0471
7.0	224.9297	0.0838	224.9162	0.0703	224.9053	0.0547
7.5	224.9193	0.0961	224.9038	0.0807	224.8913	0.0627
8.0	224.9082	0.1094	224.8906	0.0918	224.8763	0.0714
8.5	224.8963	0.1235	224.8765	0.1036	224.8604	0.0806
9.0	224.8838	0.1384	224.8615	0.1161	224.8435	0.0903
9.5	224.8705	0.1542	224.8457	0.1294	224.8256	0.1006
10.0	224.8565	0.1709	224.8290	0.1433	224.8068	0.1115
10.5	224.8418	0.1883	224.8115	0.1580	224.7870	0.1229
11.0	224.8264	0.2067	224.7931	0.1734	224.7662	0.1349
11.5	224.8102	0.2259	224.7739	0.1895	224.7445	0.1474
12.0	224.7933	0.2459	224.7538	0.2063	224.7218	0.1605
12.5	224.7758	0.2668	224.7329	0.2238	224.6981	0.1741
13.0	224.7575	0.2886	224.7111	0.2421	224.6735	0.1883
13.5	224.7384	0.3112	224.6884	0.2610	224.6479	0.2030
14.0	224.7187	0.3346	224.6650	0.2807	224.6214	0.2183
14.5	224.6982	0.3589	224.6406	0.3010	224.5939	0.2341
15.0	224.6770	0.3840	224.6154	0.3221	224.5654	0.2505
15.5	224.6551	0.4100	224.5893	0.3439	224.5360	0.2674
16.0	224.6325	0.4368	224.5624	0.3664	224.5056	0.2849
16.5	224.6092	0.4645	224.5347	0.3896	224.4742	0.3029
17.0	224.5851	0.4930	224.5060	0.4135	224.4419	0.3215
17.5	224.5604	0.5224	224.4766	0.4381	224.4087	0.3406
18.0	224.5349	0.5525	224.4462	0.4634	224.3744	0.3603
18.5	224.5087	0.5836	224.4151	0.4894	224.3392	0.3805
19.0	224.4817	0.6155	224.3830	0.5161	224.3031	0.4013
19.5	224.4541	0.6482	224.3502	0.5436	224.2660	0.4226
20.0	224.4257	0.6817	224.3164	0.5717	224.2279	0.4445
20.5	224.3966	0.7161	224.2819	0.6005	224.1889	0.4669
21.0	224.3668	0.7514	224.2464	0.6300	224.1489	0.4898
21.5	224.3363	0.7874	224.2101	0.6603	224.1079	0.5133
22.0	224.3050	0.8243	224.1730	0.6912	224.0660	0.5373
22.5	224.2730	0.8621	224.1350	0.7228	224.0232	0.5619
23.0	224.2403	0.9006	224.0962	0.7551	223.9794	0.5870
23.5	224.2069	0.9400	224.0565	0.7881	223.9346	0.6126
24.0	224.1728	0.9803	224.0159	0.8218	223.8889	0.6388
24.5	224.1379	1.0214	223.9745	0.8562	223.8422	0.6655
25.0	224.1023	1.0633	223.9323	0.8913	223.7946	0.6928

TABLE I. $a_r(q) = U + iV$, $q = \rho e^{i\phi}$ $r = 15$

ρ	$\phi = 80°$		$\phi = 85°$		$\phi = 90°$	
	U	V	U	V	U	V
0.0	225.0000	0.0000	225.0000	0.0000	225.0000	0.0000
0.5	224.9995	0.0002	224.9994	0.0001	224.9994	−0.0000
1.0	224.9979	0.0008	224.9978	0.0004	224.9978	−0.0000
1.5	224.9953	0.0017	224.9951	0.0009	224.9950	−0.0000
2.0	224.9916	0.0031	224.9912	0.0016	224.9911	−0.0000
2.5	224.9869	0.0048	224.9863	0.0024	224.9860	−0.0000
3.0	224.9811	0.0069	224.9802	0.0035	224.9799	−0.0000
3.5	224.9743	0.0094	224.9731	0.0047	224.9727	−0.0000
4.0	224.9664	0.0122	224.9648	0.0062	224.9643	−0.0000
4.5	224.9575	0.0155	224.9555	0.0078	224.9548	−0.0000
5.0	224.9476	0.0191	224.9451	0.0097	224.9442	−0.0000
5.5	224.9366	0.0231	224.9335	0.0117	224.9325	−0.0000
6.0	224.9245	0.0275	224.9209	0.0139	224.9197	−0.0000
6.5	224.9114	0.0322	224.9071	0.0164	224.9057	−0.0000
7.0	224.8972	0.0374	224.8923	0.0190	224.8907	−0.0000
7.5	224.8820	0.0429	224.8764	0.0218	224.8745	−0.0000
8.0	224.8658	0.0488	224.8594	0.0248	224.8572	−0.0000
8.5	224.8485	0.0551	224.8412	0.0280	224.8388	−0.0000
9.0	224.8302	0.0618	224.8220	0.0314	224.8193	−0.0000
9.5	224.8108	0.0688	224.8017	0.0349	224.7987	−0.0000
10.0	224.7904	0.0763	224.7803	0.0387	224.7769	−0.0000
10.5	224.7689	0.0841	224.7578	0.0427	224.7541	−0.0000
11.0	224.7464	0.0922	224.7342	0.0468	224.7301	−0.0000
11.5	224.7228	0.1008	224.7095	0.0512	224.7050	−0.0000
12.0	224.6982	0.1097	224.6837	0.0557	224.6789	−0.0000
12.5	224.6725	0.1191	224.6569	0.0604	224.6516	−0.0000
13.0	224.6458	0.1288	224.6289	0.0654	224.6232	−0.0000
13.5	224.6181	0.1388	224.5998	0.0705	224.5937	−0.0000
14.0	224.5893	0.1493	224.5697	0.0758	224.5630	−0.0000
14.5	224.5595	0.1601	224.5384	0.0813	224.5313	−0.0000
15.0	224.5286	0.1713	224.5061	0.0870	224.4985	−0.0000
15.5	224.4967	0.1829	224.4726	0.0928	224.4645	−0.0000
16.0	224.4637	0.1948	224.4381	0.0989	224.4295	−0.0000
16.5	224.4298	0.2072	224.4025	0.1052	224.3933	−0.0000
17.0	224.3947	0.2199	224.3658	0.1116	224.3561	−0.0000
17.5	224.3587	0.2330	224.3280	0.1183	224.3177	−0.0000
18.0	224.3215	0.2464	224.2892	0.1251	224.2783	−0.0000
18.5	224.2834	0.2602	224.2492	0.1321	224.2377	−0.0000
19.0	224.2442	0.2744	224.2082	0.1393	224.1960	−0.0000
19.5	224.2040	0.2890	224.1660	0.1467	224.1533	−0.0000
20.0	224.1627	0.3039	224.1228	0.1543	224.1094	−0.0000
20.5	224.1204	0.3192	224.0785	0.1620	224.0644	−0.0000
21.0	224.0771	0.3349	224.0332	0.1700	224.0184	−0.0000
21.5	224.0327	0.3510	223.9867	0.1781	223.9712	−0.0000
22.0	223.9873	0.3674	223.9392	0.1865	223.9229	−0.0000
22.5	223.9409	0.3842	223.8905	0.1950	223.8736	−0.0000
23.0	223.8934	0.4013	223.8408	0.2037	223.8231	−0.0000
23.5	223.8449	0.4189	223.7901	0.2126	223.7716	−0.0000
24.0	223.7954	0.4367	223.7382	0.2217	223.7190	−0.0000
24.5	223.7449	0.4550	223.6853	0.2309	223.6652	−0.0000
25.0	223.6933	0.4736	223.6313	0.2404	223.6104	−0.0000

TABLE II. VALUES OF $b_r(q)$

Associated with odd periodic solutions

$$b_r(q) = U + iV$$

$$q = \rho e^{i\phi}$$

ρ	$\phi = 5°$		$\phi = 10°$		$\phi = 15°$	
	U	V	U	V	U	V
0.0	1.0000	0.0000	1.0000	0.0000	1.0000	0.0000
0.5	0.4730	−0.0485	0.4799	−0.0966	0.4913	−0.1437
1.0	−0.1050	−0.1051	−0.0894	−0.2092	−0.0635	−0.3110
1.5	−0.7248	−0.1676	−0.6994	−0.3335	−0.6574	−0.4958
2.0	−1.3787	−0.2343	−1.3430	−0.4662	−1.2839	−0.6932
2.5	−2.0608	−0.3041	−2.0145	−0.6050	−1.9377	−0.8997
3.0	−2.7663	−0.3760	−2.7092	−0.7483	−2.6145	−1.1130
3.5	−3.4913	−0.4497	−3.4233	−0.8949	−3.3107	−1.3314
4.0	−4.2328	−0.5246	−4.1540	−1.0441	−4.0234	−1.5535
4.5	−4.9885	−0.6005	−4.8988	−1.1952	−4.7502	−1.7786
5.0	−5.7565	−0.6771	−5.6559	−1.3479	−5.4892	−2.0060
5.5	−6.5350	−0.7544	−6.4236	−1.5018	−6.2388	−2.2354
6.0	−7.3230	−0.8322	−7.2007	−1.6568	−6.9979	−2.4663
6.5	−8.1193	−0.9105	−7.9861	−1.8127	−7.7652	−2.6985
7.0	−8.9230	−0.9891	−8.7789	−1.9694	−8.5400	−2.9319
7.5	−9.7334	−1.0681	−9.5784	−2.1267	−9.3214	−3.1662
8.0	−10.5499	−1.1474	−10.3839	−2.2845	−10.1088	−3.4015
8.5	−11.3719	−1.2269	−11.1950	−2.4429	−10.9018	−3.6375
9.0	−12.1989	−1.3066	−12.0111	−2.6018	−11.6998	−3.8742
9.5	−13.0305	−1.3866	−12.8318	−2.7611	−12.5024	−4.1115
10.0	−13.8665	−1.4668	−13.6568	−2.9208	−13.3092	−4.3494
10.5	−14.7064	−1.5471	−14.4857	−3.0808	−14.1200	−4.5878
11.0	−15.5499	−1.6276	−15.3183	−3.2412	−14.9344	−4.8267
11.5	−16.3970	−1.7083	−16.1544	−3.4018	−15.7523	−5.0661
12.0	−17.2472	−1.7891	−16.9936	−3.5628	−16.5734	−5.3059
12.5	−18.1004	−1.8700	−17.8359	−3.7240	−17.3974	−5.5461
13.0	−18.9565	−1.9510	−18.6810	−3.8854	−18.2243	−5.7867
13.5	−19.8153	−2.0322	−19.5288	−4.0471	−19.0538	−6.0276
14.0	−20.6766	−2.1135	−20.3791	−4.2090	−19.8859	−6.2688
14.5	−21.5403	−2.1949	−21.2317	−4.3712	−20.7203	−6.5104
15.0	−22.4062	−2.2764	−22.0867	−4.5335	−21.5570	−6.7522
15.5	−23.2743	−2.3579	−22.9438	−4.6960	−22.3958	−6.9944
16.0	−24.1445	−2.4396	−23.8029	−4.8587	−23.2366	−7.2368
16.5	−25.0166	−2.5214	−24.6640	−5.0215	−24.0794	−7.4794
17.0	−25.8906	−2.6032	−25.5270	−5.1845	−24.9241	−7.7223
17.5	−26.7664	−2.6851	−26.3917	−5.3477	−25.7705	−7.9654
18.0	−27.6439	−2.7671	−27.2582	−5.5110	−26.6187	−8.2088
18.5	−28.5230	−2.8492	−28.1263	−5.6745	−27.4684	−8.4523
19.0	−29.4038	−2.9313	−28.9959	−5.8381	−28.3198	−8.6961
19.5	−30.2860	−3.0135	−29.8671	−6.0018	−29.1726	−8.9401
20.0	−31.1697	−3.0957	−30.7397	−6.1656	−30.0269	−9.1842
20.5	−32.0548	−3.1780	−31.6137	−6.3296	−30.8825	−9.4285
21.0	−32.9412	−3.2604	−32.4891	−6.4937	−31.7395	−9.6730
21.5	−33.8289	−3.3428	−33.3657	−6.6579	−32.5978	−9.9177
22.0	−34.7179	−3.4253	−34.2436	−6.8222	−33.4573	−10.1626
22.5	−35.6081	−3.5079	−35.1228	−6.9867	−34.3181	−10.4076
23.0	−36.4995	−3.5904	−36.0031	−7.1512	−35.1800	−10.6527
23.5	−37.3920	−3.6731	−36.8845	−7.3158	−36.0430	−10.8980
24.0	−38.2856	−3.7558	−37.7670	−7.4805	−36.9072	−11.1434
24.5	−39.1803	−3.8385	−38.6506	−7.6453	−37.7723	−11.3890
25.0	−40.0760	−3.9213	−39.5352	−7.8102	−38.6385	−11.6347

TABLE II. $b_r(q) = U + iV, \quad q = \rho e^{i\phi}$ $r = 1$

ρ	$\phi=20°$		$\phi=25°$		$\phi=30°$	
	U	V	U	V	U	V
0.0	1.0000	0.0000	1.0000	0.0000	1.0000	0.0000
0.5	0.5072	-0.1895	0.5273	-0.2334	0.5514	-0.2752
1.0	-0.0277	-0.4097	0.0176	-0.5041	0.0720	-0.5933
1.5	-0.5992	-0.6529	-0.5254	-0.8031	-0.4369	-0.9447
2.0	-1.2019	-0.9129	-1.0979	-1.1230	-0.9730	-1.3212
2.5	-1.8313	-1.1852	-1.6961	-1.4584	-1.5336	-1.7164
3.0	-2.4833	-1.4666	-2.3165	-1.8052	-2.1157	-2.1255
3.5	-3.1545	-1.7547	-2.9559	-2.1605	-2.7167	-2.5449
4.0	-3.8421	-2.0479	-3.6116	-2.5223	-3.3339	-2.9722
4.5	-4.5438	-2.3450	-4.2814	-2.8891	-3.9652	-3.4055
5.0	-5.2577	-2.6453	-4.9634	-3.2598	-4.6087	-3.8435
5.5	-5.9823	-2.9482	-5.6561	-3.6336	-5.2629	-4.2853
6.0	-6.7162	-3.2531	-6.3581	-4.0101	-5.9264	-4.7302
6.5	-7.4585	-3.5598	-7.0685	-4.3888	-6.5983	-5.1778
7.0	-8.2082	-3.8680	-7.7862	-4.7693	-7.2776	-5.6275
7.5	-8.9645	-4.1775	-8.5106	-5.1514	-7.9634	-6.0792
8.0	-9.7268	-4.4882	-9.2410	-5.5350	-8.6553	-6.5326
8.5	-10.4947	-4.7999	-9.9768	-5.9199	-9.3526	-6.9875
9.0	-11.2675	-5.1125	-10.7177	-6.3059	-10.0548	-7.4437
9.5	-12.0449	-5.4259	-11.4630	-6.6929	-10.7616	-7.9012
10.0	-12.8265	-5.7401	-12.2126	-7.0809	-11.4725	-8.3598
10.5	-13.6121	-6.0550	-12.9661	-7.4697	-12.1873	-8.8195
11.0	-14.4013	-6.3706	-13.7232	-7.8594	-12.9057	-9.2801
11.5	-15.1939	-6.6868	-14.4837	-8.2498	-13.6274	-9.7416
12.0	-15.9897	-7.0035	-15.2473	-8.6409	-14.3523	-10.2039
12.5	-16.7885	-7.3207	-16.0139	-9.0326	-15.0801	-10.6670
13.0	-17.5900	-7.6385	-16.7833	-9.4250	-15.8106	-11.1308
13.5	-18.3942	-7.9567	-17.5553	-9.8179	-16.5437	-11.5953
14.0	-19.2009	-8.2753	-18.3298	-10.2114	-17.2793	-12.0605
14.5	-20.0100	-8.5944	-19.1066	-10.6054	-18.0172	-12.5262
15.0	-20.8213	-8.9138	-19.8856	-10.9999	-18.7573	-12.9926
15.5	-21.6347	-9.2336	-20.6667	-11.3948	-19.4995	-13.4595
16.0	-22.4502	-9.5538	-21.4499	-11.7902	-20.2437	-13.9270
16.5	-23.2676	-9.8743	-22.2349	-12.1860	-20.9898	-14.3949
17.0	-24.0868	-10.1951	-23.0218	-12.5822	-21.7376	-14.8633
17.5	-24.9078	-10.5163	-23.8105	-12.9788	-22.4872	-15.3322
18.0	-25.7305	-10.8377	-24.6008	-13.3758	-23.2385	-15.8015
18.5	-26.5548	-11.1594	-25.3927	-13.7731	-23.9914	-16.2713
19.0	-27.3807	-11.4814	-26.1862	-14.1707	-24.7457	-16.7414
19.5	-28.2080	-11.8037	-26.9811	-14.5687	-25.5016	-17.2120
20.0	-29.0368	-12.1262	-27.7775	-14.9670	-26.2588	-17.6829
20.5	-29.8670	-12.4489	-28.5752	-15.3656	-27.0174	-18.1542
21.0	-30.6985	-12.7719	-29.3743	-15.7645	-27.7773	-18.6258
21.5	-31.5313	-13.0951	-30.1746	-16.1637	-28.5385	-19.0977
22.0	-32.3653	-13.4185	-30.9761	-16.5631	-29.3009	-19.5700
22.5	-33.2005	-13.7422	-31.7789	-16.9628	-30.0644	-20.0426
23.0	-34.0369	-14.0660	-32.5827	-17.3628	-30.8291	-20.5155
23.5	-34.8744	-14.3900	-33.3877	-17.7629	-31.5949	-20.9887
24.0	-35.7129	-14.7143	-34.1938	-18.1634	-32.3617	-21.4622
24.5	-36.5526	-15.0387	-35.0009	-18.5640	-33.1296	-21.9359
25.0	-37.3932	-15.3632	-35.8090	-18.9649	-33.8985	-22.4099

ρ	$\phi=35°$		$\phi=40°$		$\phi=45°$	
	U	V	U	V	U	V
0.0	1.0000	0.0000	1.0000	0.0000	1.0000	0.0000
0.5	0.5793	-0.3143	0.6106	-0.3505	0.6451	-0.3834
1.0	0.1348	-0.6764	0.2053	-0.7525	0.2827	-0.8209
1.5	-0.3346	-1.0764	-0.2196	-1.1965	-0.0932	-1.3039
2.0	-0.8284	-1.5055	-0.6656	-1.6736	-0.4863	-1.8237
2.5	-1.3452	-1.9565	-1.1327	-2.1760	-0.8983	-2.3723
3.0	-1.8828	-2.4240	-1.6199	-2.6976	-1.3293	-2.9430
3.5	-2.4390	-2.9038	-2.1252	-3.2335	-1.7780	-3.5303
4.0	-3.0113	-3.3929	-2.6466	-3.7802	-2.2428	-4.1300
4.5	-3.5977	-3.8891	-3.1821	-4.3351	-2.7218	-4.7390
5.0	-4.1964	-4.3908	-3.7301	-4.8964	-3.2134	-5.3553
5.5	-4.8058	-4.8970	-4.2888	-5.4628	-3.7158	-5.9773
6.0	-5.4247	-5.4067	-4.8569	-6.0333	-4.2277	-6.6038
6.5	-6.0518	-5.9195	-5.4334	-6.6071	-4.7480	-7.2341
7.0	-6.6863	-6.4349	-6.0172	-7.1839	-5.2757	-7.8676
7.5	-7.3274	-6.9524	-6.6076	-7.7631	-5.8100	-8.5038
8.0	-7.9745	-7.4719	-7.2040	-8.3445	-6.3502	-9.1424
8.5	-8.6269	-7.9932	-7.8057	-8.9279	-6.8956	-9.7832
9.0	-9.2843	-8.5160	-8.4123	-9.5131	-7.4459	-10.4259
9.5	-9.9461	-9.0402	-9.0233	-10.0998	-8.0006	-11.0704
10.0	-10.6121	-9.5658	-9.6384	-10.6880	-8.5593	-11.7165
10.5	-11.2819	-10.0925	-10.2573	-11.2775	-9.1217	-12.3641
11.0	-11.9553	-10.6203	-10.8797	-11.8683	-9.6876	-13.0130
11.5	-12.6320	-11.1492	-11.5054	-12.4602	-10.2567	-13.6633
12.0	-13.3117	-11.6790	-12.1341	-13.0533	-10.8288	-14.3147
12.5	-13.9944	-12.2097	-12.7656	-13.6473	-11.4037	-14.9673
13.0	-14.6798	-12.7412	-13.3999	-14.2423	-11.9813	-15.6210
13.5	-15.3677	-13.2736	-14.0366	-14.8382	-12.5613	-16.2756
14.0	-16.0581	-13.8067	-14.6758	-15.4350	-13.1436	-16.9312
14.5	-16.7507	-14.3405	-15.3172	-16.0326	-13.7282	-17.5878
15.0	-17.4455	-14.8750	-15.9607	-16.6309	-14.3149	-18.2451
15.5	-18.1424	-15.4102	-16.6063	-17.2300	-14.9036	-18.9033
16.0	-18.8413	-15.9459	-17.2538	-17.8298	-15.4941	-19.5623
16.5	-19.5420	-16.4822	-17.9032	-18.4302	-16.0865	-20.2220
17.0	-20.2445	-17.0191	-18.5543	-19.0313	-16.6806	-20.8824
17.5	-20.9487	-17.5566	-19.2071	-19.6329	-17.2764	-21.5435
18.0	-21.6545	-18.0945	-19.8615	-20.2352	-17.8737	-22.2053
18.5	-22.3619	-18.6329	-20.5175	-20.8380	-18.4726	-22.8677
19.0	-23.0709	-19.1718	-21.1749	-21.4413	-19.0729	-23.5306
19.5	-23.7812	-19.7112	-21.8337	-22.0452	-19.6747	-24.1942
20.0	-24.4930	-20.2510	-22.4940	-22.6495	-20.2777	-24.8583
20.5	-25.2061	-20.7912	-23.1555	-23.2544	-20.8821	-25.5229
21.0	-25.9204	-21.3318	-23.8183	-23.8596	-21.4877	-26.1881
21.5	-26.6360	-21.8728	-24.4823	-24.4654	-22.0945	-26.8537
22.0	-27.3529	-22.4141	-25.1476	-25.0715	-22.7025	-27.5198
22.5	-28.0708	-22.9559	-25.8139	-25.6781	-23.3116	-28.1864
23.0	-28.7899	-23.4979	-26.4814	-26.2851	-23.9218	-28.8534
23.5	-29.5101	-24.0404	-27.1499	-26.8924	-24.5330	-29.5209
24.0	-30.2313	-24.5831	-27.8195	-27.5002	-25.1452	-30.1888
24.5	-30.9536	-25.1262	-28.4900	-28.1082	-25.7585	-30.8570
25.0	-31.6768	-25.6696	-29.1616	-28.7167	-26.3727	-31.5257

TABLE II. $b_r(q) = U + iV$, $q = \rho e^{i\phi}$ $r = 1$

ρ	$\phi=50°$		$\phi=55°$		$\phi=60°$	
	U	V	U	V	U	V
0.0	1.0000	0.0000	1.0000	0.0000	1.0000	0.0000
0.5	0.6824	−0.4128	0.7220	−0.4384	0.7637	−0.4600
1.0	0.3661	−0.8809	0.4546	−0.9319	0.5471	−0.9735
1.5	0.0432	−1.3972	0.1879	−1.4755	0.3393	−1.5379
2.0	−0.2924	−1.9540	−0.0861	−2.0628	0.1303	−2.1488
2.5	−0.6442	−2.5432	−0.3731	−2.6863	−0.0876	−2.7997
3.0	−1.0137	−3.1575	−0.6760	−3.3382	−0.3196	−3.4828
3.5	−1.4004	−3.7908	−0.9958	−4.0119	−0.5677	−4.1907
4.0	−1.8033	−4.4383	−1.3318	−4.7018	−0.8322	−4.9171
4.5	−2.2206	−5.0965	−1.6825	−5.4037	−1.1119	−5.6569
5.0	−2.6506	−5.7628	−2.0462	−6.1145	−1.4051	−6.4067
5.5	−3.0916	−6.4353	−2.4212	−6.8322	−1.7100	−7.1639
6.0	−3.5423	−7.1128	−2.8061	−7.5553	−2.0250	−7.9268
6.5	−4.0014	−7.7945	−3.1994	−8.2828	−2.3486	−8.6943
7.0	−4.4679	−8.4796	−3.6002	−9.0140	−2.6798	−9.4656
7.5	−4.9410	−9.1676	−4.0076	−9.7483	−3.0175	−10.2402
8.0	−5.4199	−9.8583	−4.4208	−10.4853	−3.3609	−11.0177
8.5	−5.9041	−10.5512	−4.8391	−11.2248	−3.7095	−11.7977
9.0	−6.3930	−11.2463	−5.2622	−11.9666	−4.0626	−12.5801
9.5	−6.8863	−11.9433	−5.6895	−12.7104	−4.4199	−13.3647
10.0	−7.3835	−12.6420	−6.1207	−13.4561	−4.7810	−14.1512
10.5	−7.8844	−13.3423	−6.5555	−14.2035	−5.1456	−14.9396
11.0	−8.3887	−14.0442	−6.9935	−14.9526	−5.5134	−15.7297
11.5	−8.8962	−14.7475	−7.4347	−15.7032	−5.8842	−16.5215
12.0	−9.4065	−15.4521	−7.8787	−16.4552	−6.2578	−17.3149
12.5	−9.9196	−16.1579	−8.3254	−17.2086	−6.6340	−18.1097
13.0	−10.4353	−16.8650	−8.7747	−17.9632	−7.0126	−18.9059
13.5	−10.9535	−17.5731	−9.2263	−18.7191	−7.3936	−19.7034
14.0	−11.4739	−18.2823	−9.6801	−19.4761	−7.7767	−20.5021
14.5	−11.9965	−18.9925	−10.1361	−20.2342	−8.1619	−21.3020
15.0	−12.5212	−19.7036	−10.5940	−20.9934	−8.5490	−22.1030
15.5	−13.0478	−20.4156	−11.0539	−21.7535	−8.9381	−22.9051
16.0	−13.5763	−21.1285	−11.5157	−22.5146	−9.3289	−23.7082
16.5	−14.1065	−21.8422	−11.9791	−23.2765	−9.7213	−24.5123
17.0	−14.6385	−22.5567	−12.4442	−24.0393	−10.1154	−25.3173
17.5	−15.1720	−23.2719	−12.9109	−24.8030	−10.5111	−26.1232
18.0	−15.7072	−23.9879	−13.3791	−25.5674	−10.9082	−26.9300
18.5	−16.2438	−24.7045	−13.8488	−26.3326	−11.3068	−27.7375
19.0	−16.7818	−25.4218	−14.3198	−27.0985	−11.7067	−28.5459
19.5	−17.3212	−26.1397	−14.7922	−27.8650	−12.1079	−29.3550
20.0	−17.8620	−26.8583	−15.2659	−28.6323	−12.5104	−30.1648
20.5	−18.4040	−27.5774	−15.7409	−29.4002	−12.9141	−30.9753
21.0	−18.9472	−28.2971	−16.2170	−30.1687	−13.3189	−31.7865
21.5	−19.4916	−29.0174	−16.6943	−30.9378	−13.7249	−32.5984
22.0	−20.0371	−29.7382	−17.1727	−31.7075	−14.1320	−33.4108
22.5	−20.5838	−30.4594	−17.6522	−32.4778	−14.5401	−34.2239
23.0	−21.1315	−31.1812	−18.1327	−33.2486	−14.9493	−35.0376
23.5	−21.6802	−31.9035	−18.6142	−34.0199	−15.3594	−35.8518
24.0	−22.2299	−32.6262	−19.0967	−34.7917	−15.7705	−36.6666
24.5	−22.7806	−33.3494	−19.5802	−35.5640	−16.1825	−37.4819
25.0	−23.3323	−34.0730	−20.0645	−36.3368	−16.5954	−38.2977

TABLE II. $b_r(q) = U + iV$, $q = \rho e^{i\phi}$ $\qquad\qquad\qquad r = 1$

ρ	φ=65°		φ=70°		φ=75°	
	U	V	U	V	U	V
0.0	1.0000	0.0000	1.0000	0.0000	1.0000	0.0000
0.5	0.8069	−0.4776	0.8512	−0.4909	0.8962	−0.4999
1.0	0.6426	−1.0053	0.7398	−1.0271	0.8378	−1.0389
1.5	0.4955	−1.5837	0.6545	−1.6123	0.8144	−1.6236
2.0	0.3543	−2.2107	0.5831	−2.2475	0.8138	−2.2584
2.5	0.2090	−2.8815	0.5136	−2.9301	0.8225	−2.9440
3.0	0.0524	−3.5887	0.4361	−3.6538	0.8276	−3.6760
3.5	−0.1198	−4.3243	0.3440	−4.4103	0.8197	−4.4463
4.0	−0.3086	−5.0811	0.2348	−5.1912	0.7938	−5.2449
4.5	−0.5133	−5.8531	0.1086	−5.9893	0.7492	−6.0631
5.0	−0.7322	−6.6359	−0.0329	−6.7992	0.6877	−6.8943
5.5	−0.9635	−7.4267	−0.1876	−7.6175	0.6119	−7.7341
6.0	−1.2052	−8.2234	−0.3532	−8.4419	0.5244	−8.5798
6.5	−1.4558	−9.0248	−0.5280	−9.2709	0.4273	−9.4299
7.0	−1.7139	−9.8301	−0.7105	−10.1037	0.3224	−10.2835
7.5	−1.9786	−10.6387	−0.8994	−10.9397	0.2111	−11.1402
8.0	−2.2489	−11.4503	−1.0940	−11.7787	0.0944	−11.9997
8.5	−2.5243	−12.2644	−1.2934	−12.6203	−0.0270	−12.8617
9.0	−2.8042	−13.0810	−1.4972	−13.4643	−0.1525	−13.7262
9.5	−3.0880	−13.8998	−1.7048	−14.3107	−0.2816	−14.5931
10.0	−3.3756	−14.7208	−1.9159	−15.1593	−0.4140	−15.4621
10.5	−3.6665	−15.5437	−2.1302	−16.0099	−0.5495	−16.3334
11.0	−3.9605	−16.3684	−2.3475	−16.8625	−0.6877	−17.2067
11.5	−4.2574	−17.1950	−2.5676	−17.7169	−0.8286	−18.0820
12.0	−4.5570	−18.0231	−2.7902	−18.5731	−0.9719	−18.9592
12.5	−4.8591	−18.8529	−3.0152	−19.4310	−1.1175	−19.8382
13.0	−5.1636	−19.6841	−3.2426	−20.2904	−1.2653	−20.7188
13.5	−5.4703	−20.5167	−3.4720	−21.1514	−1.4151	−21.6011
14.0	−5.7791	−21.3507	−3.7036	−22.0138	−1.5669	−22.4850
14.5	−6.0900	−22.1859	−3.9370	−22.8776	−1.7206	−23.3702
15.0	−6.4027	−23.0223	−4.1723	−23.7427	−1.8760	−24.2569
15.5	−6.7172	−23.8599	−4.4094	−24.6090	−2.0332	−25.1449
16.0	−7.0335	−24.6986	−4.6481	−25.4765	−2.1919	−26.0342
16.5	−7.3514	−25.5383	−4.8884	−26.3451	−2.3522	−26.9246
17.0	−7.6709	−26.3791	−5.1303	−27.2147	−2.5140	−27.8162
17.5	−7.9919	−27.2208	−5.3736	−28.0854	−2.6772	−28.7089
18.0	−8.3143	−28.0634	−5.6183	−28.9571	−2.8418	−29.6026
18.5	−8.6381	−28.9068	−5.8643	−29.8297	−3.0076	−30.4974
19.0	−8.9633	−29.7512	−6.1117	−30.7032	−3.1747	−31.3931
19.5	−9.2897	−30.5963	−6.3603	−31.5776	−3.3431	−32.2897
20.0	−9.6174	−31.4422	−6.6100	−32.4529	−3.5125	−33.1872
20.5	−9.9462	−32.2889	−6.8610	−33.3289	−3.6831	−34.0855
21.0	−10.2761	−33.1363	−7.1130	−34.2057	−3.8548	−34.9847
21.5	−10.6072	−33.9843	−7.3661	−35.0832	−4.0274	−35.8847
22.0	−10.9393	−34.8331	−7.6202	−35.9615	−4.2011	−36.7854
22.5	−11.2725	−35.6825	−7.8753	−36.8404	−4.3758	−37.6868
23.0	−11.6066	−36.5325	−8.1314	−37.7200	−4.5514	−38.5890
23.5	−11.9417	−37.3832	−8.3884	−38.6003	−4.7279	−39.4919
24.0	−12.2777	−38.2344	−8.6463	−39.4812	−4.9052	−40.3954
24.5	−12.6147	−39.0862	−8.9051	−40.3627	−5.0834	−41.2996
25.0	−12.9525	−39.9385	−9.1648	−41.2448	−5.2625	−42.2044

TABLE II. $b_r(q) = U + iV$, $q = \rho e^{i\phi}$ $\qquad r=1$

ρ	$\phi=80°$		$\phi=85°$		$\phi=90°$	
	U	V	U	V	U	V
0.0	1.0000	0.0000	1.0000	0.0000	1.0000	0.0000
0.5	0.9415	-0.5048	0.9866	-0.5054	1.0312	-0.5020
1.0	0.9352	-1.0408	1.0311	-1.0330	1.1243	-1.0159
1.5	0.9728	-1.6175	1.1278	-1.5944	1.2770	-1.5549
2.0	1.0431	-2.2430	1.2677	-2.2012	1.4838	-2.1334
2.5	1.1317	-2.9219	1.4370	-2.8630	1.7332	-2.7663
3.0	1.2229	-3.6533	1.6173	-3.5837	2.0057	-3.4648
3.5	1.3030	-4.4297	1.7898	-4.3582	2.2760	-4.2286
4.0	1.3641	-5.2399	1.9418	-5.1737	2.5235	-5.0442
4.5	1.4040	-6.0726	2.0688	-6.0159	2.7401	-5.8918
5.0	1.4245	-6.9193	2.1728	-6.8732	2.9281	-6.7555
5.5	1.4291	-7.7747	2.2582	-7.7386	3.0938	-7.6259
6.0	1.4208	-8.6355	2.3294	-8.6084	3.2435	-8.4988
6.5	1.4026	-9.5001	2.3901	-9.4809	3.3822	-9.3726
7.0	1.3764	-10.3678	2.4429	-10.3555	3.5130	-10.2471
7.5	1.3440	-11.2381	2.4896	-11.2322	3.6384	-11.1226
8.0	1.3064	-12.1109	2.5316	-12.1109	3.7596	-11.9995
8.5	1.2644	-12.9861	2.5697	-12.9918	3.8775	-12.8783
9.0	1.2186	-13.8637	2.6044	-13.8750	3.9928	-13.7593
9.5	1.1695	-14.7437	2.6362	-14.7605	4.1058	-14.6426
10.0	1.1174	-15.6260	2.6654	-15.6485	4.2166	-15.5284
10.5	1.0625	-16.5106	2.6921	-16.5388	4.3253	-16.4168
11.0	1.0050	-17.3973	2.7164	-17.4315	4.4321	-17.3077
11.5	0.9451	-18.2862	2.7386	-18.3264	4.5369	-18.2011
12.0	0.8829	-19.1770	2.7587	-19.2236	4.6399	-19.0969
12.5	0.8185	-20.0698	2.7767	-20.1228	4.7410	-19.9950
13.0	0.7521	-20.9645	2.7928	-21.0239	4.8402	-20.8952
13.5	0.6836	-21.8608	2.8071	-21.9270	4.9377	-21.7976
14.0	0.6134	-22.7589	2.8195	-22.8319	5.0335	-22.7018
14.5	0.5413	-23.6584	2.8302	-23.7384	5.1276	-23.6079
15.0	0.4675	-24.5595	2.8393	-24.6465	5.2201	-24.5157
15.5	0.3921	-25.4620	2.8468	-25.5562	5.3110	-25.4251
16.0	0.3151	-26.3658	2.8528	-26.4673	5.4005	-26.3361
16.5	0.2366	-27.2709	2.8573	-27.3797	5.4885	-27.2485
17.0	0.1567	-28.1772	2.8604	-28.2934	5.5752	-28.1622
17.5	0.0754	-29.0847	2.8622	-29.2083	5.6606	-29.0772
18.0	-0.0072	-29.9933	2.8627	-30.1244	5.7447	-29.9934
18.5	-0.0910	-30.9029	2.8620	-31.0417	5.8277	-30.9108
19.0	-0.1761	-31.8136	2.8601	-31.9599	5.9095	-31.8294
19.5	-0.2623	-32.7252	2.8571	-32.8793	5.9902	-32.7489
20.0	-0.3497	-33.6378	2.8530	-33.7995	6.0698	-33.6695
20.5	-0.4381	-34.5513	2.8479	-34.7208	6.1485	-34.5911
21.0	-0.5276	-35.4656	2.8417	-35.6429	6.2262	-35.5136
21.5	-0.6181	-36.3808	2.8346	-36.5659	6.3029	-36.4371
22.0	-0.7095	-37.2967	2.8266	-37.4898	6.3788	-37.3614
22.5	-0.8019	-38.2135	2.8176	-38.4144	6.4538	-38.2865
23.0	-0.8952	-39.1310	2.8078	-39.3399	6.5279	-39.2125
23.5	-0.9894	-40.0492	2.7972	-40.2661	6.6013	-40.1392
24.0	-1.0844	-40.9681	2.7857	-41.1931	6.6739	-41.0668
24.5	-1.1802	-41.8877	2.7734	-42.1207	6.7457	-41.9950
25.0	-1.2768	-42.8080	2.7604	-43.0491	6.8168	-42.9240

322-566 O - 69 - 9

TABLE II. $b_r(q) = U + iV$, $q = \rho e^{i\phi}$ $r = 2$

ρ	$\phi = 5°$		$\phi = 10°$		$\phi = 15°$	
	U	V	U	V	U	V
0.0	4.0000	0.0000	4.0000	0.0000	4.0000	0.0000
0.5	3.9795	−0.0036	3.9804	−0.0071	3.9820	−0.0104
1.0	3.9183	−0.0143	3.9220	−0.0283	3.9280	−0.0414
1.5	3.8170	−0.0320	3.8252	−0.0630	3.8385	−0.0922
2.0	3.6770	−0.0560	3.6911	−0.1105	3.7142	−0.1619
2.5	3.4996	−0.0860	3.5210	−0.1698	3.5560	−0.2490
3.0	3.2868	−0.1214	3.3164	−0.2397	3.3650	−0.3520
3.5	3.0406	−0.1615	3.0792	−0.3192	3.1427	−0.4693
4.0	2.7630	−0.2058	2.8112	−0.4069	2.8905	−0.5990
4.5	2.4562	−0.2536	2.5143	−0.5020	2.6103	−0.7397
5.0	2.1223	−0.3046	2.1907	−0.6032	2.3036	−0.8899
5.5	1.7634	−0.3582	1.8421	−0.7098	1.9722	−1.0481
6.0	1.3812	−0.4141	1.4704	−0.8209	1.6178	−1.2132
6.5	0.9777	−0.4720	1.0773	−0.9360	1.2422	−1.3842
7.0	0.5544	−0.5314	0.6645	−1.0543	0.8467	−1.5602
7.5	0.1128	−0.5923	0.2334	−1.1755	0.4330	−1.7406
8.0	−0.3456	−0.6545	−0.2146	−1.2992	0.0024	−1.9246
8.5	−0.8196	−0.7177	−0.6782	−1.4250	−0.4440	−2.1119
9.0	−1.3081	−0.7818	−1.1563	−1.5527	−0.9049	−2.3020
9.5	−1.8100	−0.8467	−1.6479	−1.6820	−1.3794	−2.4945
10.0	−2.3245	−0.9124	−2.1521	−1.8128	−1.8664	−2.6892
10.5	−2.8507	−0.9787	−2.6679	−1.9448	−2.3652	−2.8858
11.0	−3.3878	−1.0456	−3.1948	−2.0781	−2.8749	−3.0842
11.5	−3.9352	−1.1131	−3.7318	−2.2123	−3.3949	−3.2841
12.0	−4.4921	−1.1810	−4.2785	−2.3476	−3.9245	−3.4855
12.5	−5.0581	−1.2493	−4.8342	−2.4837	−4.4632	−3.6882
13.0	−5.6327	−1.3181	−5.3985	−2.6207	−5.0104	−3.8921
13.5	−6.2153	−1.3873	−5.9708	−2.7583	−5.5657	−4.0972
14.0	−6.8055	−1.4568	−6.5507	−2.8967	−6.1285	−4.3032
14.5	−7.4030	−1.5266	−7.1378	−3.0358	−6.6986	−4.5103
15.0	−8.0073	−1.5968	−7.7318	−3.1755	−7.2755	−4.7183
15.5	−8.6181	−1.6672	−8.3323	−3.3157	−7.8588	−4.9271
16.0	−9.2351	−1.7379	−8.9390	−3.4565	−8.4484	−5.1368
16.5	−9.8581	−1.8089	−9.5516	−3.5979	−9.0439	−5.3472
17.0	−10.4867	−1.8801	−10.1699	−3.7397	−9.6449	−5.5583
17.5	−11.1207	−1.9516	−10.7935	−3.8820	−10.2514	−5.7702
18.0	−11.7599	−2.0232	−11.4223	−4.0247	−10.8630	−5.9828
18.5	−12.4040	−2.0951	−12.0561	−4.1679	−11.4795	−6.1959
19.0	−13.0529	−2.1672	−12.6946	−4.3114	−12.1008	−6.4097
19.5	−13.7064	−2.2395	−13.3376	−4.4554	−12.7266	−6.6241
20.0	−14.3643	−2.3120	−13.9851	−4.5997	−13.3568	−6.8390
20.5	−15.0264	−2.3847	−14.6368	−4.7444	−13.9911	−7.0545
21.0	−15.6926	−2.4575	−15.2925	−4.8895	−14.6296	−7.2705
21.5	−16.3627	−2.5306	−15.9522	−5.0349	−15.2719	−7.4870
22.0	−17.0366	−2.6037	−16.6156	−5.1806	−15.9180	−7.7040
22.5	−17.7142	−2.6771	−17.2827	−5.3267	−16.5677	−7.9215
23.0	−18.3953	−2.7506	−17.9534	−5.4730	−17.2210	−8.1394
23.5	−19.0799	−2.8242	−18.6274	−5.6196	−17.8776	−8.3578
24.0	−19.7678	−2.8980	−19.3048	−5.7665	−18.5376	−8.5766
24.5	−20.4589	−2.9719	−19.9854	−5.9137	−19.2007	−8.7958
25.0	−21.1531	−3.0459	−20.6690	−6.0612	−19.8670	−9.0154

TABLE II. $b_r(q) = U + iV$, $q = \rho e^{i\phi}$ $r = 2$

ρ	$\phi = 20°$		$\phi = 25°$		$\phi = 30°$	
	U	V	U	V	U	V
0.0	4.0000	0.0000	4.0000	0.0000	4.0000	0.0000
0.5	3.9840	-0.0134	3.9866	-0.0159	3.9896	-0.0180
1.0	3.9362	-0.0532	3.9464	-0.0635	3.9582	-0.0719
1.5	3.8567	-0.1188	3.8792	-0.1419	3.9054	-0.1608
2.0	3.7458	-0.2088	3.7849	-0.2498	3.8307	-0.2837
2.5	3.6039	-0.3216	3.6635	-0.3855	3.7334	-0.4389
3.0	3.4316	-0.4554	3.5148	-0.5471	3.6128	-0.6244
3.5	3.2299	-0.6081	3.3393	-0.7321	3.4685	-0.8378
4.0	2.9998	-0.7776	3.1372	-0.9382	3.3002	-1.0766
4.5	2.7426	-0.9617	2.9092	-1.1628	3.1077	-1.3379
5.0	2.4595	-1.1586	2.6564	-1.4036	2.8916	-1.6191
5.5	2.1521	-1.3664	2.3798	-1.6583	2.6523	-1.9174
6.0	1.8220	-1.5836	2.0806	-1.9250	2.3907	-2.2305
6.5	1.4706	-1.8087	1.7602	-2.2019	2.1081	-2.5561
7.0	1.0994	-2.0407	1.4200	-2.4874	1.8054	-2.8924
7.5	0.7099	-2.2784	1.0613	-2.7803	1.4841	-3.2377
8.0	0.3033	-2.5212	0.6855	-3.0795	1.1454	-3.5906
8.5	-0.1191	-2.7682	0.2937	-3.3841	0.7906	-3.9500
9.0	-0.5561	-3.0190	-0.1129	-3.6934	0.4207	-4.3151
9.5	-1.0067	-3.2730	-0.5332	-4.0067	0.0370	-4.6850
10.0	-1.4699	-3.5299	-0.9662	-4.3236	-0.3596	-5.0591
10.5	-1.9450	-3.7894	-1.4111	-4.6437	-0.7682	-5.4370
11.0	-2.4310	-4.0512	-1.8671	-4.9666	-1.1879	-5.8182
11.5	-2.9274	-4.3151	-2.3333	-5.2920	-1.6180	-6.2025
12.0	-3.4334	-4.5808	-2.8093	-5.6198	-2.0577	-6.5895
12.5	-3.9484	-4.8483	-3.2942	-5.9498	-2.5065	-6.9789
13.0	-4.4719	-5.1174	-3.7877	-6.2816	-2.9639	-7.3707
13.5	-5.0035	-5.3879	-4.2892	-6.6154	-3.4292	-7.7646
14.0	-5.5427	-5.6599	-4.7983	-6.9508	-3.9020	-8.1605
14.5	-6.0890	-5.9331	-5.3146	-7.2877	-4.3820	-8.5583
15.0	-6.6422	-6.2075	-5.8376	-7.6262	-4.8688	-8.9578
15.5	-7.2018	-6.4831	-6.3670	-7.9661	-5.3619	-9.3590
16.0	-7.7676	-6.7598	-6.9026	-8.3073	-5.8611	-9.7618
16.5	-8.3393	-7.0375	-7.4440	-8.6498	-6.3660	-10.1661
17.0	-8.9165	-7.3161	-7.9910	-8.9935	-6.8765	-10.5718
17.5	-9.4991	-7.5957	-8.5433	-9.3384	-7.3923	-10.9788
18.0	-10.0868	-7.8762	-9.1006	-9.6843	-7.9131	-11.3872
18.5	-10.6794	-8.1575	-9.6628	-10.0313	-8.4387	-11.7968
19.0	-11.2768	-8.4396	-10.2297	-10.3793	-8.9689	-12.2076
19.5	-11.8786	-8.7226	-10.8011	-10.7283	-9.5036	-12.6195
20.0	-12.4848	-9.0062	-11.3768	-11.0782	-10.0425	-13.0326
20.5	-13.0951	-9.2906	-11.9566	-11.4290	-10.5855	-13.4467
21.0	-13.7095	-9.5757	-12.5404	-11.7806	-11.1325	-13.8619
21.5	-14.3278	-9.8614	-13.1281	-12.1331	-11.6833	-14.2780
22.0	-14.9498	-10.1478	-13.7195	-12.4864	-12.2377	-14.6951
22.5	-15.5754	-10.4348	-14.3144	-12.8404	-12.7957	-15.1131
23.0	-16.2045	-10.7224	-14.9128	-13.1952	-13.3571	-15.5320
23.5	-16.8370	-11.0106	-15.5146	-13.5508	-13.9219	-15.9518
24.0	-17.4728	-11.2994	-16.1196	-13.9070	-14.4898	-16.3724
24.5	-18.1117	-11.5887	-16.7278	-14.2639	-15.0609	-16.7939
25.0	-18.7538	-11.8785	-17.3390	-14.6215	-15.6350	-17.2161

TABLE II. $b_r(q) = U + iV$, $q = \rho e^{i\phi}$ $r=2$

ρ	$\phi=35°$		$\phi=40°$		$\phi=45°$	
	U	V	U	V	U	V
0.0	4.0000	0.0000	4.0000	0.0000	4.0000	0.0000
0.5	3.9929	-0.0196	3.9964	-0.0205	4.0000	-0.0208
1.0	3.9712	-0.0781	3.9852	-0.0819	3.9996	-0.0833
1.5	3.9345	-0.1750	3.9657	-0.1840	3.9982	-0.1875
2.0	3.8818	-0.3094	3.9368	-0.3261	3.9942	-0.3331
2.5	3.8118	-0.4800	3.8968	-0.5074	3.9859	-0.5200
3.0	3.7234	-0.6849	3.8438	-0.7265	3.9710	-0.7474
3.5	3.6151	-0.9220	3.7757	-0.9817	3.9467	-1.0143
4.0	3.4859	-1.1887	3.6906	-1.2708	3.9103	-1.3191
4.5	3.3349	-1.4822	3.5868	-1.5909	3.8589	-1.6594
5.0	3.1617	-1.7994	3.4627	-1.9390	3.7900	-2.0323
5.5	2.9662	-2.1373	3.3176	-2.3117	3.7016	-2.4343
6.0	2.7489	-2.4930	3.1511	-2.7057	3.5926	-2.8617
6.5	2.5105	-2.8639	2.9635	-3.1179	3.4624	-3.3107
7.0	2.2520	-3.2476	2.7554	-3.5453	3.3111	-3.7777
7.5	1.9744	-3.6421	2.5278	-3.9854	3.1397	-4.2597
8.0	1.6791	-4.0456	2.2820	-4.4360	2.9490	-4.7539
8.5	1.3673	-4.4568	2.0191	-4.8955	2.7406	-5.2581
9.0	1.0403	-4.8745	1.7405	-5.3625	2.5157	-5.7706
9.5	0.6990	-5.2978	1.4473	-5.8357	2.2757	-6.2900
10.0	0.3447	-5.7260	1.1408	-6.3144	2.0220	-6.8153
10.5	-0.0217	-6.1585	0.8219	-6.7979	1.7556	-7.3456
11.0	-0.3994	-6.5948	0.4917	-7.2854	1.4776	-7.8804
11.5	-0.7875	-7.0345	0.1509	-7.7768	1.1890	-8.4192
12.0	-1.1853	-7.4772	-0.1996	-8.2715	0.8907	-8.9616
12.5	-1.5922	-7.9228	-0.5592	-8.7693	0.5832	-9.5073
13.0	-2.0076	-8.3711	-0.9273	-9.2700	0.2673	-10.0560
13.5	-2.4309	-8.8217	-1.3033	-9.7734	-0.0564	-10.6076
14.0	-2.8618	-9.2746	-1.6867	-10.2793	-0.3875	-11.1619
14.5	-3.2997	-9.7296	-2.0772	-10.7875	-0.7255	-11.7187
15.0	-3.7443	-10.1867	-2.4743	-11.2979	-1.0700	-12.2780
15.5	-4.1953	-10.6456	-2.8776	-11.8105	-1.4207	-12.8395
16.0	-4.6522	-11.1063	-3.2868	-12.3251	-1.7772	-13.4033
16.5	-5.1149	-11.5688	-3.7017	-12.8416	-2.1392	-13.9692
17.0	-5.5830	-12.0329	-4.1220	-13.3599	-2.5065	-14.5371
17.5	-6.0564	-12.4985	-4.5474	-13.8800	-2.8788	-15.1070
18.0	-6.5347	-12.9657	-4.9776	-14.4018	-3.2559	-15.6787
18.5	-7.0177	-13.4343	-5.4126	-14.9252	-3.6376	-16.2523
19.0	-7.5054	-13.9042	-5.8521	-15.4502	-4.0237	-16.8276
19.5	-7.9974	-14.3755	-6.2958	-15.9767	-4.4141	-17.4045
20.0	-8.4936	-14.8481	-6.7437	-16.5046	-4.8085	-17.9831
20.5	-8.9938	-15.3219	-7.1956	-17.0339	-5.2068	-18.5633
21.0	-9.4980	-15.7969	-7.6514	-17.5646	-5.6088	-19.1449
21.5	-10.0059	-16.2731	-8.1108	-18.0966	-6.0145	-19.7280
22.0	-10.5175	-16.7504	-8.5738	-18.6298	-6.4237	-20.3126
22.5	-11.0325	-17.2287	-9.0402	-19.1643	-6.8363	-20.8984
23.0	-11.5509	-17.7081	-9.5100	-19.6999	-7.2522	-21.4856
23.5	-12.0726	-18.1885	-9.9830	-20.2367	-7.6712	-22.0741
24.0	-12.5975	-18.6698	-10.4591	-20.7746	-8.0933	-22.6639
24.5	-13.1254	-19.1521	-10.9382	-21.3136	-8.5183	-23.2548
25.0	-13.6563	-19.6353	-11.4203	-21.8536	-8.9462	-23.8469

TABLE II. $b_r(q) = U + iV$, $q = \rho e^{i\phi}$ $r = 2$

ρ	$\phi = 50°$		$\phi = 55°$		$\phi = 60°$	
	U	V	U	V	U	V
0.0	4.0000	0.0000	4.0000	0.0000	4.0000	0.0000
0.5	4.0036	-0.0205	4.0071	-0.0196	4.0104	-0.0181
1.0	4.0141	-0.0822	4.0282	-0.0785	4.0415	-0.0725
1.5	4.0308	-0.1852	4.0627	-0.1773	4.0928	-0.1640
2.0	4.0523	-0.3300	4.1094	-0.3168	4.1635	-0.2937
2.5	4.0768	-0.5169	4.1666	-0.4980	4.2524	-0.4632
3.0	4.1016	-0.7462	4.2319	-0.7220	4.3576	-0.6746
3.5	4.1239	-1.0176	4.3022	-0.9898	4.4762	-0.9300
4.0	4.1398	-1.3305	4.3735	-1.3021	4.6045	-1.2317
4.5	4.1458	-1.6834	4.4412	-1.6586	4.7375	-1.5813
5.0	4.1380	-2.0739	4.5002	-2.0583	4.8688	-1.9797
5.5	4.1130	-2.4988	4.5454	-2.4983	4.9915	-2.4256
6.0	4.0683	-2.9539	4.5724	-2.9747	5.0986	-2.9159
6.5	4.0022	-3.4348	4.5779	-3.4825	5.1842	-3.4451
7.0	3.9144	-3.9373	4.5603	-4.0163	5.2446	-4.0063
7.5	3.8050	-4.4573	4.5193	-4.5708	5.2784	-4.5924
8.0	3.6752	-4.9914	4.4556	-5.1413	5.2862	-5.1970
8.5	3.5264	-5.5366	4.3711	-5.7243	5.2700	-5.8150
9.0	3.3600	-6.0909	4.2674	-6.3168	5.2324	-6.4427
9.5	3.1778	-6.6526	4.1468	-6.9169	5.1761	-7.0774
10.0	2.9812	-7.2204	4.0110	-7.5229	5.1036	-7.7176
10.5	2.7716	-7.7934	3.8616	-8.1341	5.0170	-8.3622
11.0	2.5501	-8.3710	3.7002	-8.7496	4.9180	-9.0107
11.5	2.3180	-8.9526	3.5280	-9.3691	4.8083	-9.6625
12.0	2.0760	-9.5379	3.3459	-9.9921	4.6889	-10.3177
12.5	1.8250	-10.1265	3.1550	-10.6185	4.5608	-10.9760
13.0	1.5656	-10.7184	2.9558	-11.2481	4.4249	-11.6373
13.5	1.2985	-11.3132	2.7491	-11.8806	4.2818	-12.3016
14.0	1.0242	-11.9109	2.5354	-12.5161	4.1319	-12.9689
14.5	0.7431	-12.5113	2.3152	-13.1545	3.9758	-13.6391
15.0	0.4557	-13.1142	2.0888	-13.7955	3.8139	-14.3121
15.5	0.1622	-13.7197	1.8566	-14.4392	3.6465	-14.9879
16.0	-0.1369	-14.3275	1.6189	-15.0855	3.4738	-15.6665
16.5	-0.4414	-14.9376	1.3760	-15.7342	3.2961	-16.3477
17.0	-0.7511	-15.5500	1.1281	-16.3854	3.1137	-17.0316
17.5	-1.0657	-16.1645	0.8755	-17.0388	2.9268	-17.7179
18.0	-1.3849	-16.7810	0.6183	-17.6945	2.7354	-18.4067
18.5	-1.7087	-17.3995	0.3568	-18.3524	2.5399	-19.0978
19.0	-2.0367	-18.0199	0.0911	-19.0123	2.3404	-19.7913
19.5	-2.3688	-18.6422	-0.1786	-19.6743	2.1370	-20.4869
20.0	-2.7050	-19.2663	-0.4521	-20.3382	1.9298	-21.1847
20.5	-3.0449	-19.8921	-0.7294	-21.0040	1.7191	-21.8846
21.0	-3.3885	-20.5195	-1.0102	-21.6717	1.5049	-22.5864
21.5	-3.7357	-21.1486	-1.2945	-22.3411	1.2873	-23.2902
22.0	-4.0863	-21.7792	-1.5822	-23.0123	1.0664	-23.9959
22.5	-4.4402	-22.4114	-1.8731	-23.6850	0.8424	-24.7033
23.0	-4.7973	-23.0450	-2.1671	-24.3594	0.6154	-25.4125
23.5	-5.1575	-23.6800	-2.4641	-25.0354	0.3854	-26.1234
24.0	-5.5207	-24.3164	-2.7641	-25.7128	0.1525	-26.8360
24.5	-5.8869	-24.9541	-3.0669	-26.3917	-0.0831	-27.5501
25.0	-6.2558	-25.5931	-3.3724	-27.0721	-0.3215	-28.2658

TABLE II. $b_r(q) = U + iV$, $q = \rho e^{i\phi}$ $r = 2$

ρ	$\phi = 65°$		$\phi = 70°$		$\phi = 75°$	
	U	V	U	V	U	V
0.0	4.0000	0.0000	4.0000	0.0000	4.0000	0.0000
0.5	4.0134	-0.0160	4.0160	-0.0134	4.0181	-0.0104
1.0	4.0535	-0.0642	4.0639	-0.0539	4.0723	-0.0420
1.5	4.1202	-0.1455	4.1439	-0.1224	4.1633	-0.0954
2.0	4.2130	-0.2612	4.2562	-0.2202	4.2916	-0.1719
2.5	4.3315	-0.4133	4.4009	-0.3495	4.4581	-0.2736
3.0	4.4744	-0.6046	4.5780	-0.5133	4.6640	-0.4033
3.5	4.6400	-0.8382	4.7869	-0.7157	4.9105	-0.5651
4.0	4.8251	-1.1182	5.0264	-0.9617	5.1986	-0.7647
4.5	5.0253	-1.4484	5.2936	-1.2579	5.5287	-1.0100
5.0	5.2339	-1.8326	5.5830	-1.6114	5.8988	-1.3120
5.5	5.4421	-2.2726	5.8851	-2.0294	6.3025	-1.6846
6.0	5.6395	-2.7674	6.1860	-2.5159	6.7247	-2.1423
6.5	5.8160	-3.3120	6.4688	-3.0690	7.1388	-2.6937
7.0	5.9641	-3.8977	6.7183	-3.6783	7.5127	-3.3300
7.5	6.0801	-4.5143	6.9259	-4.3281	7.8250	-4.0242
8.0	6.1644	-5.1523	7.0913	-5.0025	8.0742	-4.7460
8.5	6.2197	-5.8042	7.2193	-5.6899	8.2718	-5.4750
9.0	6.2501	-6.4649	7.3170	-6.3829	8.4313	-6.2017
9.5	6.2594	-7.1311	7.3907	-7.0780	8.5640	-6.9232
10.0	6.2512	-7.8013	7.4456	-7.7739	8.6775	-7.6397
10.5	6.2283	-8.4744	7.4857	-8.4702	8.7772	-8.3526
11.0	6.1931	-9.1503	7.5138	-9.1672	8.8664	-9.0633
11.5	6.1474	-9.8287	7.5321	-9.8654	8.9476	-9.7732
12.0	6.0923	-10.5097	7.5422	-10.5652	9.0222	-10.4836
12.5	6.0292	-11.1934	7.5449	-11.2672	9.0911	-11.1954
13.0	5.9587	-11.8800	7.5413	-11.9716	9.1551	-11.9094
13.5	5.8815	-12.5694	7.5318	-12.6788	9.2145	-12.6261
14.0	5.7981	-13.2618	7.5169	-13.3890	9.2696	-13.3459
14.5	5.7090	-13.9572	7.4969	-14.1023	9.3206	-14.0691
15.0	5.6144	-14.6555	7.4721	-14.8188	9.3676	-14.7958
15.5	5.5147	-15.3569	7.4427	-15.5385	9.4106	-15.5262
16.0	5.4101	-16.0612	7.4088	-16.2614	9.4497	-16.2603
16.5	5.3008	-16.7683	7.3707	-16.9875	9.4850	-16.9980
17.0	5.1871	-17.4783	7.3283	-17.7168	9.5166	-17.7392
17.5	5.0690	-18.1911	7.2820	-18.4491	9.5443	-18.4839
18.0	4.9468	-18.9065	7.2317	-19.1843	9.5684	-19.2320
18.5	4.8206	-19.6245	7.1776	-19.9225	9.5889	-19.9833
19.0	4.6905	-20.3450	7.1198	-20.6634	9.6058	-20.7377
19.5	4.5567	-21.0680	7.0584	-21.4070	9.6192	-21.4950
20.0	4.4193	-21.7932	6.9936	-22.1531	9.6293	-22.2553
20.5	4.2784	-22.5208	6.9253	-22.9017	9.6360	-23.0182
21.0	4.1341	-23.2505	6.8538	-23.6528	9.6396	-23.7838
21.5	3.9865	-23.9824	6.7791	-24.4061	9.6400	-24.5518
22.0	3.8358	-24.7162	6.7013	-25.1616	9.6374	-25.3223
22.5	3.6820	-25.4521	6.6206	-25.9192	9.6319	-26.0950
23.0	3.5253	-26.1898	6.5369	-26.6789	9.6235	-26.8699
23.5	3.3657	-26.9294	6.4504	-27.4406	9.6124	-27.6470
24.0	3.2032	-27.6707	6.3612	-28.2042	9.5986	-28.4261
24.5	3.0381	-28.4137	6.2694	-28.9696	9.5822	-29.2071
25.0	2.8704	-29.1585	6.1750	-29.7368	9.5633	-29.9901

TABLE II. $b_r(q) = U + iV$, $q = \rho e^{i\phi}$ $\qquad\qquad r=2$

ρ	$\phi=80°$		$\phi=85°$		$\phi=90°$	
	U	V	U	V	U	V
0.0	4.0000	0.0000	4.0000	0.0000	4.0000	0.0000
0.5	4.0196	-0.0071	4.0205	-0.0036	4.0209	0.0000
1.0	4.0786	-0.0287	4.0824	-0.0146	4.0837	0.0000
1.5	4.1776	-0.0653	4.1864	-0.0332	4.1894	0.0000
2.0	4.3178	-0.1179	4.3339	-0.0600	4.3394	0.0000
2.5	4.5007	-0.1881	4.5270	-0.0958	4.5359	0.0000
3.0	4.7286	-0.2780	4.7687	-0.1418	4.7823	0.0000
3.5	5.0043	-0.3911	5.0631	-0.2000	5.0831	0.0000
4.0	5.3316	-0.5323	5.4159	-0.2734	5.4448	0.0000
4.5	5.7147	-0.7094	5.8353	-0.3666	5.8772	0.0000
5.0	6.1584	-0.9344	6.3331	-0.4882	6.3953	0.0000
5.5	6.6655	-1.2268	6.9268	-0.6543	7.0249	0.0000
6.0	7.2302	-1.6171	7.6411	-0.9009	7.8166	0.0000
6.5	7.8215	-2.1438	8.4939	-1.3187	8.9074	0.0000
7.0	8.3686	-2.8204	9.3632	-2.0726	11.2147	-0.8921
7.5	8.8058	-3.5943	9.9471	-3.0506	11.3918	-2.5878
8.0	9.1327	-4.3911	10.3007	-3.9784	11.5801	-3.6257
8.5	9.3844	-5.1740	10.5625	-4.8244	11.7793	-4.4916
9.0	9.5911	-5.9357	10.7873	-5.6136	11.9888	-5.2743
9.5	9.7710	-6.6789	10.9960	-6.3662	12.2084	-6.0095
10.0	9.9346	-7.4085	11.1977	-7.0951	12.4373	-6.7161
10.5	10.0878	-8.1287	11.3966	-7.8092	12.6749	-7.4052
11.0	10.2341	-8.8433	11.5948	-8.5144	12.9205	-8.0842
11.5	10.3755	-9.5550	11.7933	-9.2151	13.1733	-8.7582
12.0	10.5133	-10.2659	11.9925	-9.9143	13.4324	-9.4311
12.5	10.6479	-10.9777	12.1922	-10.6143	13.6968	-10.1054
13.0	10.7798	-11.6915	12.3921	-11.3167	13.9654	-10.7834
13.5	10.9089	-12.4083	12.5919	-12.0229	14.2372	-11.4665
14.0	11.0354	-13.1286	12.7911	-12.7335	14.5110	-12.1559
14.5	11.1590	-13.8529	12.9891	-13.4492	14.7860	-12.8521
15.0	11.2796	-14.5814	13.1855	-14.1702	15.0609	-13.5556
15.5	11.3971	-15.3143	13.3798	-14.8968	15.3350	-14.2666
16.0	11.5115	-16.0515	13.5717	-15.6288	15.6074	-14.9849
16.5	11.6224	-16.7930	13.7607	-16.3663	15.8775	-15.7102
17.0	11.7300	-17.5388	13.9466	-17.1089	16.1446	-16.4423
17.5	11.8341	-18.2885	14.1293	-17.8564	16.4084	-17.1807
18.0	11.9347	-19.0422	14.3085	-18.6087	16.6685	-17.9249
18.5	12.0319	-19.7996	14.4842	-19.3653	16.9247	-18.6744
19.0	12.1255	-20.5606	14.6564	-20.1260	17.1770	-19.4287
19.5	12.2158	-21.3249	14.8251	-20.8905	17.4254	-20.1875
20.0	12.3027	-22.0923	14.9903	-21.6586	17.6699	-20.9502
20.5	12.3863	-22.8628	15.1520	-22.4301	17.9106	-21.7165
21.0	12.4667	-23.6362	15.3105	-23.2046	18.1476	-22.4861
21.5	12.5439	-24.4122	15.4657	-23.9820	18.3810	-23.2588
22.0	12.6182	-25.1908	15.6178	-24.7622	18.6112	-24.0342
22.5	12.6895	-25.9719	15.7669	-25.5449	18.8382	-24.8121
23.0	12.7580	-26.7553	15.9131	-26.3300	19.0621	-25.5925
23.5	12.8238	-27.5409	16.0566	-27.1175	19.2832	-26.3751
24.0	12.8869	-28.3287	16.1974	-27.9071	19.5017	-27.1599
24.5	12.9474	-29.1185	16.3357	-28.6988	19.7175	-27.9467
25.0	13.0055	-29.9103	16.4715	-29.4926	19.9310	-28.7355

TABLE II. $b_r(q) = U + iV$, $q = \rho e^{i\phi}$ $r = 3$

ρ	$\phi = 5°$		$\phi = 10°$		$\phi = 15°$	
	U	V	U	V	U	V
0.0	9.0000	0.0000	9.0000	0.0000	9.0000	0.0000
0.5	9.0135	0.0022	9.0130	0.0044	9.0122	0.0065
1.0	9.0473	0.0071	9.0458	0.0141	9.0435	0.0210
1.5	9.0920	0.0125	9.0900	0.0249	9.0867	0.0372
2.0	9.1401	0.0166	9.1384	0.0334	9.1354	0.0505
2.5	9.1856	0.0184	9.1853	0.0374	9.1845	0.0574
3.0	9.2239	0.0171	9.2262	0.0353	9.2294	0.0557
3.5	9.2514	0.0122	9.2574	0.0263	9.2667	0.0438
4.0	9.2652	0.0035	9.2762	0.0096	9.2935	0.0208
4.5	9.2634	-0.0091	9.2804	-0.0148	9.3075	-0.0137
5.0	9.2445	-0.0258	9.2685	-0.0472	9.3072	-0.0599
5.5	9.2074	-0.0463	9.2394	-0.0872	9.2910	-0.1176
6.0	9.1516	-0.0705	9.1922	-0.1348	9.2582	-0.1865
6.5	9.0766	-0.0984	9.1265	-0.1895	9.2078	-0.2662
7.0	8.9824	-0.1295	9.0421	-0.2509	9.1397	-0.3561
7.5	8.8691	-0.1638	8.9389	-0.3186	9.0534	-0.4554
8.0	8.7368	-0.2010	8.8171	-0.3921	8.9490	-0.5636
8.5	8.5861	-0.2408	8.6770	-0.4709	8.8266	-0.6799
9.0	8.4172	-0.2830	8.5189	-0.5546	8.6865	-0.8036
9.5	8.2308	-0.3273	8.3433	-0.6427	8.5290	-0.9341
10.0	8.0274	-0.3737	8.1507	-0.7348	8.3545	-1.0706
10.5	7.8076	-0.4218	7.9417	-0.8304	8.1636	-1.2126
11.0	7.5720	-0.4715	7.7170	-0.9293	7.9568	-1.3596
11.5	7.3214	-0.5227	7.4770	-1.0311	7.7346	-1.5109
12.0	7.0562	-0.5751	7.2224	-1.1354	7.4978	-1.6662
12.5	6.7771	-0.6287	6.9539	-1.2422	7.2468	-1.8251
13.0	6.4847	-0.6834	6.6719	-1.3510	6.9822	-1.9871
13.5	6.1795	-0.7390	6.3772	-1.4617	6.7047	-2.1520
14.0	5.8622	-0.7955	6.0702	-1.5742	6.4148	-2.3194
14.5	5.5332	-0.8527	5.7514	-1.6882	6.1131	-2.4892
15.0	5.1930	-0.9107	5.4214	-1.8036	5.8000	-2.6611
15.5	4.8421	-0.9693	5.0807	-1.9203	5.4761	-2.8350
16.0	4.4810	-1.0285	4.7297	-2.0383	5.1418	-3.0106
16.5	4.1101	-1.0883	4.3689	-2.1573	4.7976	-3.1878
17.0	3.7298	-1.1486	3.9986	-2.2773	4.4439	-3.3666
17.5	3.3405	-1.2093	3.6193	-2.3983	4.0811	-3.5467
18.0	2.9425	-1.2705	3.2313	-2.5201	3.7096	-3.7281
18.5	2.5362	-1.3321	2.8349	-2.6428	3.3298	-3.9108
19.0	2.1219	-1.3941	2.4306	-2.7662	2.9419	-4.0946
19.5	1.6999	-1.4565	2.0185	-2.8904	2.5463	-4.2794
20.0	1.2705	-1.5192	1.5990	-3.0153	2.1432	-4.4653
20.5	0.8340	-1.5823	1.1724	-3.1408	1.7330	-4.6522
21.0	0.3906	-1.6456	0.7389	-3.2669	1.3160	-4.8399
21.5	-0.0595	-1.7093	0.2988	-3.3936	0.8923	-5.0285
22.0	-0.5159	-1.7732	-0.1477	-3.5209	0.4622	-5.2180
22.5	-0.9786	-1.8374	-0.6004	-3.6488	0.0259	-5.4083
23.0	-1.4472	-1.9019	-1.0591	-3.7771	-0.4164	-5.5993
23.5	-1.9216	-1.9666	-1.5236	-3.9060	-0.8644	-5.7911
24.0	-2.4017	-2.0316	-1.9937	-4.0353	-1.3180	-5.9836
24.5	-2.8871	-2.0968	-2.4692	-4.1651	-1.7770	-6.1767
25.0	-3.3779	-2.1622	-2.9500	-4.2953	-2.2412	-6.3706

TABLE II. $b_r(q) = U + iV, \quad q = \rho e^{i\phi}$ $r = 3$

ρ	$\phi = 20°$		$\phi = 25°$		$\phi = 30°$	
	U	V	U	V	U	V
0.0	9.0000	0.0000	9.0000	0.0000	9.0000	0.0000
0.5	9.0110	0.0084	9.0095	0.0101	9.0078	0.0116
1.0	9.0402	0.0275	9.0359	0.0336	9.0307	0.0392
1.5	9.0819	0.0494	9.0755	0.0614	9.0675	0.0729
2.0	9.1309	0.0681	9.1245	0.0862	9.1159	0.1046
2.5	9.1826	0.0791	9.1790	0.1025	9.1730	0.1279
3.0	9.2328	0.0792	9.2354	0.1065	9.2357	0.1381
3.5	9.2781	0.0664	9.2902	0.0953	9.3011	0.1316
4.0	9.3157	0.0394	9.3408	0.0673	9.3663	0.1062
4.5	9.3431	−0.0026	9.3845	0.0212	9.4288	0.0603
5.0	9.3584	−0.0599	9.4193	−0.0434	9.4861	−0.0071
5.5	9.3601	−0.1324	9.4433	−0.1267	9.5363	−0.0963
6.0	9.3470	−0.2197	9.4550	−0.2285	9.5775	−0.2075
6.5	9.3180	−0.3215	9.4530	−0.3484	9.6078	−0.3402
7.0	9.2724	−0.4369	9.4362	−0.4855	9.6259	−0.4940
7.5	9.2097	−0.5652	9.4039	−0.6391	9.6304	−0.6680
8.0	9.1297	−0.7055	9.3552	−0.8081	9.6202	−0.8611
8.5	9.0323	−0.8570	9.2899	−0.9914	9.5943	−1.0722
9.0	8.9174	−1.0186	9.2076	−1.1879	9.5523	−1.2998
9.5	8.7852	−1.1894	9.1083	−1.3964	9.4935	−1.5426
10.0	8.6362	−1.3685	8.9921	−1.6157	9.4178	−1.7990
10.5	8.4706	−1.5552	8.8592	−1.8448	9.3252	−2.0678
11.0	8.2889	−1.7486	8.7100	−2.0826	9.2159	−2.3475
11.5	8.0918	−1.9480	8.5450	−2.3281	9.0902	−2.6369
12.0	7.8796	−2.1528	8.3646	−2.5805	8.9486	−2.9348
12.5	7.6531	−2.3623	8.1695	−2.8389	8.7917	−3.2402
13.0	7.4128	−2.5761	7.9602	−3.1028	8.6200	−3.5521
13.5	7.1594	−2.7938	7.7374	−3.3714	8.4343	−3.8698
14.0	6.8933	−3.0148	7.5016	−3.6444	8.2351	−4.1926
14.5	6.6152	−3.2390	7.2535	−3.9211	8.0232	−4.5198
15.0	6.3255	−3.4660	6.9937	−4.2013	7.7991	−4.8511
15.5	6.0249	−3.6955	6.7226	−4.4847	7.5636	−5.1860
16.0	5.7138	−3.9273	6.4409	−4.7708	7.3171	−5.5242
16.5	5.3927	−4.1613	6.1490	−5.0595	7.0602	−5.8653
17.0	5.0620	−4.3972	5.8474	−5.3506	6.7935	−6.2091
17.5	4.7221	−4.6349	5.5365	−5.6439	6.5174	−6.5554
18.0	4.3735	−4.8743	5.2168	−5.9392	6.2324	−6.9041
18.5	4.0164	−5.1153	4.8887	−6.2364	5.9388	−7.2549
19.0	3.6513	−5.3578	4.5524	−6.5354	5.6372	−7.6078
19.5	3.2784	−5.6017	4.2084	−6.8361	5.3277	−7.9626
20.0	2.8981	−5.8469	3.8569	−7.1384	5.0108	−8.3192
20.5	2.5107	−6.0934	3.4983	−7.4423	4.6868	−8.6776
21.0	2.1164	−6.3410	3.1328	−7.7475	4.3559	−9.0376
21.5	1.7155	−6.5898	2.7608	−8.0542	4.0184	−9.3993
22.0	1.3081	−6.8397	2.3823	−8.3622	3.6746	−9.7625
22.5	0.8946	−7.0907	1.9977	−8.6715	3.3247	−10.1272
23.0	0.4752	−7.3426	1.6072	−8.9820	2.9690	−10.4933
23.5	0.0500	−7.5955	1.2109	−9.2937	2.6075	−10.8608
24.0	−0.3808	−7.8494	0.8092	−9.6065	2.2406	−11.2297
24.5	−0.8169	−8.1041	0.4021	−9.9204	1.8684	−11.5999
25.0	−1.2583	−8.3598	−0.0102	−10.2355	1.4911	−11.9713

TABLE II. $b_{\mathrm{r}}(q) = U + iV$, $q = \rho e^{i\phi}$ $\qquad r = 3$

ρ	$\phi=35°$		$\phi=40°$		$\phi=45°$	
	U	V	U	V	U	V
0.0	9.0000	0.0000	9.0000	0.0000	9.0000	0.0000
0.5	9.0058	0.0128	9.0036	0.0137	9.0013	0.0142
1.0	9.0247	0.0441	9.0178	0.0482	9.0102	0.0513
1.5	9.0577	0.0838	9.0461	0.0938	9.0325	0.1026
2.0	9.1046	0.1232	9.0901	0.1416	9.0722	0.1593
2.5	9.1635	0.1552	9.1498	0.1839	9.1307	0.2135
3.0	9.2324	0.1741	9.2237	0.2143	9.2080	0.2581
3.5	9.3085	0.1758	9.3100	0.2279	9.3029	0.2874
4.0	9.3892	0.1573	9.4062	0.2209	9.4134	0.2970
4.5	9.4720	0.1164	9.5097	0.1907	9.5371	0.2835
5.0	9.5542	0.0518	9.6182	0.1353	9.6718	0.2442
5.5	9.6338	-0.0374	9.7292	0.0531	9.8151	0.1770
6.0	9.7084	-0.1516	9.8403	-0.0566	9.9645	0.0804
6.5	9.7759	-0.2909	9.9492	-0.1946	10.1176	-0.0469
7.0	9.8345	-0.4549	10.0534	-0.3610	10.2718	-0.2058
7.5	9.8823	-0.6432	10.1507	-0.5557	10.4241	-0.3970
8.0	9.9176	-0.8546	10.2386	-0.7780	10.5718	-0.6206
8.5	9.9389	-1.0880	10.3150	-1.0270	10.7117	-0.8762
9.0	9.9443	-1.3420	10.3777	-1.3012	10.8407	-1.1629
9.5	9.9348	-1.6148	10.4251	-1.5990	10.9559	-1.4791
10.0	9.9077	-1.9048	10.4557	-1.9182	11.0546	-1.8226
10.5	9.8634	-2.2102	10.4685	-2.2567	11.1348	-2.1906
11.0	9.8018	-2.5291	10.4629	-2.6122	11.1950	-2.5801
11.5	9.7229	-2.8600	10.4388	-2.9824	11.2345	-2.9880
12.0	9.6273	-3.2012	10.3965	-3.3651	11.2533	-3.4112
12.5	9.5153	-3.5514	10.3363	-3.7584	11.2519	-3.8470
13.0	9.3878	-3.9094	10.2591	-4.1608	11.2310	-4.2929
13.5	9.2453	-4.2741	10.1657	-4.5707	11.1919	-4.7470
14.0	9.0887	-4.6446	10.0571	-4.9870	11.1359	-5.2077
14.5	8.9187	-5.0202	9.9341	-5.4088	11.0642	-5.6739
15.0	8.7360	-5.4003	9.7978	-5.8352	10.9780	-6.1445
15.5	8.5414	-5.7843	9.6489	-6.2658	10.8786	-6.6190
16.0	8.3355	-6.1719	9.4883	-6.7000	10.7669	-7.0967
16.5	8.1190	-6.5627	9.3167	-7.1374	10.6439	-7.5775
17.0	7.8924	-6.9564	9.1349	-7.5778	10.5105	-8.0610
17.5	7.6563	-7.3528	8.9434	-8.0210	10.3674	-8.5470
18.0	7.4112	-7.7518	8.7428	-8.4667	10.2152	-9.0355
18.5	7.1575	-8.1531	8.5336	-8.9148	10.0544	-9.5262
19.0	6.8957	-8.5566	8.3164	-9.3653	9.8857	-10.0193
19.5	6.6261	-8.9622	8.0913	-9.8179	9.7094	-10.5145
20.0	6.3490	-9.3699	7.8590	-10.2727	9.5259	-11.0119
20.5	6.0649	-9.7794	7.6196	-10.7296	9.3356	-11.5114
21.0	5.7740	-10.1909	7.3736	-11.1884	9.1388	-12.0130
21.5	5.4765	-10.6041	7.1211	-11.6491	8.9358	-12.5166
22.0	5.1728	-11.0191	6.8625	-12.1118	8.7268	-13.0223
22.5	4.8631	-11.4357	6.5980	-12.5763	8.5120	-13.5299
23.0	4.5476	-11.8539	6.3277	-13.0425	8.2918	-14.0395
23.5	4.2264	-12.2737	6.0520	-13.5105	8.0661	-14.5510
24.0	3.8999	-12.6951	5.7710	-13.9802	7.8354	-15.0644
24.5	3.5681	-13.1179	5.4849	-14.4516	7.5997	-15.5796
25.0	3.2313	-13.5422	5.1938	-14.9246	7.3591	-16.0966

TABLE II. $b_r(q) = U+iV$, $q = \rho e^{i\phi}$ $r=3$

ρ	$\phi=50°$		$\phi=55°$		$\phi=60°$	
	U	V	U	V	U	V
0.0	9.0000	0.0000	9.0000	0.0000	9.0000	0.0000
0.5	8.9989	0.0144	8.9965	0.0141	8.9941	0.0135
1.0	9.0019	0.0533	8.9932	0.0540	8.9841	0.0533
1.5	9.0171	0.1097	8.9999	0.1147	8.9811	0.1171
2.0	9.0504	0.1756	9.0247	0.1896	8.9949	0.2003
2.5	9.1054	0.2430	9.0733	0.2711	9.0336	0.2963
3.0	9.1836	0.3043	9.1488	0.3514	9.1022	0.3972
3.5	9.2845	0.3532	9.2522	0.4235	9.2034	0.4955
4.0	9.4069	0.3845	9.3828	0.4812	9.3374	0.5842
4.5	9.5488	0.3939	9.5394	0.5198	9.5036	0.6580
5.0	9.7082	0.3782	9.7202	0.5355	9.7005	0.7123
5.5	9.8829	0.3348	9.9234	0.5249	9.9270	0.7436
6.0	10.0707	0.2613	10.1473	0.4852	10.1819	0.7488
6.5	10.2693	0.1557	10.3901	0.4138	10.4641	0.7247
7.0	10.4760	0.0161	10.6497	0.3077	10.7728	0.6680
7.5	10.6881	-0.1591	10.9238	0.1640	11.1071	0.5748
8.0	10.9022	-0.3714	11.2094	-0.0202	11.4654	0.4405
8.5	11.1145	-0.6216	11.5026	-0.2480	11.8455	0.2595
9.0	11.3206	-0.9100	11.7984	-0.5221	12.2433	0.0253
9.5	11.5161	-1.2358	12.0902	-0.8441	12.6521	-0.2690
10.0	11.6963	-1.5971	12.3706	-1.2139	13.0611	-0.6295
10.5	11.8571	-1.9909	12.6316	-1.6291	13.4556	-1.0586
11.0	11.9955	-2.4130	12.8662	-2.0844	13.8186	-1.5520
11.5	12.1094	-2.8589	13.0693	-2.5726	14.1358	-2.0973
12.0	12.1982	-3.3238	13.2389	-3.0855	14.4004	-2.6774
12.5	12.2624	-3.8035	13.3755	-3.6154	14.6139	-3.2757
13.0	12.3032	-4.2942	13.4815	-4.1563	14.7829	-3.8803
13.5	12.3225	-4.7930	13.5604	-4.7035	14.9158	-4.4843
14.0	12.3221	-5.2979	13.6158	-5.2542	15.0201	-5.0844
14.5	12.3042	-5.8073	13.6511	-5.8066	15.1020	-5.6799
15.0	12.2705	-6.3202	13.6691	-6.3600	15.1661	-6.2709
15.5	12.2226	-6.8359	13.6723	-6.9139	15.2160	-6.8583
16.0	12.1620	-7.3540	13.6626	-7.4683	15.2541	-7.4431
16.5	12.0899	-7.8742	13.6417	-8.0233	15.2823	-8.0261
17.0	12.0073	-8.3966	13.6107	-8.5793	15.3020	-8.6084
17.5	11.9151	-8.9209	13.5708	-9.1363	15.3141	-9.1905
18.0	11.8141	-9.4473	13.5226	-9.6947	15.3194	-9.7733
18.5	11.7048	-9.9757	13.4669	-10.2547	15.3185	-10.3571
19.0	11.5879	-10.5062	13.4042	-10.8165	15.3117	-10.9426
19.5	11.4637	-11.0388	13.3348	-11.3802	15.2994	-11.5298
20.0	11.3327	-11.5736	13.2592	-11.9460	15.2817	-12.1193
20.5	11.1952	-12.1104	13.1777	-12.5140	15.2590	-12.7111
21.0	11.0515	-12.6494	13.0904	-13.0843	15.2314	-13.3054
21.5	10.9018	-13.1906	12.9977	-13.6569	15.1989	-13.9023
22.0	10.7465	-13.7339	12.8997	-14.2317	15.1616	-14.5019
22.5	10.5857	-14.2794	12.7966	-14.8090	15.1198	-15.1042
23.0	10.4196	-14.8270	12.6885	-15.3886	15.0734	-15.7091
23.5	10.2483	-15.3767	12.5756	-15.9705	15.0226	-16.3168
24.0	10.0722	-15.9284	12.4581	-16.5548	14.9675	-16.9271
24.5	9.8913	-16.4822	12.3360	-17.1413	14.9080	-17.5401
25.0	9.7057	-17.0380	12.2094	-17.7301	14.8443	-18.1556

TABLE II. $b_r(q) = U + iV$, $q = \rho e^{i\phi}$ $r = 3$

ρ	$\phi = 65°$		$\phi = 70°$		$\phi = 75°$	
	U	V	U	V	U	V
0.0	9.0000	0.0000	9.0000	0.0000	9.0000	0.0000
0.5	8.9918	0.0124	8.9897	0.0110	8.9879	0.0092
1.0	8.9750	0.0511	8.9660	0.0472	8.9575	0.0417
1.5	8.9610	0.1165	8.9402	0.1125	8.9192	0.1045
2.0	8.9614	0.2067	8.9245	0.2076	8.8852	0.2018
2.5	8.9862	0.3167	8.9311	0.3302	8.8691	0.3345
3.0	9.0429	0.4391	8.9702	0.4741	8.8840	0.4985
3.5	9.1361	0.5660	9.0486	0.6309	8.9399	0.6857
4.0	9.2672	0.6895	9.1694	0.7922	9.0419	0.8864
4.5	9.4363	0.8036	9.3334	0.9507	9.1917	1.0922
5.0	9.6423	0.9032	9.5398	1.1010	9.3884	1.2968
5.5	9.8845	0.9847	9.7877	1.2393	9.6308	1.4963
6.0	10.1620	1.0450	10.0767	1.3629	9.9180	1.6885
6.5	10.4749	1.0811	10.4073	1.4697	10.2503	1.8724
7.0	10.8236	1.0899	10.7809	1.5579	10.6289	2.0480
7.5	11.2092	1.0678	11.2001	1.6252	11.0567	2.2157
8.0	11.6330	1.0097	11.6691	1.6690	11.5382	2.3766
8.5	12.0967	0.9089	12.1943	1.6853	12.0806	2.5326
9.0	12.6017	0.7557	12.7849	1.6675	12.6946	2.6871
9.5	13.1473	0.5360	13.4552	1.6044	13.3969	2.8470
10.0	13.7271	0.2301	14.2270	1.4736	14.2148	3.0273
10.5	14.3219	-0.1858	15.1337	1.2222	15.1943	3.2695
11.0	14.8902	-0.7277	16.1891	0.6991	16.3874	3.7115
11.5	15.3778	-1.3789	17.0927	-0.3109	17.5731	4.6263
12.0	15.7548	-2.0865	17.5136	-1.3964	18.3455	5.7293
12.5	16.0332	-2.8002	17.7312	-2.3124	18.8897	6.7223
13.0	16.2415	-3.4957	17.8859	-3.1116	19.3502	7.6147
13.5	16.4038	-4.1679	18.0171	-3.8388	19.7764	8.4379
14.0	16.5360	-4.8188	18.1385	-4.5199	20.1880	9.2132
14.5	16.6479	-5.4526	18.2557	-5.1702	20.5943	9.9544
15.0	16.7458	-6.0734	18.3712	-5.7997	21.0002	10.6706
15.5	16.8334	-6.6847	18.4860	-6.4153	21.4086	11.3686
16.0	16.9130	-7.2893	18.6008	-7.0218	21.8211	12.0533
16.5	16.9864	-7.8896	18.7155	-7.6226	22.2386	12.7287
17.0	17.0543	-8.4874	18.8300	-8.2204	22.6616	13.3977
17.5	17.1176	-9.0841	18.9442	-8.8173	23.0902	14.0630
18.0	17.1765	-9.6809	19.0577	-9.4146	23.5245	14.7266
18.5	17.2314	-10.2786	19.1701	-10.0136	23.9640	15.3903
19.0	17.2822	-10.8780	19.2812	-10.6152	24.4085	16.0555
19.5	17.3292	-11.4796	19.3904	-11.2200	24.8573	16.7235
20.0	17.3722	-12.0838	19.4976	-11.8284	25.3099	17.3953
20.5	17.4113	-12.6908	19.6023	-12.4408	25.7655	18.0715
21.0	17.4464	-13.3009	19.7042	-13.0574	26.2234	18.7529
21.5	17.4776	-13.9142	19.8031	-13.6784	26.6829	19.4397
22.0	17.5047	-14.5308	19.8988	-14.3036	27.1432	20.1323
22.5	17.5278	-15.1507	19.9910	-14.9332	27.6036	20.8307
23.0	17.5469	-15.7738	20.0797	-15.5670	28.0635	21.5348
23.5	17.5619	-16.4002	20.1646	-16.2049	28.5222	22.2444
24.0	17.5728	-17.0298	20.2456	-16.8468	28.9794	22.9593
24.5	17.5797	-17.6625	20.3228	-17.4926	29.4345	23.6792
25.0	17.5827	-18.2983	20.3961	-18.1421	29.8873	24.4036

ρ	$\phi = 80°$		$\phi = 85°$		$\phi = 90°$	
	U	V	U	V	U	V
0.0	9.0000	0.0000	9.0000	0.0000	9.0000	0.0000
0.5	8.9863	0.0070	8.9852	0.0046	8.9844	0.0020
1.0	8.9498	0.0346	8.9433	0.0260	8.9382	0.0159
1.5	8.8988	0.0923	8.8799	0.0757	8.8636	0.0549
2.0	8.8445	0.1882	8.8041	0.1657	8.7660	0.1336
2.5	8.8013	0.3271	8.7295	0.3055	8.6568	0.2670
3.0	8.7851	0.5084	8.6747	0.4994	8.5556	0.4665
3.5	8.8097	0.7249	8.6584	0.7427	8.4873	0.7323
4.0	8.8836	0.9657	8.6937	1.0232	8.4725	1.0514
4.5	9.0092	1.2204	8.7851	1.3274	8.5191	1.4051
5.0	9.1857	1.4813	8.9309	1.6447	8.6247	1.7783
5.5	9.4107	1.7437	9.1272	1.9695	8.7826	2.1631
6.0	9.6822	2.0060	9.3700	2.3000	8.9861	2.5571
6.5	9.9992	2.2683	9.6564	2.6368	9.2299	2.9611
7.0	10.3618	2.5318	9.9845	2.9821	9.5100	3.3775
7.5	10.7711	2.7995	10.3530	3.3396	9.8228	3.8099
8.0	11.2296	3.0753	10.7612	3.7143	10.1653	4.2626
8.5	11.7405	3.3652	11.2079	4.1125	10.5338	4.7402
9.0	12.3076	3.6784	11.6909	4.5417	10.9238	5.2473
9.5	12.9345	4.0283	12.2059	5.0110	11.3295	5.7880
10.0	13.6210	4.4357	12.7445	5.5296	11.7439	6.3652
10.5	14.3558	4.9284	13.2939	6.1044	12.1587	6.9796
11.0	15.1053	5.5330	13.8373	6.7369	12.5659	7.6289
11.5	15.8153	6.2492	14.3583	7.4202	12.9590	8.3087
12.0	16.4447	7.0373	14.8462	8.1411	13.3337	9.0126
12.5	16.9909	7.8485	15.2977	8.8848	13.6883	9.7342
13.0	17.4738	8.6538	15.7158	9.6390	14.0233	10.4678
13.5	17.9141	9.4425	16.1062	10.3960	14.3405	11.2088
14.0	18.3271	10.2130	16.4750	11.1514	14.6422	11.9541
14.5	18.7231	10.9672	16.8275	11.9032	14.9311	12.7019
15.0	19.1086	11.7078	17.1678	12.6511	15.2093	13.4509
15.5	19.4880	12.4377	17.4994	13.3953	15.4788	14.2006
16.0	19.8641	13.1595	17.8244	14.1365	15.7412	14.9508
16.5	20.2389	13.8754	18.1448	14.8756	15.9978	15.7017
17.0	20.6134	14.5874	18.4618	15.6134	16.2495	16.4534
17.5	20.9885	15.2970	18.7763	16.3506	16.4973	17.2060
18.0	21.3645	16.0057	19.0888	17.0881	16.7416	17.9600
18.5	21.7417	16.7146	19.3998	17.8264	16.9829	18.7156
19.0	22.1200	17.4248	19.7096	18.5661	17.2215	19.4729
19.5	22.4993	18.1368	20.0182	19.3076	17.4577	20.2322
20.0	22.8794	18.8515	20.3257	20.0513	17.6917	20.9937
20.5	23.2600	19.5693	20.6321	20.7975	17.9234	21.7575
21.0	23.6408	20.2906	20.9374	21.5464	18.1531	22.5237
21.5	24.0214	21.0156	21.2413	22.2982	18.3808	23.2924
22.0	24.4017	21.7444	21.5439	23.0528	18.6064	24.0635
22.5	24.7811	22.4771	21.8450	23.8105	18.8300	24.8372
23.0	25.1595	23.2138	22.1446	24.5712	19.0517	25.6134
23.5	25.5366	23.9543	22.4425	25.3348	19.2713	26.3921
24.0	25.9121	24.6985	22.7387	26.1013	19.4889	27.1733
24.5	26.2860	25.4463	23.0330	26.8707	19.7046	27.9569
25.0	26.6579	26.1976	23.3256	27.6428	19.9183	28.7428

TABLE II. $b_r(q) = U + iV$, $q = \rho e^{i\phi}$ $r = 4$

ρ	$\phi=5°$		$\phi=10°$		$\phi=15°$	
	U	V	U	V	U	V
0.0	16.0000	0.0000	16.0000	0.0000	16.0000	0.0000
0.5	16.0082	0.0014	16.0078	0.0028	16.0072	0.0041
1.0	16.0325	0.0057	16.0310	0.0112	16.0287	0.0164
1.5	16.0722	0.0124	16.0691	0.0245	16.0640	0.0359
2.0	16.1260	0.0213	16.1209	0.0420	16.1125	0.0618
2.5	16.1924	0.0317	16.1852	0.0628	16.1733	0.0926
3.0	16.2696	0.0431	16.2604	0.0856	16.2451	0.1267
3.5	16.3556	0.0549	16.3447	0.1093	16.3265	0.1625
4.0	16.4481	0.0665	16.4362	0.1327	16.4160	0.1981
4.5	16.5451	0.0773	16.5328	0.1547	16.5118	0.2321
5.0	16.6444	0.0869	16.6327	0.1744	16.6123	0.2630
5.5	16.7441	0.0948	16.7339	0.1908	16.7156	0.2893
6.0	16.8422	0.1006	16.8345	0.2033	16.8200	0.3101
6.5	16.9370	0.1041	16.9328	0.2112	16.9239	0.3243
7.0	17.0270	0.1050	17.0273	0.2141	17.0256	0.3312
7.5	17.1107	0.1031	17.1165	0.2115	17.1236	0.3302
8.0	17.1869	0.0985	17.1991	0.2034	17.2167	0.3209
8.5	17.2545	0.0909	17.2740	0.1894	17.3034	0.3030
9.0	17.3125	0.0803	17.3401	0.1695	17.3829	0.2763
9.5	17.3603	0.0668	17.3967	0.1438	17.4539	0.2408
10.0	17.3970	0.0504	17.4429	0.1122	17.5158	0.1966
10.5	17.4222	0.0312	17.4781	0.0750	17.5676	0.1437
11.0	17.4355	0.0092	17.5018	0.0322	17.6088	0.0824
11.5	17.4365	-0.0154	17.5137	-0.0160	17.6388	0.0129
12.0	17.4250	-0.0425	17.5134	-0.0693	17.6572	-0.0644
12.5	17.4009	-0.0720	17.5006	-0.1274	17.6635	-0.1492
13.0	17.3641	-0.1039	17.4754	-0.1902	17.6577	-0.2412
13.5	17.3145	-0.1378	17.4375	-0.2573	17.6394	-0.3398
14.0	17.2523	-0.1738	17.3870	-0.3285	17.6086	-0.4448
14.5	17.1775	-0.2116	17.3239	-0.4035	17.5653	-0.5557
15.0	17.0903	-0.2512	17.2484	-0.4821	17.5095	-0.6720
15.5	16.9908	-0.2924	17.1606	-0.5639	17.4412	-0.7934
16.0	16.8793	-0.3351	17.0607	-0.6488	17.3606	-0.9195
16.5	16.7560	-0.3792	16.9488	-0.7365	17.2680	-1.0499
17.0	16.6212	-0.4245	16.8252	-0.8268	17.1634	-1.1843
17.5	16.4750	-0.4711	16.6903	-0.9194	17.0471	-1.3224
18.0	16.3177	-0.5187	16.5441	-1.0143	16.9195	-1.4637
18.5	16.1498	-0.5673	16.3871	-1.1112	16.7807	-1.6082
19.0	15.9713	-0.6168	16.2194	-1.2099	16.6311	-1.7554
19.5	15.7826	-0.6672	16.0415	-1.3103	16.4709	-1.9052
20.0	15.5840	-0.7184	15.8535	-1.4123	16.3005	-2.0573
20.5	15.3758	-0.7703	15.6557	-1.5158	16.1201	-2.2116
21.0	15.1581	-0.8229	15.4484	-1.6205	15.9300	-2.3679
21.5	14.9314	-0.8761	15.2320	-1.7266	15.7306	-2.5260
22.0	14.6958	-0.9299	15.0066	-1.8337	15.5221	-2.6858
22.5	14.4517	-0.9842	14.7726	-1.9420	15.3048	-2.8472
23.0	14.1992	-1.0390	14.5301	-2.0512	15.0789	-3.0101
23.5	13.9385	-1.0943	14.2795	-2.1614	14.8448	-3.1743
24.0	13.6701	-1.1501	14.0209	-2.2724	14.6026	-3.3398
24.5	13.3939	-1.2062	13.7546	-2.3843	14.3526	-3.5065
25.0	13.1103	-1.2628	13.4809	-2.4969	14.0951	-3.6743

TABLE II. $b_r(q) = U + iV$, $q = \rho e^{i\phi}$ $\qquad\qquad$ $r = 4$

ρ	$\phi=20°$		$\phi=25°$		$\phi=30°$	
	U	V	U	V	U	V
0.0	16.0000	0.0000	16.0000	0.0000	16.0000	0.0000
0.5	16.0064	0.0053	16.0054	0.0064	16.0042	0.0072
1.0	16.0255	0.0211	16.0215	0.0252	16.0168	0.0285
1.5	16.0571	0.0464	16.0485	0.0556	16.0384	0.0633
2.0	16.1010	0.0801	16.0865	0.0965	16.0694	0.1104
2.5	16.1567	0.1206	16.1357	0.1459	16.1105	0.1681
3.0	16.2236	0.1658	16.1959	0.2020	16.1623	0.2343
3.5	16.3007	0.2137	16.2671	0.2622	16.2255	0.3067
4.0	16.3870	0.2622	16.3486	0.3241	16.3002	0.3826
4.5	16.4812	0.3092	16.4399	0.3853	16.3866	0.4592
5.0	16.5819	0.3527	16.5399	0.4433	16.4841	0.5338
5.5	16.6876	0.3910	16.6474	0.4959	16.5922	0.6035
6.0	16.7967	0.4224	16.7612	0.5410	16.7098	0.6660
6.5	16.9075	0.4457	16.8797	0.5770	16.8358	0.7189
7.0	17.0185	0.4597	17.0016	0.6022	16.9688	0.7604
7.5	17.1283	0.4636	17.1251	0.6156	17.1073	0.7887
8.0	17.2353	0.4568	17.2489	0.6161	17.2498	0.8026
8.5	17.3382	0.4387	17.3715	0.6029	17.3947	0.8008
9.0	17.4357	0.4091	17.4915	0.5756	17.5407	0.7826
9.5	17.5268	0.3677	17.6076	0.5337	17.6860	0.7472
10.0	17.6103	0.3147	17.7184	0.4772	17.8293	0.6942
10.5	17.6852	0.2499	17.8228	0.4059	17.9692	0.6235
11.0	17.7508	0.1737	17.9197	0.3199	18.1042	0.5348
11.5	17.8063	0.0864	18.0082	0.2196	18.2330	0.4283
12.0	17.8511	−0.0117	18.0872	0.1053	18.3544	0.3041
12.5	17.8845	−0.1202	18.1559	−0.0226	18.4672	0.1627
13.0	17.9062	−0.2386	18.2137	−0.1635	18.5703	0.0047
13.5	17.9158	−0.3663	18.2598	−0.3167	18.6626	−0.1693
14.0	17.9130	−0.5028	18.2939	−0.4817	18.7433	−0.3586
14.5	17.8977	−0.6475	18.3155	−0.6575	18.8116	−0.5621
15.0	17.8698	−0.7999	18.3243	−0.8436	18.8669	−0.7790
15.5	17.8292	−0.9593	18.3202	−1.0390	18.9089	−1.0081
16.0	17.7761	−1.1253	18.3031	−1.2431	18.9371	−1.2486
16.5	17.7106	−1.2972	18.2730	−1.4551	18.9515	−1.4992
17.0	17.6328	−1.4746	18.2301	−1.6742	18.9520	−1.7590
17.5	17.5429	−1.6569	18.1744	−1.8998	18.9388	−2.0270
18.0	17.4412	−1.8438	18.1063	−2.1313	18.9121	−2.3024
18.5	17.3280	−2.0349	18.0260	−2.3680	18.8721	−2.5842
19.0	17.2036	−2.2297	17.9339	−2.6095	18.8193	−2.8718
19.5	17.0682	−2.4280	17.8302	−2.8553	18.7540	−3.1645
20.0	16.9223	−2.6293	17.7154	−3.1049	18.6767	−3.4617
20.5	16.7660	−2.8335	17.5898	−3.3581	18.5879	−3.7629
21.0	16.5998	−3.0404	17.4538	−3.6143	18.4880	−4.0676
21.5	16.4239	−3.2496	17.3077	−3.8735	18.3774	−4.3755
22.0	16.2387	−3.4610	17.1520	−4.1353	18.2566	−4.6863
22.5	16.0445	−3.6744	16.9869	−4.3994	18.1261	−4.9997
23.0	15.8416	−3.8898	16.8128	−4.6658	17.9862	−5.3155
23.5	15.6302	−4.1068	16.6301	−4.9342	17.8374	−5.6335
24.0	15.4106	−4.3255	16.4389	−5.2045	17.6799	−5.9535
24.5	15.1832	−4.5457	16.2398	−5.4766	17.5143	−6.2754
25.0	14.9481	−4.7674	16.0328	−5.7503	17.3407	−6.5990

TABLE II. $b_r(q) = U+iV$, $q=\rho e^{i\phi}$ $r=4$

ρ	$\phi=35°$ U	V	$\phi=40°$ U	V	$\phi=45°$ U	V
0.0	16.0000	0.0000	16.0000	0.0000	16.0000	0.0000
0.5	16.0029	0.0078	16.0015	0.0082	16.0000	0.0083
1.0	16.0117	0.0311	16.0061	0.0327	16.0004	0.0333
1.5	16.0270	0.0693	16.0147	0.0732	16.0019	0.0750
2.0	16.0499	0.1214	16.0285	0.1291	16.0059	0.1331
2.5	16.0814	0.1862	16.0491	0.1995	16.0143	0.2074
3.0	16.1230	0.2618	16.0785	0.2832	16.0294	0.2973
3.5	16.1759	0.3459	16.1186	0.3782	16.0540	0.4017
4.0	16.2413	0.4360	16.1716	0.4823	16.0910	0.5189
4.5	16.3200	0.5292	16.2391	0.5926	16.1432	0.6464
5.0	16.4124	0.6223	16.3228	0.7061	16.2132	0.7814
5.5	16.5186	0.7122	16.4233	0.8191	16.3030	0.9201
6.0	16.6380	0.7960	16.5411	0.9284	16.4140	1.0588
6.5	16.7699	0.8709	16.6758	1.0304	16.5466	1.1934
7.0	16.9132	0.9343	16.8267	1.1223	16.7007	1.3203
7.5	17.0664	0.9842	16.9927	1.2010	16.8756	1.4360
8.0	17.2281	1.0186	17.1726	1.2644	17.0702	1.5374
8.5	17.3969	1.0361	17.3647	1.3103	17.2832	1.6218
9.0	17.5710	1.0353	17.5676	1.3369	17.5131	1.6871
9.5	17.7488	1.0152	17.7796	1.3427	17.7583	1.7312
10.0	17.9289	0.9750	17.9990	1.3264	18.0174	1.7524
10.5	18.1094	0.9140	18.2241	1.2869	18.2887	1.7489
11.0	18.2888	0.8317	18.4532	1.2233	18.5705	1.7193
11.5	18.4654	0.7281	18.6844	1.1347	18.8613	1.6619
12.0	18.6377	0.6028	18.9158	1.0204	19.1589	1.5754
12.5	18.8038	0.4562	19.1453	0.8800	19.4613	1.4583
13.0	18.9624	0.2885	19.3707	0.7134	19.7660	1.3092
13.5	19.1117	0.1002	19.5897	0.5207	20.0701	1.1271
14.0	19.2503	−0.1077	19.8002	0.3021	20.3702	0.9113
14.5	19.3769	−0.3344	19.9997	0.0587	20.6627	0.6616
15.0	19.4903	−0.5785	20.1861	−0.2083	20.9435	0.3786
15.5	19.5897	−0.8389	20.3575	−0.4974	21.2087	0.0640
16.0	19.6742	−1.1141	20.5123	−0.8064	21.4548	−0.2799
16.5	19.7434	−1.4026	20.6494	−1.1334	21.6785	−0.6495
17.0	19.7971	−1.7028	20.7679	−1.4758	21.8780	−1.0409
17.5	19.8352	−2.0134	20.8677	−1.8315	22.0522	−1.4499
18.0	19.8580	−2.3330	20.9488	−2.1981	22.2012	−1.8724
18.5	19.8658	−2.6604	21.0118	−2.5739	22.3260	−2.3048
19.0	19.8591	−2.9944	21.0574	−2.9570	22.4281	−2.7441
19.5	19.8385	−3.3342	21.0865	−3.3460	22.5092	−3.1882
20.0	19.8044	−3.6789	21.1001	−3.7397	22.5715	−3.6352
20.5	19.7577	−4.0279	21.0991	−4.1373	22.6166	−4.0840
21.0	19.6988	−4.3805	21.0847	−4.5379	22.6464	−4.5339
21.5	19.6285	−4.7363	21.0576	−4.9411	22.6623	−4.9845
22.0	19.5473	−5.0949	21.0189	−5.3465	22.6658	−5.4354
22.5	19.4558	−5.4560	20.9692	−5.7538	22.6581	−5.8867
23.0	19.3545	−5.8194	20.9093	−6.1627	22.6400	−6.3384
23.5	19.2439	−6.1849	20.8399	−6.5733	22.6126	−6.7904
24.0	19.1245	−6.5523	20.7615	−6.9853	22.5764	−7.2431
24.5	18.9967	−6.9215	20.6747	−7.3987	22.5321	−7.6963
25.0	18.8608	−7.2925	20.5799	−7.8135	22.4802	−8.1504

TABLE II. $b_r(q) = U + iV$, $q = \rho e^{i\phi}$ $\qquad$ $r = 4$

ρ	$\phi = 50°$		$\phi = 55°$		$\phi = 60°$	
	U	V	U	V	U	V
0.0	16.0000	0.0000	16.0000	0.0000	16.0000	0.0000
0.5	15.9986	0.0082	15.9972	0.0078	15.9958	0.0072
1.0	15.9946	0.0329	15.9889	0.0316	15.9835	0.0292
1.5	15.9887	0.0745	15.9758	0.0716	15.9635	0.0666
2.0	15.9825	0.1331	15.9591	0.1289	15.9365	0.1205
2.5	15.9777	0.2092	15.9405	0.2045	15.9039	0.1928
3.0	15.9769	0.3031	15.9224	0.2994	15.8677	0.2852
3.5	15.9833	0.4146	15.9080	0.4147	15.8305	0.4002
4.0	16.0004	0.5429	15.9014	0.5510	15.7964	0.5400
4.5	16.0323	0.6866	15.9072	0.7083	15.7704	0.7063
5.0	16.0826	0.8432	15.9307	0.8852	15.7588	0.8999
5.5	16.1549	1.0093	15.9770	1.0791	15.7689	1.1198
6.0	16.2520	1.1808	16.0509	1.2859	15.8078	1.3627
6.5	16.3754	1.3533	16.1557	1.5007	15.8816	1.6233
7.0	16.5260	1.5220	16.2935	1.7177	15.9944	1.8948
7.5	16.7035	1.6827	16.4648	1.9317	16.1479	2.1699
8.0	16.9072	1.8317	16.6691	2.1378	16.3420	2.4425
8.5	17.1358	1.9656	16.9054	2.3320	16.5754	2.7073
9.0	17.3881	2.0817	17.1721	2.5111	16.8460	2.9605
9.5	17.6625	2.1776	17.4680	2.6724	17.1521	3.1994
10.0	17.9579	2.2513	17.7920	2.8139	17.4924	3.4223
10.5	18.2730	2.3006	18.1431	2.9337	17.8660	3.6279
11.0	18.6066	2.3237	18.5210	3.0298	18.2728	3.8151
11.5	18.9576	2.3184	18.9254	3.1002	18.7133	3.9829
12.0	19.3248	2.2823	19.3565	3.1425	19.1890	4.1304
12.5	19.7068	2.2129	19.8148	3.1538	19.7020	4.2563
13.0	20.1016	2.1073	20.3009	3.1302	20.2557	4.3588
13.5	20.5068	1.9622	20.8152	3.0667	20.8551	4.4355
14.0	20.9189	1.7741	21.3579	2.9566	21.5073	4.4827
14.5	21.3331	1.5397	21.9280	2.7907	22.2226	4.4945
15.0	21.7428	1.2564	22.5214	2.5570	23.0174	4.4609
15.5	22.1401	0.9231	23.1283	2.2406	23.9186	4.3623
16.0	22.5157	0.5414	23.7285	1.8270	24.9761	4.1515
16.5	22.8609	0.1162	24.2890	1.3112	26.2801	3.6605
17.0	23.1686	−0.3446	24.7725	0.7106	27.4603	2.3436
17.5	23.4353	−0.8310	25.1588	0.0635	27.7534	1.0285
18.0	23.6614	−1.3334	25.4541	−0.5916	27.8569	0.0600
18.5	23.8498	−1.8438	25.6787	−1.2320	27.9310	−0.7399
19.0	24.0050	−2.3564	25.8532	−1.8496	28.0000	−1.4448
19.5	24.1320	−2.8677	25.9927	−2.4442	28.0700	−2.0899
20.0	24.2352	−3.3759	26.1079	−3.0185	28.1423	−2.6946
20.5	24.3186	−3.8800	26.2054	−3.5760	28.2173	−3.2711
21.0	24.3853	−4.3802	26.2899	−4.1201	28.2946	−3.8273
21.5	24.4380	−4.8767	26.3642	−4.6535	28.3740	−4.3691
22.0	24.4785	−5.3701	26.4305	−5.1788	28.4549	−4.9005
22.5	24.5086	−5.8610	26.4900	−5.6979	28.5370	−5.4246
23.0	24.5294	−6.3499	26.5437	−6.2125	28.6198	−5.9437
23.5	24.5418	−6.8374	26.5923	−6.7241	28.7028	−6.4599
24.0	24.5468	−7.3241	26.6362	−7.2336	28.7856	−6.9744
24.5	24.5448	−7.8105	26.6757	−7.7420	28.8679	−7.4886
25.0	24.5364	−8.2969	26.7110	−8.2500	28.9493	−8.0032

-121-

TABLE II. $b_r(q) = U + iV$, $q = \rho e^{i\phi}$ $\quad\quad r = 4$

ρ	$\phi = 65°$		$\phi = 70°$		$\phi = 75°$	
	U	V	U	V	U	V
0.0	16.0000	0.0000	16.0000	0.0000	16.0000	0.0000
0.5	15.9946	0.0064	15.9936	0.0054	15.9928	0.0042
1.0	15.9786	0.0259	15.9744	0.0218	15.9709	0.0170
1.5	15.9522	0.0593	15.9422	0.0501	15.9341	0.0392
2.0	15.9155	0.1080	15.8970	0.0917	15.8816	0.0720
2.5	15.8694	0.1741	15.8384	0.1488	15.8125	0.1175
3.0	15.8150	0.2603	15.7667	0.2245	15.7255	0.1787
3.5	15.7540	0.3699	15.6822	0.3228	15.6196	0.2596
4.0	15.6896	0.5068	15.5863	0.4490	15.4935	0.3661
4.5	15.6263	0.6751	15.4819	0.6096	15.3471	0.5062
5.0	15.5710	0.8787	15.3745	0.8120	15.1821	0.6909
5.5	15.5325	1.1195	15.2737	1.0634	15.0050	0.9343
6.0	15.5214	1.3966	15.1934	1.3682	14.8309	1.2513
6.5	15.5479	1.7051	15.1506	1.7245	14.6862	1.6506
7.0	15.6199	2.0367	15.1607	2.1224	14.6031	2.1238
7.5	15.7414	2.3813	15.2324	2.5466	14.6030	2.6444
8.0	15.9124	2.7296	15.3664	2.9817	14.6873	3.1827
8.5	16.1307	3.0746	15.5581	3.4163	14.8446	3.7188
9.0	16.3930	3.4113	15.8008	3.8442	15.0612	4.2441
9.5	16.6963	3.7371	16.0888	4.2625	15.3260	4.7566
10.0	17.0379	4.0508	16.4175	4.6708	15.6312	5.2579
10.5	17.4165	4.3520	16.7836	5.0701	15.9716	5.7505
11.0	17.8313	4.6411	17.1851	5.4620	16.3435	6.2376
11.5	18.2825	4.9188	17.6209	5.8490	16.7446	6.7226
12.0	18.7712	5.1864	18.0907	6.2337	17.1730	7.2089
12.5	19.2996	5.4453	18.5947	6.6195	17.6272	7.7001
13.0	19.8707	5.6978	19.1333	7.0102	18.1057	8.1998
13.5	20.4888	5.9467	19.7068	7.4108	18.6066	8.7118
14.0	21.1600	6.1968	20.3155	7.8272	19.1277	9.2400
14.5	21.8919	6.4552	20.9583	8.2664	19.6658	9.7878
15.0	22.6942	6.7343	21.6322	8.7370	20.2170	10.3584
15.5	23.5768	7.0558	22.3309	9.2478	20.7765	10.9539
16.0	24.5429	7.4581	23.0443	9.8061	21.3390	11.5753
16.5	25.5657	7.9963	23.7580	10.4153	21.8991	12.2218
17.0	26.5623	8.7028	24.4571	11.0720	22.4519	12.8911
17.5	27.4444	9.5260	25.1297	11.7666	22.9938	13.5798
18.0	28.2005	10.3789	25.7699	12.4865	23.5227	14.2839
18.5	28.8659	11.2136	26.3778	13.2196	24.0376	14.9992
19.0	29.4741	12.0168	26.9570	13.9571	24.5389	15.7223
19.5	30.0473	12.7884	27.5128	14.6931	25.0276	16.4502
20.0	30.5993	13.5320	28.0500	15.4245	25.5051	17.1808
20.5	31.1387	14.2522	28.5733	16.1499	25.9730	17.9126
21.0	31.6711	14.9527	29.0863	16.8688	26.4329	18.6445
21.5	32.2003	15.6370	29.5918	17.5816	26.8862	19.3761
22.0	32.7288	16.3081	30.0923	18.2888	27.3341	20.1071
22.5	33.2585	16.9684	30.5893	18.9912	27.7777	20.8374
23.0	33.7906	17.6202	31.0843	19.6897	28.2179	21.5672
23.5	34.3260	18.2653	31.5783	20.3849	28.6554	22.2965
24.0	34.8652	18.9054	32.0720	21.0779	29.0908	23.0257
24.5	35.4088	19.5420	32.5660	21.7693	29.5245	23.7550
25.0	35.9568	20.1764	33.0606	22.4598	29.9570	24.4847

TABLE II. $b_r(q) = U + iV$, $q = \rho e^{i\phi}$ $r=4$

ρ	$\phi=80°$		$\phi=85°$		$\phi=90°$	
	U	V	U	V	U	V
0.0	16.0000	0.0000	16.0000	0.0000	16.0000	0.0000
0.5	15.9922	0.0029	15.9918	0.0015	15.9916	0.0000
1.0	15.9684	0.0116	15.9668	0.0059	15.9663	0.0000
1.5	15.9281	0.0269	15.9244	0.0137	15.9231	0.0000
2.0	15.8701	0.0496	15.8630	0.0253	15.8605	0.0000
2.5	15.7928	0.0813	15.7805	0.0416	15.7764	0.0000
3.0	15.6939	0.1244	15.6740	0.0638	15.6672	0.0000
3.5	15.5706	0.1822	15.5393	0.0940	15.5285	0.0000
4.0	15.4190	0.2598	15.3705	0.1350	15.3536	0.0000
4.5	15.2348	0.3649	15.1594	0.1918	15.1326	0.0000
5.0	15.0132	0.5098	14.8940	0.2728	14.8504	0.0000
5.5	14.7512	0.7141	14.5567	0.3942	14.4810	0.0000
6.0	14.4546	1.0085	14.1225	0.5923	13.9736	0.0000
6.5	14.1541	1.4317	13.5734	0.9577	13.1907	0.0000
7.0	13.9202	1.9976	13.0309	1.6555	11.2147	0.8921
7.5	13.8186	2.6538	12.7966	2.5742	11.3918	2.5878
8.0	13.8494	3.3265	12.8149	3.4395	11.5801	3.6257
8.5	13.9769	3.9795	12.9466	4.2201	11.7793	4.4916
9.0	14.1707	4.6061	13.1364	4.9417	11.9888	5.2743
9.5	14.4120	5.2100	13.3624	5.6246	12.2084	6.0095
10.0	14.6899	5.7968	13.6146	6.2826	12.4373	6.7161
10.5	14.9975	6.3722	13.8875	6.9250	12.6749	7.4052
11.0	15.3306	6.9410	14.1778	7.5584	12.9205	8.0842
11.5	15.6860	7.5075	14.4829	8.1880	13.1733	8.7582
12.0	16.0615	8.0754	14.8009	8.8176	13.4324	9.4311
12.5	16.4547	8.6480	15.1299	9.4504	13.6968	10.1054
13.0	16.8638	9.2283	15.4683	10.0886	13.9654	10.7834
13.5	17.2864	9.8189	15.8141	10.7343	14.2372	11.4665
14.0	17.7202	10.4220	16.1658	11.3889	14.5110	12.1559
14.5	18.1626	11.0392	16.5214	12.0533	14.7860	12.8521
15.0	18.6108	11.6717	16.8793	12.7281	15.0609	13.5556
15.5	19.0621	12.3199	17.2379	13.4134	15.3350	14.2666
16.0	19.5137	12.9839	17.5957	14.1091	15.6074	14.9849
16.5	19.9631	13.6628	17.9513	14.8147	15.8775	15.7102
17.0	20.4082	14.3554	18.3038	15.5295	16.1446	16.4423
17.5	20.8474	15.0600	18.6523	16.2528	16.4084	17.1807
18.0	21.2798	15.7750	18.9962	16.9836	16.6685	17.9249
18.5	21.7046	16.4986	19.3352	17.7210	16.9247	18.6744
19.0	22.1219	17.2291	19.6693	18.4643	17.1770	19.4287
19.5	22.5318	17.9651	19.9983	19.2126	17.4254	20.1875
20.0	22.9348	18.7053	20.3224	19.9652	17.6699	20.9502
20.5	23.3313	19.4489	20.6419	20.7215	17.9106	21.7165
21.0	23.7221	20.1951	20.9570	21.4811	18.1476	22.4861
21.5	24.1077	20.9434	21.2679	22.2436	18.3810	23.2588
22.0	24.4887	21.6933	21.5751	23.0086	18.6112	24.0342
22.5	24.8658	22.4446	21.8787	23.7759	18.8382	24.8121
23.0	25.2394	23.1972	22.1791	24.5453	19.0621	25.5925
23.5	25.6099	23.9511	22.4766	25.3167	19.2832	26.3751
24.0	25.9778	24.7061	22.7713	26.0900	19.5017	27.1599
24.5	26.3434	25.4624	23.0634	26.8650	19.7175	27.9467
25.0	26.7068	26.2199	23.3532	27.6419	19.9310	28.7355

TABLE II. $b_r(q) = U + iV$, $q = \rho e^{i\phi}$ $r = 5$

ρ	$\phi = 5°$		$\phi = 10°$		$\phi = 15°$	
	U	V	U	V	U	V
0.0	25.0000	0.0000	25.0000	0.0000	25.0000	0.0000
0.5	25.0051	0.0009	25.0049	0.0018	25.0045	0.0026
1.0	25.0205	0.0036	25.0196	0.0071	25.0180	0.0104
1.5	25.0462	0.0081	25.0441	0.0160	25.0406	0.0235
2.0	25.0821	0.0145	25.0783	0.0285	25.0722	0.0417
2.5	25.1282	0.0225	25.1224	0.0444	25.1129	0.0650
3.0	25.1843	0.0323	25.1760	0.0637	25.1625	0.0932
3.5	25.2503	0.0437	25.2392	0.0861	25.2211	0.1262
4.0	25.3258	0.0565	25.3118	0.1115	25.2886	0.1636
4.5	25.4105	0.0706	25.3933	0.1395	25.3648	0.2050
5.0	25.5040	0.0858	25.4835	0.1697	25.4496	0.2499
5.5	25.6055	0.1018	25.5819	0.2017	25.5427	0.2977
6.0	25.7146	0.1185	25.6881	0.2351	25.6437	0.3477
6.5	25.8304	0.1355	25.8013	0.2692	25.7524	0.3992
7.0	25.9521	0.1525	25.9209	0.3035	25.8681	0.4513
7.5	26.0789	0.1693	26.0461	0.3375	25.9904	0.5034
8.0	26.2099	0.1855	26.1763	0.3706	26.1186	0.5545
8.5	26.3442	0.2010	26.3104	0.4023	26.2520	0.6039
9.0	26.4808	0.2154	26.4476	0.4321	26.3899	0.6507
9.5	26.6187	0.2285	26.5871	0.4594	26.5314	0.6943
10.0	26.7571	0.2402	26.7280	0.4838	26.6758	0.7338
10.5	26.8950	0.2501	26.8692	0.5050	26.8222	0.7688
11.0	27.0315	0.2582	27.0100	0.5225	26.9696	0.7986
11.5	27.1658	0.2643	27.1495	0.5362	27.1173	0.8228
12.0	27.2971	0.2682	27.2869	0.5456	27.2643	0.8408
12.5	27.4247	0.2700	27.4213	0.5507	27.4100	0.8525
13.0	27.5477	0.2695	27.5521	0.5513	27.5533	0.8573
13.5	27.6656	0.2666	27.6785	0.5471	27.6936	0.8553
14.0	27.7778	0.2614	27.7999	0.5383	27.8301	0.8461
14.5	27.8836	0.2537	27.9156	0.5246	27.9621	0.8297
15.0	27.9827	0.2438	28.0250	0.5062	28.0889	0.8061
15.5	28.0745	0.2314	28.1278	0.4830	28.2100	0.7751
16.0	28.1586	0.2167	28.2234	0.4551	28.3247	0.7370
16.5	28.2347	0.1998	28.3113	0.4226	28.4325	0.6917
17.0	28.3026	0.1806	28.3914	0.3856	28.5331	0.6395
17.5	28.3619	0.1593	28.4631	0.3441	28.6258	0.5804
18.0	28.4124	0.1359	28.5263	0.2984	28.7104	0.5147
18.5	28.4539	0.1105	28.5806	0.2486	28.7865	0.4426
19.0	28.4864	0.0831	28.6261	0.1948	28.8539	0.3643
19.5	28.5098	0.0539	28.6624	0.1372	28.9122	0.2801
20.0	28.5238	0.0230	28.6895	0.0760	28.9614	0.1902
20.5	28.5286	-0.0097	28.7073	0.0114	29.0012	0.0949
21.0	28.5241	-0.0439	28.7157	-0.0564	29.0316	-0.0054
21.5	28.5104	-0.0796	28.7148	-0.1273	29.0525	-0.1105
22.0	28.4874	-0.1167	28.7045	-0.2011	29.0638	-0.2201
22.5	28.4552	-0.1552	28.6849	-0.2776	29.0655	-0.3340
23.0	28.4139	-0.1949	28.6561	-0.3567	29.0578	-0.4518
23.5	28.3636	-0.2357	28.6181	-0.4382	29.0405	-0.5734
24.0	28.3044	-0.2777	28.5710	-0.5218	29.0139	-0.6983
24.5	28.2364	-0.3207	28.5150	-0.6076	28.9779	-0.8265
25.0	28.1597	-0.3647	28.4501	-0.6953	28.9328	-0.9577

ρ	$\phi=20°$		$\phi=25°$		$\phi=30°$	
	U	V	U	V	U	V
0.0	25.0000	0.0000	25.0000	0.0000	25.0000	0.0000
0.5	25.0040	0.0033	25.0033	0.0040	25.0026	0.0045
1.0	25.0160	0.0134	25.0134	0.0160	25.0104	0.0181
1.5	25.0359	0.0302	25.0301	0.0359	25.0234	0.0406
2.0	25.0639	0.0536	25.0536	0.0639	25.0417	0.0723
2.5	25.0999	0.0836	25.0840	0.0998	25.0654	0.1129
3.0	25.1441	0.1201	25.1212	0.1434	25.0945	0.1625
3.5	25.1963	0.1628	25.1655	0.1947	25.1294	0.2210
4.0	25.2568	0.2114	25.2171	0.2534	25.1704	0.2882
4.5	25.3256	0.2654	25.2762	0.3189	25.2178	0.3637
5.0	25.4026	0.3243	25.3432	0.3909	25.2722	0.4473
5.5	25.4879	0.3874	25.4181	0.4686	25.3341	0.5384
6.0	25.5815	0.4540	25.5015	0.5512	25.4041	0.6363
6.5	25.6832	0.5230	25.5934	0.6379	25.4828	0.7401
7.0	25.7929	0.5937	25.6941	0.7276	25.5709	0.8490
7.5	25.9102	0.6649	25.8036	0.8190	25.6689	0.9616
8.0	26.0347	0.7356	25.9219	0.9110	25.7772	1.0766
8.5	26.1662	0.8047	26.0490	1.0023	25.8962	1.1926
9.0	26.3038	0.8711	26.1845	1.0915	26.0261	1.3080
9.5	26.4471	0.9339	26.3281	1.1774	26.1669	1.4213
10.0	26.5954	0.9921	26.4792	1.2585	26.3183	1.5307
10.5	26.7477	1.0447	26.6373	1.3338	26.4801	1.6347
11.0	26.9034	1.0909	26.8015	1.4020	26.6516	1.7318
11.5	27.0615	1.1301	26.9711	1.4622	26.8322	1.8206
12.0	27.2211	1.1615	27.1453	1.5133	27.0210	1.8997
12.5	27.3815	1.1845	27.3231	1.5547	27.2173	1.9679
13.0	27.5417	1.1988	27.5035	1.5854	27.4200	2.0242
13.5	27.7008	1.2040	27.6857	1.6050	27.6282	2.0677
14.0	27.8581	1.1997	27.8686	1.6129	27.8407	2.0976
14.5	28.0126	1.1857	28.0514	1.6087	28.0565	2.1132
15.0	28.1636	1.1619	28.2330	1.5921	28.2746	2.1138
15.5	28.3103	1.1282	28.4126	1.5628	28.4938	2.0991
16.0	28.4520	1.0846	28.5892	1.5209	28.7130	2.0687
16.5	28.5880	1.0312	28.7619	1.4661	28.9312	2.0223
17.0	28.7177	0.9681	28.9300	1.3985	29.1472	1.9597
17.5	28.8405	0.8955	29.0925	1.3183	29.3600	1.8808
18.0	28.9558	0.8135	29.2487	1.2256	29.5684	1.7858
18.5	29.0632	0.7224	29.3978	1.1208	29.7714	1.6746
19.0	29.1622	0.6227	29.5392	1.0040	29.9679	1.5477
19.5	29.2523	0.5145	29.6723	0.8758	30.1570	1.4053
20.0	29.3334	0.3983	29.7964	0.7366	30.3376	1.2480
20.5	29.4051	0.2744	29.9111	0.5869	30.5088	1.0763
21.0	29.4672	0.1433	30.0159	0.4272	30.6699	0.8909
21.5	29.5194	0.0053	30.1105	0.2582	30.8202	0.6926
22.0	29.5618	−0.1390	30.1946	0.0803	30.9590	0.4822
22.5	29.5942	−0.2894	30.2680	−0.1057	31.0860	0.2606
23.0	29.6165	−0.4453	30.3305	−0.2993	31.2007	0.0288
23.5	29.6289	−0.6064	30.3822	−0.4999	31.3029	−0.2124
24.0	29.6313	−0.7723	30.4230	−0.7068	31.3925	−0.4619
24.5	29.6239	−0.9426	30.4529	−0.9196	31.4696	−0.7190
25.0	29.6067	−1.1170	30.4722	−1.1377	31.5343	−0.9828

TABLE II. $b_r(q) = U + iV$, $q = \rho e^{i\phi}$ $r = 5$

ρ	$\phi=35°$		$\phi=40°$		$\phi=45°$	
	U	V	U	V	U	V
0.0	25.0000	0.0000	25.0000	0.0000	25.0000	0.0000
0.5	25.0018	0.0049	25.0009	0.0051	25.0000	0.0052
1.0	25.0071	0.0196	25.0036	0.0205	25.0000	0.0208
1.5	25.0160	0.0441	25.0081	0.0462	25.0000	0.0469
2.0	25.0285	0.0784	25.0145	0.0822	24.9999	0.0835
2.5	25.0448	0.1226	25.0227	0.1286	24.9999	0.1307
3.0	25.0648	0.1767	25.0330	0.1855	25.0000	0.1886
3.5	25.0891	0.2407	25.0456	0.2531	25.0005	0.2576
4.0	25.1178	0.3146	25.0610	0.3314	25.0015	0.3378
4.5	25.1516	0.3982	25.0795	0.4206	25.0036	0.4298
5.0	25.1911	0.4914	25.1020	0.5209	25.0074	0.5339
5.5	25.2371	0.5940	25.1292	0.6324	25.0136	0.6507
6.0	25.2904	0.7055	25.1624	0.7550	25.0234	0.7807
6.5	25.3520	0.8254	25.2027	0.8885	25.0381	0.9242
7.0	25.4231	0.9528	25.2517	1.0328	25.0595	1.0818
7.5	25.5047	1.0867	25.3109	1.1870	25.0895	1.2534
8.0	25.5978	1.2259	25.3822	1.3504	25.1306	1.4390
8.5	25.7035	1.3689	25.4671	1.5216	25.1853	1.6378
9.0	25.8224	1.5140	25.5673	1.6990	25.2563	1.8486
9.5	25.9551	1.6592	25.6842	1.8806	25.3461	2.0697
10.0	26.1021	1.8027	25.8189	2.0641	25.4573	2.2985
10.5	26.2632	1.9424	25.9722	2.2470	25.5915	2.5323
11.0	26.4384	2.0764	26.1444	2.4269	25.7503	2.7676
11.5	26.6271	2.2028	26.3355	2.6011	25.9341	3.0012
12.0	26.8288	2.3197	26.5451	2.7673	26.1430	3.2297
12.5	27.0425	2.4255	26.7724	2.9233	26.3765	3.4501
13.0	27.2675	2.5188	27.0167	3.0670	26.6337	3.6597
13.5	27.5026	2.5982	27.2769	3.1967	26.9136	3.8561
14.0	27.7467	2.6625	27.5519	3.3108	27.2149	4.0374
14.5	27.9988	2.7108	27.8405	3.4079	27.5364	4.2018
15.0	28.2576	2.7421	28.1417	3.4867	27.8772	4.3479
15.5	28.5220	2.7556	28.4542	3.5460	28.2360	4.4742
16.0	28.7908	2.7505	28.7770	3.5847	28.6121	4.5796
16.5	29.0627	2.7262	29.1088	3.6017	29.0045	4.6625
17.0	29.3364	2.6822	29.4483	3.5959	29.4126	4.7217
17.5	29.6106	2.6180	29.7944	3.5664	29.8356	4.7556
18.0	29.8838	2.5333	30.1454	3.5119	30.2727	4.7624
18.5	30.1547	2.4277	30.4998	3.4316	30.7231	4.7402
19.0	30.4217	2.3013	30.8558	3.3244	31.1857	4.6865
19.5	30.6833	2.1541	31.2113	3.1895	31.6591	4.5987
20.0	30.9379	1.9864	31.5639	3.0262	32.1411	4.4737
20.5	31.1838	1.7987	31.9110	2.8342	32.6288	4.3083
21.0	31.4196	1.5916	32.2497	2.6135	33.1182	4.0990
21.5	31.6439	1.3661	32.5771	2.3646	33.6036	3.8427
22.0	31.8552	1.1234	32.8899	2.0887	34.0777	3.5377
22.5	32.0526	0.8647	33.1854	1.7878	34.5315	3.1840
23.0	32.2352	0.5916	33.4611	1.4643	34.9558	2.7851
23.5	32.4024	0.3056	33.7150	1.1213	35.3421	2.3476
24.0	32.5537	0.0084	33.9462	0.7619	35.6849	1.8814
24.5	32.6892	−0.2986	34.1541	0.3895	35.9826	1.3968
25.0	32.8090	−0.6139	34.3391	0.0073	36.2374	0.9036

ρ	$\phi=50°$		$\phi=55°$		$\phi=60°$	
	U	V	U	V	U	V
0.0	25.0000	0.0000	25.0000	0.0000	25.0000	0.0000
0.5	24.9991	0.0051	24.9982	0.0049	24.9974	0.0045
1.0	24.9964	0.0205	24.9929	0.0196	24.9898	0.0180
1.5	24.9918	0.0462	24.9839	0.0441	24.9765	0.0406
2.0	24.9854	0.0822	24.9713	0.0784	24.9581	0.0722
2.5	24.9771	0.1287	24.9550	0.1227	24.9343	0.1129
3.0	24.9670	0.1858	24.9349	0.1771	24.9049	0.1629
3.5	24.9551	0.2539	24.9110	0.2420	24.8697	0.2224
4.0	24.9415	0.3334	24.8831	0.3179	24.8284	0.2919
4.5	24.9265	0.4248	24.8512	0.4054	24.7806	0.3719
5.0	24.9105	0.5290	24.8154	0.5053	24.7260	0.4633
5.5	24.8941	0.6467	24.7757	0.6189	24.6641	0.5672
6.0	24.8779	0.7790	24.7324	0.7474	24.5944	0.6852
6.5	24.8634	0.9271	24.6862	0.8928	24.5166	0.8193
7.0	24.8519	1.0922	24.6379	1.0571	24.4304	0.9720
7.5	24.8456	1.2755	24.5891	1.2427	24.3357	1.1467
8.0	24.8473	1.4780	24.5420	1.4524	24.2334	1.3478
8.5	24.8601	1.7004	24.5001	1.6889	24.1251	1.5806
9.0	24.8881	1.9426	24.4681	1.9546	24.0144	1.8514
9.5	24.9354	2.2038	24.4520	2.2512	23.9078	2.1672
10.0	25.0065	2.4818	24.4591	2.5784	23.8156	2.5339
10.5	25.1052	2.7735	24.4972	2.9337	23.7523	2.9540
11.0	25.2346	3.0746	24.5733	3.3119	23.7350	3.4233
11.5	25.3967	3.3804	24.6923	3.7056	23.7776	3.9294
12.0	25.5921	3.6860	24.8565	4.1067	23.8871	4.4553
12.5	25.8205	3.9869	25.0654	4.5077	24.0620	4.9847
13.0	26.0807	4.2793	25.3167	4.9022	24.2956	5.5059
13.5	26.3713	4.5601	25.6074	5.2859	24.5800	6.0122
14.0	26.6905	4.8270	25.9342	5.6559	24.9076	6.5008
14.5	27.0368	5.0779	26.2942	6.0106	25.2727	6.9713
15.0	27.4087	5.3117	26.6850	6.3492	25.6710	7.4243
15.5	27.8054	5.5271	27.1051	6.6714	26.0994	7.8614
16.0	28.2260	5.7233	27.5534	6.9774	26.5561	8.2842
16.5	28.6701	5.8992	28.0294	7.2673	27.0399	8.6945
17.0	29.1378	6.0540	28.5333	7.5415	27.5502	9.0943
17.5	29.6292	6.1864	29.0656	7.8005	28.0871	9.4855
18.0	30.1451	6.2951	29.6276	8.0448	28.6507	9.8704
18.5	30.6864	6.3783	30.2212	8.2750	29.2417	10.2515
19.0	31.2546	6.4337	30.8491	8.4916	29.8611	10.6316
19.5	31.8515	6.4580	31.5149	8.6957	30.5096	11.0139
20.0	32.4795	6.4471	32.2234	8.8885	31.1881	11.4026
20.5	33.1413	6.3947	32.9813	9.0723	31.8972	11.8024
21.0	33.8399	6.2921	33.7977	9.2506	32.6364	12.2193
21.5	34.5780	6.1260	34.6854	9.4304	33.4041	12.6601
22.0	35.3556	5.8757	35.6624	9.6256	34.1962	13.1322
22.5	36.1636	5.5099	36.7519	9.8663	35.0057	13.6424
23.0	36.9669	4.9883	37.9700	10.2194	35.8224	14.1952
23.5	37.6834	4.2925	39.2622	10.7970	36.6342	14.7913
24.0	38.2223	3.4873	40.4453	11.6217	37.4295	15.4259
24.5	38.5808	2.6836	41.4204	12.5363	38.2001	16.0905
25.0	38.8196	1.9382	42.2429	13.4274	38.9422	16.7749

TABLE II. $b_r(q) = U + iV$, $q = \rho e^{i\phi}$ $\qquad\qquad$ $r=5$

ρ	$\phi=65°$		$\phi=70°$		$\phi=75°$	
	U	V	U	V	U	V
0.0	25.0000	0.0000	25.0000	0.0000	25.0000	0.0000
0.5	24.9967	0.0040	24.9960	0.0033	24.9955	0.0026
1.0	24.9866	0.0159	24.9840	0.0134	24.9820	0.0104
1.5	24.9698	0.0359	24.9641	0.0301	24.9594	0.0234
2.0	24.9462	0.0637	24.9360	0.0534	24.9277	0.0414
2.5	24.9157	0.0996	24.8997	0.0833	24.8869	0.0645
3.0	24.8779	0.1435	24.8549	0.1197	24.8366	0.0924
3.5	24.8327	0.1956	24.8013	0.1627	24.7765	0.1249
4.0	24.7795	0.2562	24.7383	0.2123	24.7061	0.1620
4.5	24.7177	0.3256	24.6651	0.2685	24.6247	0.2031
5.0	24.6466	0.4045	24.5808	0.3315	24.5312	0.2481
5.5	24.5651	0.4936	24.4839	0.4016	24.4243	0.2966
6.0	24.4720	0.5942	24.3728	0.4794	24.3022	0.3481
6.5	24.3660	0.7080	24.2453	0.5654	24.1626	0.4019
7.0	24.2450	0.8373	24.0983	0.6607	24.0022	0.4575
7.5	24.1073	0.9852	23.9280	0.7671	23.8169	0.5139
8.0	23.9504	1.1566	23.7293	0.8870	23.6010	0.5698
8.5	23.7719	1.3578	23.4951	1.0242	23.3466	0.6231
9.0	23.5702	1.5987	23.2155	1.1851	23.0423	0.6703
9.5	23.3454	1.8930	22.8757	1.3809	22.6708	0.7046
10.0	23.1034	2.2606	22.4535	1.6341	22.2043	0.7108
10.5	22.8633	2.7254	21.9152	1.9976	21.5965	0.6477
11.0	22.6662	3.3035	21.2465	2.6226	20.7949	0.3771
11.5	22.5663	3.9782	20.7477	3.7244	20.0200	−0.3739
12.0	22.5931	4.6969	20.7492	4.8917	19.6775	−1.3204
12.5	22.7345	5.4095	20.9716	5.8798	19.5817	−2.1646
13.0	22.9621	6.0922	21.2738	6.7417	19.5876	−2.9154
13.5	23.2515	6.7401	21.6161	7.5225	19.6454	−3.6043
14.0	23.5868	7.3557	21.9846	8.2484	19.7346	−4.2523
14.5	23.9581	7.9439	22.3733	8.9353	19.8454	−4.8730
15.0	24.3591	8.5093	22.7790	9.5938	19.9721	−5.4753
15.5	24.7861	9.0563	23.2003	10.2313	20.1110	−6.0658
16.0	25.2367	9.5887	23.6361	10.8535	20.2596	−6.6489
16.5	25.7091	10.1098	24.0856	11.4646	20.4160	−7.2283
17.0	26.2025	10.6228	24.5483	12.0682	20.5787	−7.8064
17.5	26.7160	11.1305	25.0235	12.6674	20.7462	−8.3855
18.0	27.2491	11.6356	25.5107	13.2647	20.9175	−8.9670
18.5	27.8012	12.1409	26.0092	13.8625	21.0915	−9.5521
19.0	28.3716	12.6490	26.5181	14.4627	21.2672	−10.1419
19.5	28.9596	13.1627	27.0365	15.0672	21.4437	−10.7370
20.0	29.5640	13.6846	27.5633	15.6775	21.6202	−11.3378
20.5	30.1833	14.2173	28.0974	16.2951	21.7959	−11.9446
21.0	30.8155	14.7634	28.6372	16.9208	21.9702	−12.5576
21.5	31.4580	15.3249	29.1813	17.5556	22.1425	−13.1768
22.0	32.1080	15.9033	29.7283	18.1998	22.3123	−13.8021
22.5	32.7622	16.4996	30.2766	18.8535	22.4790	−14.4334
23.0	33.4170	17.1138	30.8249	19.5167	22.6424	−15.0704
23.5	34.0693	17.7452	31.3718	20.1889	22.8022	−15.7129
24.0	34.7162	18.3920	31.9163	20.8694	22.9580	−16.3606
24.5	35.3555	19.0521	32.4575	21.5575	23.1098	−17.0132
25.0	35.9859	19.7232	32.9948	22.2523	23.2575	−17.6704

TABLE II. $b_r(q) = U + iV$, $q = \rho e^{i\phi}$ $r = 5$

ρ	$\phi = 80°$		$\phi = 85°$		$\phi = 90°$	
	U	V	U	V	U	V
0.0	25.0000	0.0000	25.0000	0.0000	25.0000	0.0000
0.5	24.9951	0.0018	24.9949	0.0009	24.9948	−0.0000
1.0	24.9804	0.0071	24.9795	0.0036	24.9792	−0.0000
1.5	24.9560	0.0160	24.9539	0.0081	24.9532	−0.0001
2.0	24.9217	0.0282	24.9181	0.0142	24.9169	−0.0002
2.5	24.8775	0.0438	24.8720	0.0218	24.8703	−0.0007
3.0	24.8234	0.0623	24.8157	0.0306	24.8136	−0.0017
3.5	24.7589	0.0836	24.7490	0.0403	24.7469	−0.0037
4.0	24.6838	0.1072	24.6719	0.0501	24.6702	−0.0073
4.5	24.5975	0.1324	24.5840	0.0594	24.5837	−0.0133
5.0	24.4993	0.1586	24.4851	0.0670	24.4876	−0.0228
5.5	24.3881	0.1846	24.3748	0.0717	24.3822	−0.0373
6.0	24.2625	0.2092	24.2523	0.0715	24.2677	−0.0585
6.5	24.1208	0.2308	24.1171	0.0642	24.1447	−0.0887
7.0	23.9607	0.2470	23.9684	0.0469	24.0138	−0.1308
7.5	23.7794	0.2548	23.8054	0.0157	23.8762	−0.1880
8.0	23.5733	0.2500	23.6277	−0.0341	23.7335	−0.2641
8.5	23.3384	0.2265	23.4355	−0.1089	23.5886	−0.3635
9.0	23.0699	0.1753	23.2302	−0.2161	23.4452	−0.4904
9.5	22.7640	0.0827	23.0158	−0.3647	23.3088	−0.6490
10.0	22.4202	−0.0719	22.8002	−0.5641	23.1864	−0.8420
10.5	22.0495	−0.3165	22.5959	−0.8212	23.0857	−1.0701
11.0	21.6850	−0.6779	22.4194	−1.1376	23.0148	−1.3315
11.5	21.3807	−1.1556	22.2868	−1.5068	22.9801	−1.6218
12.0	21.1771	−1.7102	22.2085	−1.9157	22.9859	−1.9350
12.5	21.0763	−2.2932	22.1875	−2.3499	23.0336	−2.2652
13.0	21.0580	−2.8755	22.2204	−2.7975	23.1227	−2.6070
13.5	21.1010	−3.4465	22.3010	−3.2511	23.2513	−2.9566
14.0	21.1891	−4.0050	22.4229	−3.7068	23.4167	−3.3116
14.5	21.3117	−4.5529	22.5801	−4.1633	23.6164	−3.6706
15.0	21.4611	−5.0932	22.7679	−4.6207	23.8479	−4.0336
15.5	21.6322	−5.6289	22.9822	−5.0800	24.1090	−4.4009
16.0	21.8211	−6.1626	23.2198	−5.5425	24.3977	−4.7734
16.5	22.0249	−6.6970	23.4781	−6.0098	24.7123	−5.1526
17.0	22.2412	−7.2339	23.7546	−6.4836	25.0514	−5.5401
17.5	22.4678	−7.7751	24.0473	−6.9655	25.4135	−5.9377
18.0	22.7031	−8.3222	24.3540	−7.4571	25.7971	−6.3475
18.5	22.9452	−8.8762	24.6729	−7.9597	26.2006	−6.7717
19.0	23.1927	−9.4382	25.0020	−8.4746	26.6220	−7.2125
19.5	23.4440	−10.0088	25.3392	−9.0029	27.0593	−7.6724
20.0	23.6979	−10.5886	25.6825	−9.5454	27.5097	−8.1533
20.5	23.9530	−11.1777	26.0297	−10.1025	27.9702	−8.6572
21.0	24.2080	−11.7762	26.3789	−10.6745	28.4371	−9.1853
21.5	24.4620	−12.3841	26.7279	−11.2611	28.9065	−9.7382
22.0	24.7138	−13.0010	27.0751	−11.8619	29.3743	−10.3158
22.5	24.9628	−13.6266	27.4187	−12.4760	29.8366	−10.9166
23.0	25.2081	−14.2604	27.7573	−13.1026	30.2902	−11.5385
23.5	25.4493	−14.9017	28.0899	−13.7402	30.7323	−12.1787
24.0	25.6859	−15.5501	28.4158	−14.3878	31.1612	−12.8340
24.5	25.9176	−16.2049	28.7344	−15.0441	31.5762	−13.5013
25.0	26.1443	−16.8655	29.0455	−15.7077	31.9774	−14.1776

TABLE II. $b_r(q) = U + iV$, $q = \rho e^{i\phi}$ $r=6$

ρ	$\phi=5°$		$\phi=10°$		$\phi=15°$	
	U	V	U	V	U	V
0.0	36.0000	0.0000	36.0000	0.0000	36.0000	0.0000
0.5	36.0035	0.0006	36.0034	0.0012	36.0031	0.0018
1.0	36.0141	0.0025	36.0134	0.0049	36.0124	0.0071
1.5	36.0317	0.0056	36.0302	0.0110	36.0278	0.0161
2.0	36.0563	0.0099	36.0537	0.0196	36.0495	0.0286
2.5	36.0881	0.0156	36.0840	0.0306	36.0774	0.0448
3.0	36.1269	0.0224	36.1211	0.0442	36.1115	0.0645
3.5	36.1728	0.0306	36.1649	0.0602	36.1519	0.0879
4.0	36.2259	0.0399	36.2155	0.0787	36.1985	0.1150
4.5	36.2861	0.0506	36.2729	0.0996	36.2514	0.1456
5.0	36.3534	0.0625	36.3372	0.1231	36.3106	0.1799
5.5	36.4278	0.0756	36.4082	0.1489	36.3761	0.2178
6.0	36.5093	0.0899	36.4861	0.1771	36.4480	0.2592
6.5	36.5977	0.1053	36.5707	0.2076	36.5263	0.3039
7.0	36.6931	0.1218	36.6620	0.2402	36.6110	0.3520
7.5	36.7952	0.1393	36.7600	0.2750	36.7021	0.4033
8.0	36.9040	0.1578	36.8646	0.3116	36.7995	0.4575
8.5	37.0193	0.1770	36.9756	0.3499	36.9034	0.5144
9.0	37.1408	0.1970	37.0930	0.3898	37.0136	0.5738
9.5	37.2682	0.2176	37.2164	0.4309	37.1301	0.6353
10.0	37.4014	0.2386	37.3458	0.4730	37.2528	0.6986
10.5	37.5399	0.2599	37.4809	0.5158	37.3817	0.7634
11.0	37.6835	0.2813	37.6214	0.5591	37.5165	0.8291
11.5	37.8316	0.3027	37.7669	0.6024	37.6571	0.8953
12.0	37.9840	0.3239	37.9172	0.6456	37.8033	0.9616
12.5	38.1401	0.3448	38.0719	0.6881	37.9548	1.0275
13.0	38.2995	0.3652	38.2305	0.7298	38.1113	1.0924
13.5	38.4617	0.3848	38.3926	0.7703	38.2726	1.1560
14.0	38.6262	0.4036	38.5578	0.8092	38.4382	1.2176
14.5	38.7925	0.4214	38.7256	0.8462	38.6077	1.2767
15.0	38.9600	0.4380	38.8955	0.8811	38.7806	1.3330
15.5	39.1283	0.4534	39.0669	0.9136	38.9567	1.3860
16.0	39.2968	0.4674	39.2394	0.9433	39.1352	1.4351
16.5	39.4649	0.4798	39.4125	0.9701	39.3158	1.4801
17.0	39.6323	0.4907	39.5856	0.9937	39.4979	1.5205
17.5	39.7983	0.4998	39.7582	1.0140	39.6809	1.5560
18.0	39.9625	0.5071	39.9299	1.0307	39.8644	1.5864
18.5	40.1245	0.5126	40.1000	1.0437	40.0478	1.6113
19.0	40.2837	0.5161	40.2682	1.0529	40.2306	1.6305
19.5	40.4398	0.5178	40.4340	1.0583	40.4122	1.6439
20.0	40.5923	0.5174	40.5968	1.0596	40.5921	1.6513
20.5	40.7409	0.5150	40.7563	1.0569	40.7698	1.6525
21.0	40.8851	0.5106	40.9121	1.0501	40.9449	1.6474
21.5	41.0247	0.5042	41.0637	1.0392	41.1167	1.6361
22.0	41.1592	0.4958	41.2108	1.0242	41.2850	1.6185
22.5	41.2885	0.4854	41.3530	1.0052	41.4492	1.5945
23.0	41.4122	0.4731	41.4901	0.9821	41.6088	1.5643
23.5	41.5300	0.4588	41.6216	0.9551	41.7637	1.5278
24.0	41.6419	0.4425	41.7474	0.9241	41.9132	1.4852
24.5	41.7474	0.4245	41.8671	0.8893	42.0572	1.4366
25.0	41.8466	0.4046	41.9806	0.8508	42.1952	1.3820

TABLE II. $b_r(q) = U + iV$, $q = \rho e^{i\phi}$ $r = 6$

ρ	$\phi=20°$		$\phi=25°$		$\phi=30°$	
	U	V	U	V	U	V
0.0	36.0000	0.0000	36.0000	0.0000	36.0000	0.0000
0.5	36.0027	0.0023	36.0023	0.0027	36.0018	0.0031
1.0	36.0109	0.0092	36.0092	0.0109	36.0071	0.0124
1.5	36.0246	0.0207	36.0207	0.0246	36.0161	0.0279
2.0	36.0438	0.0368	36.0367	0.0438	36.0285	0.0495
2.5	36.0684	0.0575	36.0574	0.0686	36.0446	0.0775
3.0	36.0986	0.0829	36.0826	0.0988	36.0642	0.1116
3.5	36.1342	0.1130	36.1125	0.1346	36.0873	0.1521
4.0	36.1754	0.1478	36.1469	0.1760	36.1140	0.1989
4.5	36.2222	0.1872	36.1861	0.2231	36.1443	0.2520
5.0	36.2745	0.2314	36.2299	0.2757	36.1782	0.3116
5.5	36.3325	0.2801	36.2785	0.3340	36.2158	0.3775
6.0	36.3962	0.3335	36.3320	0.3979	36.2572	0.4500
6.5	36.4657	0.3915	36.3904	0.4673	36.3025	0.5290
7.0	36.5411	0.4538	36.4539	0.5424	36.3520	0.6145
7.5	36.6224	0.5205	36.5228	0.6228	36.4056	0.7065
8.0	36.7098	0.5913	36.5970	0.7086	36.4639	0.8051
8.5	36.8033	0.6659	36.6770	0.7996	36.5270	0.9102
9.0	36.9032	0.7442	36.7630	0.8955	36.5953	1.0218
9.5	37.0094	0.8257	36.8551	0.9961	36.6693	1.1396
10.0	37.1221	0.9102	36.9538	1.1010	36.7494	1.2635
10.5	37.2413	0.9970	37.0593	1.2099	36.8361	1.3933
11.0	37.3672	1.0859	37.1719	1.3222	36.9301	1.5286
11.5	37.4996	1.1761	37.2918	1.4374	37.0317	1.6689
12.0	37.6387	1.2672	37.4194	1.5549	37.1418	1.8137
12.5	37.7843	1.3586	37.5548	1.6740	37.2608	1.9623
13.0	37.9364	1.4494	37.6983	1.7938	37.3893	2.1140
13.5	38.0947	1.5392	37.8499	1.9137	37.5278	2.2678
14.0	38.2591	1.6272	38.0096	2.0326	37.6767	2.4228
14.5	38.4293	1.7127	38.1774	2.1498	37.8364	2.5778
15.0	38.6049	1.7951	38.3532	2.2644	38.0071	2.7317
15.5	38.7856	1.8736	38.5368	2.3753	38.1887	2.8833
16.0	38.9709	1.9477	38.7278	2.4818	38.3815	3.0314
16.5	39.1605	2.0167	38.9259	2.5829	38.5850	3.1748
17.0	39.3537	2.0801	39.1307	2.6778	38.7991	3.3123
17.5	39.5500	2.1374	39.3416	2.7657	39.0232	3.4427
18.0	39.7490	2.1880	39.5581	2.8460	39.2570	3.5649
18.5	39.9499	2.2316	39.7795	2.9179	39.4998	3.6781
19.0	40.1523	2.2678	40.0054	2.9808	39.7510	3.7811
19.5	40.3554	2.2961	40.2349	3.0342	40.0098	3.8733
20.0	40.5588	2.3164	40.4674	3.0776	40.2755	3.9538
20.5	40.7618	2.3284	40.7021	3.1105	40.5473	4.0219
21.0	40.9638	2.3319	40.9385	3.1327	40.8244	4.0771
21.5	41.1642	2.3268	41.1757	3.1437	41.1059	4.1187
22.0	41.3625	2.3129	41.4131	3.1433	41.3911	4.1463
22.5	41.5580	2.2902	41.6498	3.1314	41.6790	4.1593
23.0	41.7503	2.2587	41.8853	3.1078	41.9688	4.1576
23.5	41.9387	2.2184	42.1187	3.0724	42.2596	4.1406
24.0	42.1228	2.1693	42.3494	3.0252	42.5505	4.1083
24.5	42.3020	2.1117	42.5766	2.9661	42.8404	4.0602
25.0	42.4760	2.0455	42.7997	2.8953	43.1286	3.9964

TABLE II. $b_r(q) = U + iV$, $q = \rho e^{i\phi}$ $r = 6$

ρ	$\phi = 35°$		$\phi = 40°$		$\phi = 45°$	
	U	V	U	V	U	V
0.0	36.0000	0.0000	36.0000	0.0000	36.0000	0.0000
0.5	36.0012	0.0034	36.0006	0.0035	36.0000	0.0036
1.0	36.0049	0.0134	36.0025	0.0141	36.0000	0.0143
1.5	36.0110	0.0302	36.0056	0.0317	36.0000	0.0321
2.0	36.0195	0.0537	36.0099	0.0563	35.9999	0.0571
2.5	36.0304	0.0840	36.0154	0.0880	35.9998	0.0893
3.0	36.0437	0.1211	36.0220	0.1268	35.9997	0.1286
3.5	36.0595	0.1649	36.0298	0.1727	35.9994	0.1751
4.0	36.0776	0.2156	36.0388	0.2257	35.9989	0.2288
4.5	36.0981	0.2732	36.0489	0.2859	35.9983	0.2898
5.0	36.1210	0.3378	36.0600	0.3535	35.9974	0.3581
5.5	36.1463	0.4094	36.0723	0.4284	35.9962	0.4339
6.0	36.1743	0.4881	36.0857	0.5108	35.9947	0.5172
6.5	36.2048	0.5741	36.1003	0.6009	35.9928	0.6083
7.0	36.2381	0.6674	36.1162	0.6988	35.9905	0.7074
7.5	36.2744	0.7682	36.1334	0.8049	35.9878	0.8148
8.0	36.3140	0.8766	36.1522	0.9193	35.9846	0.9308
8.5	36.3571	0.9927	36.1728	1.0425	35.9812	1.0560
9.0	36.4042	1.1168	36.1956	1.1746	35.9775	1.1907
9.5	36.4558	1.2488	36.2209	1.3162	35.9738	1.3357
10.0	36.5124	1.3888	36.2493	1.4676	35.9704	1.4917
10.5	36.5748	1.5369	36.2815	1.6293	35.9676	1.6595
11.0	36.6436	1.6930	36.3183	1.8016	35.9662	1.8401
11.5	36.7198	1.8569	36.3609	1.9849	35.9670	2.0345
12.0	36.8044	2.0284	36.4103	2.1795	35.9711	2.2439
12.5	36.8983	2.2070	36.4681	2.3855	35.9800	2.4693
13.0	37.0026	2.3922	36.5358	2.6029	35.9956	2.7119
13.5	37.1185	2.5830	36.6153	2.8312	36.0204	2.9726
14.0	37.2468	2.7786	36.7084	3.0699	36.0572	3.2518
14.5	37.3886	2.9776	36.8170	3.3180	36.1093	3.5496
15.0	37.5447	3.1788	36.9430	3.5739	36.1805	3.8652
15.5	37.7156	3.3806	37.0880	3.8360	36.2744	4.1969
16.0	37.9018	3.5813	37.2534	4.1020	36.3945	4.5422
16.5	38.1035	3.7794	37.4401	4.3695	36.5437	4.8975
17.0	38.3208	3.9731	37.6488	4.6362	36.7238	5.2587
17.5	38.5533	4.1607	37.8795	4.8994	36.9359	5.6214
18.0	38.8006	4.3407	38.1320	5.1567	37.1797	5.9815
18.5	39.0623	4.5116	38.4057	5.4061	37.4544	6.3352
19.0	39.3376	4.6721	38.6998	5.6454	37.7585	6.6795
19.5	39.6257	4.8210	39.0134	5.8731	38.0902	7.0119
20.0	39.9260	4.9571	39.3455	6.0875	38.4479	7.3305
20.5	40.2374	5.0794	39.6951	6.2875	38.8298	7.6340
21.0	40.5592	5.1870	40.0611	6.4719	39.2345	7.9215
21.5	40.8904	5.2791	40.4428	6.6397	39.6607	8.1921
22.0	41.2303	5.3549	40.8391	6.7900	40.1075	8.4453
22.5	41.5777	5.4136	41.2495	6.9219	40.5742	8.6807
23.0	41.9320	5.4545	41.6731	7.0346	41.0604	8.8980
23.5	42.2921	5.4771	42.1093	7.1271	41.5658	9.0965
24.0	42.6571	5.4805	42.5575	7.1985	42.0907	9.2758
24.5	43.0258	5.4642	43.0172	7.2476	42.6351	9.4352
25.0	43.3973	5.4275	43.4876	7.2732	43.1998	9.5740

TABLE II. $b_r(q) = U + iV$, $q = \rho e^{i\phi}$ $\qquad\qquad r = 6$

ρ	$\phi = 50°$		$\phi = 55°$		$\phi = 60°$	
	U	V	U	V	U	V
0.0	36.0000	0.0000	36.0000	0.0000	36.0000	0.0000
0.5	35.9994	0.0035	35.9988	0.0034	35.9982	0.0031
1.0	35.9975	0.0141	35.9951	0.0134	35.9929	0.0124
1.5	35.9944	0.0316	35.9890	0.0302	35.9839	0.0278
2.0	35.9900	0.0563	35.9804	0.0537	35.9714	0.0494
2.5	35.9843	0.0879	35.9693	0.0838	35.9553	0.0772
3.0	35.9773	0.1265	35.9557	0.1206	35.9355	0.1110
3.5	35.9690	0.1722	35.9396	0.1641	35.9121	0.1510
4.0	35.9592	0.2250	35.9208	0.2142	35.8849	0.1970
4.5	35.9479	0.2848	35.8993	0.2710	35.8539	0.2490
5.0	35.9350	0.3517	35.8750	0.3344	35.8191	0.3070
5.5	35.9205	0.4258	35.8477	0.4045	35.7802	0.3710
6.0	35.9042	0.5073	35.8174	0.4814	35.7370	0.4408
6.5	35.8860	0.5962	35.7837	0.5650	35.6895	0.5165
7.0	35.8657	0.6928	35.7464	0.6556	35.6371	0.5980
7.5	35.8431	0.7973	35.7053	0.7533	35.5796	0.6853
8.0	35.8181	0.9101	35.6599	0.8583	35.5165	0.7784
8.5	35.7906	1.0317	35.6098	0.9709	35.4472	0.8774
9.0	35.7601	1.1626	35.5545	1.0915	35.3710	0.9824
9.5	35.7267	1.3036	35.4934	1.2208	35.2870	1.0934
10.0	35.6901	1.4555	35.4257	1.3594	35.1942	1.2107
10.5	35.6502	1.6195	35.3507	1.5083	35.0911	1.3347
11.0	35.6070	1.7969	35.2673	1.6687	34.9762	1.4656
11.5	35.5605	1.9893	35.1746	1.8422	34.8475	1.6042
12.0	35.5112	2.1987	35.0713	2.0309	34.7023	1.7514
12.5	35.4598	2.4275	34.9562	2.2376	34.5375	1.9083
13.0	35.4074	2.6783	34.8281	2.4660	34.3489	2.0767
13.5	35.3560	2.9544	34.6856	2.7210	34.1309	2.2590
14.0	35.3088	3.2589	34.5283	3.0094	33.8760	2.4589
14.5	35.2701	3.5953	34.3568	3.3402	33.5731	2.6825
15.0	35.2460	3.9660	34.1748	3.7255	33.2056	2.9396
15.5	35.2444	4.3720	33.9917	4.1802	32.7463	3.2500
16.0	35.2743	4.8118	33.8276	4.7189	32.1449	3.6609
16.5	35.3444	5.2804	33.7152	5.3464	31.3111	4.3406
17.0	35.4614	5.7699	33.6916	6.0456	30.6147	5.8346
17.5	35.6288	6.2703	33.7770	6.7783	30.8190	7.3154
18.0	35.8465	6.7720	33.9650	7.5061	31.2260	8.4385
18.5	36.1113	7.2670	34.2353	8.2063	31.6756	9.3819
19.0	36.4188	7.7495	34.5673	8.8712	32.1430	10.2195
19.5	36.7643	8.2162	34.9457	9.5006	32.6222	10.9867
20.0	37.1434	8.6652	35.3601	10.0977	33.1114	11.7032
20.5	37.5526	9.0958	35.8038	10.6661	33.6103	12.3816
21.0	37.9888	9.5081	36.2723	11.2095	34.1188	13.0302
21.5	38.4499	9.9025	36.7628	11.7314	34.6371	13.6552
22.0	38.9345	10.2796	37.2734	12.2344	35.1654	14.2613
22.5	39.4414	10.6403	37.8031	12.7214	35.7039	14.8522
23.0	39.9702	10.9853	38.3511	13.1945	36.2528	15.4308
23.5	40.5207	11.3155	38.9172	13.6560	36.8122	15.9998
24.0	41.0930	11.6317	39.5011	14.1077	37.3823	16.5615
24.5	41.6879	11.9348	40.1031	14.5517	37.9630	17.1180
25.0	42.3060	12.2256	40.7231	14.9898	38.5543	17.6710

ρ	$\phi=65°$		$\phi=70°$		$\phi=75°$	
	U	V	U	V	U	V
0.0	36.0000	0.0000	36.0000	0.0000	36.0000	0.0000
0.5	35.9977	0.0027	35.9973	0.0023	35.9969	0.0018
1.0	35.9908	0.0109	35.9891	0.0092	35.9876	0.0071
1.5	35.9793	0.0246	35.9754	0.0206	35.9722	0.0161
2.0	35.9633	0.0437	35.9562	0.0367	35.9505	0.0285
2.5	35.9426	0.0682	35.9316	0.0572	35.9228	0.0445
3.0	35.9173	0.0981	35.9015	0.0823	35.8888	0.0639
3.5	35.8873	0.1334	35.8660	0.1118	35.8488	0.0868
4.0	35.8527	0.1739	35.8250	0.1456	35.8026	0.1131
4.5	35.8133	0.2196	35.7784	0.1838	35.7503	0.1426
5.0	35.7691	0.2705	35.7263	0.2261	35.6920	0.1752
5.5	35.7199	0.3264	35.6687	0.2724	35.6277	0.2109
6.0	35.6657	0.3871	35.6053	0.3225	35.5573	0.2492
6.5	35.6062	0.4526	35.5362	0.3762	35.4809	0.2901
7.0	35.5412	0.5227	35.4612	0.4332	35.3986	0.3331
7.5	35.4703	0.5971	35.3800	0.4931	35.3103	0.3778
8.0	35.3930	0.6755	35.2925	0.5554	35.2160	0.4237
8.5	35.3089	0.7578	35.1983	0.6197	35.1158	0.4702
9.0	35.2173	0.8436	35.0970	0.6852	35.0096	0.5164
9.5	35.1172	0.9325	34.9880	0.7511	34.8975	0.5613
10.0	35.0078	1.0239	34.8708	0.8165	34.7794	0.6039
10.5	34.8875	1.1175	34.7446	0.8802	34.6553	0.6427
11.0	34.7549	1.2125	34.6084	0.9406	34.5253	0.6761
11.5	34.6079	1.3080	34.4613	0.9961	34.3895	0.7022
12.0	34.4441	1.4031	34.3020	1.0443	34.2482	0.7188
12.5	34.2602	1.4963	34.1293	1.0824	34.1020	0.7231
13.0	34.0523	1.5856	33.9419	1.1069	33.9518	0.7124
13.5	33.8154	1.6681	33.7387	1.1133	33.7985	0.6834
14.0	33.5430	1.7394	33.5191	1.0958	33.6446	0.6327
14.5	33.2269	1.7923	33.2839	1.0475	33.4928	0.5569
15.0	32.8571	1.8145	33.0355	0.9600	33.3468	0.4532
15.5	32.4231	1.7844	32.7799	0.8245	33.2114	0.3193
16.0	31.9217	1.6637	32.5272	0.6338	33.0916	0.1544
16.5	31.3792	1.3973	32.2912	0.3844	32.9928	-0.0410
17.0	30.8782	0.9528	32.0868	0.0796	32.9197	-0.2646
17.5	30.5068	0.3819	31.9254	-0.2710	32.8755	-0.5133
18.0	30.2760	-0.2282	31.8126	-0.6549	32.8625	-0.7833
18.5	30.1503	-0.8298	31.7480	-1.0600	32.8810	-1.0707
19.0	30.0958	-1.4092	31.7275	-1.4777	32.9307	-1.3724
19.5	30.0899	-1.9662	31.7456	-1.9021	33.0100	-1.6857
20.0	30.1185	-2.5046	31.7966	-2.3302	33.1172	-2.0089
20.5	30.1725	-3.0282	31.8757	-2.7606	33.2502	-2.3408
21.0	30.2458	-3.5410	31.9786	-3.1931	33.4071	-2.6809
21.5	30.3342	-4.0460	32.1017	-3.6279	33.5858	-3.0292
22.0	30.4345	-4.5459	32.2421	-4.0657	33.7845	-3.3857
22.5	30.5444	-5.0428	32.3972	-4.5073	34.0015	-3.7509
23.0	30.6619	-5.5385	32.5650	-4.9535	34.2350	-4.1255
23.5	30.7856	-6.0344	32.7435	-5.4050	34.4834	-4.5102
24.0	30.9141	-6.5318	32.9310	-5.8627	34.7452	-4.9056
24.5	31.0462	-7.0315	33.1260	-6.3273	35.0188	-5.3126
25.0	31.1810	-7.5345	33.3271	-6.7992	35.3028	-5.7319

TABLE II. $b_r(q) = U + iV, \quad q = \rho e^{i\phi}$ $r = 6$

ρ	$\phi=80°$		$\phi=85°$		$\phi=90°$	
	U	V	U	V	U	V
0.0	36.0000	0.0000	36.0000	0.0000	36.0000	0.0000
0.5	35.9966	0.0012	35.9965	0.0006	35.9964	0.0000
1.0	35.9866	0.0049	35.9859	0.0025	35.9857	0.0000
1.5	35.9698	0.0110	35.9684	0.0056	35.9679	0.0000
2.0	35.9464	0.0195	35.9438	0.0099	35.9429	0.0000
2.5	35.9162	0.0304	35.9122	0.0154	35.9109	0.0000
3.0	35.8795	0.0437	35.8737	0.0222	35.8718	0.0000
3.5	35.8361	0.0593	35.8284	0.0301	35.8258	0.0000
4.0	35.7862	0.0772	35.7762	0.0392	35.7728	0.0000
4.5	35.7298	0.0973	35.7172	0.0494	35.7130	0.0000
5.0	35.6669	0.1195	35.6517	0.0606	35.6466	0.0000
5.5	35.5978	0.1437	35.5797	0.0728	35.5736	0.0000
6.0	35.5225	0.1696	35.5014	0.0858	35.4944	0.0000
6.5	35.4411	0.1971	35.4172	0.0996	35.4092	0.0000
7.0	35.3539	0.2257	35.3272	0.1139	35.3183	0.0000
7.5	35.2611	0.2553	35.2319	0.1286	35.2223	0.0000
8.0	35.1629	0.2853	35.1318	0.1433	35.1216	0.0000
8.5	35.0597	0.3150	35.0275	0.1578	35.0170	0.0000
9.0	34.9519	0.3440	34.9195	0.1716	34.9092	0.0000
9.5	34.8400	0.3712	34.8088	0.1843	34.7991	0.0000
10.0	34.7245	0.3958	34.6964	0.1953	34.6879	0.0000
10.5	34.6061	0.4166	34.5833	0.2041	34.5768	0.0000
11.0	34.4858	0.4324	34.4709	0.2098	34.4674	0.0000
11.5	34.3645	0.4415	34.3606	0.2118	34.3612	0.0000
12.0	34.2434	0.4426	34.2542	0.2093	34.2601	0.0000
12.5	34.1241	0.4338	34.1535	0.2014	34.1660	0.0000
13.0	34.0082	0.4133	34.0606	0.1874	34.0810	0.0000
13.5	33.8980	0.3795	33.9776	0.1665	34.0073	0.0000
14.0	33.7957	0.3307	33.9068	0.1382	33.9470	0.0000
14.5	33.7041	0.2657	33.8505	0.1019	33.9022	0.0000
15.0	33.6259	0.1834	33.8109	0.0575	33.8751	0.0000
15.5	33.5643	0.0835	33.7901	0.0047	33.8675	0.0000
16.0	33.5219	−0.0341	33.7900	−0.0562	33.8811	0.0000
16.5	33.5013	−0.1687	33.8124	−0.1250	33.9174	0.0000
17.0	33.5048	−0.3193	33.8586	−0.2013	33.9775	0.0000
17.5	33.5339	−0.4847	33.9298	−0.2848	34.0627	0.0000
18.0	33.5896	−0.6635	34.0268	−0.3748	34.1735	0.0000
18.5	33.6725	−0.8542	34.1502	−0.4710	34.3107	0.0000
19.0	33.7827	−1.0558	34.3002	−0.5731	34.4747	0.0000
19.5	33.9199	−1.2672	34.4772	−0.6807	34.6659	0.0000
20.0	34.0835	−1.4880	34.6812	−0.7939	34.8845	0.0000
20.5	34.2729	−1.7176	34.9122	−0.9125	35.1309	0.0000
21.0	34.4872	−1.9561	35.1702	−1.0368	35.4054	0.0000
21.5	34.7257	−2.2037	35.4553	−1.1670	35.7083	0.0000
22.0	34.9875	−2.4608	35.7675	−1.3038	36.0402	0.0000
22.5	35.2717	−2.7282	36.1069	−1.4478	36.4018	0.0000
23.0	35.5775	−3.0067	36.4739	−1.5998	36.7939	0.0000
23.5	35.9039	−3.2975	36.8688	−1.7610	37.2177	0.0000
24.0	36.2501	−3.6016	37.2919	−1.9329	37.6746	0.0000
24.5	36.6149	−3.9207	37.7439	−2.1171	38.1666	0.0000
25.0	36.9972	−4.2561	38.2253	−2.3159	38.6961	0.0000

TABLE II. $b_r(q) = U + iV$, $q = \rho e^{i\phi}$ $r = 7$

ρ	$\phi = 5°$		$\phi = 10°$		$\phi = 15°$	
	U	V	U	V	U	V
0.0	49.0000	0.0000	49.0000	0.0000	49.0000	0.0000
0.5	49.0026	0.0005	49.0024	0.0009	49.0023	0.0013
1.0	49.0103	0.0018	49.0098	0.0036	49.0090	0.0052
1.5	49.0231	0.0041	49.0220	0.0080	49.0203	0.0117
2.0	49.0411	0.0072	49.0392	0.0143	49.0361	0.0209
2.5	49.0642	0.0113	49.0612	0.0223	49.0564	0.0326
3.0	49.0924	0.0163	49.0882	0.0321	49.0813	0.0470
3.5	49.1259	0.0222	49.1201	0.0438	49.1106	0.0640
4.0	49.1645	0.0291	49.1569	0.0573	49.1445	0.0837
4.5	49.2083	0.0368	49.1987	0.0726	49.1830	0.1060
5.0	49.2574	0.0455	49.2455	0.0897	49.2260	0.1310
5.5	49.3116	0.0552	49.2972	0.1087	49.2736	0.1588
6.0	49.3712	0.0658	49.3539	0.1295	49.3258	0.1892
6.5	49.4359	0.0773	49.4157	0.1522	49.3826	0.2223
7.0	49.5060	0.0898	49.4825	0.1768	49.4440	0.2582
7.5	49.5814	0.1032	49.5543	0.2032	49.5101	0.2969
8.0	49.6621	0.1176	49.6312	0.2315	49.5808	0.3383
8.5	49.7481	0.1329	49.7132	0.2617	49.6562	0.3824
9.0	49.8394	0.1491	49.8003	0.2937	49.7363	0.4293
9.5	49.9360	0.1663	49.8925	0.3276	49.8212	0.4789
10.0	50.0380	0.1844	49.9898	0.3633	49.9109	0.5312
10.5	50.1452	0.2033	50.0922	0.4007	50.0053	0.5862
11.0	50.2577	0.2231	50.1998	0.4399	50.1047	0.6438
11.5	50.3754	0.2438	50.3125	0.4807	50.2089	0.7040
12.0	50.4983	0.2652	50.4302	0.5231	50.3180	0.7666
12.5	50.6263	0.2873	50.5531	0.5671	50.4320	0.8316
13.0	50.7594	0.3101	50.6809	0.6124	50.5511	0.8989
13.5	50.8974	0.3334	50.8138	0.6590	50.6751	0.9683
14.0	51.0402	0.3574	50.9516	0.7068	50.8042	1.0397
14.5	51.1877	0.3817	51.0943	0.7556	50.9383	1.1129
15.0	51.3397	0.4065	51.2417	0.8052	51.0775	1.1877
15.5	51.4962	0.4315	51.3938	0.8556	51.2217	1.2638
16.0	51.6569	0.4567	51.5505	0.9065	51.3709	1.3411
16.5	51.8216	0.4820	51.7116	0.9576	51.5251	1.4192
17.0	51.9901	0.5072	51.8770	1.0089	51.6843	1.4979
17.5	52.1623	0.5324	52.0464	1.0601	51.8483	1.5769
18.0	52.3377	0.5573	52.2197	1.1110	52.0171	1.6559
18.5	52.5163	0.5818	52.3968	1.1614	52.1905	1.7345
19.0	52.6976	0.6059	52.5773	1.2110	52.3685	1.8123
19.5	52.8815	0.6294	52.7610	1.2596	52.5508	1.8892
20.0	53.0676	0.6522	52.9477	1.3070	52.7373	1.9646
20.5	53.2556	0.6742	53.1371	1.3529	52.9277	2.0383
21.0	53.4453	0.6953	53.3288	1.3972	53.1219	2.1099
21.5	53.6362	0.7155	53.5227	1.4397	53.3195	2.1790
22.0	53.8281	0.7345	53.7183	1.4801	53.5204	2.2453
22.5	54.0206	0.7524	53.9155	1.5182	53.7241	2.3086
23.0	54.2135	0.7690	54.1137	1.5539	53.9304	2.3684
23.5	54.4063	0.7842	54.3128	1.5869	54.1390	2.4245
24.0	54.5988	0.7981	54.5123	1.6172	54.3495	2.4767
24.5	54.7907	0.8105	54.7120	1.6446	54.5615	2.5246
25.0	54.9815	0.8213	54.9114	1.6689	54.7748	2.5680

TABLE II. $b_r(q) = U + iV$, $q = \rho e^{i\phi}$ $r = 7$

ρ	$\phi=20°$		$\phi=25°$		$\phi=30°$	
	U	V	U	V	U	V
0.0	49.0000	0.0000	49.0000	0.0000	49.0000	0.0000
0.5	49.0020	0.0017	49.0017	0.0020	49.0013	0.0023
1.0	49.0080	0.0067	49.0067	0.0080	49.0052	0.0090
1.5	49.0180	0.0151	49.0151	0.0180	49.0117	0.0203
2.0	49.0319	0.0268	49.0268	0.0319	49.0208	0.0361
2.5	49.0499	0.0419	49.0418	0.0499	49.0325	0.0564
3.0	49.0718	0.0604	49.0602	0.0719	49.0468	0.0813
3.5	49.0978	0.0823	49.0820	0.0980	49.0637	0.1107
4.0	49.1277	0.1075	49.1071	0.1281	49.0831	0.1447
4.5	49.1617	0.1362	49.1355	0.1622	49.1052	0.1832
5.0	49.1997	0.1684	49.1672	0.2005	49.1297	0.2264
5.5	49.2417	0.2039	49.2023	0.2428	49.1569	0.2742
6.0	49.2877	0.2430	49.2408	0.2893	49.1865	0.3266
6.5	49.3378	0.2856	49.2826	0.3399	49.2188	0.3837
7.0	49.3919	0.3317	49.3277	0.3947	49.2535	0.4455
7.5	49.4501	0.3813	49.3762	0.4538	49.2909	0.5120
8.0	49.5124	0.4345	49.4281	0.5171	49.3307	0.5834
8.5	49.5788	0.4912	49.4835	0.5846	49.3732	0.6596
9.0	49.6494	0.5515	49.5422	0.6565	49.4182	0.7406
9.5	49.7243	0.6154	49.6045	0.7326	49.4658	0.8266
10.0	49.8034	0.6829	49.6704	0.8132	49.5161	0.9176
10.5	49.8868	0.7539	49.7399	0.8981	49.5692	1.0137
11.0	49.9746	0.8284	49.8131	0.9875	49.6250	1.1150
11.5	50.0669	0.9065	49.8901	1.0812	49.6838	1.2214
12.0	50.1637	0.9879	49.9711	1.1793	49.7455	1.3332
12.5	50.2652	1.0728	50.0562	1.2819	49.8105	1.4503
13.0	50.3715	1.1609	50.1455	1.3888	49.8788	1.5729
13.5	50.4826	1.2521	50.2393	1.5000	49.9507	1.7010
14.0	50.5987	1.3464	50.3377	1.6155	50.0264	1.8347
14.5	50.7199	1.4435	50.4410	1.7352	50.1063	1.9741
15.0	50.8464	1.5432	50.5494	1.8589	50.1905	2.1191
15.5	50.9782	1.6454	50.6632	1.9865	50.2797	2.2698
16.0	51.1155	1.7497	50.7826	2.1177	50.3740	2.4262
16.5	51.2583	1.8559	50.9080	2.2524	50.4741	2.5881
17.0	51.4069	1.9636	51.0397	2.3902	50.5805	2.7555
17.5	51.5612	2.0725	51.1780	2.5308	50.6936	2.9281
18.0	51.7213	2.1822	51.3230	2.6738	50.8142	3.1057
18.5	51.8874	2.2922	51.4753	2.8188	50.9427	3.2880
19.0	52.0593	2.4022	51.6348	2.9652	51.0798	3.4744
19.5	52.2371	2.5117	51.8020	3.1125	51.2261	3.6645
20.0	52.4207	2.6202	51.9770	3.2601	51.3822	3.8576
20.5	52.6100	2.7271	52.1600	3.4074	51.5487	4.0530
21.0	52.8049	2.8321	52.3509	3.5537	51.7260	4.2499
21.5	53.0053	2.9345	52.5499	3.6982	51.9144	4.4473
22.0	53.2110	3.0339	52.7569	3.8403	52.1145	4.6442
22.5	53.4216	3.1298	52.9719	3.9793	52.3262	4.8396
23.0	53.6370	3.2217	53.1946	4.1144	52.5497	5.0325
23.5	53.8569	3.3092	53.4248	4.2448	52.7851	5.2217
24.0	54.0809	3.3917	53.6623	4.3701	53.0320	5.4063
24.5	54.3086	3.4689	53.9067	4.4893	53.2904	5.5851
25.0	54.5397	3.5404	54.1577	4.6020	53.5599	5.7572

322-566 O - 69 - 11

TABLE II. $b_r(q) = U + iV$, $q = \rho e^{i\phi}$ $r = 7$

ρ	$\phi = 35°$		$\phi = 40°$		$\phi = 45°$	
	U	V	U	V	U	V
0.0	49.0000	0.0000	49.0000	0.0000	49.0000	0.0000
0.5	49.0009	0.0024	49.0005	0.0026	49.0000	0.0026
1.0	49.0036	0.0098	49.0018	0.0103	49.0000	0.0104
1.5	49.0080	0.0220	49.0041	0.0231	49.0000	0.0234
2.0	49.0142	0.0392	49.0072	0.0410	49.0000	0.0417
2.5	49.0222	0.0612	49.0112	0.0641	48.9999	0.0651
3.0	49.0320	0.0882	49.0162	0.0924	48.9999	0.0938
3.5	49.0435	0.1201	49.0219	0.1257	48.9998	0.1276
4.0	49.0567	0.1569	49.0286	0.1643	48.9996	0.1667
4.5	49.0716	0.1986	49.0360	0.2080	48.9993	0.2109
5.0	49.0883	0.2454	49.0443	0.2568	48.9990	0.2604
5.5	49.1067	0.2971	49.0533	0.3109	48.9985	0.3151
6.0	49.1267	0.3538	49.0632	0.3701	48.9979	0.3751
6.5	49.1484	0.4155	49.0737	0.4346	48.9970	0.4402
7.0	49.1718	0.4824	49.0850	0.5043	48.9959	0.5106
7.5	49.1967	0.5543	49.0969	0.5792	48.9946	0.5863
8.0	49.2233	0.6314	49.1095	0.6595	48.9929	0.6672
8.5	49.2515	0.7136	49.1226	0.7452	48.9908	0.7534
9.0	49.2813	0.8012	49.1364	0.8363	48.9882	0.8450
9.5	49.3127	0.8941	49.1506	0.9329	48.9850	0.9420
10.0	49.3458	0.9925	49.1653	1.0351	48.9813	1.0445
10.5	49.3804	1.0964	49.1805	1.1431	48.9767	1.1525
11.0	49.4168	1.2059	49.1960	1.2569	48.9713	1.2662
11.5	49.4548	1.3213	49.2119	1.3767	48.9649	1.3857
12.0	49.4947	1.4426	49.2282	1.5027	48.9573	1.5112
12.5	49.5364	1.5701	49.2447	1.6352	48.9484	1.6428
13.0	49.5802	1.7039	49.2616	1.7744	48.9380	1.7809
13.5	49.6261	1.8442	49.2789	1.9206	48.9260	1.9258
14.0	49.6745	1.9913	49.2965	2.0742	48.9121	2.0777
14.5	49.7255	2.1453	49.3146	2.2357	48.8962	2.2372
15.0	49.7795	2.3067	49.3334	2.4054	48.8779	2.4049
15.5	49.8368	2.4756	49.3529	2.5840	48.8571	2.5813
16.0	49.8980	2.6523	49.3736	2.7720	48.8336	2.7672
16.5	49.9636	2.8370	49.3957	2.9701	48.8073	2.9637
17.0	50.0342	3.0300	49.4198	3.1791	48.7779	3.1718
17.5	50.1106	3.2314	49.4466	3.3998	48.7455	3.3929
18.0	50.1937	3.4414	49.4768	3.6329	48.7101	3.6286
18.5	50.2843	3.6600	49.5117	3.8794	48.6720	3.8809
19.0	50.3837	3.8871	49.5525	4.1400	48.6318	4.1519
19.5	50.4929	4.1224	49.6008	4.4156	48.5905	4.4443
20.0	50.6132	4.3656	49.6587	4.7066	48.5497	4.7611
20.5	50.7457	4.6160	49.7286	5.0133	48.5120	5.1056
21.0	50.8918	4.8727	49.8128	5.3356	48.4813	5.4812
21.5	51.0526	5.1348	49.9144	5.6728	48.4628	5.8908
22.0	51.2291	5.4009	50.0360	6.0236	48.4639	6.3364
22.5	51.4222	5.6695	50.1805	6.3861	48.4930	6.8177
23.0	51.6326	5.9390	50.3500	6.7577	48.5596	7.3315
23.5	51.8607	6.2078	50.5464	7.1353	48.6718	7.8708
24.0	52.1066	6.4741	50.7706	7.5156	48.8350	8.4261
24.5	52.3704	6.7362	51.0230	7.8950	49.0508	8.9867
25.0	52.6516	6.9924	51.3032	8.2705	49.3170	9.5431

TABLE II. $b_r(q) = U + iV$, $q = \rho e^{i\phi}$ $r=7$

ρ	$\phi=50°$ U	$\phi=50°$ V	$\phi=55°$ U	$\phi=55°$ V	$\phi=60°$ U	$\phi=60°$ V
0.0	49.0000	0.0000	49.0000	0.0000	49.0000	0.0000
0.5	48.9995	0.0026	48.9991	0.0024	48.9987	0.0023
1.0	48.9982	0.0103	48.9964	0.0098	48.9948	0.0090
1.5	48.9959	0.0231	48.9920	0.0220	48.9883	0.0203
2.0	48.9927	0.0410	48.9857	0.0391	48.9792	0.0361
2.5	48.9886	0.0641	48.9777	0.0611	48.9674	0.0563
3.0	48.9836	0.0923	48.9678	0.0880	48.9531	0.0811
3.5	48.9776	0.1256	48.9562	0.1198	48.9361	0.1103
4.0	48.9707	0.1640	48.9427	0.1564	48.9165	0.1440
4.5	48.9627	0.2075	48.9273	0.1978	48.8942	0.1821
5.0	48.9538	0.2561	48.9102	0.2441	48.8693	0.2246
5.5	48.9439	0.3098	48.8911	0.2951	48.8417	0.2716
6.0	48.9328	0.3686	48.8701	0.3510	48.8114	0.3229
6.5	48.9207	0.4324	48.8472	0.4116	48.7785	0.3785
7.0	48.9075	0.5014	48.8222	0.4770	48.7428	0.4384
7.5	48.8930	0.5753	48.7953	0.5471	48.7043	0.5026
8.0	48.8773	0.6544	48.7663	0.6218	48.6631	0.5709
8.5	48.8602	0.7385	48.7351	0.7012	48.6190	0.6433
9.0	48.8418	0.8276	48.7017	0.7852	48.5721	0.7198
9.5	48.8217	0.9218	48.6659	0.8737	48.5222	0.8002
10.0	48.8001	1.0210	48.6277	0.9667	48.4692	0.8844
10.5	48.7766	1.1254	48.5869	1.0641	48.4132	0.9723
11.0	48.7512	1.2349	48.5434	1.1658	48.3539	1.0637
11.5	48.7236	1.3495	48.4968	1.2718	48.2913	1.1584
12.0	48.6935	1.4694	48.4470	1.3821	48.2251	1.2562
12.5	48.6608	1.5946	48.3937	1.4964	48.1552	1.3569
13.0	48.6251	1.7253	48.3365	1.6147	48.0812	1.4602
13.5	48.5860	1.8616	48.2749	1.7369	48.0030	1.5657
14.0	48.5431	2.0036	48.2086	1.8630	47.9202	1.6730
14.5	48.4959	2.1518	48.1369	1.9927	47.8323	1.7817
15.0	48.4438	2.3063	48.0590	2.1261	47.7388	1.8912
15.5	48.3862	2.4677	47.9742	2.2628	47.6392	2.0009
16.0	48.3222	2.6364	47.8815	2.4029	47.5328	2.1100
16.5	48.2510	2.8131	47.7796	2.5462	47.4189	2.2177
17.0	48.1716	2.9987	47.6672	2.6925	47.2965	2.3228
17.5	48.0827	3.1942	47.5425	2.8416	47.1645	2.4241
18.0	47.9829	3.4011	47.4033	2.9933	47.0220	2.5200
18.5	47.8704	3.6212	47.2472	3.1472	46.8676	2.6086
19.0	47.7434	3.8567	47.0709	3.3029	46.7000	2.6874
19.5	47.5995	4.1110	46.8702	3.4596	46.5180	2.7536
20.0	47.4360	4.3884	46.6399	3.6162	46.3203	2.8033
20.5	47.2496	4.6950	46.3730	3.7706	46.1061	2.8318
21.0	47.0372	5.0397	46.0601	3.9193	45.8757	2.8336
21.5	46.7957	5.4359	45.6881	4.0555	45.6305	2.8018
22.0	46.5249	5.9042	45.2387	4.1653	45.3743	2.7291
22.5	46.2338	6.4760	44.6887	4.2187	45.1140	2.6088
23.0	45.9572	7.1917	44.0216	4.1489	44.8595	2.4364
23.5	45.7771	8.0697	43.2916	3.8440	44.6229	2.2113
24.0	45.7841	9.0454	42.6819	3.2812	44.4153	1.9382
24.5	45.9810	10.0077	42.2912	2.6181	44.2448	1.6258
25.0	46.3069	10.9002	42.0637	1.9680	44.1151	1.2841

TABLE II. $b_r(q) = U + iV,\ q = \rho e^{i\phi}$ $r = 7$

ρ	$\phi=65°$		$\phi=70°$		$\phi=75°$	
	U	V	U	V	U	V
0.0	49.0000	0.0000	49.0000	0.0000	49.0000	0.0000
0.5	48.9983	0.0020	48.9980	0.0017	48.9977	0.0013
1.0	48.9933	0.0080	48.9920	0.0067	48.9910	0.0052
1.5	48.9849	0.0179	48.9820	0.0151	48.9797	0.0117
2.0	48.9732	0.0319	48.9681	0.0268	48.9639	0.0208
2.5	48.9581	0.0498	48.9501	0.0418	48.9436	0.0325
3.0	48.9397	0.0717	48.9282	0.0601	48.9189	0.0468
3.5	48.9179	0.0975	48.9023	0.0818	48.8896	0.0636
4.0	48.8928	0.1273	48.8724	0.1067	48.8559	0.0830
4.5	48.8643	0.1609	48.8385	0.1349	48.8177	0.1049
5.0	48.8324	0.1985	48.8007	0.1664	48.7750	0.1294
5.5	48.7972	0.2399	48.7589	0.2011	48.7279	0.1563
6.0	48.7586	0.2851	48.7132	0.2390	48.6764	0.1857
6.5	48.7167	0.3342	48.6635	0.2800	48.6205	0.2176
7.0	48.6714	0.3869	48.6100	0.3241	48.5603	0.2519
7.5	48.6226	0.4433	48.5525	0.3713	48.4957	0.2886
8.0	48.5706	0.5034	48.4912	0.4215	48.4269	0.3276
8.5	48.5151	0.5670	48.4260	0.4746	48.3539	0.3690
9.0	48.4563	0.6340	48.3571	0.5306	48.2768	0.4126
9.5	48.3940	0.7043	48.2845	0.5893	48.1956	0.4584
10.0	48.3284	0.7778	48.2082	0.6506	48.1106	0.5064
10.5	48.2594	0.8543	48.1283	0.7144	48.0219	0.5564
11.0	48.1870	0.9336	48.0450	0.7805	47.9296	0.6083
11.5	48.1111	1.0154	47.9583	0.8486	47.8339	0.6622
12.0	48.0318	1.0996	47.8684	0.9186	47.7352	0.7177
12.5	47.9490	1.1857	47.7755	0.9902	47.6336	0.7749
13.0	47.8627	1.2733	47.6798	1.0629	47.5297	0.8335
13.5	47.7729	1.3621	47.5814	1.1364	47.4237	0.8933
14.0	47.6794	1.4514	47.4807	1.2103	47.3161	0.9540
14.5	47.5823	1.5406	47.3779	1.2839	47.2076	1.0155
15.0	47.4815	1.6291	47.2735	1.3568	47.0987	1.0774
15.5	47.3768	1.7159	47.1678	1.4280	46.9903	1.1393
16.0	47.2684	1.8002	47.0612	1.4970	46.8830	1.2009
16.5	47.1559	1.8807	46.9545	1.5627	46.7778	1.2617
17.0	47.0396	1.9563	46.8482	1.6243	46.6758	1.3212
17.5	46.9194	2.0254	46.7430	1.6806	46.5780	1.3789
18.0	46.7953	2.0865	46.6398	1.7305	46.4856	1.4343
18.5	46.6678	2.1377	46.5396	1.7729	46.3998	1.4867
19.0	46.5371	2.1769	46.4434	1.8065	46.3221	1.5355
19.5	46.4041	2.2020	46.3526	1.8301	46.2538	1.5803
20.0	46.2697	2.2106	46.2685	1.8426	46.1964	1.6203
20.5	46.1354	2.2004	46.1927	1.8429	46.1511	1.6552
21.0	46.0032	2.1691	46.1267	1.8301	46.1195	1.6843
21.5	45.8754	2.1147	46.0721	1.8035	46.1029	1.7072
22.0	45.7550	2.0357	46.0308	1.7627	46.1024	1.7237
22.5	45.6452	1.9311	46.0043	1.7073	46.1194	1.7333
23.0	45.5493	1.8009	45.9941	1.6373	46.1547	1.7358
23.5	45.4704	1.6459	46.0015	1.5530	46.2093	1.7311
24.0	45.4113	1.4674	46.0277	1.4548	46.2839	1.7190
24.5	45.3739	1.2676	46.0735	1.3432	46.3791	1.6994
25.0	45.3593	1.0487	46.1394	1.2186	46.4955	1.6723

TABLE II. $b_r(q) = U + iV,\ q = \rho e^{i\phi}$ $r = 7$

ρ	$\phi=80°$		$\phi=85°$		$\phi=90°$	
	U	V	U	V	U	V
0.0	49.0000	0.0000	49.0000	0.0000	49.0000	0.0000
0.5	48.9976	0.0009	48.9974	0.0005	48.9974	0.0000
1.0	48.9902	0.0036	48.9897	0.0018	48.9896	0.0000
1.5	48.9780	0.0080	48.9769	0.0041	48.9766	0.0000
2.0	48.9609	0.0142	48.9590	0.0072	48.9584	0.0000
2.5	48.9389	0.0222	48.9359	0.0113	48.9350	0.0000
3.0	48.9120	0.0320	48.9078	0.0162	48.9064	0.0000
3.5	48.8803	0.0435	48.8746	0.0221	48.8726	0.0000
4.0	48.8437	0.0567	48.8362	0.0288	48.8337	0.0000
4.5	48.8023	0.0717	48.7929	0.0364	48.7897	0.0000
5.0	48.7561	0.0885	48.7445	0.0449	48.7406	0.0000
5.5	48.7051	0.1069	48.6911	0.0543	48.6863	0.0001
6.0	48.6493	0.1270	48.6327	0.0645	48.6270	0.0001
6.5	48.5888	0.1488	48.5693	0.0757	48.5627	0.0002
7.0	48.5236	0.1723	48.5011	0.0877	48.4933	0.0004
7.5	48.4538	0.1975	48.4279	0.1006	48.4189	0.0007
8.0	48.3794	0.2244	48.3500	0.1145	48.3396	0.0011
8.5	48.3005	0.2529	48.2673	0.1293	48.2554	0.0016
9.0	48.2172	0.2830	48.1799	0.1451	48.1662	0.0024
9.5	48.1295	0.3149	48.0879	0.1620	48.0722	0.0036
10.0	48.0378	0.3484	47.9914	0.1800	47.9734	0.0052
10.5	47.9420	0.3835	47.8905	0.1993	47.8698	0.0074
11.0	47.8424	0.4205	47.7854	0.2199	47.7614	0.0103
11.5	47.7392	0.4591	47.6762	0.2420	47.6484	0.0142
12.0	47.6326	0.4995	47.5631	0.2658	47.5307	0.0193
12.5	47.5232	0.5418	47.4464	0.2915	47.4084	0.0260
13.0	47.4111	0.5859	47.3263	0.3195	47.2815	0.0346
13.5	47.2969	0.6321	47.2032	0.3499	47.1501	0.0456
14.0	47.1811	0.6802	47.0774	0.3833	47.0144	0.0595
14.5	47.0643	0.7306	46.9495	0.4200	46.8743	0.0770
15.0	46.9473	0.7831	46.8199	0.4606	46.7301	0.0989
15.5	46.8308	0.8380	46.6893	0.5057	46.5819	0.1260
16.0	46.7157	0.8954	46.5585	0.5558	46.4299	0.1594
16.5	46.6032	0.9553	46.4283	0.6116	46.2745	0.2003
17.0	46.4943	1.0179	46.2997	0.6741	46.1160	0.2502
17.5	46.3903	1.0831	46.1739	0.7438	45.9552	0.3105
18.0	46.2925	1.1512	46.0523	0.8216	45.7927	0.3830
18.5	46.2024	1.2219	45.9363	0.9083	45.6298	0.4697
19.0	46.1216	1.2954	45.8278	1.0045	45.4678	0.5725
19.5	46.0515	1.3714	45.7284	1.1108	45.3087	0.6935
20.0	45.9938	1.4498	45.6402	1.2277	45.1549	0.8347
20.5	45.9500	1.5303	45.5654	1.3554	45.0094	0.9979
21.0	45.9216	1.6127	45.5059	1.4937	44.8756	1.1841
21.5	45.9101	1.6964	45.4639	1.6426	44.7572	1.3940
22.0	45.9168	1.7811	45.4412	1.8012	44.6584	1.6274
22.5	45.9428	1.8664	45.4398	1.9690	44.5830	1.8828
23.0	45.9892	1.9516	45.4610	2.1448	44.5342	2.1584
23.5	46.0570	2.0362	45.5060	2.3277	44.5145	2.4514
24.0	46.1467	2.1199	45.5758	2.5164	44.5257	2.7587
24.5	46.2591	2.2020	45.6710	2.7099	44.5685	3.0774
25.0	46.3945	2.2821	45.7919	2.9071	44.6427	3.4048

TABLE II. $b_r(q) = U + iV$, $q = \rho e^{i\phi}$ $\qquad\qquad r = 8$

ρ	$\phi = 5°$		$\phi = 10°$		$\phi = 15°$	
	U	V	U	V	U	V
0.0	64.0000	0.0000	64.0000	0.0000	64.0000	0.0000
0.5	64.0020	0.0003	64.0019	0.0007	64.0017	0.0010
1.0	64.0078	0.0014	64.0075	0.0027	64.0069	0.0040
1.5	64.0176	0.0031	64.0168	0.0061	64.0155	0.0089
2.0	64.0313	0.0055	64.0298	0.0109	64.0275	0.0159
2.5	64.0489	0.0086	64.0466	0.0170	64.0430	0.0248
3.0	64.0704	0.0124	64.0672	0.0245	64.0619	0.0358
3.5	64.0958	0.0169	64.0914	0.0333	64.0842	0.0487
4.0	64.1252	0.0221	64.1195	0.0435	64.1101	0.0636
4.5	64.1585	0.0280	64.1512	0.0551	64.1393	0.0806
5.0	64.1958	0.0346	64.1868	0.0681	64.1720	0.0996
5.5	64.2370	0.0419	64.2261	0.0825	64.2082	0.1206
6.0	64.2822	0.0499	64.2692	0.0983	64.2479	0.1436
6.5	64.3314	0.0586	64.3160	0.1155	64.2910	0.1687
7.0	64.3845	0.0681	64.3667	0.1341	64.3376	0.1959
7.5	64.4417	0.0783	64.4212	0.1541	64.3877	0.2251
8.0	64.5029	0.0892	64.4795	0.1755	64.4413	0.2564
8.5	64.5681	0.1008	64.5416	0.1984	64.4984	0.2898
9.0	64.6373	0.1132	64.6075	0.2227	64.5590	0.3253
9.5	64.7106	0.1263	64.6774	0.2485	64.6231	0.3630
10.0	64.7880	0.1401	64.7511	0.2758	64.6908	0.4027
10.5	64.8695	0.1547	64.8286	0.3045	64.7621	0.4446
11.0	64.9550	0.1701	64.9101	0.3347	64.8369	0.4887
11.5	65.0447	0.1862	64.9955	0.3664	64.9152	0.5350
12.0	65.1386	0.2030	65.0849	0.3996	64.9972	0.5834
12.5	65.2365	0.2206	65.1781	0.4342	65.0828	0.6341
13.0	65.3387	0.2390	65.2754	0.4704	65.1721	0.6869
13.5	65.4450	0.2581	65.3766	0.5081	65.2650	0.7419
14.0	65.5555	0.2779	65.4819	0.5472	65.3616	0.7992
14.5	65.6701	0.2985	65.5911	0.5878	65.4619	0.8586
15.0	65.7889	0.3199	65.7044	0.6299	65.5659	0.9203
15.5	65.9119	0.3419	65.8217	0.6734	65.6737	0.9841
16.0	66.0391	0.3646	65.9430	0.7183	65.7854	1.0501
16.5	66.1705	0.3880	66.0685	0.7646	65.9008	1.1182
17.0	66.3060	0.4121	66.1979	0.8123	66.0202	1.1884
17.5	66.4456	0.4368	66.3315	0.8612	66.1435	1.2607
18.0	66.5893	0.4620	66.4691	0.9115	66.2707	1.3350
18.5	66.7371	0.4879	66.6108	0.9629	66.4019	1.4113
19.0	66.8888	0.5143	66.7566	1.0154	66.5372	1.4894
19.5	67.0446	0.5411	66.9064	1.0691	66.6766	1.5694
20.0	67.2043	0.5684	67.0602	1.1237	66.8200	1.6511
20.5	67.3678	0.5961	67.2180	1.1791	66.9677	1.7344
21.0	67.5351	0.6241	67.3798	1.2354	67.1195	1.8191
21.5	67.7060	0.6524	67.5455	1.2924	67.2755	1.9053
22.0	67.8806	0.6809	67.7151	1.3499	67.4358	1.9926
22.5	68.0587	0.7095	67.8886	1.4078	67.6004	2.0810
23.0	68.2401	0.7382	68.0657	1.4661	67.7693	2.1703
23.5	68.4248	0.7669	68.2466	1.5245	67.9424	2.2602
24.0	68.6126	0.7955	68.4310	1.5830	68.1199	2.3506
24.5	68.8034	0.8240	68.6190	1.6413	68.3016	2.4413
25.0	68.9970	0.8523	68.8103	1.6994	68.4875	2.5321

TABLE II. $b_r(q) = U + iV$, $q = \rho e^{i\phi}$ $r = 8$

ρ	$\phi=20°$		$\phi=25°$		$\phi=30°$	
	U	V	U	V	U	V
0.0	64.0000	0.0000	64.0000	0.0000	64.0000	0.0000
0.5	64.0015	0.0013	64.0013	0.0015	64.0010	0.0017
1.0	64.0061	0.0051	64.0051	0.0061	64.0040	0.0069
1.5	64.0137	0.0115	64.0115	0.0137	64.0089	0.0155
2.0	64.0243	0.0204	64.0204	0.0243	64.0159	0.0275
2.5	64.0380	0.0319	64.0319	0.0380	64.0248	0.0430
3.0	64.0547	0.0460	64.0459	0.0548	64.0357	0.0619
3.5	64.0745	0.0626	64.0625	0.0746	64.0486	0.0843
4.0	64.0973	0.0818	64.0816	0.0974	64.0634	0.1101
4.5	64.1232	0.1036	64.1033	0.1234	64.0802	0.1394
5.0	64.1521	0.1280	64.1275	0.1524	64.0990	0.1722
5.5	64.1840	0.1549	64.1542	0.1845	64.1197	0.2085
6.0	64.2190	0.1845	64.1835	0.2197	64.1424	0.2482
6.5	64.2571	0.2167	64.2153	0.2581	64.1670	0.2915
7.0	64.2982	0.2516	64.2497	0.2995	64.1936	0.3382
7.5	64.3424	0.2891	64.2866	0.3441	64.2221	0.3885
8.0	64.3896	0.3293	64.3260	0.3919	64.2525	0.4423
8.5	64.4399	0.3721	64.3680	0.4428	64.2849	0.4997
9.0	64.4933	0.4177	64.4124	0.4969	64.3191	0.5607
9.5	64.5497	0.4659	64.4595	0.5543	64.3553	0.6252
10.0	64.6093	0.5169	64.5090	0.6148	64.3933	0.6934
10.5	64.6719	0.5707	64.5611	0.6787	64.4333	0.7652
11.0	64.7376	0.6272	64.6157	0.7458	64.4751	0.8407
11.5	64.8065	0.6865	64.6729	0.8162	64.5188	0.9199
12.0	64.8785	0.7487	64.7326	0.8899	64.5643	1.0028
12.5	64.9536	0.8136	64.7948	0.9670	64.6117	1.0894
13.0	65.0320	0.8814	64.8597	1.0475	64.6610	1.1799
13.5	65.1135	0.9521	64.9271	1.1315	64.7122	1.2742
14.0	65.1982	1.0256	64.9971	1.2189	64.7652	1.3724
14.5	65.2862	1.1020	65.0698	1.3098	64.8200	1.4745
15.0	65.3775	1.1814	65.1452	1.4042	64.8768	1.5807
15.5	65.4722	1.2636	65.2233	1.5022	64.9355	1.6909
16.0	65.5702	1.3488	65.3041	1.6038	64.9961	1.8053
16.5	65.6717	1.4369	65.3878	1.7090	65.0587	1.9239
17.0	65.7768	1.5279	65.4744	1.8180	65.1233	2.0468
17.5	65.8854	1.6218	65.5640	1.9306	65.1900	2.1741
18.0	65.9976	1.7185	65.6567	2.0471	65.2588	2.3060
18.5	66.1136	1.8181	65.7525	2.1673	65.3299	2.4424
19.0	66.2335	1.9205	65.8517	2.2913	65.4033	2.5836
19.5	66.3573	2.0257	65.9543	2.4191	65.4791	2.7297
20.0	66.4851	2.1335	66.0605	2.5508	65.5577	2.8807
20.5	66.6171	2.2440	66.1705	2.6863	65.6390	3.0368
21.0	66.7534	2.3569	66.2845	2.8257	65.7233	3.1981
21.5	66.8941	2.4723	66.4027	2.9688	65.8108	3.3649
22.0	67.0393	2.5899	66.5254	3.1157	65.9019	3.5371
22.5	67.1892	2.7096	66.6526	3.2662	65.9969	3.7149
23.0	67.3439	2.8312	66.7849	3.4203	66.0961	3.8985
23.5	67.5035	2.9545	66.9223	3.5779	66.1999	4.0878
24.0	67.6681	3.0794	67.0653	3.7388	66.3087	4.2830
24.5	67.8379	3.2055	67.2141	3.9027	66.4232	4.4841
25.0	68.0129	3.3327	67.3690	4.0695	66.5438	4.6910

ρ	$\phi = 35°$		$\phi = 40°$		$\phi = 45°$	
	U	V	U	V	U	V
0.0	64.0000	0.0000	64.0000	0.0000	64.0000	0.0000
0.5	64.0007	0.0019	64.0003	0.0020	64.0000	0.0020
1.0	64.0027	0.0075	64.0014	0.0078	64.0000	0.0079
1.5	64.0061	0.0168	64.0031	0.0176	64.0000	0.0179
2.0	64.0108	0.0298	64.0055	0.0313	64.0000	0.0317
2.5	64.0169	0.0466	64.0086	0.0489	64.0000	0.0496
3.0	64.0244	0.0672	64.0124	0.0704	63.9999	0.0714
3.5	64.0332	0.0914	64.0168	0.0958	63.9999	0.0972
4.0	64.0433	0.1194	64.0219	0.1251	63.9998	0.1270
4.5	64.0548	0.1512	64.0276	0.1584	63.9997	0.1607
5.0	64.0675	0.1867	64.0341	0.1955	63.9996	0.1984
5.5	64.0816	0.2260	64.0411	0.2366	63.9994	0.2401
6.0	64.0970	0.2691	64.0488	0.2817	63.9991	0.2857
6.5	64.1137	0.3159	64.0571	0.3306	63.9988	0.3353
7.0	64.1317	0.3665	64.0660	0.3835	63.9984	0.3889
7.5	64.1510	0.4209	64.0755	0.4404	63.9978	0.4464
8.0	64.1715	0.4791	64.0855	0.5012	63.9972	0.5079
8.5	64.1933	0.5411	64.0961	0.5659	63.9964	0.5733
9.0	64.2163	0.6070	64.1073	0.6346	63.9954	0.6428
9.5	64.2406	0.6767	64.1190	0.7073	63.9943	0.7161
10.0	64.2660	0.7503	64.1312	0.7839	63.9930	0.7935
10.5	64.2927	0.8278	64.1438	0.8645	63.9914	0.8748
11.0	64.3205	0.9091	64.1569	0.9492	63.9895	0.9600
11.5	64.3494	0.9944	64.1704	1.0378	63.9874	1.0492
12.0	64.3795	1.0837	64.1842	1.1305	63.9849	1.1424
12.5	64.4107	1.1769	64.1984	1.2273	63.9820	1.2395
13.0	64.4429	1.2742	64.2129	1.3281	63.9787	1.3406
13.5	64.4762	1.3756	64.2276	1.4330	63.9748	1.4456
14.0	64.5106	1.4811	64.2425	1.5421	63.9704	1.5546
14.5	64.5459	1.5908	64.2576	1.6553	63.9654	1.6675
15.0	64.5823	1.7047	64.2727	1.7728	63.9596	1.7844
15.5	64.6196	1.8230	64.2879	1.8946	63.9530	1.9053
16.0	64.6579	1.9457	64.3030	2.0208	63.9455	2.0302
16.5	64.6970	2.0730	64.3179	2.1514	63.9369	2.1592
17.0	64.7372	2.2048	64.3326	2.2866	63.9270	2.2921
17.5	64.7782	2.3415	64.3470	2.4264	63.9159	2.4292
18.0	64.8201	2.4830	64.3609	2.5710	63.9031	2.5704
18.5	64.8629	2.6297	64.3743	2.7206	63.8886	2.7159
19.0	64.9067	2.7816	64.3870	2.8754	63.8721	2.8656
19.5	64.9515	2.9390	64.3989	3.0355	63.8533	3.0197
20.0	64.9972	3.1021	64.4099	3.2012	63.8319	3.1783
20.5	65.0441	3.2712	64.4198	3.3729	63.8077	3.3416
21.0	65.0922	3.4466	64.4286	3.5509	63.7801	3.5097
21.5	65.1416	3.6286	64.4360	3.7355	63.7487	3.6829
22.0	65.1925	3.8176	64.4419	3.9273	63.7131	3.8614
22.5	65.2451	4.0139	64.4462	4.1268	63.6726	4.0456
23.0	65.2998	4.2179	64.4488	4.3347	63.6267	4.2359
23.5	65.3569	4.4302	64.4495	4.5517	63.5745	4.4329
24.0	65.4168	4.6512	64.4485	4.7787	63.5151	4.6370
24.5	65.4800	4.8813	64.4456	5.0167	63.4477	4.8491
25.0	65.5473	5.1211	64.4409	5.2669	63.3709	5.0701

TABLE II. $b_r(q) = U + iV$, $q = \rho e^{i\phi}$ $\qquad\qquad r = 8$

ρ	$\phi = 50°$		$\phi = 55°$		$\phi = 60°$	
	U	V	U	V	U	V
0.0	64.0000	0.0000	64.0000	0.0000	64.0000	0.0000
0.5	63.9997	0.0020	63.9993	0.0019	63.9990	0.0017
1.0	63.9986	0.0078	63.9973	0.0075	63.9960	0.0069
1.5	63.9969	0.0176	63.9939	0.0168	63.9911	0.0155
2.0	63.9945	0.0313	63.9891	0.0298	63.9841	0.0275
2.5	63.9914	0.0488	63.9830	0.0466	63.9752	0.0429
3.0	63.9875	0.0703	63.9755	0.0671	63.9643	0.0618
3.5	63.9830	0.0957	63.9667	0.0913	63.9513	0.0841
4.0	63.9778	0.1250	63.9564	0.1192	63.9364	0.1098
4.5	63.9718	0.1582	63.9448	0.1508	63.9195	0.1389
5.0	63.9651	0.1952	63.9318	0.1862	63.9006	0.1715
5.5	63.9577	0.2362	63.9174	0.2252	63.8797	0.2074
6.0	63.9496	0.2811	63.9016	0.2679	63.8567	0.2467
6.5	63.9406	0.3298	63.8844	0.3143	63.8318	0.2893
7.0	63.9309	0.3824	63.8658	0.3644	63.8048	0.3354
7.5	63.9205	0.4389	63.8457	0.4181	63.7758	0.3847
8.0	63.9092	0.4992	63.8242	0.4754	63.7447	0.4374
8.5	63.8971	0.5634	63.8012	0.5364	63.7116	0.4935
9.0	63.8841	0.6314	63.7768	0.6011	63.6765	0.5528
9.5	63.8704	0.7033	63.7509	0.6693	63.6393	0.6154
10.0	63.8557	0.7790	63.7234	0.7411	63.6001	0.6812
10.5	63.8401	0.8584	63.6945	0.8164	63.5588	0.7503
11.0	63.8236	0.9417	63.6641	0.8953	63.5154	0.8226
11.5	63.8062	1.0288	63.6321	0.9777	63.4700	0.8980
12.0	63.7877	1.1196	63.5985	1.0636	63.4225	0.9766
12.5	63.7682	1.2141	63.5634	1.1529	63.3730	1.0582
13.0	63.7477	1.3124	63.5266	1.2455	63.3214	1.1429
13.5	63.7260	1.4143	63.4882	1.3415	63.2678	1.2306
14.0	63.7031	1.5198	63.4481	1.4408	63.2121	1.3211
14.5	63.6789	1.6290	63.4064	1.5432	63.1543	1.4146
15.0	63.6534	1.7417	63.3628	1.6488	63.0946	1.5107
15.5	63.6264	1.8579	63.3175	1.7574	63.0328	1.6095
16.0	63.5980	1.9776	63.2703	1.8689	62.9691	1.7108
16.5	63.5678	2.1006	63.2212	1.9831	62.9034	1.8145
17.0	63.5359	2.2270	63.1701	2.1001	62.8358	1.9204
17.5	63.5019	2.3567	63.1169	2.2195	62.7663	2.0284
18.0	63.4659	2.4895	63.0615	2.3412	62.6949	2.1382
18.5	63.4274	2.6254	63.0039	2.4650	62.6217	2.2496
19.0	63.3863	2.7643	62.9438	2.5906	62.5468	2.3623
19.5	63.3423	2.9061	62.8811	2.7177	62.4701	2.4760
20.0	63.2951	3.0506	62.8157	2.8462	62.3919	2.5904
20.5	63.2442	3.1978	62.7473	2.9755	62.3120	2.7050
21.0	63.1893	3.3475	62.6756	3.1053	62.2307	2.8194
21.5	63.1297	3.4995	62.6006	3.2350	62.1480	2.9330
22.0	63.0650	3.6536	62.5217	3.3643	62.0640	3.0453
22.5	62.9945	3.8097	62.4388	3.4924	61.9790	3.1557
23.0	62.9173	3.9675	62.3514	3.6187	61.8929	3.2634
23.5	62.8326	4.1267	62.2591	3.7424	61.8061	3.3676
24.0	62.7393	4.2870	62.1616	3.8625	61.7188	3.4676
24.5	62.6361	4.4480	62.0583	3.9779	61.6313	3.5623
25.0	62.5216	4.6093	61.9489	4.0876	61.5439	3.6507

TABLE II. $b_r(q) = U + iV$, $q = \rho e^{i\phi}$ $r = 8$

ρ	$\phi = 65°$		$\phi = 70°$		$\phi = 75°$	
	U	V	U	V	U	V
0.0	64.0000	0.0000	64.0000	0.0000	64.0000	0.0000
0.5	63.9987	0.0015	63.9985	0.0013	63.9983	0.0010
1.0	63.9949	0.0061	63.9939	0.0051	63.9931	0.0040
1.5	63.9885	0.0137	63.9863	0.0115	63.9845	0.0089
2.0	63.9796	0.0243	63.9757	0.0204	63.9725	0.0159
2.5	63.9681	0.0380	63.9620	0.0319	63.9571	0.0248
3.0	63.9541	0.0547	63.9453	0.0459	63.9382	0.0357
3.5	63.9375	0.0744	63.9255	0.0624	63.9159	0.0485
4.0	63.9183	0.0971	63.9028	0.0815	63.8901	0.0633
4.5	63.8966	0.1228	63.8769	0.1030	63.8610	0.0801
5.0	63.8724	0.1516	63.8481	0.1271	63.8284	0.0988
5.5	63.8456	0.1833	63.8162	0.1537	63.7924	0.1195
6.0	63.8162	0.2180	63.7813	0.1828	63.7530	0.1421
6.5	63.7843	0.2557	63.7434	0.2144	63.7102	0.1666
7.0	63.7498	0.2963	63.7024	0.2484	63.6640	0.1931
7.5	63.7127	0.3399	63.6584	0.2849	63.6145	0.2214
8.0	63.6731	0.3864	63.6114	0.3238	63.5615	0.2516
8.5	63.6309	0.4358	63.5615	0.3652	63.5052	0.2838
9.0	63.5862	0.4881	63.5085	0.4089	63.4456	0.3178
9.5	63.5389	0.5432	63.4525	0.4551	63.3826	0.3536
10.0	63.4891	0.6013	63.3935	0.5037	63.3162	0.3913
10.5	63.4367	0.6621	63.3316	0.5546	63.2466	0.4309
11.0	63.3818	0.7258	63.2668	0.6079	63.1736	0.4723
11.5	63.3243	0.7922	63.1990	0.6635	63.0974	0.5156
12.0	63.2644	0.8614	63.1283	0.7215	63.0179	0.5607
12.5	63.2020	0.9333	63.0547	0.7818	62.9352	0.6076
13.0	63.1371	1.0079	62.9783	0.8444	62.8493	0.6565
13.5	63.0698	1.0852	62.8992	0.9092	62.7602	0.7072
14.0	63.0002	1.1650	62.8173	0.9764	62.6680	0.7598
14.5	62.9282	1.2473	62.7327	1.0458	62.5728	0.8143
15.0	62.8539	1.3322	62.6456	1.1175	62.4745	0.8708
15.5	62.7775	1.4194	62.5559	1.1914	62.3733	0.9293
16.0	62.6990	1.5090	62.4639	1.2676	62.2693	0.9899
16.5	62.6184	1.6008	62.3697	1.3460	62.1625	1.0527
17.0	62.5360	1.6948	62.2733	1.4267	62.0530	1.1177
17.5	62.4518	1.7908	62.1750	1.5095	61.9411	1.1851
18.0	62.3660	1.8886	62.0751	1.5947	61.8267	1.2551
18.5	62.2789	1.9882	61.9736	1.6821	61.7102	1.3277
19.0	62.1906	2.0893	61.8710	1.7717	61.5917	1.4032
19.5	62.1013	2.1918	61.7676	1.8635	61.4715	1.4818
20.0	62.0114	2.2954	61.6636	1.9576	61.3499	1.5638
20.5	61.9211	2.3997	61.5596	2.0539	61.2271	1.6493
21.0	61.8308	2.5047	61.4560	2.1524	61.1037	1.7388
21.5	61.7410	2.6098	61.3533	2.2531	60.9800	1.8326
22.0	61.6519	2.7147	61.2522	2.3560	60.8567	1.9311
22.5	61.5642	2.8191	61.1532	2.4609	60.7342	2.0346
23.0	61.4784	2.9223	61.0572	2.5679	60.6133	2.1436
23.5	61.3950	3.0241	60.9649	2.6769	60.4947	2.2586
24.0	61.3147	3.1237	60.8772	2.7876	60.3795	2.3801
24.5	61.2382	3.2207	60.7949	2.9000	60.2685	2.5083
25.0	61.1661	3.3144	60.7191	3.0139	60.1630	2.6439

TABLE II. $b_r(q) = U + iV$, $q = \rho e^{i\phi}$ $\qquad\qquad r = 8$

ρ	$\phi = 80°$		$\phi = 85°$		$\phi = 90°$	
	U	V	U	V	U	V
0.0	64.0000	0.0000	64.0000	0.0000	64.0000	0.0000
0.5	63.9981	0.0007	63.9980	0.0003	63.9980	0.0000
1.0	63.9925	0.0027	63.9922	0.0014	63.9921	0.0000
1.5	63.9832	0.0061	63.9824	0.0031	63.9821	0.0000
2.0	63.9702	0.0109	63.9687	0.0055	63.9683	0.0000
2.5	63.9534	0.0169	63.9512	0.0086	63.9504	0.0000
3.0	63.9329	0.0244	63.9297	0.0124	63.9286	0.0000
3.5	63.9087	0.0332	63.9044	0.0168	63.9029	0.0000
4.0	63.8808	0.0433	63.8751	0.0220	63.8732	0.0000
4.5	63.8492	0.0548	63.8420	0.0278	63.8396	0.0000
5.0	63.8139	0.0676	63.8050	0.0343	63.8020	0.0000
5.5	63.7749	0.0817	63.7641	0.0415	63.7605	0.0000
6.0	63.7322	0.0972	63.7194	0.0493	63.7152	0.0000
6.5	63.6858	0.1139	63.6709	0.0578	63.6659	0.0000
7.0	63.6358	0.1320	63.6185	0.0670	63.6127	0.0000
7.5	63.5821	0.1514	63.5623	0.0768	63.5557	0.0000
8.0	63.5248	0.1720	63.5023	0.0873	63.4948	0.0000
8.5	63.4638	0.1940	63.4385	0.0984	63.4300	0.0000
9.0	63.3993	0.2172	63.3709	0.1102	63.3614	0.0000
9.5	63.3311	0.2417	63.2996	0.1227	63.2890	0.0000
10.0	63.2593	0.2675	63.2245	0.1357	63.2127	0.0000
10.5	63.1839	0.2945	63.1456	0.1495	63.1327	0.0000
11.0	63.1050	0.3229	63.0629	0.1639	63.0488	0.0000
11.5	63.0225	0.3525	62.9766	0.1789	62.9611	0.0000
12.0	62.9364	0.3834	62.8865	0.1946	62.8696	0.0000
12.5	62.8469	0.4156	62.7926	0.2110	62.7743	0.0000
13.0	62.7538	0.4491	62.6950	0.2281	62.6751	0.0000
13.5	62.6572	0.4840	62.5936	0.2459	62.5721	0.0000
14.0	62.5571	0.5203	62.4885	0.2645	62.4653	0.0000
14.5	62.4535	0.5580	62.3795	0.2838	62.3545	0.0000
15.0	62.3464	0.5972	62.2668	0.3039	62.2397	0.0000
15.5	62.2359	0.6381	62.1501	0.3250	62.1209	0.0000
16.0	62.1220	0.6806	62.0295	0.3469	61.9979	0.0000
16.5	62.0046	0.7248	61.9049	0.3700	61.8707	0.0000
17.0	61.8838	0.7711	61.7762	0.3941	61.7391	0.0000
17.5	61.7596	0.8194	61.6432	0.4196	61.6029	0.0000
18.0	61.6320	0.8701	61.5059	0.4464	61.4620	0.0000
18.5	61.5010	0.9233	61.3640	0.4748	61.3161	0.0000
19.0	61.3666	0.9794	61.2174	0.5051	61.1648	0.0000
19.5	61.2289	1.0386	61.0659	0.5375	61.0079	0.0000
20.0	61.0880	1.1015	60.9091	0.5722	60.8449	0.0000
20.5	60.9438	1.1684	60.7468	0.6097	60.6754	0.0000
21.0	60.7964	1.2399	60.5785	0.6504	60.4986	0.0000
21.5	60.6459	1.3167	60.4038	0.6949	60.3139	0.0000
22.0	60.4926	1.3994	60.2223	0.7438	60.1204	0.0000
22.5	60.3364	1.4888	60.0333	0.7979	59.9172	0.0000
23.0	60.1778	1.5860	59.8363	0.8581	59.7029	0.0000
23.5	60.0171	1.6919	59.6303	0.9257	59.4760	0.0000
24.0	59.8547	1.8079	59.4148	1.0019	59.2348	0.0000
24.5	59.6913	1.9351	59.1886	1.0886	58.9771	0.0000
25.0	59.5277	2.0751	58.9510	1.1879	58.6999	0.0000

ρ	$\phi = 5°$		$\phi = 10°$		$\phi = 15°$	
	U	V	U	V	U	V
0.0	81.0000	0.0000	81.0000	0.0000	81.0000	0.0000
0.5	81.0015	0.0003	81.0015	0.0005	81.0014	0.0008
1.0	81.0062	0.0011	81.0059	0.0021	81.0054	0.0031
1.5	81.0139	0.0024	81.0132	0.0048	81.0122	0.0070
2.0	81.0246	0.0043	81.0235	0.0086	81.0217	0.0125
2.5	81.0385	0.0068	81.0367	0.0134	81.0338	0.0195
3.0	81.0554	0.0098	81.0529	0.0193	81.0487	0.0281
3.5	81.0754	0.0133	81.0720	0.0262	81.0663	0.0383
4.0	81.0986	0.0174	81.0940	0.0343	81.0866	0.0501
4.5	81.1248	0.0220	81.1190	0.0434	81.1097	0.0634
5.0	81.1541	0.0272	81.1470	0.0536	81.1354	0.0783
5.5	81.1865	0.0329	81.1779	0.0649	81.1639	0.0948
6.0	81.2220	0.0392	81.2118	0.0772	81.1951	0.1129
6.5	81.2606	0.0461	81.2486	0.0907	81.2290	0.1325
7.0	81.3023	0.0535	81.2884	0.1053	81.2656	0.1538
7.5	81.3472	0.0614	81.3312	0.1209	81.3050	0.1767
8.0	81.3952	0.0699	81.3769	0.1377	81.3471	0.2012
8.5	81.4463	0.0790	81.4256	0.1556	81.3919	0.2273
9.0	81.5006	0.0887	81.4774	0.1745	81.4395	0.2550
9.5	81.5580	0.0989	81.5321	0.1947	81.4898	0.2844
10.0	81.6186	0.1097	81.5898	0.2159	81.5429	0.3154
10.5	81.6824	0.1210	81.6506	0.2383	81.5987	0.3480
11.0	81.7493	0.1330	81.7144	0.2618	81.6573	0.3824
11.5	81.8195	0.1455	81.7812	0.2865	81.7187	0.4183
12.0	81.8928	0.1587	81.8510	0.3123	81.7828	0.4560
12.5	81.9694	0.1724	81.9239	0.3393	81.8498	0.4954
13.0	82.0491	0.1867	81.9998	0.3674	81.9195	0.5364
13.5	82.1322	0.2016	82.0788	0.3967	81.9920	0.5792
14.0	82.2184	0.2171	82.1609	0.4272	82.0673	0.6237
14.5	82.3080	0.2332	82.2461	0.4589	82.1454	0.6699
15.0	82.4008	0.2500	82.3344	0.4918	82.2263	0.7179
15.5	82.4968	0.2673	82.4258	0.5260	82.3101	0.7676
16.0	82.5962	0.2853	82.5203	0.5613	82.3967	0.8191
16.5	82.6989	0.3038	82.6180	0.5978	82.4862	0.8724
17.0	82.8050	0.3230	82.7188	0.6356	82.5785	0.9274
17.5	82.9143	0.3429	82.8228	0.6746	82.6737	0.9843
18.0	83.0270	0.3633	82.9300	0.7148	82.7718	1.0430
18.5	83.1431	0.3844	83.0404	0.7563	82.8728	1.1035
19.0	83.2625	0.4061	83.1540	0.7990	82.9768	1.1658
19.5	83.3854	0.4284	83.2708	0.8429	83.0837	1.2299
20.0	83.5116	0.4513	83.3908	0.8881	83.1936	1.2959
20.5	83.6411	0.4748	83.5141	0.9345	83.3064	1.3638
21.0	83.7741	0.4990	83.6407	0.9821	83.4223	1.4335
21.5	83.9105	0.5237	83.7705	1.0309	83.5413	1.5050
22.0	84.0503	0.5490	83.9037	1.0809	83.6633	1.5784
22.5	84.1936	0.5749	84.0401	1.1322	83.7884	1.6536
23.0	84.3402	0.6014	84.1799	1.1846	83.9166	1.7306
23.5	84.4902	0.6284	84.3230	1.2381	84.0480	1.8094
24.0	84.6436	0.6560	84.4694	1.2927	84.1826	1.8901
24.5	84.8003	0.6841	84.6193	1.3485	84.3204	1.9724
25.0	84.9605	0.7126	84.7724	1.4053	84.4615	2.0566

TABLE II. $b_r(q) = U+iV$, $q=\rho e^{i\phi}$ $r=9$

ρ	$\phi=20°$		$\phi=25°$		$\phi=30°$	
	U	V	U	V	U	V
0.0	81.0000	0.0000	81.0000	0.0000	81.0000	0.0000
0.5	81.0012	0.0010	81.0010	0.0012	81.0008	0.0014
1.0	81.0048	0.0040	81.0040	0.0048	81.0031	0.0054
1.5	81.0108	0.0090	81.0090	0.0108	81.0070	0.0122
2.0	81.0192	0.0161	81.0161	0.0192	81.0125	0.0217
2.5	81.0299	0.0251	81.0251	0.0299	81.0195	0.0338
3.0	81.0431	0.0362	81.0362	0.0431	81.0281	0.0487
3.5	81.0587	0.0493	81.0492	0.0587	81.0383	0.0663
4.0	81.0766	0.0644	81.0643	0.0767	81.0500	0.0867
4.5	81.0970	0.0815	81.0813	0.0971	81.0632	0.1097
5.0	81.1197	0.1006	81.1004	0.1199	81.0780	0.1355
5.5	81.1449	0.1218	81.1215	0.1451	81.0944	0.1640
6.0	81.1724	0.1450	81.1446	0.1728	81.1123	0.1952
6.5	81.2024	0.1703	81.1696	0.2029	81.1317	0.2292
7.0	81.2347	0.1976	81.1967	0.2354	81.1527	0.2659
7.5	81.2695	0.2270	81.2258	0.2703	81.1753	0.3054
8.0	81.3066	0.2584	81.2569	0.3077	81.1993	0.3476
8.5	81.3462	0.2920	81.2899	0.3476	81.2249	0.3925
9.0	81.3882	0.3275	81.3250	0.3899	81.2520	0.4403
9.5	81.4325	0.3652	81.3621	0.4347	81.2807	0.4908
10.0	81.4793	0.4050	81.4011	0.4820	81.3108	0.5441
10.5	81.5285	0.4469	81.4422	0.5318	81.3425	0.6002
11.0	81.5801	0.4909	81.4852	0.5841	81.3756	0.6591
11.5	81.6341	0.5370	81.5302	0.6389	81.4103	0.7208
12.0	81.6906	0.5853	81.5772	0.6962	81.4464	0.7853
12.5	81.7494	0.6358	81.6262	0.7561	81.4841	0.8527
13.0	81.8107	0.6884	81.6772	0.8185	81.5232	0.9229
13.5	81.8744	0.7431	81.7301	0.8835	81.5638	0.9960
14.0	81.9405	0.8001	81.7850	0.9511	81.6058	1.0719
14.5	82.0091	0.8593	81.8419	1.0213	81.6493	1.1507
15.0	82.0801	0.9207	81.9007	1.0940	81.6942	1.2325
15.5	82.1536	0.9844	81.9616	1.1695	81.7406	1.3171
16.0	82.2295	1.0503	82.0243	1.2476	81.7884	1.4047
16.5	82.3078	1.1185	82.0891	1.3283	81.8376	1.4953
17.0	82.3886	1.1890	82.1558	1.4118	81.8882	1.5888
17.5	82.4720	1.2618	82.2246	1.4980	81.9402	1.6854
18.0	82.5578	1.3369	82.2952	1.5869	81.9936	1.7850
18.5	82.6461	1.4144	82.3679	1.6786	82.0484	1.8876
19.0	82.7369	1.4942	82.4426	1.7732	82.1046	1.9934
19.5	82.8303	1.5764	82.5193	1.8705	82.1621	2.1023
20.0	82.9262	1.6611	82.5979	1.9707	82.2209	2.2143
20.5	83.0247	1.7481	82.6786	2.0739	82.2811	2.3296
21.0	83.1258	1.8376	82.7614	2.1799	82.3426	2.4481
21.5	83.2296	1.9295	82.8462	2.2890	82.4055	2.5700
22.0	83.3361	2.0239	82.9331	2.4010	82.4697	2.6953
22.5	83.4453	2.1208	83.0221	2.5161	82.5352	2.8239
23.0	83.5572	2.2202	83.1133	2.6344	82.6021	2.9561
23.5	83.6720	2.3221	83.2067	2.7557	82.6703	3.0919
24.0	83.7896	2.4266	83.3023	2.8803	82.7398	3.2314
24.5	83.9101	2.5335	83.4003	3.0082	82.8108	3.3746
25.0	84.0336	2.6429	83.5006	3.1393	82.8831	3.5217

TABLE II. $b_r(q) = U + iV$, $q = \rho e^{i\phi}$ $r=9$

ρ	$\phi=35°$		$\phi=40°$		$\phi=45°$	
	U	V	U	V	U	V
0.0	81.0000	0.0000	81.0000	0.0000	81.0000	0.0000
0.5	81.0005	0.0015	81.0003	0.0015	81.0000	0.0016
1.0	81.0021	0.0059	81.0011	0.0062	81.0000	0.0062
1.5	81.0048	0.0132	81.0024	0.0138	81.0000	0.0141
2.0	81.0085	0.0235	81.0043	0.0246	81.0000	0.0250
2.5	81.0133	0.0367	81.0068	0.0385	81.0000	0.0391
3.0	81.0192	0.0529	81.0097	0.0554	81.0000	0.0562
3.5	81.0261	0.0720	81.0132	0.0754	81.0000	0.0766
4.0	81.0341	0.0940	81.0173	0.0985	80.9999	0.1000
4.5	81.0432	0.1190	81.0219	0.1247	80.9999	0.1266
5.0	81.0533	0.1470	81.0269	0.1539	80.9998	0.1562
5.5	81.0644	0.1779	81.0325	0.1863	80.9997	0.1891
6.0	81.0766	0.2117	81.0387	0.2217	80.9996	0.2250
6.5	81.0899	0.2485	81.0453	0.2602	80.9994	0.2641
7.0	81.1041	0.2883	81.0524	0.3019	80.9992	0.3062
7.5	81.1194	0.3310	81.0601	0.3466	80.9990	0.3516
8.0	81.1358	0.3767	81.0682	0.3944	80.9987	0.4000
8.5	81.1531	0.4254	81.0768	0.4453	80.9983	0.4515
9.0	81.1715	0.4771	81.0859	0.4993	80.9979	0.5062
9.5	81.1908	0.5317	81.0954	0.5564	80.9973	0.5640
10.0	81.2112	0.5894	81.1054	0.6166	80.9967	0.6249
10.5	81.2326	0.6500	81.1159	0.6799	80.9960	0.6890
11.0	81.2549	0.7137	81.1268	0.7463	80.9952	0.7561
11.5	81.2782	0.7803	81.1381	0.8158	80.9943	0.8264
12.0	81.3025	0.8500	81.1498	0.8885	80.9932	0.8998
12.5	81.3277	0.9227	81.1619	0.9643	80.9920	0.9763
13.0	81.3538	0.9985	81.1744	1.0432	80.9906	1.0559
13.5	81.3809	1.0773	81.1873	1.1252	80.9891	1.1386
14.0	81.4089	1.1591	81.2006	1.2103	80.9873	1.2245
14.5	81.4378	1.2440	81.2141	1.2986	80.9854	1.3134
15.0	81.4675	1.3320	81.2280	1.3900	80.9832	1.4054
15.5	81.4982	1.4231	81.2422	1.4846	80.9808	1.5005
16.0	81.5297	1.5172	81.2567	1.5822	80.9782	1.5987
16.5	81.5620	1.6145	81.2714	1.6831	80.9752	1.6999
17.0	81.5951	1.7149	81.2864	1.7871	80.9719	1.8043
17.5	81.6290	1.8185	81.3015	1.8942	80.9683	1.9116
18.0	81.6637	1.9252	81.3168	2.0045	80.9644	2.0220
18.5	81.6991	2.0352	81.3323	2.1180	80.9600	2.1355
19.0	81.7352	2.1483	81.3478	2.2346	80.9552	2.2519
19.5	81.7720	2.2647	81.3634	2.3544	80.9500	2.3713
20.0	81.8095	2.3844	81.3790	2.4775	80.9442	2.4938
20.5	81.8475	2.5074	81.3945	2.6037	80.9378	2.6191
21.0	81.8862	2.6338	81.4099	2.7331	80.9308	2.7474
21.5	81.9254	2.7635	81.4252	2.8658	80.9231	2.8786
22.0	81.9650	2.8967	81.4402	3.0017	80.9147	3.0126
22.5	82.0052	3.0335	81.4549	3.1409	80.9054	3.1495
23.0	82.0457	3.1738	81.4691	3.2834	80.8952	3.2892
23.5	82.0867	3.3178	81.4829	3.4292	80.8840	3.4317
24.0	82.1279	3.4655	81.4961	3.5784	80.8716	3.5768
24.5	82.1694	3.6171	81.5085	3.7311	80.8580	3.7246
25.0	82.2111	3.7727	81.5201	3.8872	80.8429	3.8751

ρ	$\phi = 50°$			$\phi = 55°$			$\phi = 60°$		
	U	V		U	V		U	V	
0.0	81.0000	0.0000		81.0000	0.0000		81.0000	0.0000	
0.5	80.9997	0.0015		80.9995	0.0015		80.9992	0.0014	
1.0	80.9989	0.0062		80.9979	0.0059		80.9969	0.0054	
1.5	80.9976	0.0138		80.9952	0.0132		80.9930	0.0122	
2.0	80.9957	0.0246		80.9914	0.0235		80.9875	0.0216	
2.5	80.9932	0.0385		80.9866	0.0367		80.9805	0.0338	
3.0	80.9902	0.0554		80.9807	0.0528		80.9719	0.0487	
3.5	80.9867	0.0754		80.9738	0.0719		80.9617	0.0663	
4.0	80.9826	0.0985		80.9657	0.0939		80.9500	0.0865	
4.5	80.9779	0.1246		80.9566	0.1188		80.9367	0.1095	
5.0	80.9727	0.1538		80.9464	0.1467		80.9218	0.1351	
5.5	80.9669	0.1861		80.9351	0.1775		80.9053	0.1635	
6.0	80.9605	0.2214		80.9227	0.2112		80.8873	0.1945	
6.5	80.9536	0.2598		80.9092	0.2478		80.8677	0.2282	
7.0	80.9461	0.3013		80.8947	0.2873		80.8465	0.2645	
7.5	80.9380	0.3459		80.8790	0.3297		80.8237	0.3036	
8.0	80.9293	0.3935		80.8622	0.3750		80.7993	0.3453	
8.5	80.9200	0.4441		80.8443	0.4232		80.7734	0.3896	
9.0	80.9101	0.4978		80.8252	0.4743		80.7458	0.4366	
9.5	80.8996	0.5545		80.8051	0.5283		80.7167	0.4862	
10.0	80.8884	0.6143		80.7838	0.5852		80.6859	0.5384	
10.5	80.8767	0.6772		80.7614	0.6449		80.6536	0.5933	
11.0	80.8642	0.7430		80.7378	0.7075		80.6196	0.6508	
11.5	80.8512	0.8119		80.7131	0.7730		80.5840	0.7109	
12.0	80.8374	0.8838		80.6872	0.8413		80.5468	0.7736	
12.5	80.8230	0.9588		80.6601	0.9124		80.5080	0.8388	
13.0	80.8080	1.0367		80.6319	0.9864		80.4676	0.9067	
13.5	80.7922	1.1176		80.6025	1.0631		80.4255	0.9771	
14.0	80.7757	1.2016		80.5719	1.1427		80.3818	1.0500	
14.5	80.7585	1.2885		80.5401	1.2251		80.3365	1.1255	
15.0	80.7406	1.3784		80.5072	1.3103		80.2896	1.2035	
15.5	80.7219	1.4712		80.4730	1.3982		80.2410	1.2841	
16.0	80.7025	1.5670		80.4376	1.4888		80.1909	1.3671	
16.5	80.6823	1.6657		80.4010	1.5822		80.1391	1.4526	
17.0	80.6613	1.7673		80.3632	1.6783		80.0857	1.5406	
17.5	80.6395	1.8718		80.3242	1.7771		80.0307	1.6310	
18.0	80.6169	1.9791		80.2840	1.8785		79.9741	1.7239	
18.5	80.5935	2.0893		80.2425	1.9826		79.9160	1.8192	
19.0	80.5692	2.2023		80.1999	2.0892		79.8563	1.9169	
19.5	80.5440	2.3180		80.1560	2.1984		79.7951	2.0169	
20.0	80.5180	2.4365		80.1110	2.3101		79.7324	2.1193	
20.5	80.4910	2.5576		80.0648	2.4243		79.6682	2.2241	
21.0	80.4630	2.6813		80.0174	2.5408		79.6026	2.3311	
21.5	80.4341	2.8077		79.9688	2.6597		79.5357	2.4404	
22.0	80.4041	2.9365		79.9191	2.7809		79.4674	2.5519	
22.5	80.3731	3.0677		79.8683	2.9043		79.3979	2.6656	
23.0	80.3410	3.2012		79.8163	3.0298		79.3273	2.7814	
23.5	80.3077	3.3370		79.7634	3.1572		79.2556	2.8994	
24.0	80.2732	3.4749		79.7094	3.2866		79.1829	3.0193	
24.5	80.2374	3.6147		79.6544	3.4176		79.1094	3.1413	
25.0	80.2003	3.7565		79.5984	3.5503		79.0352	3.2651	

TABLE II. $b_r(q) = U + iV$, $q = \rho e^{i\phi}$ $\qquad$ $r = 9$

ρ	$\phi = 65°$		$\phi = 70°$		$\phi = 75°$	
	U	V	U	V	U	V
0.0	81.0000	0.0000	81.0000	0.0000	81.0000	0.0000
0.5	80.9990	0.0012	80.9988	0.0010	80.9986	0.0008
1.0	80.9960	0.0048	80.9952	0.0040	80.9946	0.0031
1.5	80.9910	0.0108	80.9892	0.0090	80.9878	0.0070
2.0	80.9839	0.0191	80.9808	0.0161	80.9784	0.0125
2.5	80.9749	0.0299	80.9701	0.0251	80.9662	0.0195
3.0	80.9638	0.0431	80.9569	0.0361	80.9513	0.0281
3.5	80.9508	0.0586	80.9414	0.0492	80.9337	0.0382
4.0	80.9357	0.0765	80.9234	0.0642	80.9134	0.0499
4.5	80.9186	0.0968	80.9031	0.0812	80.8905	0.0632
5.0	80.8995	0.1195	80.8803	0.1002	80.8648	0.0779
5.5	80.8784	0.1445	80.8552	0.1212	80.8364	0.0943
6.0	80.8553	0.1719	80.8277	0.1442	80.8054	0.1121
6.5	80.8302	0.2017	80.7978	0.1692	80.7718	0.1315
7.0	80.8030	0.2338	80.7655	0.1961	80.7352	0.1525
7.5	80.7738	0.2683	80.7309	0.2250	80.6961	0.1749
8.0	80.7427	0.3051	80.6938	0.2558	80.6543	0.1989
8.5	80.7095	0.3443	80.6544	0.2886	80.6098	0.2243
9.0	80.6742	0.3857	80.6126	0.3233	80.5626	0.2513
9.5	80.6370	0.4295	80.5684	0.3600	80.5128	0.2798
10.0	80.5977	0.4756	80.5218	0.3986	80.4604	0.3097
10.5	80.5565	0.5240	80.4729	0.4391	80.4052	0.3412
11.0	80.5132	0.5747	80.4216	0.4815	80.3474	0.3741
11.5	80.4678	0.6276	80.3679	0.5258	80.2870	0.4085
12.0	80.4205	0.6829	80.3118	0.5720	80.2239	0.4443
12.5	80.3711	0.7404	80.2534	0.6201	80.1582	0.4816
13.0	80.3197	0.8002	80.1926	0.6701	80.0898	0.5204
13.5	80.2663	0.8622	80.1295	0.7219	80.0189	0.5606
14.0	80.2109	0.9264	80.0640	0.7756	79.9452	0.6022
14.5	80.1535	0.9929	79.9961	0.8312	79.8690	0.6452
15.0	80.0940	1.0615	79.9259	0.8886	79.7901	0.6897
15.5	80.0325	1.1324	79.8534	0.9478	79.7087	0.7356
16.0	79.9691	1.2055	79.7785	1.0089	79.6246	0.7829
16.5	79.9036	1.2808	79.7013	1.0718	79.5378	0.8316
17.0	79.8362	1.3583	79.6217	1.1365	79.4485	0.8817
17.5	79.7668	1.4379	79.5399	1.2031	79.3566	0.9332
18.0	79.6955	1.5197	79.4557	1.2715	79.2620	0.9861
18.5	79.6222	1.6037	79.3692	1.3418	79.1648	1.0405
19.0	79.5470	1.6899	79.2804	1.4139	79.0650	1.0963
19.5	79.4699	1.7783	79.1893	1.4879	78.9625	1.1535
20.0	79.3909	1.8688	79.0960	1.5639	78.8573	1.2122
20.5	79.3101	1.9615	79.0004	1.6417	78.7495	1.2724
21.0	79.2276	2.0564	78.9025	1.7215	78.6389	1.3341
21.5	79.1433	2.1535	78.8024	1.8034	78.5257	1.3974
22.0	79.0574	2.2529	78.7001	1.8873	78.4096	1.4623
22.5	78.9699	2.3545	78.5957	1.9734	78.2908	1.5288
23.0	78.8809	2.4584	78.4891	2.0617	78.1691	1.5972
23.5	78.7904	2.5646	78.3803	2.1523	78.0445	1.6673
24.0	78.6987	2.6731	78.2695	2.2453	77.9169	1.7394
24.5	78.6058	2.7841	78.1567	2.3409	77.7863	1.8135
25.0	78.5119	2.8975	78.0419	2.4392	77.6525	1.8899

TABLE II. $b_r(q) = U + iV$, $q = \rho e^{i\phi}$　　　　　　$r = 9$

ρ	$\phi = 80°$		$\phi = 85°$		$\phi = 90°$	
	U	V	U	V	U	V
0.0	81.0000	0.0000	81.0000	0.0000	81.0000	0.0000
0.5	80.9985	0.0005	80.9985	0.0003	80.9984	-0.0000
1.0	80.9941	0.0021	80.9938	0.0011	80.9937	-0.0000
1.5	80.9868	0.0048	80.9862	0.0024	80.9859	-0.0000
2.0	80.9765	0.0085	80.9754	0.0043	80.9750	-0.0000
2.5	80.9633	0.0134	80.9615	0.0068	80.9609	-0.0000
3.0	80.9472	0.0192	80.9446	0.0098	80.9438	-0.0000
3.5	80.9281	0.0262	80.9246	0.0133	80.9235	-0.0000
4.0	80.9061	0.0341	80.9016	0.0173	80.9001	-0.0000
4.5	80.8812	0.0432	80.8755	0.0219	80.8736	-0.0000
5.0	80.8533	0.0533	80.8463	0.0271	80.8440	-0.0000
5.5	80.8226	0.0645	80.8141	0.0327	80.8112	-0.0000
6.0	80.7889	0.0767	80.7788	0.0389	80.7754	-0.0000
6.5	80.7523	0.0899	80.7405	0.0457	80.7365	-0.0000
7.0	80.7128	0.1042	80.6991	0.0529	80.6945	-0.0000
7.5	80.6704	0.1196	80.6547	0.0607	80.6495	-0.0000
8.0	80.6251	0.1360	80.6073	0.0690	80.6013	-0.0000
8.5	80.5770	0.1534	80.5569	0.0778	80.5501	-0.0000
9.0	80.5259	0.1718	80.5034	0.0872	80.4959	-0.0000
9.5	80.4720	0.1912	80.4470	0.0971	80.4386	-0.0000
10.0	80.4152	0.2117	80.3875	0.1074	80.3782	-0.0000
10.5	80.3555	0.2332	80.3251	0.1183	80.3148	-0.0000
11.0	80.2929	0.2557	80.2596	0.1297	80.2484	-0.0000
11.5	80.2276	0.2791	80.1912	0.1416	80.1790	-0.0000
12.0	80.1593	0.3036	80.1199	0.1540	80.1066	-0.0001
12.5	80.0883	0.3291	80.0455	0.1669	80.0312	-0.0001
13.0	80.0144	0.3555	79.9683	0.1803	79.9528	-0.0001
13.5	79.9376	0.3829	79.8881	0.1941	79.8715	-0.0002
14.0	79.8581	0.4113	79.8049	0.2085	79.7872	-0.0002
14.5	79.7757	0.4406	79.7188	0.2233	79.6999	-0.0003
15.0	79.6905	0.4709	79.6299	0.2386	79.6097	-0.0004
15.5	79.6025	0.5021	79.5380	0.2543	79.5166	-0.0005
16.0	79.5117	0.5342	79.4432	0.2704	79.4205	-0.0007
16.5	79.4181	0.5673	79.3454	0.2870	79.3216	-0.0010
17.0	79.3217	0.6013	79.2448	0.3041	79.2198	-0.0013
17.5	79.2224	0.6363	79.1413	0.3215	79.1151	-0.0016
18.0	79.1204	0.6721	79.0349	0.3393	79.0076	-0.0021
18.5	79.0155	0.7089	78.9256	0.3575	78.8972	-0.0027
19.0	78.9077	0.7465	78.8134	0.3760	78.7840	-0.0035
19.5	78.7970	0.7851	78.6983	0.3948	78.6679	-0.0045
20.0	78.6835	0.8245	78.5802	0.4139	78.5491	-0.0057
20.5	78.5670	0.8648	78.4591	0.4333	78.4275	-0.0071
21.0	78.4475	0.9060	78.3351	0.4528	78.3031	-0.0089
21.5	78.3250	0.9481	78.2081	0.4725	78.1759	-0.0111
22.0	78.1994	0.9910	78.0779	0.4923	78.0460	-0.0138
22.5	78.0706	1.0349	77.9447	0.5122	77.9134	-0.0171
23.0	77.9386	1.0796	77.8083	0.5320	77.7781	-0.0210
23.5	77.8031	1.1252	77.6686	0.5517	77.6400	-0.0257
24.0	77.6642	1.1718	77.5255	0.5711	77.4994	-0.0314
24.5	77.5216	1.2192	77.3791	0.5902	77.3560	-0.0381
25.0	77.3751	1.2676	77.2290	0.6088	77.2101	-0.0461

322-566 O - 69 - 12

TABLE II. $b_r(q) = U + iV$, $q = \rho e^{i\phi}$ $\qquad\qquad r=10$

ρ	$\phi=5°$		$\phi=10°$		$\phi=15°$	
	U	V	U	V	U	V
0.0	100.0000	0.0000	100.0000	0.0000	100.0000	0.0000
0.5	100.0012	0.0002	100.0012	0.0004	100.0011	0.0006
1.0	100.0050	0.0009	100.0047	0.0017	100.0044	0.0025
1.5	100.0112	0.0020	100.0107	0.0039	100.0098	0.0057
2.0	100.0199	0.0035	100.0190	0.0069	100.0175	0.0101
2.5	100.0311	0.0055	100.0297	0.0108	100.0273	0.0158
3.0	100.0448	0.0079	100.0427	0.0156	100.0394	0.0227
3.5	100.0610	0.0108	100.0582	0.0212	100.0536	0.0310
4.0	100.0796	0.0140	100.0760	0.0277	100.0700	0.0404
4.5	100.1008	0.0178	100.0962	0.0350	100.0886	0.0512
5.0	100.1244	0.0220	100.1187	0.0433	100.1094	0.0632
5.5	100.1506	0.0266	100.1437	0.0524	100.1324	0.0765
6.0	100.1793	0.0316	100.1710	0.0623	100.1576	0.0911
6.5	100.2104	0.0372	100.2007	0.0732	100.1849	0.1070
7.0	100.2441	0.0431	100.2329	0.0849	100.2145	0.1241
7.5	100.2803	0.0495	100.2674	0.0975	100.2463	0.1425
8.0	100.3190	0.0564	100.3043	0.1110	100.2803	0.1622
8.5	100.3602	0.0637	100.3436	0.1254	100.3165	0.1832
9.0	100.4039	0.0714	100.3853	0.1406	100.3548	0.2055
9.5	100.4502	0.0796	100.4294	0.1568	100.3954	0.2291
10.0	100.4990	0.0883	100.4759	0.1738	100.4382	0.2540
10.5	100.5503	0.0974	100.5248	0.1918	100.4833	0.2802
11.0	100.6042	0.1070	100.5762	0.2106	100.5305	0.3077
11.5	100.6606	0.1170	100.6299	0.2304	100.5799	0.3366
12.0	100.7196	0.1275	100.6861	0.2511	100.6316	0.3667
12.5	100.7811	0.1385	100.7448	0.2726	100.6855	0.3982
13.0	100.8452	0.1499	100.8058	0.2951	100.7416	0.4311
13.5	100.9119	0.1618	100.8693	0.3185	100.8000	0.4652
14.0	100.9811	0.1742	100.9353	0.3429	100.8605	0.5007
14.5	101.0529	0.1870	101.0037	0.3682	100.9234	0.5376
15.0	101.1274	0.2004	101.0745	0.3944	100.9884	0.5758
15.5	101.2044	0.2142	101.1479	0.4215	101.0557	0.6154
16.0	101.2840	0.2285	101.2237	0.4496	101.1253	0.6564
16.5	101.3663	0.2432	101.3019	0.4787	101.1971	0.6988
17.0	101.4511	0.2585	101.3827	0.5087	101.2712	0.7425
17.5	101.5386	0.2743	101.4659	0.5397	101.3475	0.7877
18.0	101.6288	0.2905	101.5517	0.5716	101.4261	0.8342
18.5	101.7216	0.3073	101.6399	0.6045	101.5070	0.8822
19.0	101.8170	0.3245	101.7307	0.6385	101.5902	0.9316
19.5	101.9152	0.3423	101.8240	0.6734	101.6756	0.9825
20.0	102.0160	0.3605	101.9198	0.7093	101.7633	1.0347
20.5	102.1195	0.3793	102.0182	0.7462	101.8534	1.0885
21.0	102.2257	0.3986	102.1191	0.7841	101.9457	1.1437
21.5	102.3346	0.4184	102.2226	0.8230	102.0404	1.2004
22.0	102.4462	0.4387	102.3287	0.8630	102.1373	1.2585
22.5	102.5606	0.4596	102.4373	0.9039	102.2366	1.3182
23.0	102.6777	0.4810	102.5485	0.9459	102.3383	1.3794
23.5	102.7975	0.5029	102.6624	0.9890	102.4423	1.4421
24.0	102.9202	0.5253	102.7788	1.0331	102.5486	1.5063
24.5	103.0456	0.5482	102.8979	1.0782	102.6574	1.5720
25.0	103.1737	0.5717	103.0196	1.1244	102.7685	1.6393

TABLE II. $b_r(q) = U + iV$, $q = \rho e^{i\phi}$ $\qquad\qquad$ $r = 10$

ρ	$\phi=20°$		$\phi=25°$		$\phi=30°$	
	U	V	U	V	U	V
0.0	100.0000	0.0000	100.0000	0.0000	100.0000	0.0000
0.5	100.0010	0.0008	100.0008	0.0010	100.0006	0.0011
1.0	100.0039	0.0032	100.0032	0.0039	100.0025	0.0044
1.5	100.0087	0.0073	100.0073	0.0087	100.0057	0.0098
2.0	100.0155	0.0130	100.0130	0.0155	100.0101	0.0175
2.5	100.0242	0.0203	100.0203	0.0242	100.0158	0.0273
3.0	100.0348	0.0292	100.0292	0.0348	100.0227	0.0394
3.5	100.0474	0.0398	100.0398	0.0474	100.0309	0.0536
4.0	100.0619	0.0520	100.0519	0.0619	100.0404	0.0700
4.5	100.0784	0.0658	100.0657	0.0784	100.0511	0.0886
5.0	100.0967	0.0813	100.0811	0.0968	100.0631	0.1094
5.5	100.1171	0.0984	100.0982	0.1172	100.0763	0.1324
6.0	100.1393	0.1171	100.1168	0.1395	100.0908	0.1577
6.5	100.1635	0.1375	100.1371	0.1638	100.1065	0.1851
7.0	100.1896	0.1595	100.1590	0.1900	100.1235	0.2147
7.5	100.2177	0.1831	100.1825	0.2182	100.1418	0.2465
8.0	100.2477	0.2085	100.2076	0.2483	100.1613	0.2805
8.5	100.2797	0.2354	100.2344	0.2804	100.1820	0.3168
9.0	100.3136	0.2641	100.2628	0.3145	100.2040	0.3552
9.5	100.3494	0.2944	100.2927	0.3505	100.2272	0.3959
10.0	100.3872	0.3263	100.3243	0.3886	100.2517	0.4389
10.5	100.4269	0.3600	100.3575	0.4286	100.2774	0.4840
11.0	100.4686	0.3953	100.3924	0.4706	100.3043	0.5314
11.5	100.5122	0.4323	100.4288	0.5146	100.3324	0.5810
12.0	100.5577	0.4710	100.4668	0.5606	100.3618	0.6329
12.5	100.6052	0.5114	100.5065	0.6086	100.3924	0.6870
13.0	100.6546	0.5535	100.5477	0.6587	100.4242	0.7434
13.5	100.7060	0.5973	100.5906	0.7107	100.4573	0.8020
14.0	100.7594	0.6429	100.6350	0.7648	100.4915	0.8629
14.5	100.8147	0.6901	100.6811	0.8209	100.5270	0.9261
15.0	100.8719	0.7391	100.7288	0.8791	100.5637	0.9916
15.5	100.9311	0.7898	100.7780	0.9393	100.6015	1.0593
16.0	100.9922	0.8423	100.8289	1.0016	100.6406	1.1294
16.5	101.0553	0.8966	100.8813	1.0659	100.6808	1.2017
17.0	101.1204	0.9526	100.9354	1.1324	100.7222	1.2764
17.5	101.1874	1.0104	100.9910	1.2009	100.7648	1.3534
18.0	101.2564	1.0700	101.0482	1.2715	100.8086	1.4327
18.5	101.3273	1.1314	101.1070	1.3442	100.8535	1.5143
19.0	101.4002	1.1946	101.1674	1.4191	100.8996	1.5983
19.5	101.4751	1.2596	101.2293	1.4960	100.9468	1.6846
20.0	101.5519	1.3265	101.2929	1.5752	100.9952	1.7733
20.5	101.6307	1.3952	101.3580	1.6564	101.0447	1.8644
21.0	101.7115	1.4657	101.4247	1.7399	101.0953	1.9578
21.5	101.7942	1.5382	101.4929	1.8255	101.1471	2.0537
22.0	101.8789	1.6125	101.5627	1.9134	101.1999	2.1520
22.5	101.9657	1.6887	101.6341	2.0034	101.2539	2.2527
23.0	102.0544	1.7668	101.7070	2.0957	101.3089	2.3558
23.5	102.1451	1.8469	101.7815	2.1903	101.3650	2.4614
24.0	102.2378	1.9289	101.8576	2.2871	101.4221	2.5695
24.5	102.3325	2.0129	101.9352	2.3862	101.4804	2.6800
25.0	102.4292	2.0989	102.0144	2.4876	101.5396	2.7931

TABLE II. $b_r(q) = U + iV$, $q = \rho e^{i\phi}$ $r = 10$

ρ	$\phi=35°$		$\phi=40°$		$\phi=45°$	
	U	V	U	V	U	V
0.0	100.0000	0.0000	100.0000	0.0000	100.0000	0.0000
0.5	100.0004	0.0012	100.0002	0.0012	100.0000	0.0013
1.0	100.0017	0.0047	100.0009	0.0050	100.0000	0.0051
1.5	100.0039	0.0107	100.0020	0.0112	100.0000	0.0114
2.0	100.0069	0.0190	100.0035	0.0199	100.0000	0.0202
2.5	100.0108	0.0297	100.0055	0.0311	100.0000	0.0316
3.0	100.0155	0.0427	100.0079	0.0448	100.0000	0.0455
3.5	100.0211	0.0582	100.0107	0.0609	100.0000	0.0619
4.0	100.0276	0.0760	100.0140	0.0796	100.0000	0.0808
4.5	100.0349	0.0961	100.0177	0.1007	99.9999	0.1023
5.0	100.0431	0.1187	100.0218	0.1244	99.9999	0.1263
5.5	100.0521	0.1437	100.0264	0.1505	99.9998	0.1528
6.0	100.0620	0.1710	100.0314	0.1791	99.9998	0.1818
6.5	100.0727	0.2007	100.0368	0.2102	99.9997	0.2134
7.0	100.0843	0.2328	100.0426	0.2439	99.9996	0.2475
7.5	100.0967	0.2673	100.0488	0.2800	99.9995	0.2841
8.0	100.1100	0.3042	100.0555	0.3186	99.9993	0.3232
8.5	100.1241	0.3435	100.0625	0.3597	99.9991	0.3649
9.0	100.1391	0.3851	100.0700	0.4032	99.9989	0.4091
9.5	100.1548	0.4292	100.0778	0.4493	99.9986	0.4558
10.0	100.1714	0.4757	100.0861	0.4979	99.9983	0.5050
10.5	100.1888	0.5246	100.0947	0.5490	99.9979	0.5568
11.0	100.2071	0.5758	100.1038	0.6027	99.9975	0.6111
11.5	100.2261	0.6295	100.1132	0.6588	99.9970	0.6679
12.0	100.2460	0.6857	100.1229	0.7174	99.9965	0.7272
12.5	100.2667	0.7442	100.1331	0.7785	99.9958	0.7891
13.0	100.2881	0.8051	100.1436	0.8422	99.9951	0.8534
13.5	100.3104	0.8685	100.1545	0.9083	99.9944	0.9203
14.0	100.3334	0.9343	100.1657	0.9770	99.9935	0.9898
14.5	100.3573	1.0026	100.1772	1.0482	99.9925	1.0617
15.0	100.3819	1.0733	100.1891	1.1219	99.9914	1.1361
15.5	100.4072	1.1464	100.2013	1.1981	99.9902	1.2131
16.0	100.4334	1.2220	100.2139	1.2768	99.9889	1.2926
16.5	100.4603	1.3000	100.2267	1.3581	99.9874	1.3746
17.0	100.4879	1.3805	100.2399	1.4419	99.9858	1.4591
17.5	100.5163	1.4634	100.2533	1.5282	99.9841	1.5461
18.0	100.5454	1.5488	100.2670	1.6170	99.9822	1.6356
18.5	100.5752	1.6367	100.2810	1.7084	99.9801	1.7277
19.0	100.6057	1.7271	100.2952	1.8023	99.9779	1.8222
19.5	100.6369	1.8200	100.3097	1.8987	99.9754	1.9192
20.0	100.6688	1.9153	100.3245	1.9976	99.9728	2.0188
20.5	100.7014	2.0131	100.3394	2.0991	99.9700	2.1208
21.0	100.7347	2.1135	100.3546	2.2031	99.9670	2.2253
21.5	100.7686	2.2163	100.3700	2.3096	99.9637	2.3322
22.0	100.8031	2.3217	100.3855	2.4187	99.9602	2.4417
22.5	100.8383	2.4296	100.4012	2.5303	99.9565	2.5535
23.0	100.8740	2.5400	100.4171	2.6444	99.9524	2.6679
23.5	100.9103	2.6530	100.4330	2.7610	99.9481	2.7847
24.0	100.9472	2.7685	100.4491	2.8801	99.9436	2.9039
24.5	100.9847	2.8865	100.4653	3.0018	99.9387	3.0255
25.0	101.0226	3.0072	100.4815	3.1260	99.9335	3.1495

TABLE II. $b_r(q) = U + iV$, $q = \rho e^{i\phi}$ $\qquad$ $r = 10$

ρ	$\phi=50°$		$\phi=55°$		$\phi=60°$	
	U	V	U	V	U	V
0.0	100.0000	0.0000	100.0000	0.0000	100.0000	0.0000
0.5	99.9998	0.0012	99.9996	0.0012	99.9994	0.0011
1.0	99.9991	0.0050	99.9983	0.0047	99.9975	0.0044
1.5	99.9980	0.0112	99.9961	0.0107	99.9943	0.0098
2.0	99.9965	0.0199	99.9931	0.0190	99.9899	0.0175
2.5	99.9945	0.0311	99.9892	0.0297	99.9842	0.0273
3.0	99.9921	0.0448	99.9844	0.0427	99.9773	0.0394
3.5	99.9892	0.0609	99.9788	0.0581	99.9691	0.0536
4.0	99.9859	0.0796	99.9723	0.0759	99.9596	0.0699
4.5	99.9822	0.1007	99.9650	0.0961	99.9488	0.0885
5.0	99.9780	0.1243	99.9567	0.1186	99.9368	0.1093
5.5	99.9733	0.1504	99.9476	0.1435	99.9235	0.1322
6.0	99.9682	0.1790	99.9376	0.1707	99.9090	0.1573
6.5	99.9627	0.2100	99.9268	0.2003	99.8932	0.1845
7.0	99.9566	0.2436	99.9150	0.2323	99.8761	0.2140
7.5	99.9502	0.2796	99.9024	0.2666	99.8577	0.2456
8.0	99.9432	0.3181	99.8889	0.3033	99.8380	0.2793
8.5	99.9358	0.3590	99.8745	0.3423	99.8171	0.3152
9.0	99.9279	0.4025	99.8592	0.3837	99.7949	0.3533
9.5	99.9196	0.4484	99.8431	0.4274	99.7714	0.3935
10.0	99.9107	0.4968	99.8260	0.4735	99.7466	0.4359
10.5	99.9014	0.5476	99.8080	0.5219	99.7206	0.4804
11.0	99.8916	0.6009	99.7891	0.5726	99.6932	0.5271
11.5	99.8812	0.6567	99.7693	0.6257	99.6646	0.5759
12.0	99.8704	0.7150	99.7486	0.6811	99.6347	0.6268
12.5	99.8591	0.7757	99.7270	0.7388	99.6034	0.6798
13.0	99.8473	0.8388	99.7044	0.7989	99.5709	0.7350
13.5	99.8349	0.9044	99.6810	0.8613	99.5371	0.7923
14.0	99.8220	0.9725	99.6566	0.9259	99.5019	0.8516
14.5	99.8086	1.0430	99.6312	0.9929	99.4655	0.9131
15.0	99.7947	1.1160	99.6049	1.0622	99.4277	0.9767
15.5	99.7802	1.1914	99.5777	1.1338	99.3887	1.0423
16.0	99.7652	1.2692	99.5495	1.2077	99.3483	1.1101
16.5	99.7496	1.3495	99.5204	1.2838	99.3066	1.1799
17.0	99.7335	1.4322	99.4903	1.3622	99.2636	1.2518
17.5	99.7168	1.5173	99.4593	1.4430	99.2192	1.3258
18.0	99.6995	1.6048	99.4273	1.5259	99.1735	1.4018
18.5	99.6816	1.6948	99.3943	1.6112	99.1266	1.4799
19.0	99.6632	1.7871	99.3604	1.6987	99.0782	1.5600
19.5	99.6441	1.8819	99.3254	1.7884	99.0286	1.6421
20.0	99.6245	1.9790	99.2895	1.8804	98.9776	1.7263
20.5	99.6042	2.0786	99.2526	1.9746	98.9253	1.8125
21.0	99.5833	2.1805	99.2147	2.0710	98.8716	1.9007
21.5	99.5619	2.2848	99.1759	2.1697	98.8166	1.9910
22.0	99.5397	2.3914	99.1360	2.2706	98.7603	2.0832
22.5	99.5170	2.5004	99.0952	2.3737	98.7027	2.1775
23.0	99.4936	2.6118	99.0534	2.4789	98.6437	2.2738
23.5	99.4696	2.7254	99.0105	2.5864	98.5834	2.3720
24.0	99.4450	2.8414	98.9668	2.6960	98.5218	2.4723
24.5	99.4197	2.9596	98.9220	2.8078	98.4588	2.5746
25.0	99.3938	3.0802	98.8763	2.9217	98.3946	2.6788

TABLE II. $b_r(q) = U + iV$, $q = \rho e^{i\phi}$ $r = 10$

ρ	$\phi = 65°$		$\phi = 70°$		$\phi = 75°$	
	U	V	U	V	U	V
0.0	100.0000	0.0000	100.0000	0.0000	100.0000	0.0000
0.5	99.9992	0.0010	99.9990	0.0008	99.9989	0.0006
1.0	99.9968	0.0039	99.9961	0.0032	99.9956	0.0025
1.5	99.9927	0.0087	99.9913	0.0073	99.9902	0.0057
2.0	99.9870	0.0155	99.9845	0.0130	99.9825	0.0101
2.5	99.9797	0.0242	99.9758	0.0203	99.9727	0.0158
3.0	99.9708	0.0348	99.9652	0.0292	99.9606	0.0227
3.5	99.9602	0.0474	99.9526	0.0397	99.9464	0.0309
4.0	99.9480	0.0619	99.9381	0.0519	99.9300	0.0404
4.5	99.9342	0.0783	99.9217	0.0657	99.9115	0.0511
5.0	99.9188	0.0966	99.9033	0.0811	99.8907	0.0630
5.5	99.9018	0.1169	99.8830	0.0981	99.8678	0.0763
6.0	99.8831	0.1391	99.8608	0.1167	99.8427	0.0907
6.5	99.8628	0.1632	99.8366	0.1369	99.8154	0.1064
7.0	99.8409	0.1892	99.8105	0.1587	99.7859	0.1234
7.5	99.8173	0.2171	99.7825	0.1821	99.7542	0.1416
8.0	99.7921	0.2469	99.7525	0.2071	99.7204	0.1610
8.5	99.7653	0.2787	99.7206	0.2337	99.6844	0.1817
9.0	99.7369	0.3123	99.6868	0.2619	99.6463	0.2036
9.5	99.7068	0.3478	99.6511	0.2916	99.6060	0.2267
10.0	99.6751	0.3852	99.6134	0.3230	99.5635	0.2511
10.5	99.6417	0.4245	99.5738	0.3559	99.5188	0.2766
11.0	99.6068	0.4657	99.5323	0.3904	99.4720	0.3034
11.5	99.5702	0.5088	99.4889	0.4264	99.4230	0.3314
12.0	99.5319	0.5537	99.4435	0.4641	99.3719	0.3606
12.5	99.4921	0.6005	99.3962	0.5032	99.3187	0.3910
13.0	99.4506	0.6491	99.3470	0.5439	99.2632	0.4226
13.5	99.4075	0.6996	99.2959	0.5862	99.2057	0.4554
14.0	99.3627	0.7519	99.2429	0.6300	99.1460	0.4894
14.5	99.3163	0.8061	99.1879	0.6753	99.0841	0.5246
15.0	99.2682	0.8621	99.1311	0.7221	99.0202	0.5609
15.5	99.2185	0.9200	99.0723	0.7705	98.9541	0.5984
16.0	99.1672	0.9797	99.0116	0.8204	98.8858	0.6371
16.5	99.1143	1.0411	98.9490	0.8717	98.8155	0.6769
17.0	99.0597	1.1044	98.8845	0.9246	98.7430	0.7179
17.5	99.0034	1.1695	98.8181	0.9790	98.6684	0.7600
18.0	98.9455	1.2364	98.7497	1.0348	98.5917	0.8033
18.5	98.8860	1.3050	98.6795	1.0921	98.5129	0.8476
19.0	98.8248	1.3755	98.6074	1.1509	98.4319	0.8931
19.5	98.7620	1.4477	98.5333	1.2112	98.3489	0.9398
20.0	98.6976	1.5217	98.4574	1.2729	98.2637	0.9875
20.5	98.6315	1.5974	98.3795	1.3360	98.1765	1.0363
21.0	98.5637	1.6749	98.2997	1.4006	98.0871	1.0862
21.5	98.4943	1.7542	98.2181	1.4666	97.9957	1.1372
22.0	98.4232	1.8352	98.1345	1.5341	97.9021	1.1892
22.5	98.3505	1.9180	98.0490	1.6030	97.8065	1.2424
23.0	98.2762	2.0025	97.9615	1.6733	97.7087	1.2965
23.5	98.2002	2.0887	97.8722	1.7450	97.6088	1.3517
24.0	98.1225	2.1767	97.7809	1.8181	97.5068	1.4079
24.5	98.0432	2.2665	97.6876	1.8927	97.4027	1.4652
25.0	97.9622	2.3580	97.5924	1.9686	97.2964	1.5234

TABLE II. $b_r(q) = U + iV$, $q = \rho e^{i\phi}$ $r = 10$

ρ	$\phi = 80°$		$\phi = 85°$		$\phi = 90°$	
	U	V	U	V	U	V
0.0	100.0000	0.0000	100.0000	0.0000	100.0000	0.0000
0.5	99.9988	0.0004	99.9988	0.0002	99.9987	0.0000
1.0	99.9953	0.0017	99.9950	0.0009	99.9949	0.0000
1.5	99.9893	0.0039	99.9888	0.0020	99.9886	0.0000
2.0	99.9810	0.0069	99.9801	0.0035	99.9798	0.0000
2.5	99.9703	0.0108	99.9689	0.0055	99.9684	0.0000
3.0	99.9573	0.0155	99.9552	0.0079	99.9546	0.0000
3.5	99.9419	0.0211	99.9391	0.0107	99.9382	0.0000
4.0	99.9241	0.0276	99.9205	0.0140	99.9192	0.0000
4.5	99.9039	0.0349	99.8993	0.0177	99.8978	0.0000
5.0	99.8814	0.0431	99.8758	0.0219	99.8738	0.0000
5.5	99.8566	0.0522	99.8497	0.0265	99.8474	0.0000
6.0	99.8293	0.0620	99.8211	0.0315	99.8184	0.0000
6.5	99.7997	0.0728	99.7901	0.0370	99.7869	0.0000
7.0	99.7678	0.0844	99.7567	0.0428	99.7529	0.0000
7.5	99.7335	0.0968	99.7207	0.0491	99.7164	0.0000
8.0	99.6968	0.1101	99.6823	0.0559	99.6775	0.0000
8.5	99.6578	0.1242	99.6415	0.0631	99.6360	0.0000
9.0	99.6164	0.1392	99.5982	0.0707	99.5920	0.0000
9.5	99.5727	0.1550	99.5524	0.0787	99.5456	0.0000
10.0	99.5267	0.1717	99.5042	0.0871	99.4966	0.0000
10.5	99.4783	0.1891	99.4536	0.0960	99.4452	0.0000
11.0	99.4276	0.2074	99.4005	0.1053	99.3913	0.0000
11.5	99.3746	0.2266	99.3450	0.1150	99.3350	0.0000
12.0	99.3193	0.2465	99.2870	0.1251	99.2762	0.0000
12.5	99.2616	0.2673	99.2267	0.1356	99.2149	0.0000
13.0	99.2016	0.2889	99.1639	0.1466	99.1512	0.0000
13.5	99.1393	0.3113	99.0987	0.1580	99.0851	0.0000
14.0	99.0747	0.3345	99.0312	0.1697	99.0165	0.0000
14.5	99.0078	0.3585	98.9612	0.1819	98.9455	0.0000
15.0	98.9387	0.3833	98.8888	0.1945	98.8721	0.0000
15.5	98.8672	0.4089	98.8141	0.2074	98.7962	0.0000
16.0	98.7934	0.4353	98.7370	0.2208	98.7180	0.0000
16.5	98.7174	0.4624	98.6575	0.2346	98.6373	0.0000
17.0	98.6391	0.4904	98.5756	0.2488	98.5543	0.0000
17.5	98.5585	0.5191	98.4914	0.2633	98.4688	0.0000
18.0	98.4757	0.5486	98.4048	0.2782	98.3810	0.0000
18.5	98.3906	0.5788	98.3159	0.2936	98.2909	0.0000
19.0	98.3032	0.6098	98.2247	0.3093	98.1983	0.0000
19.5	98.2137	0.6416	98.1312	0.3253	98.1035	0.0000
20.0	98.1218	0.6741	98.0353	0.3418	98.0063	0.0000
20.5	98.0278	0.7073	97.9372	0.3586	97.9067	0.0000
21.0	97.9315	0.7412	97.8367	0.3757	97.8049	0.0000
21.5	97.8330	0.7759	97.7340	0.3932	97.7008	0.0000
22.0	97.7323	0.8112	97.6290	0.4111	97.5944	0.0000
22.5	97.6294	0.8472	97.5218	0.4293	97.4857	0.0000
23.0	97.5243	0.8839	97.4123	0.4478	97.3748	0.0000
23.5	97.4169	0.9213	97.3006	0.4666	97.2617	0.0000
24.0	97.3074	0.9593	97.1867	0.4857	97.1464	0.0000
24.5	97.1957	0.9979	97.0706	0.5051	97.0289	0.0000
25.0	97.0818	1.0371	96.9524	0.5248	96.9092	0.0000

ρ	$\phi=5°$		$\phi=10°$		$\phi=15°$	
	U	V	U	V	U	V
0.0	121.0000	0.0000	121.0000	0.0000	121.0000	0.0000
0.5	121.0010	0.0002	121.0010	0.0004	121.0009	0.0005
1.0	121.0041	0.0007	121.0039	0.0014	121.0036	0.0021
1.5	121.0092	0.0016	121.0088	0.0032	121.0081	0.0047
2.0	121.0164	0.0029	121.0157	0.0057	121.0144	0.0083
2.5	121.0256	0.0045	121.0245	0.0089	121.0226	0.0130
3.0	121.0369	0.0065	121.0352	0.0128	121.0325	0.0188
3.5	121.0503	0.0089	121.0480	0.0175	121.0442	0.0255
4.0	121.0657	0.0116	121.0627	0.0228	121.0577	0.0334
4.5	121.0831	0.0147	121.0793	0.0289	121.0731	0.0422
5.0	121.1026	0.0181	121.0979	0.0357	121.0902	0.0521
5.5	121.1242	0.0219	121.1185	0.0432	121.1092	0.0631
6.0	121.1478	0.0261	121.1410	0.0514	121.1300	0.0751
6.5	121.1735	0.0306	121.1656	0.0603	121.1525	0.0882
7.0	121.2013	0.0355	121.1920	0.0700	121.1769	0.1023
7.5	121.2311	0.0408	121.2205	0.0804	121.2031	0.1174
8.0	121.2630	0.0464	121.2509	0.0915	121.2311	0.1337
8.5	121.2969	0.0524	121.2833	0.1033	121.2610	0.1510
9.0	121.3330	0.0588	121.3176	0.1158	121.2926	0.1693
9.5	121.3711	0.0656	121.3540	0.1291	121.3260	0.1887
10.0	121.4112	0.0727	121.3923	0.1431	121.3613	0.2092
10.5	121.4535	0.0802	121.4326	0.1579	121.3984	0.2307
11.0	121.4978	0.0880	121.4748	0.1733	121.4373	0.2533
11.5	121.5442	0.0963	121.5191	0.1895	121.4780	0.2770
12.0	121.5927	0.1049	121.5653	0.2065	121.5206	0.3017
12.5	121.6433	0.1139	121.6136	0.2242	121.5650	0.3275
13.0	121.6960	0.1232	121.6638	0.2426	121.6112	0.3545
13.5	121.7508	0.1330	121.7160	0.2618	121.6592	0.3824
14.0	121.8077	0.1431	121.7702	0.2817	121.7091	0.4115
14.5	121.8667	0.1536	121.8264	0.3024	121.7608	0.4417
15.0	121.9278	0.1645	121.8847	0.3238	121.8143	0.4730
15.5	121.9910	0.1757	121.9449	0.3460	121.8697	0.5053
16.0	122.0564	0.1874	122.0071	0.3689	121.9269	0.5388
16.5	122.1238	0.1994	122.0714	0.3926	121.9859	0.5734
17.0	122.1934	0.2119	122.1377	0.4171	122.0468	0.6091
17.5	122.2652	0.2247	122.2060	0.4423	122.1095	0.6459
18.0	122.3390	0.2379	122.2763	0.4683	122.1741	0.6838
18.5	122.4150	0.2516	122.3487	0.4951	122.2405	0.7229
19.0	122.4932	0.2656	122.4231	0.5227	122.3088	0.7631
19.5	122.5735	0.2800	122.4995	0.5510	122.3789	0.8044
20.0	122.6559	0.2948	122.5780	0.5801	122.4509	0.8469
20.5	122.7406	0.3100	122.6585	0.6101	122.5248	0.8905
21.0	122.8274	0.3257	122.7411	0.6408	122.6005	0.9353
21.5	122.9164	0.3417	122.8257	0.6723	122.6781	0.9812
22.0	123.0075	0.3581	122.9124	0.7046	122.7576	1.0283
22.5	123.1009	0.3750	123.0012	0.7378	122.8389	1.0766
23.0	123.1964	0.3923	123.0920	0.7717	122.9221	1.1260
23.5	123.2942	0.4100	123.1850	0.8065	123.0072	1.1767
24.0	123.3941	0.4281	123.2800	0.8421	123.0942	1.2285
24.5	123.4963	0.4466	123.3771	0.8785	123.1831	1.2815
25.0	123.6007	0.4656	123.4763	0.9158	123.2738	1.3358

TABLE II. $b_r(q) = U + iV$, $q = \rho e^{i\phi}$ $r = 11$

ρ	$\phi=20°$		$\phi=25°$		$\phi=30°$	
	U	V	U	V	U	V
0.0	121.0000	0.0000	121.0000	0.0000	121.0000	0.0000
0.5	121.0008	0.0007	121.0007	0.0008	121.0005	0.0009
1.0	121.0032	0.0027	121.0027	0.0032	121.0021	0.0036
1.5	121.0072	0.0060	121.0060	0.0072	121.0047	0.0081
2.0	121.0128	0.0107	121.0107	0.0128	121.0083	0.0144
2.5	121.0199	0.0167	121.0167	0.0200	121.0130	0.0226
3.0	121.0287	0.0241	121.0241	0.0287	121.0187	0.0325
3.5	121.0391	0.0328	121.0328	0.0391	121.0255	0.0442
4.0	121.0511	0.0429	121.0428	0.0511	121.0333	0.0578
4.5	121.0646	0.0543	121.0542	0.0647	121.0422	0.0731
5.0	121.0798	0.0670	121.0669	0.0799	121.0521	0.0903
5.5	121.0966	0.0811	121.0810	0.0966	121.0630	0.1092
6.0	121.1149	0.0965	121.0964	0.1150	121.0749	0.1300
6.5	121.1349	0.1133	121.1131	0.1350	121.0879	0.1526
7.0	121.1564	0.1315	121.1312	0.1566	121.1020	0.1770
7.5	121.1796	0.1509	121.1506	0.1798	121.1170	0.2032
8.0	121.2043	0.1718	121.1713	0.2047	121.1331	0.2313
8.5	121.2307	0.1940	121.1934	0.2311	121.1503	0.2611
9.0	121.2586	0.2176	121.2168	0.2592	121.1684	0.2928
9.5	121.2882	0.2425	121.2416	0.2888	121.1876	0.3263
10.0	121.3193	0.2688	121.2677	0.3201	121.2079	0.3617
10.5	121.3521	0.2964	121.2951	0.3530	121.2291	0.3988
11.0	121.3864	0.3254	121.3238	0.3876	121.2514	0.4378
11.5	121.4224	0.3558	121.3539	0.4238	121.2747	0.4786
12.0	121.4600	0.3876	121.3853	0.4616	121.2990	0.5213
12.5	121.4991	0.4208	121.4181	0.5010	121.3243	0.5658
13.0	121.5399	0.4553	121.4521	0.5421	121.3507	0.6122
13.5	121.5822	0.4912	121.4875	0.5848	121.3781	0.6604
14.0	121.6262	0.5286	121.5243	0.6292	121.4065	0.7104
14.5	121.6718	0.5673	121.5623	0.6752	121.4359	0.7623
15.0	121.7190	0.6074	121.6017	0.7229	121.4663	0.8160
15.5	121.7677	0.6489	121.6424	0.7723	121.4977	0.8717
16.0	121.8181	0.6918	121.6845	0.8233	121.5301	0.9291
16.5	121.8701	0.7362	121.7278	0.8760	121.5635	0.9885
17.0	121.9237	0.7819	121.7725	0.9303	121.5980	1.0497
17.5	121.9789	0.8291	121.8185	0.9863	121.6334	1.1128
18.0	122.0358	0.8777	121.8658	1.0441	121.6698	1.1777
18.5	122.0942	0.9278	121.9145	1.1035	121.7072	1.2446
19.0	122.1542	0.9793	121.9644	1.1646	121.7456	1.3133
19.5	122.2159	1.0322	122.0157	1.2274	121.7850	1.3839
20.0	122.2791	1.0866	122.0683	1.2919	121.8253	1.4565
20.5	122.3440	1.1424	122.1222	1.3581	121.8666	1.5309
21.0	122.4105	1.1998	122.1774	1.4260	121.9089	1.6072
21.5	122.4786	1.2585	122.2339	1.4957	121.9522	1.6855
22.0	122.5483	1.3188	122.2917	1.5671	121.9964	1.7657
22.5	122.6196	1.3805	122.3509	1.6402	122.0416	1.8478
23.0	122.6926	1.4438	122.4113	1.7151	122.0878	1.9318
23.5	122.7671	1.5085	122.4730	1.7917	122.1349	2.0177
24.0	122.8433	1.5748	122.5361	1.8701	122.1829	2.1056
24.5	122.9211	1.6425	122.6004	1.9503	122.2319	2.1955
25.0	123.0005	1.7118	122.6660	2.0322	122.2818	2.2873

TABLE II. $b_r(q) = U + iV$, $q = \rho e^{i\phi}$ $\qquad\qquad$ r=11

ρ	$\phi=35°$		$\phi=40°$		$\phi=45°$	
	U	V	U	V	U	V
0.0	121.0000	0.0000	121.0000	0.0000	121.0000	0.0000
0.5	121.0004	0.0010	121.0002	0.0010	121.0000	0.0010
1.0	121.0014	0.0039	121.0007	0.0041	121.0000	0.0042
1.5	121.0032	0.0088	121.0016	0.0092	121.0000	0.0094
2.0	121.0057	0.0157	121.0029	0.0164	121.0000	0.0167
2.5	121.0089	0.0245	121.0045	0.0256	121.0000	0.0260
3.0	121.0128	0.0352	121.0065	0.0369	121.0000	0.0375
3.5	121.0174	0.0480	121.0088	0.0503	121.0000	0.0510
4.0	121.0228	0.0627	121.0116	0.0657	121.0000	0.0667
4.5	121.0288	0.0793	121.0146	0.0831	121.0000	0.0844
5.0	121.0356	0.0979	121.0180	0.1026	120.9999	0.1042
5.5	121.0430	0.1185	121.0218	0.1242	120.9999	0.1260
6.0	121.0512	0.1410	121.0259	0.1478	120.9999	0.1500
6.5	121.0601	0.1655	121.0304	0.1734	120.9998	0.1760
7.0	121.0697	0.1920	121.0352	0.2011	120.9998	0.2042
7.5	121.0799	0.2204	121.0404	0.2309	120.9997	0.2344
8.0	121.0909	0.2508	121.0459	0.2627	120.9996	0.2667
8.5	121.1026	0.2832	121.0518	0.2966	120.9995	0.3010
9.0	121.1150	0.3175	121.0580	0.3326	120.9994	0.3375
9.5	121.1280	0.3539	121.0646	0.3706	120.9992	0.3760
10.0	121.1418	0.3921	121.0715	0.4107	120.9991	0.4167
10.5	121.1562	0.4324	121.0787	0.4528	120.9988	0.4594
11.0	121.1714	0.4746	121.0862	0.4970	120.9986	0.5042
11.5	121.1872	0.5189	121.0941	0.5432	120.9983	0.5510
12.0	121.2037	0.5651	121.1023	0.5915	120.9980	0.6000
12.5	121.2209	0.6133	121.1109	0.6419	120.9977	0.6510
13.0	121.2387	0.6634	121.1197	0.6944	120.9973	0.7041
13.5	121.2573	0.7156	121.1289	0.7489	120.9969	0.7593
14.0	121.2765	0.7697	121.1384	0.8055	120.9964	0.8166
14.5	121.2964	0.8259	121.1482	0.8641	120.9958	0.8760
15.0	121.3169	0.8840	121.1583	0.9248	120.9952	0.9374
15.5	121.3381	0.9441	121.1687	0.9876	120.9945	1.0009
16.0	121.3600	1.0063	121.1793	1.0525	120.9938	1.0666
16.5	121.3825	1.0704	121.1903	1.1194	120.9930	1.1342
17.0	121.4057	1.1365	121.2016	1.1884	120.9921	1.2040
17.5	121.4295	1.2047	121.2132	1.2595	120.9911	1.2758
18.0	121.4539	1.2748	121.2250	1.3327	120.9901	1.3498
18.5	121.4790	1.3470	121.2371	1.4079	120.9889	1.4258
19.0	121.5047	1.4212	121.2495	1.4852	120.9877	1.5038
19.5	121.5311	1.4974	121.2621	1.5646	120.9863	1.5840
20.0	121.5581	1.5756	121.2750	1.6461	120.9849	1.6662
20.5	121.5857	1.6559	121.2881	1.7297	120.9833	1.7505
21.0	121.6139	1.7382	121.3015	1.8153	120.9816	1.8369
21.5	121.6427	1.8225	121.3151	1.9031	120.9798	1.9254
22.0	121.6721	1.9089	121.3290	1.9929	120.9779	2.0159
22.5	121.7021	1.9973	121.3431	2.0848	120.9758	2.1085
23.0	121.7327	2.0877	121.3574	2.1788	120.9736	2.2031
23.5	121.7639	2.1802	121.3719	2.2749	120.9713	2.2999
24.0	121.7956	2.2747	121.3867	2.3730	120.9688	2.3986
24.5	121.8279	2.3713	121.4016	2.4733	120.9661	2.4995
25.0	121.8608	2.4699	121.4167	2.5756	120.9633	2.6024

ρ	$\phi = 50°$		$\phi = 55°$		$\phi = 60°$	
	U	V	U	V	U	V
0.0	121.0000	0.0000	121.0000	0.0000	121.0000	0.0000
0.5	120.9998	0.0010	120.9996	0.0010	120.9995	0.0009
1.0	120.9993	0.0041	120.9986	0.0039	120.9979	0.0036
1.5	120.9984	0.0092	120.9968	0.0088	120.9953	0.0081
2.0	120.9971	0.0164	120.9943	0.0157	120.9917	0.0144
2.5	120.9955	0.0256	120.9911	0.0245	120.9870	0.0225
3.0	120.9935	0.0369	120.9872	0.0352	120.9812	0.0325
3.5	120.9911	0.0503	120.9825	0.0480	120.9745	0.0442
4.0	120.9884	0.0656	120.9772	0.0626	120.9667	0.0577
4.5	120.9853	0.0831	120.9711	0.0793	120.9578	0.0730
5.0	120.9819	0.1026	120.9643	0.0978	120.9479	0.0902
5.5	120.9780	0.1241	120.9568	0.1184	120.9369	0.1091
6.0	120.9738	0.1477	120.9486	0.1409	120.9249	0.1298
6.5	120.9693	0.1733	120.9397	0.1653	120.9119	0.1523
7.0	120.9643	0.2010	120.9300	0.1917	120.8978	0.1766
7.5	120.9590	0.2307	120.9196	0.2200	120.8827	0.2027
8.0	120.9533	0.2625	120.9085	0.2503	120.8665	0.2306
8.5	120.9473	0.2963	120.8967	0.2826	120.8492	0.2603
9.0	120.9408	0.3322	120.8841	0.3167	120.8309	0.2917
9.5	120.9340	0.3701	120.8708	0.3529	120.8116	0.3250
10.0	120.9268	0.4100	120.8568	0.3909	120.7912	0.3600
10.5	120.9192	0.4520	120.8420	0.4309	120.7697	0.3968
11.0	120.9112	0.4960	120.8265	0.4729	120.7472	0.4354
11.5	120.9028	0.5421	120.8103	0.5167	120.7237	0.4758
12.0	120.8940	0.5902	120.7933	0.5625	120.6990	0.5179
12.5	120.8848	0.6403	120.7756	0.6103	120.6733	0.5618
13.0	120.8752	0.6925	120.7571	0.6599	120.6466	0.6075
13.5	120.8652	0.7467	120.7379	0.7115	120.6188	0.6549
14.0	120.8548	0.8030	120.7179	0.7651	120.5899	0.7041
14.5	120.8440	0.8612	120.6972	0.8205	120.5599	0.7551
15.0	120.8327	0.9216	120.6758	0.8778	120.5289	0.8078
15.5	120.8211	0.9839	120.6535	0.9371	120.4968	0.8622
16.0	120.8090	1.0482	120.6305	0.9983	120.4637	0.9184
16.5	120.7965	1.1146	120.6068	1.0614	120.4294	0.9763
17.0	120.7836	1.1830	120.5822	1.1264	120.3941	1.0360
17.5	120.7702	1.2535	120.5569	1.1933	120.3577	1.0974
18.0	120.7564	1.3259	120.5309	1.2621	120.3203	1.1605
18.5	120.7421	1.4004	120.5040	1.3328	120.2817	1.2254
19.0	120.7274	1.4768	120.4764	1.4054	120.2421	1.2920
19.5	120.7122	1.5553	120.4480	1.4799	120.2013	1.3603
20.0	120.6966	1.6358	120.4187	1.5562	120.1595	1.4303
20.5	120.6805	1.7183	120.3888	1.6345	120.1166	1.5020
21.0	120.6640	1.8028	120.3580	1.7146	120.0726	1.5754
21.5	120.6469	1.8893	120.3264	1.7966	120.0275	1.6506
22.0	120.6294	1.9778	120.2940	1.8805	119.9813	1.7274
22.5	120.6114	2.0683	120.2608	1.9662	119.9340	1.8059
23.0	120.5930	2.1608	120.2267	2.0538	119.8856	1.8861
23.5	120.5740	2.2553	120.1919	2.1433	119.8361	1.9679
24.0	120.5546	2.3518	120.1563	2.2346	119.7855	2.0515
24.5	120.5346	2.4502	120.1198	2.3278	119.7338	2.1367
25.0	120.5141	2.5506	120.0825	2.4228	119.6809	2.2235

TABLE II. $b_r(q) = U + iV$, $q = \rho e^{i\phi}$ $r = 11$

| ρ | $\phi=65°$ | | $\phi=70°$ | | $\phi=75°$ | |
	U	V	U	V	U	V
0.0	121.0000	0.0000	121.0000	0.0000	121.0000	0.0000
0.5	120.9993	0.0008	120.9992	0.0007	120.9991	0.0005
1.0	120.9973	0.0032	120.9968	0.0027	120.9964	0.0021
1.5	120.9940	0.0072	120.9928	0.0060	120.9919	0.0047
2.0	120.9893	0.0128	120.9872	0.0107	120.9856	0.0083
2.5	120.9833	0.0199	120.9801	0.0167	120.9774	0.0130
3.0	120.9759	0.0287	120.9713	0.0241	120.9675	0.0187
3.5	120.9672	0.0391	120.9609	0.0328	120.9558	0.0255
4.0	120.9571	0.0510	120.9489	0.0428	120.9423	0.0333
4.5	120.9458	0.0646	120.9354	0.0542	120.9269	0.0422
5.0	120.9330	0.0797	120.9202	0.0669	120.9098	0.0520
5.5	120.9190	0.0965	120.9035	0.0809	120.8909	0.0629
6.0	120.9036	0.1148	120.8851	0.0963	120.8702	0.0749
6.5	120.8868	0.1347	120.8652	0.1130	120.8476	0.0879
7.0	120.8687	0.1562	120.8436	0.1310	120.8233	0.1019
7.5	120.8493	0.1792	120.8205	0.1504	120.7972	0.1169
8.0	120.8285	0.2039	120.7958	0.1710	120.7693	0.1330
8.5	120.8064	0.2301	120.7695	0.1930	120.7395	0.1501
9.0	120.7830	0.2579	120.7416	0.2163	120.7080	0.1682
9.5	120.7582	0.2873	120.7121	0.2410	120.6747	0.1874
10.0	120.7320	0.3183	120.6810	0.2669	120.6396	0.2075
10.5	120.7045	0.3508	120.6483	0.2942	120.6027	0.2287
11.0	120.6757	0.3849	120.6140	0.3227	120.5641	0.2509
11.5	120.6455	0.4205	120.5782	0.3526	120.5236	0.2741
12.0	120.6140	0.4577	120.5407	0.3838	120.4814	0.2983
12.5	120.5811	0.4965	120.5017	0.4162	120.4373	0.3235
13.0	120.5469	0.5368	120.4611	0.4500	120.3915	0.3498
13.5	120.5114	0.5786	120.4188	0.4851	120.3439	0.3770
14.0	120.4745	0.6220	120.3751	0.5214	120.2946	0.4052
14.5	120.4362	0.6670	120.3297	0.5590	120.2434	0.4345
15.0	120.3966	0.7135	120.2827	0.5980	120.1905	0.4647
15.5	120.3557	0.7615	120.2341	0.6382	120.1358	0.4959
16.0	120.3134	0.8111	120.1840	0.6796	120.0793	0.5281
16.5	120.2697	0.8621	120.1323	0.7224	120.0211	0.5612
17.0	120.2247	0.9147	120.0790	0.7664	119.9611	0.5954
17.5	120.1784	0.9689	120.0241	0.8116	119.8993	0.6305
18.0	120.1307	1.0245	119.9677	0.8582	119.8358	0.6666
18.5	120.0816	1.0816	119.9096	0.9060	119.7705	0.7037
19.0	120.0313	1.1403	119.8500	0.9550	119.7035	0.7417
19.5	119.9795	1.2004	119.7888	1.0052	119.6347	0.7807
20.0	119.9264	1.2621	119.7261	1.0568	119.5642	0.8206
20.5	119.8719	1.3252	119.6617	1.1095	119.4919	0.8615
21.0	119.8161	1.3898	119.5958	1.1635	119.4179	0.9033
21.5	119.7590	1.4559	119.5284	1.2187	119.3421	0.9461
22.0	119.7004	1.5234	119.4593	1.2751	119.2646	0.9898
22.5	119.6406	1.5925	119.3887	1.3327	119.1853	1.0345
23.0	119.5793	1.6629	119.3165	1.3915	119.1044	1.0800
23.5	119.5167	1.7349	119.2427	1.4515	119.0217	1.1265
24.0	119.4528	1.8083	119.1674	1.5128	118.9372	1.1739
24.5	119.3875	1.8831	119.0905	1.5752	118.8511	1.2222
25.0	119.3208	1.9594	119.0121	1.6388	118.7632	1.2714

TABLE II.　$b_r(q) = U + iV,\ q = \rho e^{i\phi}$　　　$r = 11$

ρ	$\phi = 80°$		$\phi = 85°$		$\phi = 90°$	
	U	V	U	V	U	V
0.0	121.0000	0.0000	121.0000	0.0000	121.0000	0.0000
0.5	120.9990	0.0004	120.9990	0.0002	120.9990	0.0000
1.0	120.9961	0.0014	120.9959	0.0007	120.9958	0.0000
1.5	120.9912	0.0032	120.9908	0.0016	120.9906	0.0000
2.0	120.9843	0.0057	120.9836	0.0029	120.9833	0.0000
2.5	120.9755	0.0089	120.9744	0.0045	120.9740	0.0000
3.0	120.9648	0.0128	120.9631	0.0065	120.9625	0.0000
3.5	120.9520	0.0174	120.9497	0.0089	120.9490	0.0000
4.0	120.9374	0.0228	120.9344	0.0116	120.9334	0.0000
4.5	120.9207	0.0288	120.9169	0.0146	120.9157	0.0000
5.0	120.9022	0.0356	120.8975	0.0181	120.8959	0.0000
5.5	120.8816	0.0431	120.8760	0.0219	120.8740	0.0000
6.0	120.8591	0.0512	120.8524	0.0260	120.8501	0.0000
6.5	120.8347	0.0601	120.8268	0.0305	120.8241	0.0000
7.0	120.8083	0.0697	120.7991	0.0354	120.7961	0.0000
7.5	120.7800	0.0800	120.7695	0.0406	120.7659	0.0000
8.0	120.7497	0.0910	120.7377	0.0462	120.7337	0.0000
8.5	120.7175	0.1026	120.7040	0.0521	120.6994	0.0000
9.0	120.6833	0.1150	120.6682	0.0584	120.6631	0.0000
9.5	120.6472	0.1281	120.6304	0.0650	120.6247	0.0000
10.0	120.6092	0.1419	120.5905	0.0720	120.5843	0.0000
10.5	120.5692	0.1564	120.5487	0.0794	120.5418	0.0000
11.0	120.5273	0.1716	120.5048	0.0871	120.4972	0.0000
11.5	120.4834	0.1874	120.4589	0.0951	120.4506	0.0000
12.0	120.4377	0.2040	120.4109	0.1035	120.4019	0.0000
12.5	120.3900	0.2212	120.3610	0.1123	120.3512	0.0000
13.0	120.3404	0.2391	120.3090	0.1214	120.2985	0.0000
13.5	120.2888	0.2577	120.2551	0.1308	120.2437	0.0000
14.0	120.2353	0.2770	120.1991	0.1406	120.1869	0.0000
14.5	120.1800	0.2970	120.1411	0.1507	120.1281	0.0000
15.0	120.1227	0.3176	120.0812	0.1612	120.0672	0.0000
15.5	120.0635	0.3389	120.0192	0.1720	120.0043	0.0000
16.0	120.0024	0.3609	119.9553	0.1832	119.9394	0.0000
16.5	119.9393	0.3836	119.8893	0.1946	119.8725	0.0000
17.0	119.8744	0.4069	119.8214	0.2065	119.8036	0.0000
17.5	119.8076	0.4309	119.7515	0.2186	119.7326	0.0000
18.0	119.7389	0.4555	119.6797	0.2311	119.6597	0.0000
18.5	119.6683	0.4808	119.6058	0.2440	119.5848	0.0000
19.0	119.5958	0.5068	119.5300	0.2571	119.5079	0.0000
19.5	119.5215	0.5334	119.4523	0.2706	119.4290	0.0000
20.0	119.4452	0.5607	119.3725	0.2844	119.3481	0.0000
20.5	119.3671	0.5886	119.2909	0.2986	119.2652	0.0000
21.0	119.2872	0.6171	119.2073	0.3131	119.1804	0.0000
21.5	119.2053	0.6463	119.1217	0.3279	119.0935	0.0000
22.0	119.1216	0.6761	119.0342	0.3430	119.0048	0.0000
22.5	119.0360	0.7065	118.9448	0.3584	118.9141	0.0001
23.0	118.9486	0.7376	118.8534	0.3742	118.8214	0.0001
23.5	118.8594	0.7693	118.7602	0.3903	118.7267	0.0001
24.0	118.7683	0.8017	118.6650	0.4067	118.6302	0.0001
24.5	118.6753	0.8346	118.5679	0.4234	118.5317	0.0002
25.0	118.5806	0.8682	118.4690	0.4404	118.4313	0.0002

TABLE II. $b_r(q) = U + iV$, $q = \rho e^{i\phi}$ $r = 12$

ρ	$\phi=5°$		$\phi=10°$		$\phi=15°$	
	U	V	U	V	U	V
0.0	144.0000	0.0000	144.0000	0.0000	144.0000	0.0000
0.5	144.0009	0.0002	144.0008	0.0003	144.0008	0.0004
1.0	144.0034	0.0006	144.0033	0.0012	144.0030	0.0017
1.5	144.0077	0.0014	144.0074	0.0027	144.0068	0.0039
2.0	144.0138	0.0024	144.0131	0.0048	144.0121	0.0070
2.5	144.0215	0.0038	144.0205	0.0075	144.0189	0.0109
3.0	144.0310	0.0055	144.0296	0.0108	144.0273	0.0157
3.5	144.0422	0.0074	144.0403	0.0147	144.0371	0.0214
4.0	144.0551	0.0097	144.0526	0.0191	144.0485	0.0280
4.5	144.0697	0.0123	144.0666	0.0242	144.0613	0.0354
5.0	144.0861	0.0152	144.0822	0.0299	144.0757	0.0437
5.5	144.1042	0.0184	144.0994	0.0362	144.0916	0.0529
6.0	144.1240	0.0219	144.1183	0.0431	144.1090	0.0630
6.5	144.1456	0.0257	144.1389	0.0506	144.1280	0.0739
7.0	144.1688	0.0298	144.1611	0.0587	144.1484	0.0858
7.5	144.1939	0.0342	144.1850	0.0674	144.1704	0.0985
8.0	144.2206	0.0389	144.2105	0.0767	144.1939	0.1121
8.5	144.2491	0.0440	144.2376	0.0866	144.2189	0.1266
9.0	144.2793	0.0493	144.2664	0.0971	144.2455	0.1419
9.5	144.3112	0.0550	144.2969	0.1082	144.2735	0.1582
10.0	144.3449	0.0609	144.3290	0.1199	144.3031	0.1753
10.5	144.3803	0.0672	144.3628	0.1323	144.3342	0.1933
11.0	144.4174	0.0737	144.3982	0.1452	144.3668	0.2122
11.5	144.4563	0.0806	144.4353	0.1588	144.4009	0.2321
12.0	144.4969	0.0878	144.4740	0.1730	144.4366	0.2528
12.5	144.5393	0.0953	144.5144	0.1877	144.4738	0.2743
13.0	144.5834	0.1032	144.5565	0.2031	144.5125	0.2968
13.5	144.6293	0.1113	144.6002	0.2191	144.5528	0.3202
14.0	144.6769	0.1197	144.6456	0.2358	144.5946	0.3445
14.5	144.7263	0.1285	144.6927	0.2530	144.6379	0.3697
15.0	144.7774	0.1376	144.7414	0.2709	144.6827	0.3958
15.5	144.8303	0.1470	144.7918	0.2894	144.7291	0.4228
16.0	144.8850	0.1567	144.8439	0.3085	144.7770	0.4507
16.5	144.9414	0.1667	144.8977	0.3283	144.8264	0.4796
17.0	144.9995	0.1771	144.9531	0.3486	144.8774	0.5093
17.5	145.0595	0.1878	145.0103	0.3697	144.9299	0.5400
18.0	145.1212	0.1988	145.0691	0.3913	144.9840	0.5716
18.5	145.1847	0.2101	145.1295	0.4136	145.0396	0.6041
19.0	145.2500	0.2217	145.1917	0.4365	145.0967	0.6375
19.5	145.3170	0.2337	145.2556	0.4600	145.1554	0.6719
20.0	145.3858	0.2460	145.3211	0.4842	145.2157	0.7072
20.5	145.4565	0.2586	145.3884	0.5090	145.2774	0.7434
21.0	145.5289	0.2716	145.4573	0.5345	145.3408	0.7806
21.5	145.6031	0.2849	145.5280	0.5607	145.4056	0.8187
22.0	145.6791	0.2985	145.6004	0.5874	145.4721	0.8577
22.5	145.7569	0.3124	145.6744	0.6149	145.5401	0.8977
23.0	145.8365	0.3267	145.7502	0.6430	145.6096	0.9387
23.5	145.9179	0.3413	145.8277	0.6717	145.6807	0.9806
24.0	146.0012	0.3563	145.9069	0.7011	145.7534	1.0235
24.5	146.0862	0.3716	145.9878	0.7312	145.8276	1.0673
25.0	146.1731	0.3872	146.0705	0.7620	145.9034	1.1121

TABLE II. $b_r(q) = U + iV$, $q = \rho e^{i\phi}$ $\quad r = 12$

ρ	$\phi = 20°$		$\phi = 25°$		$\phi = 30°$	
	U	V	U	V	$\overline{U}$	V
0.0	144.0000	0.0000	144.0000	0.0000	144.0000	0.0000
0.5	144.0007	0.0006	144.0006	0.0007	144.0004	0.0008
1.0	144.0027	0.0022	144.0022	0.0027	144.0017	0.0030
1.5	144.0060	0.0051	144.0051	0.0060	144.0039	0.0068
2.0	144.0107	0.0090	144.0090	0.0107	144.0070	0.0121
2.5	144.0167	0.0140	144.0140	0.0167	144.0109	0.0189
3.0	144.0241	0.0202	144.0202	0.0241	144.0157	0.0273
3.5	144.0328	0.0275	144.0275	0.0328	144.0214	0.0371
4.0	144.0429	0.0360	144.0360	0.0429	144.0280	0.0485
4.5	144.0542	0.0455	144.0455	0.0543	144.0354	0.0613
5.0	144.0670	0.0562	144.0562	0.0670	144.0437	0.0757
5.5	144.0810	0.0680	144.0680	0.0811	144.0529	0.0916
6.0	144.0964	0.0810	144.0809	0.0965	144.0629	0.1091
6.5	144.1132	0.0951	144.0949	0.1133	144.0738	0.1280
7.0	144.1313	0.1103	144.1101	0.1314	144.0856	0.1485
7.5	144.1507	0.1266	144.1264	0.1508	144.0982	0.1705
8.0	144.1715	0.1441	144.1438	0.1716	144.1118	0.1940
8.5	144.1936	0.1627	144.1623	0.1938	144.1262	0.2190
9.0	144.2170	0.1824	144.1820	0.2173	144.1414	0.2456
9.5	144.2418	0.2033	144.2028	0.2422	144.1576	0.2737
10.0	144.2679	0.2253	144.2247	0.2684	144.1745	0.3033
10.5	144.2954	0.2485	144.2477	0.2960	144.1924	0.3344
11.0	144.3242	0.2728	144.2718	0.3249	144.2111	0.3671
11.5	144.3544	0.2982	144.2971	0.3552	144.2307	0.4013
12.0	144.3859	0.3248	144.3234	0.3868	144.2512	0.4370
12.5	144.4187	0.3525	144.3509	0.4199	144.2725	0.4743
13.0	144.4529	0.3814	144.3795	0.4542	144.2946	0.5131
13.5	144.4885	0.4114	144.4093	0.4900	144.3177	0.5535
14.0	144.5253	0.4426	144.4401	0.5271	144.3416	0.5953
14.5	144.5636	0.4750	144.4721	0.5656	144.3663	0.6388
15.0	144.6031	0.5085	144.5052	0.6054	144.3919	0.6837
15.5	144.6440	0.5432	144.5394	0.6467	144.4184	0.7303
16.0	144.6863	0.5790	144.5747	0.6893	144.4457	0.7783
16.5	144.7299	0.6160	144.6111	0.7333	144.4738	0.8280
17.0	144.7749	0.6542	144.6487	0.7787	144.5029	0.8791
17.5	144.8211	0.6935	144.6873	0.8254	144.5327	0.9318
18.0	144.8688	0.7340	144.7271	0.8736	144.5634	0.9861
18.5	144.9178	0.7757	144.7680	0.9232	144.5950	1.0420
19.0	144.9681	0.8186	144.8100	0.9741	144.6274	1.0994
19.5	145.0198	0.8626	144.8531	1.0265	144.6606	1.1584
20.0	145.0728	0.9079	144.8973	1.0802	144.6947	1.2189
20.5	145.1272	0.9543	144.9426	1.1354	144.7296	1.2810
21.0	145.1830	1.0020	144.9891	1.1920	144.7653	1.3447
21.5	145.2400	1.0508	145.0366	1.2499	144.8019	1.4100
22.0	145.2985	1.1009	145.0853	1.3093	144.8393	1.4768
22.5	145.3583	1.1521	145.1350	1.3702	144.8776	1.5453
23.0	145.4194	1.2046	145.1859	1.4324	144.9166	1.6153
23.5	145.4819	1.2583	145.2378	1.4961	144.9565	1.6869
24.0	145.5457	1.3132	145.2909	1.5612	144.9973	1.7601
24.5	145.6109	1.3693	145.3451	1.6277	145.0388	1.8349
25.0	145.6775	1.4266	145.4003	1.6957	145.0811	1.9113

TABLE II. $b_r(q) = U + iV$, $q = \rho e^{i\phi}$ $r = 12$

ρ	$\phi = 35°$		$\phi = 40°$		$\phi = 45°$	
	U	V	U	V	U	V
0.0	144.0000	0.0000	144.0000	0.0000	144.0000	0.0000
0.5	144.0003	0.0008	144.0002	0.0009	144.0000	0.0009
1.0	144.0012	0.0033	144.0006	0.0034	144.0000	0.0035
1.5	144.0027	0.0074	144.0014	0.0077	144.0000	0.0079
2.0	144.0048	0.0131	144.0024	0.0138	144.0000	0.0140
2.5	144.0075	0.0205	144.0038	0.0215	144.0000	0.0219
3.0	144.0108	0.0296	144.0055	0.0310	144.0000	0.0315
3.5	144.0146	0.0403	144.0074	0.0422	144.0000	0.0428
4.0	144.0191	0.0526	144.0097	0.0551	144.0000	0.0559
4.5	144.0242	0.0665	144.0123	0.0697	144.0000	0.0708
5.0	144.0299	0.0822	144.0151	0.0861	144.0000	0.0874
5.5	144.0361	0.0994	144.0183	0.1042	143.9999	0.1058
6.0	144.0430	0.1183	144.0218	0.1240	143.9999	0.1259
6.5	144.0504	0.1389	144.0256	0.1455	143.9999	0.1477
7.0	144.0585	0.1611	144.0296	0.1688	143.9999	0.1713
7.5	144.0671	0.1849	144.0340	0.1937	143.9998	0.1967
8.0	144.0764	0.2104	144.0386	0.2205	143.9998	0.2238
8.5	144.0862	0.2376	144.0436	0.2489	143.9997	0.2526
9.0	144.0966	0.2664	144.0488	0.2790	143.9996	0.2832
9.5	144.1076	0.2968	144.0544	0.3109	143.9995	0.3156
10.0	144.1192	0.3289	144.0602	0.3445	143.9994	0.3496
10.5	144.1313	0.3627	144.0663	0.3799	143.9993	0.3855
11.0	144.1441	0.3981	144.0727	0.4169	143.9992	0.4231
11.5	144.1574	0.4351	144.0794	0.4557	143.9990	0.4624
12.0	144.1713	0.4739	144.0863	0.4962	143.9988	0.5035
12.5	144.1858	0.5142	144.0936	0.5385	143.9986	0.5463
13.0	144.2009	0.5563	144.1011	0.5825	143.9984	0.5909
13.5	144.2165	0.6000	144.1089	0.6282	143.9982	0.6372
14.0	144.2327	0.6453	144.1170	0.6756	143.9979	0.6853
14.5	144.2495	0.6924	144.1253	0.7248	143.9975	0.7351
15.0	144.2669	0.7411	144.1340	0.7757	143.9972	0.7867
15.5	144.2848	0.7914	144.1428	0.8283	143.9968	0.8400
16.0	144.3033	0.8434	144.1520	0.8827	143.9964	0.8951
16.5	144.3224	0.8971	144.1614	0.9388	143.9959	0.9519
17.0	144.3420	0.9525	144.1711	0.9967	143.9954	1.0104
17.5	144.3622	1.0095	144.1810	1.0562	143.9948	1.0707
18.0	144.3829	1.0682	144.1912	1.1176	143.9942	1.1328
18.5	144.4042	1.1286	144.2016	1.1806	143.9935	1.1966
19.0	144.4261	1.1907	144.2123	1.2454	143.9928	1.2621
19.5	144.4485	1.2544	144.2233	1.3120	143.9920	1.3294
20.0	144.4714	1.3199	144.2344	1.3802	143.9911	1.3984
20.5	144.4949	1.3870	144.2459	1.4503	143.9902	1.4692
21.0	144.5189	1.4558	144.2575	1.5220	143.9892	1.5417
21.5	144.5435	1.5263	144.2694	1.5955	143.9882	1.6160
22.0	144.5686	1.5984	144.2815	1.6708	143.9870	1.6920
22.5	144.5942	1.6723	144.2938	1.7478	143.9858	1.7698
23.0	144.6204	1.7479	144.3064	1.8265	143.9845	1.8493
23.5	144.6471	1.8251	144.3192	1.9070	143.9831	1.9305
24.0	144.6743	1.9041	144.3322	1.9892	143.9816	2.0135
24.5	144.7020	1.9847	144.3454	2.0732	143.9800	2.0982
25.0	144.7302	2.0671	144.3588	2.1589	143.9784	2.1847

TABLE II. $b_r(q) = U + iV$, $q = \rho e^{i\phi}$ $r = 12$

ρ	$\phi = 50°$		$\phi = 55°$		$\phi = 60°$	
	U	V	U	V	U	V
0.0	144.0000	0.0000	144.0000	0.0000	144.0000	0.0000
0.5	143.9998	0.0009	143.9997	0.0008	143.9996	0.0008
1.0	143.9994	0.0034	143.9988	0.0033	143.9983	0.0030
1.5	143.9986	0.0077	143.9973	0.0074	143.9961	0.0068
2.0	143.9976	0.0138	143.9952	0.0131	143.9930	0.0121
2.5	143.9962	0.0215	143.9925	0.0205	143.9891	0.0189
3.0	143.9945	0.0310	143.9892	0.0296	143.9843	0.0272
3.5	143.9926	0.0422	143.9853	0.0402	143.9786	0.0371
4.0	143.9903	0.0551	143.9809	0.0526	143.9720	0.0484
4.5	143.9877	0.0697	143.9758	0.0665	143.9646	0.0613
5.0	143.9848	0.0861	143.9701	0.0821	143.9563	0.0757
5.5	143.9816	0.1041	143.9638	0.0994	143.9471	0.0916
6.0	143.9781	0.1239	143.9569	0.1182	143.9370	0.1089
6.5	143.9743	0.1454	143.9494	0.1388	143.9261	0.1278
7.0	143.9701	0.1687	143.9413	0.1609	143.9143	0.1483
7.5	143.9657	0.1936	143.9326	0.1847	143.9016	0.1702
8.0	143.9609	0.2203	143.9233	0.2101	143.8880	0.1936
8.5	143.9559	0.2487	143.9134	0.2372	143.8735	0.2185
9.0	143.9505	0.2788	143.9029	0.2659	143.8582	0.2450
9.5	143.9448	0.3106	143.8917	0.2962	143.8420	0.2729
10.0	143.9388	0.3441	143.8800	0.3282	143.8249	0.3023
10.5	143.9324	0.3794	143.8676	0.3618	143.8069	0.3333
11.0	143.9258	0.4164	143.8547	0.3970	143.7881	0.3657
11.5	143.9188	0.4551	143.8411	0.4339	143.7683	0.3996
12.0	143.9115	0.4954	143.8269	0.4724	143.7477	0.4350
12.5	143.9039	0.5376	143.8121	0.5125	143.7262	0.4720
13.0	143.8959	0.5814	143.7967	0.5542	143.7038	0.5104
13.5	143.8876	0.6269	143.7807	0.5976	143.6805	0.5503
14.0	143.8790	0.6742	143.7640	0.6426	143.6563	0.5917
14.5	143.8701	0.7231	143.7467	0.6892	143.6312	0.6345
15.0	143.8608	0.7738	143.7288	0.7374	143.6053	0.6789
15.5	143.8511	0.8261	143.7103	0.7873	143.5784	0.7247
16.0	143.8412	0.8802	143.6911	0.8388	143.5507	0.7720
16.5	143.8309	0.9360	143.6713	0.8918	143.5220	0.8208
17.0	143.8202	0.9935	143.6509	0.9465	143.4925	0.8711
17.5	143.8092	1.0527	143.6298	1.0028	143.4621	0.9228
18.0	143.7979	1.1136	143.6082	1.0608	143.4307	0.9760
18.5	143.7861	1.1762	143.5858	1.1203	143.3985	1.0307
19.0	143.7741	1.2405	143.5629	1.1814	143.3654	1.0869
19.5	143.7617	1.3065	143.5392	1.2441	143.3314	1.1445
20.0	143.7489	1.3742	143.5150	1.3085	143.2964	1.2035
20.5	143.7357	1.4436	143.4901	1.3744	143.2606	1.2641
21.0	143.7222	1.5146	143.4646	1.4419	143.2239	1.3260
21.5	143.7083	1.5874	143.4384	1.5110	143.1862	1.3895
22.0	143.6941	1.6619	143.4115	1.5818	143.1476	1.4543
22.5	143.6794	1.7381	143.3840	1.6541	143.1082	1.5206
23.0	143.6644	1.8159	143.3558	1.7279	143.0678	1.5884
23.5	143.6490	1.8954	143.3270	1.8034	143.0265	1.6576
24.0	143.6332	1.9767	143.2975	1.8805	142.9843	1.7282
24.5	143.6171	2.0596	143.2674	1.9591	142.9412	1.8003
25.0	143.6005	2.1442	143.2365	2.0393	142.8971	1.8738

322-566 O - 69 - 13

TABLE II. $b_r(q) = U + iV$, $q = \rho e^{i\phi}$ $r = 12$

ρ	$\phi = 65°$		$\phi = 70°$		$\phi = 75°$	
	U	V	U	V	U	V
0.0	144.0000	0.0000	144.0000	0.0000	144.0000	0.0000
0.5	143.9994	0.0007	143.9993	0.0006	143.9992	0.0004
1.0	143.9978	0.0027	143.9973	0.0022	143.9970	0.0017
1.5	143.9949	0.0060	143.9940	0.0051	143.9932	0.0039
2.0	143.9910	0.0107	143.9893	0.0090	143.9879	0.0070
2.5	143.9860	0.0167	143.9833	0.0140	143.9811	0.0109
3.0	143.9798	0.0241	143.9759	0.0202	143.9727	0.0157
3.5	143.9725	0.0328	143.9672	0.0275	143.9629	0.0214
4.0	143.9640	0.0428	143.9571	0.0359	143.9518	0.0280
4.5	143.9545	0.0542	143.9458	0.0455	143.9387	0.0354
5.0	143.9438	0.0669	143.9330	0.0562	143.9243	0.0437
5.5	143.9320	0.0810	143.9190	0.0679	143.9084	0.0528
6.0	143.9191	0.0964	143.9036	0.0808	143.8910	0.0629
6.5	143.9050	0.1131	143.8869	0.0949	143.8721	0.0738
7.0	143.8898	0.1311	143.8688	0.1100	143.8517	0.0855
7.5	143.8735	0.1505	143.8494	0.1262	143.8298	0.0982
8.0	143.8561	0.1712	143.8286	0.1436	143.8063	0.1117
8.5	143.8376	0.1932	143.8065	0.1621	143.7814	0.1261
9.0	143.8179	0.2166	143.7831	0.1817	143.7549	0.1413
9.5	143.7971	0.2413	143.7583	0.2024	143.7269	0.1574
10.0	143.7752	0.2673	143.7322	0.2242	143.6975	0.1743
10.5	143.7521	0.2946	143.7048	0.2471	143.6665	0.1922
11.0	143.7279	0.3233	143.6760	0.2712	143.6340	0.2108
11.5	143.7026	0.3533	143.6459	0.2963	143.6000	0.2304
12.0	143.6762	0.3846	143.6145	0.3225	143.5645	0.2508
12.5	143.6486	0.4172	143.5817	0.3498	143.5275	0.2720
13.0	143.6199	0.4511	143.5476	0.3783	143.4890	0.2941
13.5	143.5901	0.4863	143.5122	0.4078	143.4491	0.3170
14.0	143.5591	0.5229	143.4754	0.4384	143.4076	0.3408
14.5	143.5271	0.5607	143.4373	0.4701	143.3646	0.3655
15.0	143.4938	0.5999	143.3978	0.5029	143.3201	0.3910
15.5	143.4595	0.6404	143.3571	0.5368	143.2741	0.4173
16.0	143.4240	0.6821	143.3150	0.5718	143.2266	0.4444
16.5	143.3874	0.7252	143.2715	0.6079	143.1777	0.4725
17.0	143.3497	0.7695	143.2268	0.6450	143.1272	0.5013
17.5	143.3109	0.8152	143.1807	0.6832	143.0753	0.5310
18.0	143.2709	0.8621	143.1332	0.7225	143.0218	0.5615
18.5	143.2298	0.9104	143.0845	0.7629	142.9669	0.5928
19.0	143.1875	0.9599	143.0344	0.8043	142.9105	0.6250
19.5	143.1441	1.0107	142.9830	0.8468	142.8526	0.6580
20.0	143.0996	1.0627	142.9302	0.8904	142.7932	0.6918
20.5	143.0539	1.1161	142.8762	0.9350	142.7324	0.7264
21.0	143.0072	1.1707	142.8208	0.9807	142.6700	0.7619
21.5	142.9592	1.2266	142.7641	1.0275	142.6062	0.7981
22.0	142.9102	1.2837	142.7060	1.0753	142.5409	0.8352
22.5	142.8600	1.3421	142.6467	1.1241	142.4742	0.8731
23.0	142.8087	1.4018	142.5860	1.1740	142.4059	0.9118
23.5	142.7562	1.4628	142.5240	1.2249	142.3362	0.9513
24.0	142.7027	1.5249	142.4606	1.2769	142.2650	0.9915
24.5	142.6479	1.5884	142.3960	1.3299	142.1924	1.0326
25.0	142.5921	1.6530	142.3300	1.3839	142.1183	1.0745

TABLE II. $b_r(q) = U + iV$, $q = \rho e^{i\phi}$ $r = 12$

ρ	$\phi=80°$		$\phi=85°$		$\phi=90°$	
	U	V	U	V	U	V
0.0	144.0000	0.0000	144.0000	0.0000	144.0000	0.0000
0.5	143.9992	0.0003	143.9991	0.0002	143.9991	0.0000
1.0	143.9967	0.0012	143.9966	0.0006	143.9965	0.0000
1.5	143.9926	0.0027	143.9923	0.0014	143.9921	0.0000
2.0	143.9869	0.0048	143.9862	0.0024	143.9860	0.0000
2.5	143.9795	0.0075	143.9785	0.0038	143.9781	0.0000
3.0	143.9704	0.0108	143.9690	0.0055	143.9685	0.0000
3.5	143.9598	0.0146	143.9578	0.0074	143.9572	0.0000
4.0	143.9474	0.0191	143.9449	0.0097	143.9441	0.0000
4.5	143.9335	0.0242	143.9303	0.0123	143.9292	0.0000
5.0	143.9179	0.0299	143.9139	0.0152	143.9126	0.0000
5.5	143.9006	0.0361	143.8959	0.0183	143.8943	0.0000
6.0	143.8818	0.0430	143.8761	0.0218	143.8742	0.0000
6.5	143.8613	0.0505	143.8546	0.0256	143.8524	0.0000
7.0	143.8391	0.0585	143.8314	0.0297	143.8288	0.0000
7.5	143.8153	0.0672	143.8065	0.0341	143.8035	0.0000
8.0	143.7899	0.0764	143.7798	0.0388	143.7764	0.0000
8.5	143.7628	0.0862	143.7515	0.0438	143.7477	0.0000
9.0	143.7341	0.0966	143.7214	0.0491	143.7171	0.0000
9.5	143.7038	0.1076	143.6897	0.0546	143.6849	0.0000
10.0	143.6719	0.1192	143.6562	0.0605	143.6509	0.0000
10.5	143.6383	0.1314	143.6210	0.0667	143.6152	0.0000
11.0	143.6031	0.1442	143.5841	0.0732	143.5777	0.0000
11.5	143.5662	0.1575	143.5455	0.0800	143.5386	0.0000
12.0	143.5277	0.1715	143.5052	0.0870	143.4976	0.0000
12.5	143.4876	0.1860	143.4632	0.0944	143.4550	0.0000
13.0	143.4459	0.2011	143.4195	0.1021	143.4107	0.0000
13.5	143.4026	0.2168	143.3742	0.1100	143.3646	0.0000
14.0	143.3576	0.2330	143.3271	0.1183	143.3168	0.0000
14.5	143.3111	0.2499	143.2783	0.1268	143.2673	0.0000
15.0	143.2629	0.2673	143.2279	0.1357	143.2161	0.0000
15.5	143.2131	0.2853	143.1757	0.1448	143.1631	0.0000
16.0	143.1616	0.3038	143.1219	0.1542	143.1085	0.0000
16.5	143.1086	0.3230	143.0664	0.1639	143.0521	0.0000
17.0	143.0540	0.3427	143.0092	0.1739	142.9941	0.0000
17.5	142.9977	0.3630	142.9503	0.1842	142.9343	0.0000
18.0	142.9399	0.3838	142.8897	0.1948	142.8729	0.0000
18.5	142.8804	0.4052	142.8275	0.2056	142.8097	0.0000
19.0	142.8194	0.4272	142.7636	0.2168	142.7449	0.0000
19.5	142.7567	0.4497	142.6981	0.2282	142.6783	0.0000
20.0	142.6925	0.4728	142.6308	0.2399	142.6101	0.0000
20.5	142.6266	0.4964	142.5620	0.2519	142.5402	0.0000
21.0	142.5592	0.5206	142.4914	0.2642	142.4686	0.0000
21.5	142.4902	0.5454	142.4192	0.2767	142.3953	0.0000
22.0	142.4196	0.5707	142.3454	0.2896	142.3204	0.0000
22.5	142.3474	0.5966	142.2699	0.3027	142.2438	0.0000
23.0	142.2736	0.6230	142.1927	0.3161	142.1655	0.0000
23.5	142.1982	0.6499	142.1139	0.3297	142.0855	0.0000
24.0	142.1213	0.6774	142.0335	0.3437	142.0039	0.0000
24.5	142.0428	0.7055	141.9514	0.3579	141.9207	0.0000
25.0	141.9628	0.7340	141.8677	0.3724	141.8357	0.0000

TABLE II. $b_r(q) = U + iV$, $q = \rho e^{i\phi}$ $\qquad\qquad$ $r = 13$

ρ	$\phi = 5°$		$\phi = 10°$		$\phi = 15°$	
	U	V	U	V	U	V
0.0	169.0000	0.0000	169.0000	0.0000	169.0000	0.0000
0.5	169.0007	0.0001	169.0007	0.0003	169.0006	0.0004
1.0	169.0029	0.0005	169.0028	0.0010	169.0026	0.0015
1.5	169.0066	0.0012	169.0063	0.0023	169.0058	0.0033
2.0	169.0117	0.0021	169.0112	0.0041	169.0103	0.0060
2.5	169.0183	0.0032	169.0175	0.0064	169.0161	0.0093
3.0	169.0264	0.0047	169.0252	0.0092	169.0232	0.0134
3.5	169.0359	0.0063	169.0343	0.0125	169.0316	0.0182
4.0	169.0469	0.0083	169.0448	0.0163	169.0412	0.0238
4.5	169.0594	0.0105	169.0566	0.0206	169.0522	0.0301
5.0	169.0733	0.0129	169.0699	0.0255	169.0644	0.0372
5.5	169.0887	0.0156	169.0846	0.0308	169.0780	0.0450
6.0	169.1056	0.0186	169.1007	0.0367	169.0928	0.0536
6.5	169.1239	0.0219	169.1182	0.0430	169.1089	0.0629
7.0	169.1437	0.0254	169.1371	0.0499	169.1263	0.0730
7.5	169.1650	0.0291	169.1574	0.0573	169.1450	0.0838
8.0	169.1877	0.0331	169.1791	0.0652	169.1650	0.0954
8.5	169.2119	0.0374	169.2022	0.0737	169.1863	0.1077
9.0	169.2376	0.0419	169.2267	0.0826	169.2089	0.1207
9.5	169.2648	0.0467	169.2526	0.0920	169.2328	0.1345
10.0	169.2934	0.0518	169.2799	0.1020	169.2579	0.1491
10.5	169.3235	0.0571	169.3087	0.1125	169.2844	0.1644
11.0	169.3551	0.0627	169.3388	0.1235	169.3121	0.1805
11.5	169.3882	0.0686	169.3703	0.1350	169.3412	0.1973
12.0	169.4227	0.0747	169.4033	0.1470	169.3715	0.2149
12.5	169.4587	0.0810	169.4376	0.1596	169.4031	0.2332
13.0	169.4963	0.0877	169.4734	0.1727	169.4361	0.2523
13.5	169.5352	0.0946	169.5106	0.1862	169.4703	0.2722
14.0	169.5757	0.1017	169.5492	0.2004	169.5058	0.2928
14.5	169.6177	0.1092	169.5892	0.2150	169.5427	0.3142
15.0	169.6611	0.1169	169.6306	0.2302	169.5808	0.3363
15.5	169.7060	0.1248	169.6734	0.2458	169.6202	0.3592
16.0	169.7524	0.1331	169.7177	0.2620	169.6609	0.3829
16.5	169.8003	0.1416	169.7633	0.2788	169.7030	0.4073
17.0	169.8497	0.1503	169.8104	0.2960	169.7463	0.4325
17.5	169.9006	0.1594	169.8590	0.3138	169.7909	0.4585
18.0	169.9530	0.1687	169.9089	0.3321	169.8369	0.4853
18.5	170.0069	0.1783	169.9602	0.3510	169.8841	0.5128
19.0	170.0623	0.1881	170.0130	0.3704	169.9327	0.5411
19.5	170.1192	0.1982	170.0672	0.3903	169.9825	0.5702
20.0	170.1776	0.2086	170.1229	0.4107	170.0337	0.6000
20.5	170.2375	0.2193	170.1800	0.4317	170.0862	0.6307
21.0	170.2989	0.2302	170.2385	0.4532	170.1400	0.6621
21.5	170.3618	0.2414	170.2984	0.4753	170.1951	0.6943
22.0	170.4262	0.2529	170.3598	0.4979	170.2515	0.7273
22.5	170.4921	0.2647	170.4226	0.5211	170.3092	0.7611
23.0	170.5596	0.2767	170.4868	0.5448	170.3682	0.7956
23.5	170.6286	0.2891	170.5525	0.5690	170.4286	0.8310
24.0	170.6991	0.3017	170.6197	0.5938	170.4903	0.8672
24.5	170.7711	0.3145	170.6882	0.6191	170.5532	0.9041
25.0	170.8446	0.3277	170.7583	0.6450	170.6176	0.9419

TABLE II. $b_r(q) = U+iV$, $q=\rho e^{i\phi}$ $\qquad$ $r=13$

ρ	$\phi=20°$		$\phi=25°$		$\phi=30°$	
	U	V	U	V	U	V
0.0	169.0000	0.0000	169.0000	0.0000	169.0000	0.0000
0.5	169.0006	0.0005	169.0005	0.0006	169.0004	0.0006
1.0	169.0023	0.0019	169.0019	0.0023	169.0015	0.0026
1.5	169.0051	0.0043	169.0043	0.0051	169.0033	0.0058
2.0	169.0091	0.0077	169.0077	0.0091	169.0060	0.0103
2.5	169.0142	0.0120	169.0120	0.0143	169.0093	0.0161
3.0	169.0205	0.0172	169.0172	0.0205	169.0134	0.0232
3.5	169.0279	0.0234	169.0234	0.0279	169.0182	0.0316
4.0	169.0365	0.0306	169.0306	0.0365	169.0238	0.0412
4.5	169.0462	0.0388	169.0387	0.0462	169.0301	0.0522
5.0	169.0570	0.0478	169.0478	0.0570	169.0372	0.0645
5.5	169.0690	0.0579	169.0579	0.0690	169.0450	0.0780
6.0	169.0821	0.0689	169.0689	0.0821	169.0535	0.0928
6.5	169.0963	0.0809	169.0808	0.0964	169.0628	0.1090
7.0	169.1117	0.0938	169.0937	0.1118	169.0729	0.1264
7.5	169.1283	0.1077	169.1076	0.1284	169.0837	0.1451
8.0	169.1459	0.1226	169.1224	0.1461	169.0952	0.1651
8.5	169.1648	0.1384	169.1382	0.1649	169.1074	0.1864
9.0	169.1847	0.1552	169.1549	0.1849	169.1204	0.2090
9.5	169.2058	0.1729	169.1726	0.2060	169.1342	0.2329
10.0	169.2280	0.1916	169.1912	0.2283	169.1486	0.2580
10.5	169.2514	0.2113	169.2108	0.2518	169.1639	0.2845
11.0	169.2760	0.2320	169.2314	0.2764	169.1798	0.3123
11.5	169.3016	0.2536	169.2529	0.3021	169.1965	0.3414
12.0	169.3284	0.2762	169.2754	0.3290	169.2139	0.3718
12.5	169.3564	0.2997	169.2988	0.3571	169.2321	0.4034
13.0	169.3855	0.3243	169.3231	0.3863	169.2510	0.4364
13.5	169.4157	0.3498	169.3485	0.4166	169.2706	0.4707
14.0	169.4471	0.3763	169.3747	0.4482	169.2910	0.5063
14.5	169.4796	0.4037	169.4019	0.4808	169.3121	0.5432
15.0	169.5133	0.4321	169.4301	0.5147	169.3339	0.5814
15.5	169.5481	0.4616	169.4593	0.5497	169.3565	0.6209
16.0	169.5840	0.4920	169.4893	0.5859	169.3798	0.6618
16.5	169.6211	0.5233	169.5204	0.6232	169.4038	0.7039
17.0	169.6594	0.5557	169.5524	0.6617	169.4286	0.7473
17.5	169.6988	0.5890	169.5853	0.7014	169.4541	0.7921
18.0	169.7393	0.6234	169.6192	0.7422	169.4803	0.8382
18.5	169.7810	0.6587	169.6540	0.7842	169.5073	0.8856
19.0	169.8238	0.6950	169.6898	0.8274	169.5349	0.9343
19.5	169.8678	0.7323	169.7265	0.8718	169.5633	0.9843
20.0	169.9129	0.7707	169.7642	0.9174	169.5924	1.0357
20.5	169.9591	0.8100	169.8028	0.9641	169.6223	1.0884
21.0	170.0065	0.8503	169.8424	1.0120	169.6528	1.1424
21.5	170.0551	0.8916	169.8829	1.0611	169.6841	1.1977
22.0	170.1048	0.9339	169.9244	1.1114	169.7161	1.2544
22.5	170.1556	0.9772	169.9668	1.1629	169.7488	1.3124
23.0	170.2076	1.0215	170.0102	1.2155	169.7823	1.3717
23.5	170.2608	1.0669	170.0545	1.2694	169.8164	1.4324
24.0	170.3151	1.1132	170.0998	1.3244	169.8513	1.4944
24.5	170.3705	1.1606	170.1460	1.3807	169.8868	1.5577
25.0	170.4271	1.2090	170.1931	1.4382	169.9231	1.6224

TABLE II. $b_r(q) = U + iV, \; q = \rho e^{i\phi}$ $r = 13$

ρ	$\phi = 35°$		$\phi = 40°$		$\phi = 45°$	
	U	V	U	V	U	V
0.0	169.0000	0.0000	169.0000	0.0000	169.0000	0.0000
0.5	169.0003	0.0007	169.0001	0.0007	169.0000	0.0007
1.0	169.0010	0.0028	169.0005	0.0029	169.0000	0.0030
1.5	169.0023	0.0063	169.0012	0.0066	169.0000	0.0067
2.0	169.0041	0.0112	169.0021	0.0117	169.0000	0.0119
2.5	169.0064	0.0175	169.0032	0.0183	169.0000	0.0186
3.0	169.0092	0.0252	169.0046	0.0264	169.0000	0.0268
3.5	169.0125	0.0343	169.0063	0.0359	169.0000	0.0365
4.0	169.0163	0.0448	169.0083	0.0469	169.0000	0.0476
4.5	169.0206	0.0566	169.0105	0.0594	169.0000	0.0603
5.0	169.0254	0.0699	169.0129	0.0733	169.0000	0.0744
5.5	169.0308	0.0846	169.0156	0.0887	169.0000	0.0900
6.0	169.0366	0.1007	169.0186	0.1055	169.0000	0.1071
6.5	169.0430	0.1182	169.0218	0.1239	168.9999	0.1257
7.0	169.0498	0.1371	169.0252	0.1436	168.9999	0.1458
7.5	169.0572	0.1574	169.0290	0.1649	168.9999	0.1674
8.0	169.0650	0.1791	169.0329	0.1876	168.9999	0.1905
8.5	169.0734	0.2022	169.0372	0.2118	168.9998	0.2150
9.0	169.0823	0.2267	169.0417	0.2375	168.9998	0.2411
9.5	169.0917	0.2526	169.0464	0.2646	168.9997	0.2686
10.0	169.1015	0.2799	169.0514	0.2932	168.9997	0.2976
10.5	169.1119	0.3086	169.0566	0.3233	168.9996	0.3281
11.0	169.1228	0.3387	169.0621	0.3548	168.9995	0.3601
11.5	169.1342	0.3702	169.0678	0.3878	168.9994	0.3936
12.0	169.1460	0.4032	169.0738	0.4223	168.9993	0.4286
12.5	169.1584	0.4375	169.0800	0.4582	168.9992	0.4650
13.0	169.1713	0.4733	169.0864	0.4957	168.9990	0.5030
13.5	169.1846	0.5104	169.0931	0.5346	168.9989	0.5424
14.0	169.1985	0.5490	169.1001	0.5749	168.9987	0.5833
14.5	169.2129	0.5890	169.1072	0.6167	168.9985	0.6257
15.0	169.2277	0.6304	169.1147	0.6600	168.9983	0.6696
15.5	169.2430	0.6732	169.1223	0.7048	168.9980	0.7150
16.0	169.2589	0.7174	169.1302	0.7511	168.9978	0.7619
16.5	169.2752	0.7630	169.1383	0.7988	168.9975	0.8102
17.0	169.2920	0.8101	169.1467	0.8480	168.9972	0.8601
17.5	169.3093	0.8585	169.1553	0.8987	168.9968	0.9114
18.0	169.3270	0.9084	169.1641	0.9508	168.9964	0.9642
18.5	169.3453	0.9597	169.1731	1.0044	168.9960	1.0186
19.0	169.3640	1.0124	169.1824	1.0596	168.9956	1.0743
19.5	169.3832	1.0666	169.1919	1.1161	168.9951	1.1316
20.0	169.4029	1.1221	169.2016	1.1742	168.9946	1.1904
20.5	169.4231	1.1791	169.2115	1.2337	168.9940	1.2507
21.0	169.4437	1.2375	169.2216	1.2947	168.9934	1.3124
21.5	169.4649	1.2974	169.2320	1.3572	168.9927	1.3756
22.0	169.4864	1.3587	169.2426	1.4212	168.9920	1.4403
22.5	169.5085	1.4214	169.2534	1.4867	168.9913	1.5065
23.0	169.5310	1.4855	169.2644	1.5536	168.9905	1.5742
23.5	169.5540	1.5510	169.2756	1.6220	168.9896	1.6434
24.0	169.5775	1.6180	169.2870	1.6919	168.9887	1.7141
24.5	169.6014	1.6865	169.2986	1.7633	168.9877	1.7862
25.0	169.6258	1.7563	169.3104	1.8362	168.9867	1.8598

TABLE II. $b_r(q) = U + iV$, $q = \rho e^{i\phi}$ $\qquad\qquad r = 13$

ρ	$\phi = 50°$		$\phi = 55°$		$\phi = 60°$	
	U	V	U	V	U	V
0.0	169.0000	0.0000	169.0000	0.0000	169.0000	0.0000
0.5	168.9999	0.0007	168.9997	0.0007	168.9996	0.0006
1.0	168.9995	0.0029	168.9990	0.0028	168.9985	0.0026
1.5	168.9988	0.0066	168.9977	0.0063	168.9967	0.0058
2.0	168.9979	0.0117	168.9959	0.0112	168.9940	0.0103
2.5	168.9968	0.0183	168.9936	0.0175	168.9907	0.0161
3.0	168.9953	0.0264	168.9908	0.0252	168.9866	0.0232
3.5	168.9937	0.0359	168.9875	0.0343	168.9818	0.0316
4.0	168.9917	0.0469	168.9837	0.0447	168.9762	0.0412
4.5	168.9895	0.0593	168.9794	0.0566	168.9699	0.0522
5.0	168.9871	0.0733	168.9745	0.0699	168.9628	0.0644
5.5	168.9843	0.0887	168.9692	0.0846	168.9550	0.0779
6.0	168.9814	0.1055	168.9633	0.1007	168.9464	0.0928
6.5	168.9781	0.1238	168.9569	0.1181	168.9371	0.1088
7.0	168.9746	0.1436	168.9501	0.1370	168.9270	0.1262
7.5	168.9708	0.1648	168.9427	0.1572	168.9162	0.1449
8.0	168.9668	0.1875	168.9347	0.1789	168.9047	0.1648
8.5	168.9625	0.2117	168.9263	0.2019	168.8924	0.1861
9.0	168.9579	0.2373	168.9174	0.2264	168.8794	0.2086
9.5	168.9531	0.2644	168.9079	0.2522	168.8656	0.2324
10.0	168.9480	0.2930	168.8979	0.2795	168.8510	0.2575
10.5	168.9426	0.3230	168.8875	0.3081	168.8357	0.2838
11.0	168.9370	0.3545	168.8765	0.3381	168.8197	0.3114
11.5	168.9311	0.3874	168.8649	0.3695	168.8029	0.3404
12.0	168.9249	0.4218	168.8529	0.4023	168.7854	0.3705
12.5	168.9185	0.4577	168.8403	0.4364	168.7671	0.4020
13.0	168.9117	0.4950	168.8272	0.4720	168.7480	0.4347
13.5	168.9048	0.5338	168.8136	0.5090	168.7282	0.4688
14.0	168.8975	0.5740	168.7995	0.5473	168.7077	0.5040
14.5	168.8899	0.6157	168.7848	0.5870	168.6864	0.5406
15.0	168.8821	0.6589	168.7697	0.6281	168.6643	0.5784
15.5	168.8740	0.7035	168.7540	0.6706	168.6415	0.6175
16.0	168.8656	0.7496	168.7377	0.7145	168.6180	0.6579
16.5	168.8569	0.7971	168.7210	0.7598	168.5936	0.6995
17.0	168.8480	0.8461	168.7037	0.8064	168.5685	0.7424
17.5	168.8387	0.8965	168.6858	0.8544	168.5427	0.7866
18.0	168.8292	0.9484	168.6675	0.9038	168.5161	0.8320
18.5	168.8194	1.0017	168.6486	0.9546	168.4888	0.8787
19.0	168.8093	1.0565	168.6292	1.0067	168.4606	0.9266
19.5	168.7989	1.1128	168.6092	1.0603	168.4318	0.9758
20.0	168.7882	1.1705	168.5887	1.1151	168.4021	1.0263
20.5	168.7772	1.2296	168.5677	1.1714	168.3717	1.0780
21.0	168.7659	1.2902	168.5461	1.2290	168.3405	1.1309
21.5	168.7543	1.3523	168.5240	1.2880	168.3086	1.1851
22.0	168.7424	1.4158	168.5013	1.3484	168.2759	1.2406
22.5	168.7302	1.4807	168.4781	1.4102	168.2424	1.2973
23.0	168.7177	1.5471	168.4544	1.4733	168.2082	1.3552
23.5	168.7049	1.6149	168.4301	1.5377	168.1732	1.4144
24.0	168.6918	1.6842	168.4052	1.6035	168.1374	1.4748
24.5	168.6784	1.7549	168.3798	1.6707	168.1009	1.5365
25.0	168.6647	1.8271	168.3539	1.7393	168.0636	1.5994

ρ	$\phi = 65°$		$\phi = 70°$		$\phi = 75°$	
	U	V	U	V	U	V
0.0	169.0000	0.0000	169.0000	0.0000	169.0000	0.0000
0.5	168.9995	0.0006	168.9994	0.0005	168.9994	0.0004
1.0	168.9981	0.0023	168.9977	0.0019	168.9974	0.0015
1.5	168.9957	0.0051	168.9949	0.0043	168.9942	0.0033
2.0	168.9923	0.0091	168.9909	0.0077	168.9897	0.0060
2.5	168.9880	0.0142	168.9858	0.0120	168.9839	0.0093
3.0	168.9828	0.0205	168.9795	0.0172	168.9768	0.0134
3.5	168.9766	0.0279	168.9721	0.0234	168.9684	0.0182
4.0	168.9694	0.0365	168.9635	0.0306	168.9588	0.0238
4.5	168.9613	0.0462	168.9538	0.0387	168.9478	0.0301
5.0	168.9522	0.0570	168.9430	0.0478	168.9356	0.0372
5.5	168.9421	0.0689	168.9310	0.0578	168.9220	0.0450
6.0	168.9311	0.0820	168.9179	0.0688	168.9072	0.0535
6.5	168.9192	0.0963	168.9037	0.0808	168.8911	0.0628
7.0	168.9062	0.1116	168.8883	0.0937	168.8737	0.0728
7.5	168.8924	0.1281	168.8718	0.1075	168.8551	0.0836
8.0	168.8775	0.1458	168.8541	0.1223	168.8351	0.0951
8.5	168.8617	0.1645	168.8353	0.1380	168.8139	0.1074
9.0	168.8450	0.1845	168.8154	0.1547	168.7913	0.1203
9.5	168.8273	0.2055	168.7943	0.1724	168.7675	0.1341
10.0	168.8086	0.2277	168.7721	0.1910	168.7424	0.1485
10.5	168.7890	0.2510	168.7487	0.2105	168.7160	0.1637
11.0	168.7684	0.2754	168.7242	0.2310	168.6884	0.1796
11.5	168.7469	0.3009	168.6986	0.2524	168.6594	0.1963
12.0	168.7244	0.3276	168.6718	0.2748	168.6292	0.2137
12.5	168.7009	0.3554	168.6439	0.2981	168.5977	0.2318
13.0	168.6765	0.3843	168.6149	0.3224	168.5649	0.2507
13.5	168.6512	0.4144	168.5847	0.3475	168.5308	0.2702
14.0	168.6248	0.4456	168.5534	0.3737	168.4955	0.2905
14.5	168.5975	0.4779	168.5209	0.4007	168.4588	0.3116
15.0	168.5693	0.5113	168.4873	0.4288	168.4209	0.3333
15.5	168.5401	0.5458	168.4526	0.4577	168.3817	0.3558
16.0	168.5099	0.5815	168.4167	0.4876	168.3413	0.3790
16.5	168.4788	0.6182	168.3797	0.5184	168.2995	0.4030
17.0	168.4467	0.6561	168.3416	0.5501	168.2565	0.4276
17.5	168.4136	0.6951	168.3024	0.5828	168.2122	0.4530
18.0	168.3796	0.7352	168.2620	0.6163	168.1667	0.4791
18.5	168.3446	0.7764	168.2204	0.6509	168.1199	0.5059
19.0	168.3087	0.8187	168.1778	0.6863	168.0718	0.5334
19.5	168.2718	0.8621	168.1340	0.7227	168.0224	0.5617
20.0	168.2339	0.9066	168.0890	0.7599	167.9717	0.5906
20.5	168.1951	0.9523	168.0430	0.7981	167.9198	0.6203
21.0	168.1553	0.9990	167.9958	0.8372	167.8666	0.6506
21.5	168.1145	1.0468	167.9474	0.8773	167.8122	0.6817
22.0	168.0728	1.0957	167.8980	0.9182	167.7565	0.7135
22.5	168.0301	1.1457	167.8474	0.9600	167.6995	0.7459
23.0	167.9865	1.1968	167.7957	1.0028	167.6413	0.7791
23.5	167.9419	1.2490	167.7428	1.0464	167.5818	0.8130
24.0	167.8963	1.3022	167.6888	1.0910	167.5210	0.8476
24.5	167.8498	1.3566	167.6337	1.1365	167.4590	0.8829
25.0	167.8023	1.4120	167.5775	1.1828	167.3957	0.9188

TABLE II. $b_r(q) = U + iV$, $q = \rho e^{i\phi}$ $\qquad$ $r = 13$

ρ	$\phi=80°$		$\phi=85°$		$\phi=90°$	
	U	V	U	V	U	V
0.0	169.0000	0.0000	169.0000	0.0000	169.0000	0.0000
0.5	168.9993	0.0003	168.9993	0.0001	168.9993	-0.0000
1.0	168.9972	0.0010	168.9971	0.0005	168.9970	-0.0000
1.5	168.9937	0.0023	168.9934	0.0012	168.9933	-0.0000
2.0	168.9888	0.0041	168.9883	0.0021	168.9881	-0.0000
2.5	168.9825	0.0064	168.9817	0.0032	168.9814	-0.0000
3.0	168.9748	0.0092	168.9736	0.0047	168.9732	-0.0000
3.5	168.9657	0.0125	168.9641	0.0063	168.9635	-0.0000
4.0	168.9553	0.0163	168.9531	0.0083	168.9524	-0.0000
4.5	168.9434	0.0206	168.9407	0.0105	168.9397	-0.0000
5.0	168.9301	0.0254	168.9267	0.0129	168.9256	-0.0000
5.5	168.9154	0.0308	168.9114	0.0156	168.9100	-0.0000
6.0	168.8994	0.0366	168.8945	0.0186	168.8929	-0.0000
6.5	168.8819	0.0430	168.8762	0.0218	168.8743	-0.0000
7.0	168.8630	0.0498	168.8565	0.0253	168.8542	-0.0000
7.5	168.8428	0.0572	168.8352	0.0290	168.8327	-0.0000
8.0	168.8211	0.0651	168.8125	0.0330	168.8097	-0.0000
8.5	168.7981	0.0734	168.7884	0.0373	168.7851	-0.0000
9.0	168.7736	0.0823	168.7628	0.0418	168.7591	-0.0000
9.5	168.7478	0.0917	168.7357	0.0465	168.7317	-0.0000
10.0	168.7206	0.1016	168.7072	0.0516	168.7027	-0.0000
10.5	168.6920	0.1120	168.6772	0.0568	168.6723	-0.0000
11.0	168.6620	0.1228	168.6458	0.0624	168.6404	-0.0000
11.5	168.6306	0.1342	168.6129	0.0681	168.6070	-0.0000
12.0	168.5978	0.1461	168.5786	0.0742	168.5721	-0.0000
12.5	168.5636	0.1585	168.5428	0.0805	168.5358	-0.0000
13.0	168.5281	0.1714	168.5056	0.0870	168.4980	-0.0000
13.5	168.4912	0.1848	168.4669	0.0938	168.4587	-0.0000
14.0	168.4528	0.1987	168.4267	0.1009	168.4180	-0.0000
14.5	168.4131	0.2131	168.3852	0.1082	168.3757	-0.0000
15.0	168.3721	0.2279	168.3421	0.1157	168.3321	-0.0000
15.5	168.3296	0.2433	168.2977	0.1235	168.2869	-0.0000
16.0	168.2857	0.2592	168.2517	0.1316	168.2403	-0.0000
16.5	168.2405	0.2755	168.2044	0.1399	168.1922	-0.0000
17.0	168.1939	0.2924	168.1556	0.1484	168.1427	-0.0000
17.5	168.1459	0.3097	168.1054	0.1572	168.0917	-0.0000
18.0	168.0966	0.3275	168.0537	0.1662	168.0392	-0.0000
18.5	168.0459	0.3459	168.0006	0.1755	167.9853	-0.0000
19.0	167.9938	0.3647	167.9460	0.1851	167.9300	-0.0000
19.5	167.9403	0.3840	167.8901	0.1949	167.8732	-0.0000
20.0	167.8855	0.4037	167.8327	0.2049	167.8149	-0.0000
20.5	167.8292	0.4240	167.7738	0.2152	167.7552	-0.0000
21.0	167.7717	0.4447	167.7136	0.2257	167.6940	-0.0000
21.5	167.7127	0.4660	167.6519	0.2365	167.6314	-0.0000
22.0	167.6524	0.4877	167.5888	0.2475	167.5674	-0.0000
22.5	167.5908	0.5098	167.5243	0.2587	167.5019	-0.0000
23.0	167.5278	0.5325	167.4583	0.2702	167.4349	-0.0000
23.5	167.4634	0.5556	167.3910	0.2820	167.3666	-0.0000
24.0	167.3976	0.5793	167.3222	0.2939	167.2968	-0.0000
24.5	167.3305	0.6033	167.2520	0.3061	167.2256	-0.0000
25.0	167.2621	0.6279	167.1804	0.3186	167.1529	-0.0000

TABLE II. $b_r(q) = U + iV$, $q = \rho e^{i\phi}$ $r = 14$

ρ	$\phi=5°$		$\phi=10°$		$\phi=15°$	
	U	V	U	V	U	V
0.0	196.0000	0.0000	196.0000	0.0000	196.0000	0.0000
0.5	196.0006	0.0001	196.0006	0.0002	196.0006	0.0003
1.0	196.0025	0.0004	196.0024	0.0009	196.0022	0.0013
1.5	196.0057	0.0010	196.0054	0.0020	196.0050	0.0029
2.0	196.0101	0.0018	196.0096	0.0035	196.0089	0.0051
2.5	196.0158	0.0028	196.0151	0.0055	196.0139	0.0080
3.0	196.0227	0.0040	196.0217	0.0079	196.0200	0.0115
3.5	196.0309	0.0055	196.0295	0.0107	196.0272	0.0157
4.0	196.0404	0.0071	196.0386	0.0140	196.0355	0.0205
4.5	196.0511	0.0090	196.0488	0.0178	196.0450	0.0260
5.0	196.0631	0.0111	196.0602	0.0219	196.0555	0.0321
5.5	196.0764	0.0135	196.0729	0.0265	196.0672	0.0388
6.0	196.0909	0.0160	196.0868	0.0316	196.0800	0.0462
6.5	196.1067	0.0188	196.1018	0.0371	196.0938	0.0542
7.0	196.1238	0.0218	196.1181	0.0430	196.1088	0.0629
7.5	196.1421	0.0251	196.1356	0.0494	196.1249	0.0722
8.0	196.1617	0.0285	196.1543	0.0562	196.1422	0.0821
8.5	196.1825	0.0322	196.1742	0.0634	196.1605	0.0927
9.0	196.2047	0.0361	196.1953	0.0711	196.1799	0.1040
9.5	196.2281	0.0402	196.2176	0.0793	196.2005	0.1159
10.0	196.2527	0.0446	196.2411	0.0878	196.2222	0.1284
10.5	196.2786	0.0492	196.2658	0.0969	196.2449	0.1416
11.0	196.3058	0.0540	196.2918	0.1063	196.2688	0.1554
11.5	196.3343	0.0590	196.3189	0.1162	196.2939	0.1699
12.0	196.3640	0.0643	196.3473	0.1266	196.3200	0.1850
12.5	196.3951	0.0698	196.3769	0.1374	196.3472	0.2008
13.0	196.4273	0.0755	196.4077	0.1486	196.3756	0.2172
13.5	196.4609	0.0814	196.4397	0.1603	196.4051	0.2343
14.0	196.4957	0.0876	196.4729	0.1724	196.4356	0.2520
14.5	196.5318	0.0939	196.5073	0.1850	196.4674	0.2704
15.0	196.5692	0.1006	196.5430	0.1980	196.5002	0.2894
15.5	196.6078	0.1074	196.5798	0.2115	196.5341	0.3091
16.0	196.6478	0.1145	196.6179	0.2254	196.5692	0.3294
16.5	196.6890	0.1218	196.6572	0.2398	196.6054	0.3504
17.0	196.7315	0.1293	196.6977	0.2546	196.6427	0.3721
17.5	196.7752	0.1371	196.7395	0.2699	196.6811	0.3944
18.0	196.8203	0.1450	196.7824	0.2856	196.7206	0.4174
18.5	196.8666	0.1533	196.8266	0.3018	196.7613	0.4410
19.0	196.9143	0.1617	196.8720	0.3184	196.8030	0.4653
19.5	196.9632	0.1704	196.9186	0.3355	196.8459	0.4902
20.0	197.0133	0.1793	196.9665	0.3530	196.8900	0.5159
20.5	197.0648	0.1884	197.0155	0.3710	196.9351	0.5421
21.0	197.1176	0.1978	197.0658	0.3895	196.9814	0.5691
21.5	197.1716	0.2074	197.1173	0.4084	197.0288	0.5967
22.0	197.2270	0.2173	197.1701	0.4278	197.0773	0.6250
22.5	197.2836	0.2273	197.2241	0.4476	197.1269	0.6539
23.0	197.3416	0.2377	197.2793	0.4679	197.1777	0.6835
23.5	197.4008	0.2482	197.3357	0.4886	197.2296	0.7138
24.0	197.4613	0.2590	197.3934	0.5099	197.2826	0.7448
24.5	197.5232	0.2700	197.4523	0.5315	197.3368	0.7764
25.0	197.5863	0.2812	197.5125	0.5537	197.3921	0.8087

TABLE II. $b_r(q) = U + iV$, $q = \rho e^{i\phi}$ $r = 14$

ρ	$\phi=20°$		$\phi=25°$		$\phi=30°$	
	U	V	U	V	U	V
0.0	196.0000	0.0000	196.0000	0.0000	196.0000	0.0000
0.5	196.0005	0.0004	196.0004	0.0005	196.0003	0.0006
1.0	196.0020	0.0016	196.0016	0.0020	196.0013	0.0022
1.5	196.0044	0.0037	196.0037	0.0044	196.0029	0.0050
2.0	196.0079	0.0066	196.0066	0.0079	196.0051	0.0089
2.5	196.0123	0.0103	196.0103	0.0123	196.0080	0.0139
3.0	196.0177	0.0148	196.0148	0.0177	196.0115	0.0200
3.5	196.0241	0.0202	196.0202	0.0241	196.0157	0.0272
4.0	196.0314	0.0264	196.0264	0.0314	196.0205	0.0355
4.5	196.0398	0.0334	196.0334	0.0398	196.0260	0.0450
5.0	196.0491	0.0412	196.0412	0.0491	196.0320	0.0555
5.5	196.0594	0.0499	196.0499	0.0594	196.0388	0.0672
6.0	196.0707	0.0594	196.0593	0.0707	196.0461	0.0800
6.5	196.0830	0.0697	196.0696	0.0830	196.0541	0.0939
7.0	196.0963	0.0808	196.0807	0.0963	196.0628	0.1089
7.5	196.1105	0.0928	196.0927	0.1106	196.0721	0.1250
8.0	196.1257	0.1056	196.1055	0.1258	196.0820	0.1422
8.5	196.1419	0.1192	196.1191	0.1420	196.0926	0.1605
9.0	196.1591	0.1336	196.1335	0.1592	196.1038	0.1800
9.5	196.1773	0.1489	196.1487	0.1774	196.1156	0.2006
10.0	196.1965	0.1650	196.1648	0.1966	196.1281	0.2222
10.5	196.2166	0.1820	196.1817	0.2168	196.1412	0.2450
11.0	196.2377	0.1997	196.1994	0.2380	196.1550	0.2690
11.5	196.2598	0.2183	196.2179	0.2601	196.1694	0.2940
12.0	196.2829	0.2378	196.2373	0.2833	196.1844	0.3202
12.5	196.3070	0.2580	196.2574	0.3074	196.2001	0.3474
13.0	196.3321	0.2792	196.2784	0.3326	196.2164	0.3758
13.5	196.3581	0.3011	196.3003	0.3587	196.2333	0.4053
14.0	196.3851	0.3239	196.3229	0.3858	196.2509	0.4360
14.5	196.4131	0.3475	196.3464	0.4139	196.2691	0.4677
15.0	196.4421	0.3719	196.3706	0.4430	196.2879	0.5006
15.5	196.4721	0.3972	196.3957	0.4731	196.3074	0.5346
16.0	196.5031	0.4233	196.4217	0.5042	196.3275	0.5697
16.5	196.5350	0.4503	196.4484	0.5363	196.3482	0.6059
17.0	196.5680	0.4781	196.4760	0.5694	196.3696	0.6433
17.5	196.6019	0.5068	196.5044	0.6036	196.3916	0.6818
18.0	196.6368	0.5363	196.5336	0.6387	196.4142	0.7214
18.5	196.6727	0.5666	196.5636	0.6748	196.4375	0.7622
19.0	196.7096	0.5978	196.5945	0.7119	196.4614	0.8041
19.5	196.7474	0.6298	196.6261	0.7500	196.4859	0.8471
20.0	196.7863	0.6627	196.6586	0.7891	196.5111	0.8912
20.5	196.8261	0.6964	196.6919	0.8293	196.5368	0.9365
21.0	196.8669	0.7310	196.7261	0.8704	196.5632	0.9829
21.5	196.9087	0.7665	196.7610	0.9125	196.5903	1.0305
22.0	196.9515	0.8028	196.7968	0.9557	196.6179	1.0792
22.5	196.9953	0.8399	196.8334	0.9999	196.6462	1.1290
23.0	197.0401	0.8779	196.8708	1.0451	196.6751	1.1799
23.5	197.0858	0.9168	196.9090	1.0913	196.7046	1.2320
24.0	197.1326	0.9565	196.9480	1.1385	196.7348	1.2853
24.5	197.1803	0.9971	196.9879	1.1868	196.7655	1.3397
25.0	197.2290	1.0386	197.0285	1.2360	196.7969	1.3952

ρ	$\phi = 35°$		$\phi = 40°$		$\phi = 45°$	
	U	V	U	V	U	V
0.0	196.0000	0.0000	196.0000	0.0000	196.0000	0.0000
0.5	196.0002	0.0006	196.0001	0.0006	196.0000	0.0006
1.0	196.0009	0.0024	196.0004	0.0025	196.0000	0.0026
1.5	196.0020	0.0054	196.0010	0.0057	196.0000	0.0058
2.0	196.0035	0.0096	196.0018	0.0101	196.0000	0.0103
2.5	196.0055	0.0151	196.0028	0.0158	196.0000	0.0160
3.0	196.0079	0.0217	196.0040	0.0227	196.0000	0.0231
3.5	196.0107	0.0295	196.0055	0.0309	196.0000	0.0314
4.0	196.0140	0.0386	196.0071	0.0404	196.0000	0.0410
4.5	196.0178	0.0488	196.0090	0.0511	196.0000	0.0519
5.0	196.0219	0.0602	196.0111	0.0631	196.0000	0.0641
5.5	196.0265	0.0729	196.0134	0.0764	196.0000	0.0776
6.0	196.0315	0.0868	196.0160	0.0909	196.0000	0.0923
6.5	196.0370	0.1018	196.0188	0.1067	196.0000	0.1083
7.0	196.0429	0.1181	196.0218	0.1237	195.9999	0.1256
7.5	196.0493	0.1356	196.0250	0.1421	195.9999	0.1442
8.0	196.0561	0.1543	196.0284	0.1616	195.9999	0.1641
8.5	196.0633	0.1742	196.0321	0.1825	195.9999	0.1853
9.0	196.0709	0.1953	196.0359	0.2046	195.9999	0.2077
9.5	196.0790	0.2176	196.0400	0.2280	195.9998	0.2314
10.0	196.0875	0.2411	196.0443	0.2526	195.9998	0.2564
10.5	196.0965	0.2658	196.0488	0.2785	195.9997	0.2827
11.0	196.1059	0.2917	196.0536	0.3057	195.9997	0.3103
11.5	196.1157	0.3189	196.0585	0.3341	195.9996	0.3391
12.0	196.1259	0.3473	196.0637	0.3638	195.9995	0.3692
12.5	196.1366	0.3768	196.0691	0.3947	195.9995	0.4006
13.0	196.1477	0.4076	196.0747	0.4270	195.9994	0.4333
13.5	196.1593	0.4396	196.0805	0.4605	195.9993	0.4673
14.0	196.1712	0.4728	196.0865	0.4952	195.9992	0.5026
14.5	196.1836	0.5072	196.0927	0.5312	195.9990	0.5391
15.0	196.1965	0.5428	196.0991	0.5685	195.9989	0.5769
15.5	196.2097	0.5797	196.1058	0.6071	195.9987	0.6160
16.0	196.2234	0.6177	196.1126	0.6469	195.9986	0.6564
16.5	196.2375	0.6570	196.1197	0.6880	195.9984	0.6981
17.0	196.2520	0.6975	196.1270	0.7304	195.9982	0.7410
17.5	196.2670	0.7392	196.1344	0.7740	195.9980	0.7852
18.0	196.2824	0.7821	196.1421	0.8189	195.9977	0.8308
18.5	196.2982	0.8263	196.1500	0.8651	195.9975	0.8775
19.0	196.3144	0.8716	196.1581	0.9125	195.9972	0.9256
19.5	196.3310	0.9182	196.1663	0.9612	195.9969	0.9750
20.0	196.3481	0.9660	196.1748	1.0112	195.9965	1.0256
20.5	196.3656	1.0150	196.1835	1.0625	195.9962	1.0775
21.0	196.3835	1.0653	196.1924	1.1150	195.9958	1.1307
21.5	196.4018	1.1167	196.2014	1.1688	195.9954	1.1852
22.0	196.4205	1.1694	196.2107	1.2239	195.9949	1.2410
22.5	196.4397	1.2233	196.2202	1.2802	195.9944	1.2980
23.0	196.4592	1.2785	196.2298	1.3378	195.9939	1.3563
23.5	196.4792	1.3348	196.2396	1.3967	195.9934	1.4159
24.0	196.4995	1.3924	196.2497	1.4569	195.9928	1.4768
24.5	196.5203	1.4512	196.2599	1.5183	195.9922	1.5390
25.0	196.5415	1.5113	196.2703	1.5810	195.9915	1.6024

TABLE II. $b_r(q) = U + iV$, $q = \rho e^{i\phi}$ $\qquad\qquad r = 14$

ρ	$\phi = 50°$		$\phi = 55°$		$\phi = 60°$	
	U	V	U	V	U	V
0.0	196.0000	0.0000	196.0000	0.0000	196.0000	0.0000
0.5	195.9999	0.0006	195.9998	0.0006	195.9997	0.0006
1.0	195.9996	0.0025	195.9991	0.0024	195.9987	0.0022
1.5	195.9990	0.0057	195.9980	0.0054	195.9971	0.0050
2.0	195.9982	0.0101	195.9965	0.0096	195.9949	0.0089
2.5	195.9972	0.0158	195.9945	0.0151	195.9920	0.0139
3.0	195.9960	0.0227	195.9921	0.0217	195.9885	0.0200
3.5	195.9945	0.0309	195.9893	0.0295	195.9843	0.0272
4.0	195.9929	0.0404	195.9860	0.0385	195.9795	0.0355
4.5	195.9910	0.0511	195.9822	0.0488	195.9740	0.0450
5.0	195.9889	0.0631	195.9781	0.0602	195.9679	0.0555
5.5	195.9865	0.0764	195.9735	0.0729	195.9612	0.0672
6.0	195.9839	0.0909	195.9684	0.0867	195.9538	0.0799
6.5	195.9812	0.1067	195.9629	0.1018	195.9458	0.0938
7.0	195.9781	0.1237	195.9570	0.1180	195.9372	0.1088
7.5	195.9749	0.1420	195.9506	0.1355	195.9278	0.1248
8.0	195.9714	0.1616	195.9438	0.1541	195.9179	0.1420
8.5	195.9677	0.1824	195.9366	0.1740	195.9073	0.1603
9.0	195.9638	0.2045	195.9289	0.1951	195.8961	0.1797
9.5	195.9597	0.2278	195.9207	0.2173	195.8842	0.2003
10.0	195.9553	0.2524	195.9121	0.2408	195.8717	0.2219
10.5	195.9507	0.2783	195.9031	0.2655	195.8585	0.2446
11.0	195.9458	0.3054	195.8936	0.2913	195.8447	0.2684
11.5	195.9408	0.3338	195.8837	0.3184	195.8303	0.2933
12.0	195.9355	0.3635	195.8734	0.3467	195.8152	0.3194
12.5	195.9299	0.3944	195.8626	0.3761	195.7994	0.3465
13.0	195.9242	0.4265	195.8513	0.4068	195.7830	0.3747
13.5	195.9182	0.4600	195.8396	0.4387	195.7660	0.4041
14.0	195.9119	0.4946	195.8275	0.4717	195.7483	0.4345
14.5	195.9055	0.5306	195.8149	0.5060	195.7300	0.4660
15.0	195.8988	0.5678	195.8018	0.5414	195.7110	0.4987
15.5	195.8919	0.6062	195.7884	0.5781	195.6914	0.5324
16.0	195.8847	0.6459	195.7744	0.6159	195.6711	0.5672
16.5	195.8773	0.6869	195.7600	0.6549	195.6502	0.6032
17.0	195.8696	0.7291	195.7452	0.6952	195.6286	0.6402
17.5	195.8617	0.7726	195.7299	0.7366	195.6064	0.6783
18.0	195.8536	0.8174	195.7141	0.7792	195.5835	0.7175
18.5	195.8452	0.8633	195.6979	0.8230	195.5600	0.7578
19.0	195.8366	0.9106	195.6813	0.8680	195.5358	0.7992
19.5	195.8278	0.9591	195.6642	0.9142	195.5110	0.8417
20.0	195.8187	1.0088	195.6466	0.9615	195.4855	0.8852
20.5	195.8093	1.0598	195.6286	1.0101	195.4593	0.9299
21.0	195.7997	1.1121	195.6101	1.0598	195.4326	0.9756
21.5	195.7899	1.1656	195.5911	1.1108	195.4051	1.0225
22.0	195.7798	1.2204	195.5717	1.1629	195.3770	1.0704
22.5	195.7694	1.2764	195.5518	1.2162	195.3483	1.1194
23.0	195.7588	1.3337	195.5315	1.2707	195.3188	1.1694
23.5	195.7479	1.3922	195.5107	1.3263	195.2888	1.2206
24.0	195.7368	1.4519	195.4894	1.3832	195.2580	1.2728
24.5	195.7255	1.5129	195.4677	1.4412	195.2267	1.3261
25.0	195.7138	1.5752	195.4455	1.5004	195.1946	1.3805

ρ	$\phi = 65°$		$\phi = 70°$		$\phi = 75°$	
	U	V	U	V	U	V
0.0	196.0000	0.0000	196.0000	0.0000	196.0000	0.0000
0.5	195.9996	0.0005	195.9995	0.0004	195.9994	0.0003
1.0	195.9984	0.0020	195.9980	0.0016	195.9978	0.0013
1.5	195.9963	0.0044	195.9956	0.0037	195.9950	0.0029
2.0	195.9934	0.0079	195.9921	0.0066	195.9911	0.0051
2.5	195.9897	0.0123	195.9877	0.0103	195.9861	0.0080
3.0	195.9852	0.0177	195.9823	0.0148	195.9800	0.0115
3.5	195.9798	0.0241	195.9759	0.0202	195.9728	0.0157
4.0	195.9736	0.0314	195.9686	0.0264	195.9645	0.0205
4.5	195.9666	0.0398	195.9602	0.0334	195.9550	0.0260
5.0	195.9588	0.0491	195.9509	0.0412	195.9445	0.0320
5.5	195.9501	0.0594	195.9406	0.0498	195.9328	0.0388
6.0	195.9407	0.0707	195.9293	0.0593	195.9201	0.0461
6.5	195.9304	0.0830	195.9170	0.0696	195.9062	0.0541
7.0	195.9192	0.0962	195.9038	0.0807	195.8912	0.0628
7.5	195.9073	0.1104	195.8895	0.0926	195.8751	0.0721
8.0	195.8945	0.1256	195.8743	0.1054	195.8579	0.0820
8.5	195.8809	0.1418	195.8581	0.1190	195.8396	0.0925
9.0	195.8665	0.1590	195.8409	0.1334	195.8202	0.1037
9.5	195.8512	0.1771	195.8228	0.1486	195.7997	0.1156
10.0	195.8351	0.1962	195.8036	0.1646	195.7780	0.1280
10.5	195.8182	0.2163	195.7835	0.1815	195.7553	0.1411
11.0	195.8005	0.2374	195.7624	0.1991	195.7315	0.1549
11.5	195.7820	0.2594	195.7403	0.2176	195.7065	0.1692
12.0	195.7626	0.2824	195.7172	0.2369	195.6805	0.1842
12.5	195.7424	0.3064	195.6932	0.2570	195.6533	0.1999
13.0	195.7214	0.3313	195.6682	0.2779	195.6250	0.2161
13.5	195.6995	0.3573	195.6421	0.2997	195.5957	0.2330
14.0	195.6768	0.3842	195.6152	0.3222	195.5652	0.2506
14.5	195.6533	0.4120	195.5872	0.3456	195.5336	0.2687
15.0	195.6290	0.4409	195.5582	0.3698	195.5009	0.2875
15.5	195.6038	0.4707	195.5283	0.3947	195.4671	0.3069
16.0	195.5778	0.5014	195.4974	0.4205	195.4322	0.3270
16.5	195.5510	0.5332	195.4655	0.4471	195.3962	0.3477
17.0	195.5234	0.5659	195.4327	0.4746	195.3592	0.3690
17.5	195.4949	0.5995	195.3988	0.5028	195.3210	0.3909
18.0	195.4656	0.6342	195.3640	0.5318	195.2817	0.4134
18.5	195.4355	0.6698	195.3282	0.5616	195.2413	0.4366
19.0	195.4045	0.7063	195.2914	0.5922	195.1998	0.4604
19.5	195.3728	0.7438	195.2537	0.6237	195.1572	0.4848
20.0	195.3402	0.7823	195.2149	0.6559	195.1135	0.5099
20.5	195.3067	0.8217	195.1752	0.6889	195.0687	0.5355
21.0	195.2725	0.8621	195.1345	0.7227	195.0228	0.5618
21.5	195.2374	0.9034	195.0929	0.7574	194.9759	0.5887
22.0	195.2015	0.9457	195.0502	0.7928	194.9278	0.6162
22.5	195.1647	0.9890	195.0066	0.8290	194.8786	0.6443
23.0	195.1271	1.0331	194.9620	0.8660	194.8283	0.6730
23.5	195.0887	1.0783	194.9165	0.9038	194.7770	0.7024
24.0	195.0495	1.1244	194.8699	0.9424	194.7245	0.7323
24.5	195.0094	1.1714	194.8224	0.9817	194.6710	0.7629
25.0	194.9685	1.2194	194.7739	1.0219	194.6164	0.7941

TABLE II. $b_r(q) = U + iV$, $q = \rho e^{i\phi}$ $r = 14$

ρ	$\phi = 80°$		$\phi = 85°$		$\phi = 90°$	
	U	V	U	V	U	V
0.0	196.0000	0.0000	196.0000	0.0000	196.0000	0.0000
0.5	195.9994	0.0002	195.9994	0.0001	195.9994	0.0000
1.0	195.9976	0.0009	195.9975	0.0004	195.9974	0.0000
1.5	195.9946	0.0020	195.9943	0.0010	195.9942	0.0000
2.0	195.9904	0.0035	195.9899	0.0018	195.9897	0.0000
2.5	195.9849	0.0055	195.9842	0.0028	195.9840	0.0000
3.0	195.9783	0.0079	195.9773	0.0040	195.9769	0.0000
3.5	195.9705	0.0107	195.9691	0.0055	195.9686	0.0000
4.0	195.9615	0.0140	195.9596	0.0071	195.9590	0.0000
4.5	195.9512	0.0178	195.9489	0.0090	195.9481	0.0000
5.0	195.9398	0.0219	195.9369	0.0111	195.9359	0.0000
5.5	195.9271	0.0265	195.9236	0.0135	195.9225	0.0000
6.0	195.9133	0.0316	195.9091	0.0160	195.9077	0.0000
6.5	195.8982	0.0370	195.8933	0.0188	195.8917	0.0000
7.0	195.8820	0.0429	195.8763	0.0218	195.8744	0.0000
7.5	195.8645	0.0493	195.8580	0.0250	195.8558	0.0000
8.0	195.8459	0.0561	195.8385	0.0285	195.8360	0.0000
8.5	195.8260	0.0633	195.8177	0.0321	195.8149	0.0000
9.0	195.8049	0.0709	195.7956	0.0360	195.7924	0.0000
9.5	195.7827	0.0790	195.7723	0.0401	195.7688	0.0000
10.0	195.7592	0.0876	195.7477	0.0445	195.7438	0.0000
10.5	195.7346	0.0965	195.7218	0.0490	195.7176	0.0000
11.0	195.7087	0.1059	195.6948	0.0538	195.6901	0.0000
11.5	195.6816	0.1157	195.6664	0.0588	195.6613	0.0000
12.0	195.6534	0.1260	195.6368	0.0640	195.6312	0.0000
12.5	195.6239	0.1367	195.6059	0.0694	195.5999	0.0000
13.0	195.5933	0.1478	195.5738	0.0750	195.5673	0.0000
13.5	195.5614	0.1594	195.5405	0.0809	195.5334	0.0000
14.0	195.5284	0.1714	195.5058	0.0870	195.4983	0.0000
14.5	195.4941	0.1838	195.4700	0.0933	195.4618	0.0000
15.0	195.4587	0.1966	195.4329	0.0998	195.4242	0.0000
15.5	195.4221	0.2099	195.3945	0.1065	195.3852	0.0000
16.0	195.3843	0.2236	195.3549	0.1135	195.3450	0.0000
16.5	195.3452	0.2377	195.3140	0.1207	195.3035	0.0000
17.0	195.3050	0.2523	195.2719	0.1281	195.2608	0.0000
17.5	195.2636	0.2673	195.2286	0.1357	195.2168	0.0000
18.0	195.2211	0.2827	195.1840	0.1435	195.1715	0.0000
18.5	195.1773	0.2985	195.1381	0.1515	195.1250	0.0000
19.0	195.1323	0.3148	195.0911	0.1598	195.0772	0.0000
19.5	195.0862	0.3315	195.0427	0.1683	195.0281	0.0000
20.0	195.0388	0.3486	194.9932	0.1769	194.9778	0.0000
20.5	194.9903	0.3661	194.9424	0.1858	194.9262	0.0000
21.0	194.9406	0.3841	194.8903	0.1949	194.8734	0.0000
21.5	194.8897	0.4025	194.8371	0.2043	194.8193	0.0000
22.0	194.8377	0.4212	194.7825	0.2138	194.7640	0.0000
22.5	194.7844	0.4405	194.7268	0.2235	194.7074	0.0000
23.0	194.7300	0.4601	194.6698	0.2335	194.6496	0.0000
23.5	194.6744	0.4801	194.6116	0.2437	194.5905	0.0000
24.0	194.6176	0.5006	194.5522	0.2541	194.5302	0.0000
24.5	194.5596	0.5215	194.4915	0.2647	194.4686	0.0000
25.0	194.5005	0.5428	194.4296	0.2755	194.4058	0.0000

ρ	$\phi = 5°$		$\phi = 10°$		$\phi = 15°$	
	U	V	U	V	U	V
0.0	225.0000	0.0000	225.0000	0.0000	225.0000	0.0000
0.5	225.0005	0.0001	225.0005	0.0002	225.0005	0.0003
1.0	225.0022	0.0004	225.0021	0.0008	225.0019	0.0011
1.5	225.0049	0.0009	225.0047	0.0017	225.0043	0.0025
2.0	225.0088	0.0016	225.0084	0.0031	225.0077	0.0045
2.5	225.0137	0.0024	225.0131	0.0048	225.0121	0.0070
3.0	225.0198	0.0035	225.0189	0.0069	225.0174	0.0100
3.5	225.0269	0.0047	225.0257	0.0094	225.0237	0.0137
4.0	225.0352	0.0062	225.0336	0.0122	225.0309	0.0179
4.5	225.0445	0.0079	225.0425	0.0155	225.0391	0.0226
5.0	225.0550	0.0097	225.0524	0.0191	225.0483	0.0279
5.5	225.0665	0.0117	225.0635	0.0231	225.0585	0.0338
6.0	225.0792	0.0140	225.0755	0.0275	225.0696	0.0402
6.5	225.0929	0.0164	225.0886	0.0323	225.0817	0.0472
7.0	225.1077	0.0190	225.1028	0.0374	225.0947	0.0547
7.5	225.1237	0.0218	225.1180	0.0430	225.1088	0.0628
8.0	225.1407	0.0248	225.1343	0.0489	225.1237	0.0715
8.5	225.1589	0.0280	225.1516	0.0552	225.1397	0.0807
9.0	225.1781	0.0314	225.1700	0.0619	225.1566	0.0905
9.5	225.1985	0.0350	225.1894	0.0690	225.1745	0.1008
10.0	225.2200	0.0388	225.2099	0.0764	225.1934	0.1117
10.5	225.2425	0.0428	225.2314	0.0843	225.2132	0.1232
11.0	225.2662	0.0470	225.2540	0.0925	225.2340	0.1352
11.5	225.2909	0.0513	225.2776	0.1011	225.2558	0.1478
12.0	225.3168	0.0559	225.3023	0.1101	225.2785	0.1610
12.5	225.3438	0.0607	225.3280	0.1195	225.3022	0.1747
13.0	225.3719	0.0656	225.3548	0.1293	225.3269	0.1890
13.5	225.4011	0.0708	225.3826	0.1394	225.3525	0.2038
14.0	225.4314	0.0762	225.4115	0.1500	225.3792	0.2192
14.5	225.4628	0.0817	225.4415	0.1609	225.4067	0.2352
15.0	225.4953	0.0875	225.4725	0.1722	225.4353	0.2517
15.5	225.5289	0.0934	225.5046	0.1839	225.4648	0.2689
16.0	225.5636	0.0995	225.5377	0.1960	225.4953	0.2865
16.5	225.5995	0.1059	225.5719	0.2085	225.5268	0.3048
17.0	225.6364	0.1124	225.6071	0.2214	225.5593	0.3236
17.5	225.6745	0.1192	225.6434	0.2347	225.5927	0.3430
18.0	225.7136	0.1261	225.6807	0.2483	225.6271	0.3629
18.5	225.7539	0.1332	225.7192	0.2624	225.6624	0.3834
19.0	225.7953	0.1406	225.7586	0.2768	225.6988	0.4045
19.5	225.8378	0.1481	225.7992	0.2916	225.7361	0.4262
20.0	225.8814	0.1558	225.8408	0.3069	225.7744	0.4484
20.5	225.9262	0.1638	225.8834	0.3225	225.8136	0.4712
21.0	225.9720	0.1719	225.9271	0.3385	225.8539	0.4946
21.5	226.0190	0.1802	225.9719	0.3549	225.8951	0.5186
22.0	226.0671	0.1888	226.0178	0.3717	225.9373	0.5431
22.5	226.1163	0.1975	226.0647	0.3889	225.9805	0.5682
23.0	226.1666	0.2064	226.1127	0.4065	226.0246	0.5939
23.5	226.2181	0.2156	226.1617	0.4244	226.0697	0.6202
24.0	226.2707	0.2249	226.2118	0.4428	226.1158	0.6470
24.5	226.3244	0.2344	226.2630	0.4616	226.1629	0.6744
25.0	226.3792	0.2442	226.3152	0.4808	226.2110	0.7024

Table II. $b_r(q) = U + iV$, $q = \rho e^{i\phi}$ $r = 15$

ρ	$\phi=20°$		$\phi=25°$		$\phi=30°$	
	U	V	U	V	U	V
0.0	225.0000	0.0000	225.0000	0.0000	225.0000	0.0000
0.5	225.0004	0.0004	225.0004	0.0004	225.0003	0.0005
1.0	225.0017	0.0014	225.0014	0.0017	225.0011	0.0019
1.5	225.0038	0.0032	225.0032	0.0038	225.0025	0.0043
2.0	225.0068	0.0057	225.0057	0.0068	225.0045	0.0077
2.5	225.0107	0.0090	225.0090	0.0107	225.0070	0.0121
3.0	225.0154	0.0129	225.0129	0.0154	225.0100	0.0174
3.5	225.0209	0.0176	225.0176	0.0209	225.0137	0.0237
4.0	225.0274	0.0230	225.0230	0.0274	225.0179	0.0309
4.5	225.0346	0.0291	225.0291	0.0346	225.0226	0.0392
5.0	225.0427	0.0359	225.0359	0.0428	225.0279	0.0483
5.5	225.0517	0.0434	225.0434	0.0517	225.0338	0.0585
6.0	225.0616	0.0517	225.0516	0.0616	225.0402	0.0696
6.5	225.0722	0.0606	225.0606	0.0723	225.0471	0.0817
7.0	225.0838	0.0703	225.0703	0.0838	225.0547	0.0948
7.5	225.0962	0.0808	225.0807	0.0962	225.0628	0.1088
8.0	225.1094	0.0919	225.0918	0.1095	225.0714	0.1238
8.5	225.1236	0.1037	225.1036	0.1236	225.0806	0.1397
9.0	225.1385	0.1163	225.1162	0.1386	225.0904	0.1567
9.5	225.1543	0.1296	225.1295	0.1544	225.1007	0.1746
10.0	225.1710	0.1436	225.1435	0.1711	225.1115	0.1934
10.5	225.1885	0.1584	225.1582	0.1887	225.1230	0.2133
11.0	225.2069	0.1738	225.1736	0.2071	225.1349	0.2341
11.5	225.2262	0.1900	225.1897	0.2264	225.1475	0.2559
12.0	225.2463	0.2069	225.2066	0.2465	225.1606	0.2786
12.5	225.2672	0.2245	225.2241	0.2675	225.1742	0.3023
13.0	225.2890	0.2429	225.2424	0.2894	225.1884	0.3270
13.5	225.3117	0.2620	225.2614	0.3121	225.2032	0.3527
14.0	225.3352	0.2818	225.2811	0.3357	225.2185	0.3794
14.5	225.3596	0.3023	225.3016	0.3601	225.2343	0.4070
15.0	225.3849	0.3235	225.3227	0.3854	225.2508	0.4356
15.5	225.4109	0.3455	225.3446	0.4116	225.2677	0.4651
16.0	225.4379	0.3682	225.3671	0.4387	225.2852	0.4957
16.5	225.4657	0.3917	225.3904	0.4666	225.3033	0.5272
17.0	225.4944	0.4158	225.4144	0.4953	225.3219	0.5597
17.5	225.5239	0.4407	225.4392	0.5250	225.3411	0.5932
18.0	225.5543	0.4664	225.4646	0.5555	225.3608	0.6276
18.5	225.5855	0.4927	225.4908	0.5869	225.3811	0.6630
19.0	225.6176	0.5198	225.5176	0.6191	225.4020	0.6995
19.5	225.6505	0.5476	225.5452	0.6522	225.4233	0.7368
20.0	225.6844	0.5762	225.5735	0.6862	225.4453	0.7752
20.5	225.7190	0.6055	225.6025	0.7211	225.4678	0.8146
21.0	225.7545	0.6355	225.6322	0.7568	225.4908	0.8549
21.5	225.7909	0.6663	225.6627	0.7934	225.5144	0.8962
22.0	225.8282	0.6978	225.6938	0.8309	225.5385	0.9385
22.5	225.8663	0.7300	225.7257	0.8693	225.5632	0.9818
23.0	225.9052	0.7630	225.7583	0.9085	225.5884	1.0261
23.5	225.9450	0.7967	225.7916	0.9486	225.6141	1.0713
24.0	225.9857	0.8311	225.8256	0.9896	225.6404	1.1176
24.5	226.0272	0.8663	225.8603	1.0315	225.6673	1.1648
25.0	226.0696	0.9023	225.8957	1.0742	225.6947	1.2130

322-566 O - 69 - 14

TABLE II. $b_r(q) = U + iV$, $q = \rho e^{i\phi}$ $\qquad$ $r = 15$

ρ	$\phi = 35°$		$\phi = 40°$		$\phi = 45°$	
	U	V	U	V	U	V
0.0	225.0000	0.0000	225.0000	0.0000	225.0000	0.0000
0.5	225.0002	0.0005	225.0001	0.0005	225.0000	0.0006
1.0	225.0008	0.0021	225.0004	0.0022	225.0000	0.0022
1.5	225.0017	0.0047	225.0009	0.0049	225.0000	0.0050
2.0	225.0031	0.0084	225.0015	0.0088	225.0000	0.0089
2.5	225.0048	0.0131	225.0024	0.0137	225.0000	0.0140
3.0	225.0069	0.0189	225.0035	0.0198	225.0000	0.0201
3.5	225.0093	0.0257	225.0047	0.0269	225.0000	0.0273
4.0	225.0122	0.0336	225.0062	0.0352	225.0000	0.0357
4.5	225.0155	0.0425	225.0078	0.0445	225.0000	0.0452
5.0	225.0191	0.0524	225.0097	0.0550	225.0000	0.0558
5.5	225.0231	0.0635	225.0117	0.0665	225.0000	0.0675
6.0	225.0275	0.0755	225.0139	0.0791	225.0000	0.0804
6.5	225.0322	0.0886	225.0164	0.0929	225.0000	0.0943
7.0	225.0374	0.1028	225.0190	0.1077	225.0000	0.1094
7.5	225.0429	0.1180	225.0218	0.1237	225.0000	0.1256
8.0	225.0488	0.1343	225.0248	0.1407	224.9999	0.1429
8.5	225.0551	0.1516	225.0279	0.1588	224.9999	0.1613
9.0	225.0618	0.1700	225.0313	0.1781	224.9999	0.1808
9.5	225.0688	0.1894	225.0349	0.1984	224.9999	0.2015
10.0	225.0762	0.2098	225.0386	0.2199	224.9999	0.2232
10.5	225.0840	0.2314	225.0426	0.2424	224.9998	0.2461
11.0	225.0922	0.2539	225.0467	0.2661	224.9998	0.2701
11.5	225.1008	0.2776	225.0510	0.2908	224.9998	0.2952
12.0	225.1097	0.3022	225.0555	0.3166	224.9997	0.3214
12.5	225.1190	0.3280	225.0602	0.3436	224.9997	0.3488
13.0	225.1287	0.3547	225.0651	0.3716	224.9996	0.3772
13.5	225.1388	0.3826	225.0702	0.4008	224.9995	0.4068
14.0	225.1492	0.4115	225.0755	0.4310	224.9995	0.4375
14.5	225.1600	0.4414	225.0809	0.4624	224.9994	0.4693
15.0	225.1712	0.4724	225.0865	0.4948	224.9993	0.5022
15.5	225.1828	0.5045	225.0923	0.5284	224.9992	0.5363
16.0	225.1947	0.5376	225.0983	0.5631	224.9991	0.5714
16.5	225.2070	0.5717	225.1045	0.5988	224.9989	0.6077
17.0	225.2197	0.6069	225.1109	0.6357	224.9988	0.6451
17.5	225.2328	0.6432	225.1174	0.6737	224.9987	0.6836
18.0	225.2462	0.6806	225.1242	0.7127	224.9985	0.7232
18.5	225.2600	0.7189	225.1311	0.7529	224.9983	0.7639
19.0	225.2742	0.7584	225.1382	0.7942	224.9981	0.8058
19.5	225.2887	0.7989	225.1454	0.8366	224.9979	0.8488
20.0	225.3036	0.8405	225.1529	0.8801	224.9977	0.8928
20.5	225.3189	0.8831	225.1605	0.9246	224.9975	0.9380
21.0	225.3345	0.9268	225.1683	0.9703	224.9972	0.9844
21.5	225.3505	0.9715	225.1763	1.0171	224.9970	1.0318
22.0	225.3669	1.0173	225.1845	1.0651	224.9967	1.0803
22.5	225.3837	1.0642	225.1928	1.1141	224.9963	1.1300
23.0	225.4008	1.1121	225.2013	1.1642	224.9960	1.1808
23.5	225.4182	1.1611	225.2100	1.2154	224.9957	1.2327
24.0	225.4361	1.2112	225.2188	1.2678	224.9953	1.2857
24.5	225.4543	1.2623	225.2278	1.3212	224.9949	1.3398
25.0	225.4728	1.3145	225.2370	1.3757	224.9944	1.3950

TABLE II. $b_r(q) = U + iV, \quad q = \rho e^{i\phi}$ $r = 15$

ρ	$\phi=50°$		$\phi=55°$		$\phi=60°$	
	U	V	U	V	U	V
0.0	225.0000	0.0000	225.0000	0.0000	225.0000	0.0000
0.5	224.9999	0.0005	224.9998	0.0005	224.9997	0.0005
1.0	224.9996	0.0022	224.9992	0.0021	224.9989	0.0019
1.5	224.9991	0.0049	224.9983	0.0047	224.9975	0.0043
2.0	224.9984	0.0088	224.9969	0.0084	224.9955	0.0077
2.5	224.9976	0.0137	224.9952	0.0131	224.9930	0.0121
3.0	224.9965	0.0198	224.9931	0.0189	224.9900	0.0174
3.5	224.9952	0.0269	224.9906	0.0257	224.9863	0.0237
4.0	224.9938	0.0352	224.9878	0.0336	224.9821	0.0309
4.5	224.9921	0.0445	224.9845	0.0425	224.9774	0.0391
5.0	224.9903	0.0550	224.9809	0.0524	224.9721	0.0483
5.5	224.9883	0.0665	224.9769	0.0634	224.9662	0.0585
6.0	224.9860	0.0791	224.9725	0.0755	224.9598	0.0696
6.5	224.9836	0.0929	224.9677	0.0886	224.9528	0.0817
7.0	224.9810	0.1077	224.9626	0.1028	224.9453	0.0947
7.5	224.9782	0.1236	224.9570	0.1180	224.9372	0.1087
8.0	224.9751	0.1407	224.9511	0.1342	224.9285	0.1237
8.5	224.9719	0.1588	224.9448	0.1515	224.9193	0.1396
9.0	224.9685	0.1780	224.9381	0.1698	224.9096	0.1565
9.5	224.9649	0.1984	224.9310	0.1892	224.8992	0.1744
10.0	224.9611	0.2198	224.9235	0.2097	224.8883	0.1932
10.5	224.9571	0.2423	224.9157	0.2311	224.8769	0.2130
11.0	224.9529	0.2659	224.9075	0.2537	224.8649	0.2337
11.5	224.9485	0.2906	224.8988	0.2772	224.8523	0.2554
12.0	224.9439	0.3164	224.8898	0.3019	224.8391	0.2781
12.5	224.9391	0.3434	224.8804	0.3275	224.8254	0.3017
13.0	224.9341	0.3714	224.8707	0.3542	224.8112	0.3263
13.5	224.9289	0.4005	224.8605	0.3820	224.7964	0.3519
14.0	224.9235	0.4307	224.8499	0.4108	224.7810	0.3784
14.5	224.9179	0.4620	224.8390	0.4406	224.7650	0.4059
15.0	224.9121	0.4944	224.8277	0.4715	224.7485	0.4343
15.5	224.9061	0.5278	224.8160	0.5034	224.7315	0.4637
16.0	224.8999	0.5624	224.8038	0.5364	224.7138	0.4941
16.5	224.8935	0.5981	224.7913	0.5704	224.6956	0.5254
17.0	224.8869	0.6349	224.7785	0.6054	224.6769	0.5576
17.5	224.8800	0.6727	224.7652	0.6415	224.6575	0.5909
18.0	224.8730	0.7117	224.7515	0.6786	224.6377	0.6250
18.5	224.8658	0.7518	224.7374	0.7168	224.6172	0.6602
19.0	224.8583	0.7929	224.7230	0.7560	224.5962	0.6962
19.5	224.8507	0.8352	224.7081	0.7963	224.5746	0.7333
20.0	224.8428	0.8785	224.6929	0.8375	224.5524	0.7713
20.5	224.8348	0.9229	224.6773	0.8799	224.5297	0.8102
21.0	224.8265	0.9685	224.6612	0.9232	224.5065	0.8501
21.5	224.8180	1.0151	224.6448	0.9676	224.4826	0.8909
22.0	224.8093	1.0628	224.6280	1.0130	224.4582	0.9327
22.5	224.8004	1.1116	224.6107	1.0595	224.4332	0.9755
23.0	224.7912	1.1615	224.5931	1.1070	224.4076	1.0192
23.5	224.7819	1.2124	224.5751	1.1555	224.3815	1.0638
24.0	224.7723	1.2645	224.5567	1.2051	224.3548	1.1094
24.5	224.7625	1.3177	224.5379	1.2557	224.3276	1.1559
25.0	224.7526	1.3719	224.5186	1.3073	224.2997	1.2034

TABLE II. $b_r(q) = U + iV$, $q = \rho e^{i\phi}$ $r=15$

| ρ | $\phi=65°$ | | $\phi=70°$ | | $\phi=75°$ | |
	U	V	U	V	U	V
0.0	225.0000	0.0000	225.0000	0.0000	225.0000	0.0000
0.5	224.9996	0.0004	224.9996	0.0004	224.9995	0.0003
1.0	224.9986	0.0017	224.9983	0.0014	224.9981	0.0011
1.5	224.9968	0.0038	224.9962	0.0032	224.9956	0.0025
2.0	224.9943	0.0068	224.9932	0.0057	224.9923	0.0045
2.5	224.9910	0.0107	224.9893	0.0090	224.9879	0.0070
3.0	224.9871	0.0154	224.9846	0.0129	224.9826	0.0100
3.5	224.9824	0.0209	224.9791	0.0176	224.9763	0.0137
4.0	224.9770	0.0274	224.9726	0.0230	224.9691	0.0179
4.5	224.9709	0.0346	224.9654	0.0290	224.9609	0.0226
5.0	224.9641	0.0427	224.9573	0.0359	224.9517	0.0279
5.5	224.9566	0.0517	224.9483	0.0434	224.9415	0.0337
6.0	224.9483	0.0615	224.9384	0.0516	224.9304	0.0402
6.5	224.9394	0.0722	224.9278	0.0606	224.9183	0.0471
7.0	224.9297	0.0838	224.9162	0.0703	224.9053	0.0547
7.5	224.9193	0.0961	224.9038	0.0807	224.8913	0.0627
8.0	224.9082	0.1094	224.8906	0.0918	224.8763	0.0714
8.5	224.8963	0.1235	224.8765	0.1036	224.8604	0.0806
9.0	224.8838	0.1384	224.8615	0.1161	224.8435	0.0903
9.5	224.8705	0.1542	224.8457	0.1294	224.8256	0.1006
10.0	224.8565	0.1709	224.8290	0.1433	224.8068	0.1115
10.5	224.8418	0.1883	224.8115	0.1580	224.7870	0.1229
11.0	224.8264	0.2067	224.7931	0.1734	224.7662	0.1349
11.5	224.8102	0.2259	224.7739	0.1895	224.7445	0.1474
12.0	224.7933	0.2459	224.7538	0.2063	224.7218	0.1605
12.5	224.7758	0.2668	224.7329	0.2238	224.6981	0.1741
13.0	224.7575	0.2886	224.7111	0.2421	224.6735	0.1883
13.5	224.7384	0.3112	224.6884	0.2610	224.6479	0.2030
14.0	224.7187	0.3346	224.6650	0.2807	224.6214	0.2183
14.5	224.6982	0.3589	224.6406	0.3010	224.5939	0.2341
15.0	224.6770	0.3840	224.6154	0.3221	224.5654	0.2505
15.5	224.6551	0.4100	224.5893	0.3439	224.5360	0.2674
16.0	224.6325	0.4368	224.5624	0.3664	224.5056	0.2849
16.5	224.6092	0.4645	224.5347	0.3896	224.4742	0.3029
17.0	224.5851	0.4930	224.5060	0.4135	224.4419	0.3215
17.5	224.5604	0.5224	224.4766	0.4381	224.4087	0.3406
18.0	224.5349	0.5525	224.4462	0.4634	224.3744	0.3603
18.5	224.5087	0.5836	224.4151	0.4894	224.3392	0.3805
19.0	224.4817	0.6155	224.3830	0.5161	224.3031	0.4013
19.5	224.4541	0.6482	224.3502	0.5436	224.2660	0.4226
20.0	224.4257	0.6817	224.3164	0.5717	224.2279	0.4445
20.5	224.3966	0.7161	224.2819	0.6005	224.1889	0.4669
21.0	224.3668	0.7514	224.2464	0.6300	224.1489	0.4898
21.5	224.3363	0.7874	224.2101	0.6603	224.1079	0.5133
22.0	224.3050	0.8243	224.1730	0.6912	224.0660	0.5373
22.5	224.2730	0.8621	224.1350	0.7228	224.0232	0.5619
23.0	224.2403	0.9006	224.0962	0.7551	223.9794	0.5870
23.5	224.2069	0.9400	224.0565	0.7881	223.9346	0.6126
24.0	224.1728	0.9803	224.0159	0.8218	223.8889	0.6388
24.5	224.1379	1.0214	223.9745	0.8562	223.8422	0.6655
25.0	224.1023	1.0633	223.9323	0.8913	223.7948	0.6928

TABLE II. $b_r(q) = U + iV$, $q = \rho e^{i\phi}$ $\qquad\qquad r = 15$

ρ	$\phi = 80°$		$\phi = 85°$		$\phi = 90°$	
	U	V	U	V	U	V
0.0	225.0000	0.0000	225.0000	0.0000	225.0000	0.0000
0.5	224.9995	0.0002	224.9994	0.0001	224.9994	0.0000
1.0	224.9979	0.0008	224.9978	0.0004	224.9978	0.0000
1.5	224.9953	0.0017	224.9951	0.0009	224.9950	0.0000
2.0	224.9916	0.0031	224.9912	0.0016	224.9911	0.0000
2.5	224.9869	0.0048	224.9863	0.0024	224.9860	0.0000
3.0	224.9811	0.0069	224.9802	0.0035	224.9799	0.0000
3.5	224.9743	0.0094	224.9731	0.0047	224.9727	0.0000
4.0	224.9664	0.0122	224.9648	0.0062	224.9643	0.0000
4.5	224.9575	0.0155	224.9555	0.0078	224.9548	0.0000
5.0	224.9476	0.0191	224.9451	0.0097	224.9442	0.0000
5.5	224.9366	0.0231	224.9335	0.0117	224.9325	0.0000
6.0	224.9245	0.0275	224.9209	0.0139	224.9197	0.0000
6.5	224.9114	0.0322	224.9071	0.0164	224.9057	0.0000
7.0	224.8972	0.0374	224.8923	0.0190	224.8907	0.0000
7.5	224.8820	0.0429	224.8764	0.0218	224.8745	0.0000
8.0	224.8658	0.0488	224.8594	0.0248	224.8572	0.0000
8.5	224.8485	0.0551	224.8412	0.0280	224.8388	0.0000
9.0	224.8302	0.0618	224.8220	0.0314	224.8193	0.0000
9.5	224.8108	0.0688	224.8017	0.0349	224.7987	0.0000
10.0	224.7904	0.0763	224.7803	0.0387	224.7769	0.0000
10.5	224.7689	0.0841	224.7578	0.0427	224.7541	0.0000
11.0	224.7464	0.0922	224.7342	0.0468	224.7301	0.0000
11.5	224.7228	0.1008	224.7095	0.0512	224.7050	0.0000
12.0	224.6982	0.1097	224.6837	0.0557	224.6789	0.0000
12.5	224.6725	0.1191	224.6569	0.0604	224.6516	0.0000
13.0	224.6458	0.1288	224.6289	0.0654	224.6232	0.0000
13.5	224.6181	0.1388	224.5998	0.0705	224.5937	0.0000
14.0	224.5893	0.1493	224.5697	0.0758	224.5630	0.0000
14.5	224.5595	0.1601	224.5384	0.0813	224.5313	0.0000
15.0	224.5286	0.1713	224.5061	0.0870	224.4985	0.0000
15.5	224.4967	0.1829	224.4726	0.0928	224.4645	0.0000
16.0	224.4637	0.1948	224.4381	0.0989	224.4295	0.0000
16.5	224.4298	0.2072	224.4025	0.1052	224.3933	0.0000
17.0	224.3947	0.2199	224.3658	0.1116	224.3561	0.0000
17.5	224.3587	0.2330	224.3280	0.1183	224.3177	0.0000
18.0	224.3215	0.2464	224.2892	0.1251	224.2783	0.0000
18.5	224.2834	0.2602	224.2492	0.1321	224.2377	0.0000
19.0	224.2442	0.2744	224.2082	0.1393	224.1960	0.0000
19.5	224.2040	0.2890	224.1660	0.1467	224.1533	0.0000
20.0	224.1627	0.3039	224.1228	0.1543	224.1094	0.0000
20.5	224.1204	0.3192	224.0785	0.1620	224.0644	0.0000
21.0	224.0771	0.3349	224.0332	0.1700	224.0184	0.0000
21.5	224.0327	0.3510	223.9867	0.1781	223.9712	0.0000
22.0	223.9873	0.3674	223.9392	0.1865	223.9229	0.0000
22.5	223.9409	0.3842	223.8905	0.1950	223.8736	0.0000
23.0	223.8934	0.4013	223.8408	0.2037	223.8231	0.0000
23.5	223.8449	0.4189	223.7901	0.2126	223.7716	0.0000
24.0	223.7954	0.4367	223.7382	0.2217	223.7190	0.0000
24.5	223.7449	0.4550	223.6853	0.2309	223.6652	0.0000
25.0	223.6933	0.4736	223.6313	0.2404	223.6104	0.0000

TABLE III. VALUES OF $a_r(q)$, $a_{r+2}(q)$

And other related functions

$$a_r(q) = U + iV, \qquad a_{r+2}(q) = U - iV$$

$$FA(q) = \tfrac{1}{2}[a_r(q) + a_{r+2}(q)], \qquad FB(q) = [a_{r+2}(q) - a_r(q)]^2$$

$$q = i\rho$$

$$r = 0,\, 4,\, 8,\, 12; \qquad r+2 = 2,\, 6,\, 10,\, 14$$

ρ	$a_r(i\rho)$	$a_{r+2}(i\rho)$	$FA(i\rho)$	$FB(i\rho)$
0.0	0.00000 000	4.00000 000	2.00000 000	16.00000 000
0.1	0.00500 548	3.99582 780	2.00041 664	15.92666 279
0.2	0.02008 831	3.98324 421	2.00166 626	15.70660 463
0.3	0.04545 239	3.96204 351	2.00374 795	15.33968 597
0.4	0.08145 407	3.93186 629	2.00666 018	14.82567 426
0.5	0.12863 012	3.89217 154	2.01040 083	14.16424 405
0.6	0.18774 404	3.84219 025	2.01496 714	13.35497 711
0.7	0.25986 133	3.78085 019	2.02035 576	12.39736 260
0.8	0.34647 362	3.70665 178	2.02656 270	11.29079 725
0.9	0.44971 265	3.61745 407	2.03358 336	10.03458 567
1.0	0.57274 468	3.51008 032	2.04141 250	8.62794 061
1.1	0.72057 223	3.37951 627	2.05004 425	7.06998 344
1.2	0.90191 600	3.21702 821	2.05947 210	5.35974 454
1.3	1.13478 731	3.00459 049	2.06968 890	3.49616 391
1.4	1.47280 284	2.68857 084	2.08068 684	1.47809 183

At $\rho = 1.46876861$

$a_0(i\rho) = a_2(i\rho) = 2.08869890$

(to 8D)

TABLE III. $a_r(i\rho)$, $a_{r+2}(i\rho)$ and Auxiliary Functions $r=0$

$$a_r(i\rho) = U+iV,\ a_{r+2}(i\rho) = U-iV,\ FB(i\rho) = (a_{r+2}-a_r)^2$$

ρ	U	V		$FB(i\rho)$
1.5	2.09245 747	-0.41704 626		-0.69571 035
1.6	2.10499 166	-0.86985 190		-3.02656 930
1.7	2.11827 963	-1.17429 752		-5.51589 868
1.8	2.13231 093	-1.42874 052		-8.16519 789
1.9	2.14707 443	-1.65650 616		-10.97605 069
2.0	2.16255 832	-1.86749 322		-13.95012 365
2.1	2.17875 015	-2.06695 212		-17.08916 435
2.2	2.19563 674	-2.25804 115		-20.39499 937
2.3	2.21320 428	-2.44282 276		-23.86953 212
2.4	2.23143 829	-2.62272 474		-27.51474 027
2.5	2.25032 359	-2.79877 978		-31.33267 310
2.6	2.26984 438	-2.97176 078		-35.32544 844
2.7	2.28998 421	-3.14226 230		-39.49524 938
2.8	2.31072 598	-3.31075 221		-43.84432 072
2.9	2.33205 200	-3.47760 568		-48.37496 509
3.0	2.35394 398	-3.64312 842		-53.08953 874
3.1	2.37638 304	-3.80757 295		-57.99044 715
3.2	2.39934 977	-3.97115 034		-63.08014 021
3.3	2.42282 423	-4.13403 880		-68.36110 720
3.4	2.44678 602	-4.29639 010		-73.83587 152
3.5	2.47121 426	-4.45833 447		-79.50698 506
3.6	2.49608 770	-4.61998 437		-85.37702 246
3.7	2.52138 468	-4.78143 742		-91.44857 508
3.8	2.54708 327	-4.94277 869		-97.72424 483
3.9	2.57316 124	-5.10408 263		-104.20663 783
4.0	2.59959 616	-5.26541 447		-110.89835 797
4.1	2.62636 544	-5.42683 150		-117.80200 042
4.2	2.65344 640	-5.58838 405		-124.92014 513
4.3	2.68081 629	-5.75011 631		-132.25535 029
4.4	2.70845 240	-5.91206 702		-139.81014 596
4.5	2.73633 212	-6.07427 007		-147.58702 772
4.6	2.76443 297	-6.23675 498		-155.58845 062
4.7	2.79273 266	-6.39954 731		-163.81682 328
4.8	2.82120 920	-6.56266 909		-172.27450 222
4.9	2.84984 094	-6.72613 906		-180.96378 668
5.0	2.87860 660	-6.88997 303		-189.88691 363

ρ	U	V	ρ	U	V
5.0	2.87860 660	-6.88997 303	10.0	4.21405 514	-15.51071 824
5.1	2.90748 535	-7.05418 410	10.1	4.23682 448	-15.68873 482
5.2	2.93645 690	-7.21878 288	10.2	4.25945 324	-15.86686 839
5.3	2.96550 149	-7.38377 772	10.3	4.28194 409	-16.04511 566
5.4	2.99459 996	-7.54917 491	10.4	4.30429 970	-16.22347 353
5.5	3.02373 383	-7.71497 882	10.5	4.32652 269	-16.40193 907
5.6	3.05288 530	-7.88119 209	10.6	4.34861 567	-16.58050 949
5.7	3.08203 727	-8.04781 580	10.7	4.37058 120	-16.75918 215
5.8	3.11117 344	-8.21484 957	10.8	4.39242 183	-16.93795 457
5.9	3.14027 825	-8.38229 173	10.9	4.41414 004	-17.11682 437
6.0	3.16933 699	-8.55013 943	11.0	4.43573 828	-17.29578 932
6.1	3.19833 571	-8.71838 878	11.1	4.45721 895	-17.47484 731
6.2	3.22726 133	-8.88703 495	11.2	4.47858 440	-17.65399 634
6.3	3.25610 158	-9.05607 228	11.3	4.49983 693	-17.83323 451
6.4	3.28484 504	-9.22549 437	11.4	4.52097 880	-18.01256 002
6.5	3.31348 111	-9.39529 421	11.5	4.54201 219	-18.19197 119
6.6	3.34200 000	-9.56546 425	11.6	4.56293 927	-18.37146 640
6.7	3.37039 273	-9.73599 645	11.7	4.58376 211	-18.55104 412
6.8	3.39865 112	-9.90688 245	11.8	4.60448 276	-18.73070 292
6.9	3.42676 776	-10.07811 353	11.9	4.62510 320	-18.91044 143
7.0	3.45473 598	-10.24968 079	12.0	4.64562 536	-19.09025 834
7.1	3.48254 983	-10.42157 511	12.1	4.66605 111	-19.27015 243
7.2	3.51020 407	-10.59378 730	12.2	4.68638 228	-19.45012 252
7.3	3.53769 412	-10.76630 808	12.3	4.70662 064	-19.63016 750
7.4	3.56501 602	-10.93912 817	12.4	4.72676 791	-19.81028 631
7.5	3.59216 644	-11.11223 832	12.5	4.74682 576	-19.99047 794
7.6	3.61914 261	-11.28562 934	12.6	4.76679 581	-20.17074 144
7.7	3.64594 230	-11.45929 216	12.7	4.78667 962	-20.35107 589
7.8	3.67256 378	-11.63321 783	12.8	4.80647 873	-20.53148 040
7.9	3.69900 579	-11.80739 757	12.9	4.82619 461	-20.71195 415
8.0	3.72526 753	-11.98182 279	13.0	4.84582 868	-20.89249 633
8.1	3.75134 860	-12.15648 507	13.1	4.86538 233	-21.07310 618
8.2	3.77724 895	-12.33137 624	13.2	4.88485 691	-21.25378 296
8.3	3.80296 891	-12.50648 836	13.3	4.90425 372	-21.43452 597
8.4	3.82850 911	-12.68181 371	13.4	4.92357 401	-21.61533 451
8.5	3.85387 048	-12.85734 483	13.5	4.94281 900	-21.79620 795
8.6	3.87905 419	-13.03307 453	13.6	4.96198 988	-21.97714 564
8.7	3.90406 166	-13.20899 586	13.7	4.98108 779	-22.15814 697
8.8	3.92889 452	-13.38510 213	13.8	5.00011 384	-22.33921 137
8.9	3.95355 457	-13.56138 693	13.9	5.01906 909	-22.52033 824
9.0	3.97804 380	-13.73784 410	14.0	5.03795 459	-22.70152 705
9.1	4.00236 432	-13.91446 772	14.1	5.05677 134	-22.88277 725
9.2	4.02651 838	-14.09125 215	14.2	5.07552 032	-23.06408 832
9.3	4.05050 832	-14.26819 199	14.3	5.09420 248	-23.24545 975
9.4	4.07433 659	-14.44528 208	14.4	5.11281 872	-23.42689 105
9.5	4.09800 569	-14.62251 750	14.5	5.13136 993	-23.60838 172
9.6	4.12151 820	-14.79989 357	14.6	5.14985 697	-23.78993 129
9.7	4.14487 674	-14.97740 581	14.7	5.16828 068	-23.97153 931
9.8	4.16808 396	-15.15505 000	14.8	5.18664 187	-24.15320 531
9.9	4.19114 253	-15.33282 208	14.9	5.20494 131	-24.33492 886
10.0	4.21405 514	-15.51071 824	15.0	5.22317 976	-24.51670 951

$$a_r(i\rho) = U + iV, \quad a_{r+2}(i\rho) = U - iV$$

ρ	U	V	ρ	U	V
15.0	5.22317 976	-24.51670 951	25.0	6.81659 977	-42.92397 295
15.2	5.25947 665	-24.88044 040	25.5	6.88701 878	-43.85365 903
15.4	5.29553 818	-25.24439 463	26.0	6.95674 878	-44.78403 288
15.6	5.33136 968	-25.60856 893	26.5	7.02580 938	-45.71507 430
15.8	5.36697 619	-25.97296 014	27.0	7.09421 933	-46.64676 407
16.0	5.40236 248	-26.33756 513	27.5	7.16199 660	-47.57908 389
16.2	5.43753 306	-26.70238 088	28.0	7.22915 838	-48.51201 636
16.4	5.47249 222	-27.06740 439	28.5	7.29572 117	-49.44554 486
16.6	5.50724 404	-27.43263 274	29.0	7.36170 073	-50.37965 356
16.8	5.54179 241	-27.79806 305	29.5	7.42711 220	-51.31432 733
17.0	5.57614 104	-28.16369 246	30.0	7.49197 007	-52.24955 174
17.2	5.61029 346	-28.52951 818	30.5	7.55628 826	-53.18531 295
17.4	5.64425 309	-28.89553 744	31.0	7.62008 008	-54.12159 775
17.6	5.67802 318	-29.26174 753	31.5	7.68335 936	-55.05839 347
17.8	5.71160 687	-29.62814 574	32.0	7.74613 536	-55.99568 794
18.0	5.74500 715	-29.99472 943	32.5	7.80842 289	-56.93346 952
18.2	5.77822 696	-30.36149 597	33.0	7.87023 231	-57.87172 699
18.4	5.81126 909	-30.72844 278	33.5	7.93157 451	-58.81044 959
18.6	5.84413 626	-31.09556 730	34.0	7.99245 999	-59.74962 696
18.8	5.87683 110	-31.46286 701	34.5	8.05289 886	-60.68924 911
19.0	5.90935 616	-31.83033 943	35.0	8.11290 084	-61.62930 646
19.2	5.94171 393	-32.19798 211	35.5	8.17247 531	-62.56978 971
19.4	5.97390 681	-32.56579 263	36.0	8.23163 132	-63.51068 995
19.6	6.00593 714	-32.93376 862	36.5	8.29037 758	-64.45199 855
19.8	6.03780 722	-33.30190 774	37.0	8.34872 251	-65.39370 716
20.0	6.06951 928	-33.67020 767	37.5	8.40667 425	-66.33580 774
20.2	6.10107 548	-34.03866 615	38.0	8.46424 064	-67.27829 250
20.4	6.13247 795	-34.40728 094	38.5	8.52142 930	-68.22115 391
20.6	6.16372 878	-34.77604 984	39.0	8.57824 756	-69.16438 468
20.8	6.19482 999	-35.14497 070	39.5	8.63470 254	-70.10797 776
21.0	6.22578 358	-35.51404 139	40.0	8.69080 111	-71.05192 630
21.2	6.25659 149	-35.88325 983	40.5	8.74654 995	-71.99622 369
21.4	6.28725 563	-36.25262 396	41.0	8.80195 551	-72.94086 350
21.6	6.31777 788	-36.62213 178	41.5	8.85702 407	-73.88583 950
21.8	6.34816 007	-36.99178 131	42.0	8.91176 168	-74.83114 564
22.0	6.37840 399	-37.36157 061	42.5	8.96617 425	-75.77677 607
22.2	6.40851 143	-37.73149 778	43.0	9.02026 749	-76.72272 509
22.4	6.43848 410	-38.10156 096	43.5	9.07404 696	-77.66898 716
22.6	6.46832 371	-38.47175 831	44.0	9.12751 806	-78.61555 692
22.8	6.49803 194	-38.84208 804	44.5	9.18068 602	-79.56242 914
23.0	6.52761 041	-39.21254 839	45.0	9.23355 594	-80.50959 875
23.2	6.55706 075	-39.58313 763	45.5	9.28613 277	-81.45706 080
23.4	6.58638 454	-39.95385 408	46.0	9.33842 133	-82.40481 051
23.6	6.61558 332	-40.32469 607	46.5	9.39042 631	-83.35284 319
23.8	6.64465 863	-40.69566 199	47.0	9.44215 227	-84.30115 430
24.0	6.67361 197	-41.06675 024	47.5	9.49360 366	-85.24973 941
24.2	6.70244 481	-41.43795 926	48.0	9.54478 479	-86.19859 420
24.4	6.73115 860	-41.80928 753	48.5	9.59569 987	-87.14771 449
24.6	6.75975 476	-42.18073 354	49.0	9.64635 303	-88.09709 618
24.8	6.78823 469	-42.55229 582	49.5	9.69674 824	-89.04673 528
25.0	6.81659 977	-42.92397 295	50.0	9.74688 942	-89.99662 789

ρ	U	V	ρ	U	V
50.0	9.74688 942	−89.99662 789	75.0	11.99490 507	−137.74983 651
50.5	9.79678 036	−90.94677 024	75.5	12.03567 046	−138.70908 906
51.0	9.84642 477	−91.89715 862	76.0	12.07630 104	−139.66847 625
51.5	9.89582 628	−92.84778 943	76.5	12.11679 813	−140.62799 675
52.0	9.94498 841	−93.79865 915	77.0	12.15716 303	−141.58764 926
52.5	9.99391 460	−94.74976 434	77.5	12.19739 705	−142.54743 249
53.0	10.04260 823	−95.70110 164	78.0	12.23750 143	−143.50734 518
53.5	10.09107 257	−96.65266 778	78.5	12.27747 742	−144.46738 609
54.0	10.13931 084	−97.60445 957	79.0	12.31732 626	−145.42755 400
54.5	10.18732 617	−98.55647 388	79.5	12.35704 914	−146.38784 770
55.0	10.23512 162	−99.50870 765	80.0	12.39664 726	−147.34826 601
55.5	10.28270 019	−100.46115 790	80.5	12.43612 177	−148.30880 776
56.0	10.33006 480	−101.41382 172	81.0	12.47547 384	−149.26947 181
56.5	10.37721 831	−102.36669 624	81.5	12.51470 459	−150.23025 702
57.0	10.42416 352	−103.31977 869	82.0	12.55381 514	−151.19116 229
57.5	10.47090 316	−104.27306 633	82.5	12.59280 658	−152.15218 651
58.0	10.51743 992	−105.22655 650	83.0	12.63168 000	−153.11332 861
58.5	10.56377 641	−106.18024 658	83.5	12.67043 647	−154.07458 753
59.0	10.60991 520	−107.13413 402	84.0	12.70907 703	−155.03596 221
59.5	10.65585 879	−108.08821 631	84.5	12.74760 272	−155.99745 163
60.0	10.70160 965	−109.04249 101	85.0	12.78601 455	−156.95905 477
60.5	10.74717 017	−109.99695 571	85.5	12.82431 353	−157.92077 062
61.0	10.79254 272	−110.95160 808	86.0	12.86250 064	−158.88259 821
61.5	10.83772 959	−111.90644 579	86.5	12.90057 687	−159.84453 655
62.0	10.88273 306	−112.86146 662	87.0	12.93854 317	−160.80658 469
62.5	10.92755 534	−113.81666 833	87.5	12.97640 049	−161.76874 169
63.0	10.97219 860	−114.77204 877	88.0	13.01414 977	−162.73100 661
63.5	11.01666 496	−115.72760 582	88.5	13.05179 191	−163.69337 854
64.0	11.06095 652	−116.68333 740	89.0	13.08932 783	−164.65585 657
64.5	11.10507 532	−117.63924 146	89.5	13.12675 843	−165.61843 981
65.0	11.14902 336	−118.59531 600	90.0	13.16408 458	−166.58112 737
65.5	11.19280 261	−119.55155 907	90.5	13.20130 715	−167.54391 840
66.0	11.23641 501	−120.50796 874	91.0	13.23842 701	−168.50681 202
66.5	11.27986 244	−121.46454 311	91.5	13.27544 499	−169.46980 741
67.0	11.32314 676	−122.42128 034	92.0	13.31236 194	−170.43290 373
67.5	11.36626 980	−123.37817 861	92.5	13.34917 867	−171.39610 015
68.0	11.40923 335	−124.33523 614	93.0	13.38589 599	−172.35939 587
68.5	11.45203 917	−125.29245 116	93.5	13.42251 471	−173.32279 008
69.0	11.49468 897	−126.24982 197	94.0	13.45903 562	−174.28628 201
69.5	11.53718 445	−127.20734 686	94.5	13.49545 950	−175.24987 086
70.0	11.57952 727	−128.16502 419	95.0	13.53178 711	−176.21355 587
70.5	11.62171 908	−129.12285 232	95.5	13.56801 922	−177.17733 629
71.0	11.66376 146	−130.08082 965	96.0	13.60415 657	−178.14121 136
71.5	11.70565 601	−131.03895 462	96.5	13.64019 991	−179.10518 036
72.0	11.74740 426	−131.99722 566	97.0	13.67614 996	−180.06924 254
72.5	11.78900 775	−132.95564 128	97.5	13.71200 744	−181.03339 719
73.0	11.83046 795	−133.91419 997	98.0	13.74777 307	−181.99764 359
73.5	11.87178 636	−134.87290 027	98.5	13.78344 755	−182.96198 106
74.0	11.91296 440	−135.83174 073	99.0	13.81903 157	−183.92640 890
74.5	11.95400 350	−136.79071 994	99.5	13.85452 582	−184.89092 641
75.0	11.99490 507	−137.74983 651	100.0	13.88993 097	−185.85553 294

ρ	$a_r(i\rho)$	$a_{r+2}(i\rho)$	ρ	$a_r(i\rho)$	$a_{r+2}(i\rho)$
0.0	16.00000 000	36.00000 000	5.0	15.49070 781	35.64434 536
0.1	15.99966 672	35.99985 714	5.1	15.48333 219	35.62998 626
0.2	15.99866 747	35.99942 858	5.2	15.47677 051	35.61533 897
0.3	15.99700 406	35.99871 432	5.3	15.47106 296	35.60040 270
0.4	15.99467 950	35.99771 439	5.4	15.46624 858	35.58517 659
0.5	15.99169 802	35.99642 884	5.5	15.46236 519	35.56965 968
0.6	15.98806 505	35.99485 769	5.6	15.45944 929	35.55385 096
0.7	15.98378 724	35.99300 101	5.7	15.45753 604	35.53774 930
0.8	15.97887 248	35.99085 887	5.8	15.45665 914	35.52135 351
0.9	15.97332 990	35.98843 133	5.9	15.45685 085	35.50466 227
1.0	15.96716 986	35.98571 847	6.0	15.45814 191	35.48767 421
1.1	15.96040 400	35.98272 039	6.1	15.46056 153	35.47038 780
1.2	15.95304 521	35.97943 719	6.2	15.46413 737	35.45280 144
1.3	15.94510 767	35.97586 896	6.3	15.46889 554	35.43491 339
1.4	15.93660 685	35.97201 581	6.4	15.47486 060	35.41672 182
1.5	15.92755 952	35.96787 788	6.5	15.48205 559	35.39822 474
1.6	15.91798 377	35.96345 526	6.6	15.49050 202	35.37942 006
1.7	15.90789 900	35.95874 810	6.7	15.50021 994	35.36030 553
1.8	15.89732 595	35.95375 652	6.8	15.51122 794	35.34087 876
1.9	15.88628 671	35.94848 065	6.9	15.52354 323	35.32113 723
2.0	15.87480 470	35.94292 062	7.0	15.53718 167	35.30107 823
2.1	15.86290 469	35.93707 657	7.1	15.55215 785	35.28069 893
2.2	15.85061 282	35.93094 864	7.2	15.56848 511	35.25999 628
2.3	15.83795 653	35.92453 694	7.3	15.58617 565	35.23896 710
2.4	15.82496 464	35.91784 162	7.4	15.60524 057	35.21760 799
2.5	15.81166 729	35.91086 280	7.5	15.62568 998	35.19591 537
2.6	15.79809 592	35.90360 058	7.6	15.64753 300	35.17388 545
2.7	15.78428 327	35.89605 510	7.7	15.67077 791	35.15151 426
2.8	15.77026 335	35.88822 645	7.8	15.69543 219	35.12879 756
2.9	15.75607 140	35.88011 473	7.9	15.72150 260	35.10573 091
3.0	15.74174 387	35.87172 001	8.0	15.74899 526	35.08230 964
3.1	15.72731 835	35.86304 238	8.1	15.77791 571	35.05852 882
3.2	15.71283 356	35.85408 188	8.2	15.80826 900	35.03438 324
3.3	15.69832 925	35.84483 856	8.3	15.84005 975	35.00986 745
3.4	15.68384 614	35.83531 243	8.4	15.87329 224	34.98497 569
3.5	15.66942 591	35.82550 349	8.5	15.90797 047	34.95970 192
3.6	15.65511 102	35.81541 173	8.6	15.94409 820	34.93403 979
3.7	15.64094 471	35.80503 710	8.7	15.98167 906	34.90798 262
3.8	15.62697 088	35.79437 952	8.8	16.02071 659	34.88152 340
3.9	15.61323 399	35.78343 889	8.9	16.06121 430	34.85465 475
4.0	15.59977 893	35.77221 508	9.0	16.10317 575	34.82736 894
4.1	15.58665 098	35.76070 792	9.1	16.14660 459	34.79965 785
4.2	15.57389 562	35.74891 722	9.2	16.19150 459	34.77151 295
4.3	15.56155 846	35.73684 272	9.3	16.23787 978	34.74292 530
4.4	15.54968 511	35.72448 415	9.4	16.28573 440	34.71388 550
4.5	15.53832 106	35.71184 117	9.5	16.33507 303	34.68438 370
4.6	15.52751 154	35.69891 342	9.6	16.38590 060	34.65440 956
4.7	15.51730 140	35.68570 047	9.7	16.43822 245	34.62395 224
4.8	15.50773 502	35.67220 184	9.8	16.49204 438	34.59300 035
4.9	15.49885 615	35.65841 700	9.9	16.54737 272	34.56154 195
5.0	15.49070 781	35.64434 536	10.0	16.60421 432	34.52956 451

ρ	$a_r(i\rho)$	$a_{r+2}(i\rho)$	$FA(i\rho)$	$FB(i\rho)$
10.0	16.60421 432	34.52956 451	25.56688 941	321.31817 921
10.1	16.66257 667	34.49705 487	25.57981 577	318.06861 251
10.2	16.72246 789	34.46399 923	25.59323 356	314.76193 410
10.3	16.78389 682	34.43038 310	25.60713 996	311.39847 797
10.4	16.84687 304	34.39619 127	25.62153 216	307.97857 027
10.5	16.91140 694	34.36140 776	25.63640 735	304.50252 860
10.6	16.97750 977	34.32601 580	25.65176 278	300.97066 138
10.7	17.04519 368	34.28999 774	25.66759 571	297.38326 726
10.8	17.11447 179	34.25333 507	25.68390 343	293.74063 463
10.9	17.18535 826	34.21600 831	25.70068 328	290.04304 112
11.0	17.25786 831	34.17799 695	25.71793 263	286.29075 323
11.1	17.33201 834	34.13927 944	25.73564 889	282.48402 594
11.2	17.40782 596	34.09983 310	25.75382 953	278.62310 239
11.3	17.48531 008	34.05963 401	25.77247 205	274.70821 359
11.4	17.56449 101	34.01865 699	25.79157 400	270.73957 822
11.5	17.64539 048	33.97687 548	25.81113 298	266.71740 235
11.6	17.72803 182	33.93426 147	25.83114 665	262.64187 930
11.7	17.81244 001	33.89078 536	25.85161 269	258.51318 948
11.8	17.89864 177	33.84641 592	25.87252 885	254.33150 025
11.9	17.98666 576	33.80112 009	25.89389 292	250.09696 584
12.0	18.07654 261	33.75486 290	25.91570 275	245.80972 722
12.1	18.16830 514	33.70760 732	25.93795 623	241.46991 207
12.2	18.26198 850	33.65931 407	25.96065 129	237.07763 473
12.3	18.35763 032	33.60994 149	25.98378 591	232.63299 615
12.4	18.45527 092	33.55944 531	26.00735 811	228.13608 386
12.5	18.55495 354	33.50777 842	26.03136 598	223.58697 201
12.6	18.65672 455	33.45489 069	26.05580 762	218.98572 132
12.7	18.76063 373	33.40072 864	26.08068 119	214.33237 912
12.8	18.86673 458	33.34523 517	26.10598 488	209.62697 935
12.9	18.97508 465	33.28834 922	26.13171 693	204.86954 264
13.0	19.08574 587	33.23000 536	26.15787 561	200.06007 627
13.1	19.19878 507	33.17013 341	26.18445 924	195.19857 428
13.2	19.31427 438	33.10865 793	26.21146 616	190.28501 744
13.3	19.43229 181	33.04549 766	26.23889 473	185.31937 340
13.4	19.55292 189	32.98056 489	26.26674 339	180.30159 664
13.5	19.67625 636	32.91376 476	26.29501 056	175.23162 860
13.6	19.80239 505	32.84499 439	26.32369 472	170.10939 768
13.7	19.93144 678	32.77414 195	26.35279 437	164.93481 934
13.8	20.06353 053	32.70108 552	26.38230 802	159.70779 617
13.9	20.19877 671	32.62569 177	26.41223 424	154.42821 788
14.0	20.33732 872	32.54781 444	26.44257 158	149.09596 146
14.1	20.47934 478	32.46729 252	26.47331 865	143.71089 115
14.2	20.62500 005	32.38394 807	26.50447 406	138.27285 856
14.3	20.77448 928	32.29758 360	26.53603 644	132.78170 271
14.4	20.92802 993	32.20797 896	26.56800 445	127.23725 009
14.5	21.08586 601	32.11488 748	26.60037 674	121.63931 472
14.6	21.24827 276	32.01803 126	26.63315 201	115.98769 822
14.7	21.41556 258	31.91709 532	26.66632 895	110.28218 983
14.8	21.58809 233	31.81172 018	26.69990 626	104.52256 651
14.9	21.76627 274	31.70149 257	26.73388 265	98.70859 297
15.0	21.95058 052	31.58593 322	26.76825 687	92.84002 171

TABLE III. $a_r(i\rho)$, $a_{r+2}(i\rho)$ and Auxiliary Functions $\qquad r=4$

$$FA(i\rho) = \tfrac{1}{2}(a_r + a_{r+2}), \quad FB(i\rho) = (a_{r+2} - a_r)^2$$

ρ	$a_r(i\rho)$	$a_{r+2}(i\rho)$	$FA(i\rho)$	$FB(i\rho)$
15.0	21.95058 052	31.58593 322	26.76825 687	92.84002 171
15.1	22.14157 418	31.46448 108	26.80302 763	86.91659 309
15.2	22.33991 526	31.33647 212	26.83819 369	80.93803 538
15.3	22.54639 706	31.20111 050	26.87375 378	74.90406 479
15.4	22.76198 483	31.05742 849	26.90970 666	68.81438 552
15.5	22.98787 316	30.90422 900	26.94605 108	62.66868 980
15.6	23.22557 080	30.74000 078	26.98278 579	56.46665 795
15.7	23.47703 084	30.56278 827	27.01990 956	50.20795 839
15.8	23.74485 989	30.36998 236	27.05742 112	43.89224 767
15.9	24.03267 453	30.15796 396	27.09531 924	37.51917 054
16.0	24.34575 583	29.92144 951	27.13360 267	31.08835 997
16.1	24.69237 916	29.65216 113	27.17227 014	24.59943 715
16.2	25.08693 746	29.33570 335	27.21132 040	18.05201 156
16.3	25.55917 888	28.94232 549	27.25075 218	11.44568 097
16.4	26.19740 005	28.38372 836	27.29056 421	4.78003 146

At $\rho = 16.47116589$

$a_4(i\rho) = a_6(i\rho) = 27.31912767$

(to 8D)

ρ	U	V		$FB(i\rho)$
16.5	27.33075 519	−0.69738 127		−1.94536 252
16.6	27.37132 384	−1.47740 805		−8.73093 817
16.7	27.41226 886	−1.97339 456		−15.57714 432
16.8	27.45358 891	−2.37088 809		−22.48444 136
16.9	27.49528 269	−2.71354 479		−29.45330 129
17.0	27.53734 883	−3.02010 793		−36.48420 767
17.1	27.57978 599	−3.30066 870		−43.57765 559
17.2	27.62259 278	−3.56139 550		−50.73415 171
17.3	27.66576 782	−3.80638 326		−57.95421 419
17.4	27.70930 970	−4.03851 373		−65.23837 270
17.5	27.75321 698	−4.25990 518		−72.58716 844
17.6	27.79748 822	−4.47216 821		−80.00115 407
17.7	27.84212 195	−4.67656 107		−87.48089 375
17.8	27.88711 667	−4.87408 871		−95.02696 311
17.9	27.93247 087	−5.06556 880		−102.63994 924
18.0	27.97818 302	−5.25167 713		−110.32045 068
18.1	28.02425 153	−5.43297 979		−118.06907 741
18.2	28.07067 483	−5.60995 657		−125.88645 084
18.3	28.11745 130	−5.78301 833		−133.77320 382
18.4	28.16457 930	−5.95252 007		−141.72998 059
18.5	28.21205 714	−6.11877 105		−149.75743 677
18.6	28.25988 314	−6.28204 265		−157.85623 940
18.7	28.30805 555	−6.44257 454		−166.02706 685
18.8	28.35657 260	−6.60057 969		−174.27060 884
18.9	28.40543 251	−6.75624 834		−182.58756 644
19.0	28.45463 344	−6.90975 130		−190.97865 200
19.1	28.50417 353	−7.06124 262		−199.44458 915
19.2	28.55405 088	−7.21086 182		−207.98611 279
19.3	28.60426 354	−7.35873 578		−216.60396 904
19.4	28.65480 956	−7.50498 027		−225.29891 520
19.5	28.70568 692	−7.64970 130		−234.07171 973
19.6	28.75689 357	−7.79299 625		−242.92316 221
19.7	28.80842 742	−7.93495 484		−251.85403 329
19.8	28.86028 635	−8.07565 995		−260.86513 463
19.9	28.91246 819	−8.21518 836		−269.95727 887
20.0	28.96497 072	−8.35361 134		−279.13128 957

ρ	U	V	ρ	U	V
20.0	28.96497 072	-8.35361 134	25.0	31.93607 422	-14.69031 374
20.1	29.01779 170	-8.49099 525	25.1	32.00086 168	-14.81447 151
20.2	29.07092 883	-8.62740 197	25.2	32.06578 763	-14.93873 237
20.3	29.12437 976	-8.76288 934	25.3	32.13084 739	-15.06310 290
20.4	29.17814 212	-8.89751 154	25.4	32.19603 628	-15.18758 943
20.5	29.23221 346	-9.03131 939	25.5	32.26134 961	-15.31219 803
20.6	29.28659 132	-9.16436 067	25.6	32.32678 266	-15.43693 451
20.7	29.34127 318	-9.29668 037	25.7	32.39233 068	-15.56180 446
20.8	29.39625 645	-9.42832 090	25.8	32.45798 894	-15.68681 320
20.9	29.45153 852	-9.55932 233	25.9	32.52375 268	-15.81196 584
21.0	29.50711 672	-9.68972 256	26.0	32.58961 713	-15.93726 724
21.1	29.56298 833	-9.81955 748	26.1	32.65557 753	-16.06272 205
21.2	29.61915 059	-9.94886 112	26.2	32.72162 910	-16.18833 468
21.3	29.67560 068	-10.07766 583	26.3	32.78776 708	-16.31410 935
21.4	29.73233 572	-10.20600 232	26.4	32.85398 671	-16.44005 003
21.5	29.78935 281	-10.33389 986	26.5	32.92028 322	-16.56616 050
21.6	29.84664 895	-10.46138 632	26.6	32.98665 186	-16.69244 435
21.7	29.90422 114	-10.58848 827	26.7	33.05308 789	-16.81890 494
21.8	29.96206 630	-10.71523 111	26.8	33.11958 660	-16.94554 545
21.9	30.02018 129	-10.84163 909	26.9	33.18614 327	-17.07236 886
22.0	30.07856 293	-10.96773 542	27.0	33.25275 322	-17.19937 795
22.1	30.13720 799	-11.09354 229	27.1	33.31941 179	-17.32657 533
22.2	30.19611 318	-11.21908 099	27.2	33.38611 434	-17.45396 341
22.3	30.25527 515	-11.34437 192	27.3	33.45285 628	-17.58154 444
22.4	30.31469 051	-11.46943 465	27.4	33.51963 301	-17.70932 048
22.5	30.37435 582	-11.59428 797	27.5	33.58644 001	-17.83729 342
22.6	30.43426 756	-11.71894 992	27.6	33.65327 277	-17.96546 499
22.7	30.49442 218	-11.84343 786	27.7	33.72012 684	-18.09383 672
22.8	30.55481 607	-11.96776 845	27.8	33.78699 779	-18.22241 004
22.9	30.61544 557	-12.09195 777	27.9	33.85388 126	-18.35118 616
23.0	30.67630 697	-12.21602 125	28.0	33.92077 292	-18.48016 617
23.1	30.73739 650	-12.33997 376	28.1	33.98766 849	-18.60935 100
23.2	30.79871 033	-12.46382 965	28.2	34.05456 377	-18.73874 144
23.3	30.86024 461	-12.58760 272	28.3	34.12145 459	-18.86833 813
23.4	30.92199 541	-12.71130 628	28.4	34.18833 684	-18.99814 157
23.5	30.98395 876	-12.83495 315	28.5	34.25520 649	-19.12815 213
23.6	31.04613 065	-12.95855 573	28.6	34.32205 955	-19.25837 004
23.7	31.10850 700	-13.08212 593	28.7	34.38889 211	-19.38879 541
23.8	31.17108 370	-13.20567 526	28.8	34.45570 033	-19.51942 821
23.9	31.23385 659	-13.32921 484	28.9	34.52248 042	-19.65026 832
24.0	31.29682 147	-13.45275 537	29.0	34.58922 868	-19.78131 547
24.1	31.35997 408	-13.57630 719	29.1	34.65594 147	-19.91256 930
24.2	31.42331 014	-13.69988 025	29.2	34.72261 524	-20.04402 932
24.3	31.48682 530	-13.82348 418	29.3	34.78924 650	-20.17569 496
24.4	31.55051 519	-13.94712 823	29.4	34.85583 186	-20.30756 554
24.5	31.61437 540	-14.07082 136	29.5	34.92236 797	-20.43964 026
24.6	31.67840 147	-14.19457 216	29.6	34.98885 159	-20.57191 827
24.7	31.74258 893	-14.31838 896	29.7	35.05527 957	-20.70439 859
24.8	31.80693 325	-14.44227 973	29.8	35.12164 880	-20.83708 018
24.9	31.87142 987	-14.56625 218	29.9	35.18795 631	-20.96996 191
25.0	31.93607 422	-14.69031 374	30.0	35.25419 916	-21.10304 256

322-566 O - 69 - 15

ρ	U	V	ρ	U	V
30.0	35.25419 916	−21.10304 256	40.0	41.36371 885	−35.11853 204
30.2	35.38647 967	−21.36979 546	40.2	41.47574 821	−35.40813 060
30.4	35.51846 869	−21.63732 778	40.4	41.58745 863	−35.69797 603
30.6	35.65014 597	−21.90562 745	40.6	41.69885 499	−35.98806 566
30.8	35.78149 262	−22.17468 148	40.8	41.80994 207	−36.27839 698
31.0	35.91249 112	−22.44447 613	41.0	41.92072 451	−36.56896 767
31.2	36.04312 533	−22.71499 698	41.2	42.03120 683	−36.85977 556
31.4	36.17338 043	−22.98622 905	41.4	42.14139 343	−37.15081 860
31.6	36.30324 296	−23.25815 690	41.6	42.25128 861	−37.44209 490
31.8	36.43270 074	−23.53076 475	41.8	42.36089 650	−37.73360 270
32.0	36.56174 287	−23.80403 651	42.0	42.47022 116	−38.02534 032
32.2	36.69035 966	−24.07795 594	42.2	42.57926 648	−38.31730 623
32.4	36.81854 265	−24.35250 668	42.4	42.68803 627	−38.60949 897
32.6	36.94628 450	−24.62767 235	42.6	42.79653 420	−38.90191 717
32.8	37.07357 897	−24.90343 661	42.8	42.90476 383	−39.19455 956
33.0	37.20042 091	−25.17978 322	43.0	43.01272 859	−39.48742 493
33.2	37.32680 613	−25.45669 611	43.2	43.12043 182	−39.78051 213
33.4	37.45273 142	−25.73415 941	43.4	43.22787 673	−40.07382 010
33.6	37.57819 445	−26.01215 752	43.6	43.33506 644	−40.36734 781
33.8	37.70319 376	−26.29067 516	43.8	43.44200 395	−40.66109 429
34.0	37.82772 865	−26.56969 735	44.0	43.54869 216	−40.95505 861
34.2	37.95179 918	−26.84920 953	44.2	43.65513 388	−41.24923 989
34.4	38.07540 609	−27.12919 750	44.4	43.76133 182	−41.54363 728
34.6	38.19855 074	−27.40964 748	44.6	43.86728 858	−41.83824 995
34.8	38.32123 510	−27.69054 616	44.8	43.97300 669	−42.13307 711
35.0	38.44346 164	−27.97188 065	45.0	44.07848 859	−42.42811 799
35.2	38.56523 334	−28.25363 854	45.2	44.18373 662	−42.72337 184
35.4	38.68655 360	−28.53580 788	45.4	44.28875 306	−43.01883 793
35.6	38.80742 623	−28.81837 720	45.6	44.39354 009	−43.31451 553
35.8	38.92785 537	−29.10133 550	45.8	44.49809 983	−43.61040 393
36.0	39.04784 549	−29.38467 226	46.0	44.60243 432	−43.90650 244
36.2	39.16740 133	−29.66837 742	46.2	44.70654 553	−44.20281 035
36.4	39.28652 786	−29.95244 140	46.4	44.81043 538	−44.49932 699
36.6	39.40523 024	−30.23685 508	46.6	44.91410 570	−44.79605 165
36.8	39.52351 382	−30.52160 976	46.8	45.01755 828	−45.09298 366
37.0	39.64138 408	−30.80669 721	47.0	45.12079 484	−45.39012 233
37.2	39.75884 661	−31.09210 961	47.2	45.22381 704	−45.68746 697
37.4	39.87590 710	−31.37783 958	47.4	45.32662 651	−45.98501 688
37.6	39.99257 127	−31.66388 011	47.6	45.42922 481	−46.28277 138
37.8	40.10884 491	−31.95022 459	47.8	45.53161 345	−46.58072 975
38.0	40.22473 381	−32.23686 681	48.0	45.63379 390	−46.87889 130
38.2	40.34024 378	−32.52380 088	48.2	45.73576 760	−47.17725 531
38.4	40.45538 059	−32.81102 129	48.4	45.83753 592	−47.47582 106
38.6	40.57014 999	−33.09852 284	48.6	45.93910 023	−47.77458 783
38.8	40.68455 769	−33.38630 066	48.8	46.04046 181	−48.07355 488
39.0	40.79860 932	−33.67435 016	49.0	46.14162 196	−48.37272 147
39.2	40.91231 047	−33.96266 706	49.2	46.24258 192	−48.67208 685
39.4	41.02566 664	−34.25124 733	49.4	46.34334 289	−48.97165 026
39.6	41.13868 323	−34.54008 723	49.6	46.44390 605	−49.27141 093
39.8	41.25136 556	−34.82918 323	49.8	46.54427 257	−49.57136 810
40.0	41.36371 885	−35.11853 204	50.0	46.64444 356	−49.87152 097

ρ	U	V	ρ	U	V
50.0	46.64444 356	−49.87152 097	75.0	57.89964 783	−88.65921 693
50.5	46.89402 282	−50.62275 415	75.5	58.10370 937	−89.45583 192
51.0	47.14240 351	−51.37519 297	76.0	58.30709 430	−90.25311 574
51.5	47.38960 148	−52.12882 457	76.5	58.50980 937	−91.05106 184
52.0	47.63563 191	−52.88363 583	77.0	58.71186 120	−91.84966 380
52.5	47.88050 942	−53.63961 342	77.5	58.91325 633	−92.64891 528
53.0	48.12424 812	−54.39674 381	78.0	59.11400 115	−93.44881 007
53.5	48.36686 175	−55.15501 333	78.5	59.31410 196	−94.24934 206
54.0	48.60836 368	−55.91440 818	79.0	59.51356 495	−95.05050 521
54.5	48.84876 701	−56.67491 453	79.5	59.71239 623	−95.85229 360
55.0	49.08808 456	−57.43651 847	80.0	59.91060 178	−96.65470 140
55.5	49.32632 897	−58.19920 612	80.5	60.10818 748	−97.45772 286
56.0	49.56351 266	−58.96296 363	81.0	60.30515 915	−98.26135 234
56.5	49.79964 791	−59.72777 721	81.5	60.50152 248	−99.06558 426
57.0	50.03474 682	−60.49363 319	82.0	60.69728 309	−99.87041 314
57.5	50.26882 140	−61.26051 799	82.5	60.89244 650	−100.67583 357
58.0	50.50188 348	−62.02841 819	83.0	61.08701 816	−101.48184 024
58.5	50.73394 482	−62.79732 053	83.5	61.28100 341	−102.28842 791
59.0	50.96501 701	−63.56721 194	84.0	61.47440 754	−103.09559 140
59.5	51.19511 155	−64.33807 954	84.5	61.66723 573	−103.90332 562
60.0	51.42423 983	−65.10991 065	85.0	61.85949 310	−104.71162 556
60.5	51.65241 310	−65.88269 283	85.5	62.05118 468	−105.52048 627
61.0	51.87964 250	−66.65641 383	86.0	62.24231 544	−106.32990 288
61.5	52.10593 903	−67.43106 167	86.5	62.43289 027	−107.13987 058
62.0	52.33131 357	−68.20662 457	87.0	62.62291 399	−107.95038 463
62.5	52.55577 687	−68.98309 101	87.5	62.81239 135	−108.76144 035
63.0	52.77933 954	−69.76044 970	88.0	63.00132 702	−109.57303 316
63.5	53.00201 205	−70.53868 958	88.5	63.18972 562	−110.38515 849
64.0	53.22380 474	−71.31779 983	89.0	63.37759 169	−111.19781 187
64.5	53.44472 777	−72.09776 987	89.5	63.56492 973	−112.01098 888
65.0	53.66479 120	−72.87858 933	90.0	63.75174 415	−112.82468 517
65.5	53.88400 489	−73.66024 809	90.5	63.93803 931	−113.63889 643
66.0	54.10237 859	−74.44273 622	91.0	64.12381 951	−114.45361 842
66.5	54.31992 188	−75.22604 404	91.5	64.30908 899	−115.26884 697
67.0	54.53664 418	−76.01016 204	92.0	64.49385 193	−116.08457 794
67.5	54.75255 475	−76.79508 095	92.5	64.67811 247	−116.90080 726
68.0	54.96766 273	−77.58079 167	93.0	64.86187 467	−117.71753 091
68.5	55.18197 707	−78.36728 533	93.5	65.04514 254	−118.53474 494
69.0	55.39550 658	−79.15455 320	94.0	65.22792 005	−119.35244 541
69.5	55.60825 992	−79.94258 676	94.5	65.41021 111	−120.17062 849
70.0	55.82024 559	−80.73137 766	95.0	65.59201 958	−120.98929 035
70.5	56.03147 195	−81.52091 772	95.5	65.77334 927	−121.80842 723
71.0	56.24194 721	−82.31119 891	96.0	65.95420 392	−122.62803 542
71.5	56.45167 944	−83.10221 338	96.5	66.13458 727	−123.44811 126
72.0	56.66067 655	−83.89395 342	97.0	66.31450 296	−124.26865 113
72.5	56.86894 632	−84.68641 147	97.5	66.49395 461	−125.08965 146
73.0	57.07649 639	−85.47958 011	98.0	66.67294 579	−125.91110 872
73.5	57.28333 427	−86.27345 205	98.5	66.85148 002	−126.73301 943
74.0	57.48946 733	−87.06802 017	99.0	67.02956 079	−127.55538 015
74.5	57.69490 282	−87.86327 742	99.5	67.20719 153	−128.37818 750
75.0	57.89964 783	−88.65921 693	100.0	67.38437 562	−129.20143 810

ρ	$a_r(i\rho)$	$a_{r+2}(i\rho)$	ρ	$a_r(i\rho)$	$a_{r+2}(i\rho)$
0.0	64.00000 000	100.00000 000	10.0	63.21323 095	99.49663 238
0.2	63.99968 254	99.99979 798	10.2	63.18175 055	99.47636 626
0.4	63.99873 018	99.99919 192	10.4	63.14967 366	99.45570 435
0.6	63.99714 295	99.99818 184	10.6	63.11700 231	99.43464 697
0.8	63.99492 091	99.99676 775	10.8	63.08373 862	99.41319 445
1.0	63.99206 417	99.99494 967	11.0	63.04988 486	99.39134 711
1.2	63.98857 284	99.99272 763	11.2	63.01544 340	99.36910 527
1.4	63.98444 706	99.99010 166	11.4	62.98041 674	99.34646 928
1.6	63.97968 700	99.98707 182	11.6	62.94480 755	99.32343 948
1.8	63.97429 286	99.98363 815	11.8	62.90861 860	99.30001 622
2.0	63.96826 485	99.97980 070	12.0	62.87185 288	99.27619 984
2.2	63.96160 324	99.97555 954	12.2	62.83451 352	99.25159 069
2.4	63.95430 828	99.97091 473	12.4	62.79660 384	99.22738 915
2.6	63.94638 028	99.96586 635	12.6	62.75812 736	99.20239 557
2.8	63.93781 956	99.96041 449	12.8	62.71908 782	99.17701 032
3.0	63.92862 647	99.95455 922	13.0	62.67948 918	99.15123 377
3.2	63.91880 140	99.94830 064	13.2	62.63933 563	99.12506 630
3.4	63.90834 473	99.94163 886	13.4	62.59863 164	99.09850 829
3.6	63.89725 691	99.93457 398	13.6	62.55738 193	99.07156 013
3.8	63.88553 837	99.92710 612	13.8	62.51559 154	99.04422 219
4.0	63.87318 961	99.91923 539	14.0	62.47326 579	99.01649 486
4.2	63.86021 113	99.91096 192	14.2	62.43041 037	98.98837 855
4.4	63.84660 345	99.90228 584	14.4	62.38703 128	98.95987 365
4.6	63.83236 713	99.89320 730	14.6	62.34313 493	98.93098 055
4.8	63.81750 277	99.88372 644	14.8	62.29872 810	98.90169 965
5.0	63.80201 096	99.87384 340	15.0	62.25381 801	98.87203 136
5.2	63.78589 236	99.86355 835	15.2	62.20841 233	98.84197 608
5.4	63.76914 762	99.85287 146	15.4	62.16251 918	98.81153 421
5.6	63.75177 744	99.84178 288	15.6	62.11614 722	98.78070 617
5.8	63.73378 255	99.83029 281	15.8	62.06930 562	98.74949 236
6.0	63.71516 369	99.81840 142	16.0	62.02200 410	98.71789 318
6.2	63.69592 165	99.80610 890	16.2	61.97425 300	98.68590 905
6.4	63.67605 725	99.79341 544	16.4	61.92606 328	98.65354 038
6.6	63.65557 133	99.78032 126	16.6	61.87744 656	98.62078 756
6.8	63.63446 477	99.76682 655	16.8	61.82841 515	98.58765 100
7.0	63.61273 849	99.75293 153	17.0	61.77898 211	98.55413 112
7.2	63.59039 344	99.73863 642	17.2	61.72916 127	98.52022 830
7.4	63.56743 062	99.72394 144	17.4	61.67896 726	98.48594 295
7.6	63.54385 105	99.70884 683	17.6	61.62841 560	98.45127 547
7.8	63.51965 581	99.69335 282	17.8	61.57752 266	98.41622 624
8.0	63.49484 602	99.67745 966	18.0	61.52630 578	98.38079 565
8.2	63.46942 283	99.66116 760	18.2	61.47478 327	98.34498 409
8.4	63.44338 747	99.64447 689	18.4	61.42297 449	98.30879 192
8.6	63.41674 120	99.62738 779	18.6	61.37089 985	98.27221 952
8.8	63.38948 534	99.60990 057	18.8	61.31858 090	98.23526 725
9.0	63.36162 127	99.59201 550	19.0	61.26604 034	98.19793 545
9.2	63.33315 045	99.57373 287	19.2	61.21330 212	98.16022 448
9.4	63.30407 438	99.55505 294	19.4	61.16039 142	98.12213 466
9.6	63.27439 466	99.53597 602	19.6	61.10733 474	98.08366 632
9.8	63.24411 293	99.51650 240	19.8	61.05415 997	98.04481 976
10.0	63.21323 095	99.49663 238	20.0	61.00089 637	98.00559 528

ρ	$a_r(i\rho)$	$a_{r+2}(i\rho)$	ρ	$a_r(i\rho)$	$a_{r+2}(i\rho)$
20.0	61.00089 637	98.00559 528	30.0	59.32670 480	95.55855 258
20.2	60.94757 467	97.96599 316	30.2	59.34131 016	95.49939 302
20.4	60.89422 710	97.92601 365	30.4	59.35889 753	95.43978 325
20.6	60.84088 744	97.88565 702	30.6	59.37951 094	95.37971 750
20.8	60.78759 103	97.84492 348	30.8	59.40319 204	95.31918 971
21.0	60.73437 487	97.80381 324	31.0	59.42998 013	95.25819 339
21.2	60.68127 760	97.76232 648	31.2	59.45991 220	95.19672 172
21.4	60.62833 956	97.72046 337	31.4	59.49302 294	95.13476 743
21.6	60.57560 281	97.67822 404	31.6	59.52934 488	95.07232 285
21.8	60.52311 118	97.63560 859	31.8	59.56890 838	95.00937 984
22.0	60.47091 026	97.59261 710	32.0	59.61174 178	94.94592 980
22.2	60.41904 745	97.54924 963	32.2	59.65787 145	94.88196 361
22.4	60.36757 191	97.50550 618	32.4	59.70732 193	94.81747 166
22.6	60.31653 467	97.46138 673	32.6	59.76011 602	94.75244 375
22.8	60.26598 850	97.41689 121	32.8	59.81627 494	94.68686 912
23.0	60.21598 802	97.37201 953	33.0	59.87581 840	94.62073 639
23.2	60.16658 959	97.32677 153	33.2	59.93876 476	94.55403 353
23.4	60.11785 135	97.28114 703	33.4	60.00513 119	94.48674 785
23.6	60.06983 314	97.23514 577	33.6	60.07493 378	94.41886 593
23.8	60.02259 647	97.18876 747	33.8	60.14818 771	94.35037 358
24.0	59.97620 449	97.14201 177	34.0	60.22490 737	94.28125 585
24.2	59.93072 189	97.09487 826	34.2	60.30510 652	94.21149 691
24.4	59.88621 485	97.04736 646	34.4	60.38879 846	94.14108 008
24.6	59.84275 096	96.99947 583	34.6	60.47599 617	94.06998 772
24.8	59.80039 910	96.95120 577	34.8	60.56671 244	93.99820 123
25.0	59.75922 937	96.90255 557	35.0	60.66096 006	93.92570 093
25.2	59.71931 292	96.85352 448	35.2	60.75875 197	93.85246 608
25.4	59.68072 190	96.80411 164	35.4	60.86010 138	93.77847 474
25.6	59.64352 927	96.75431 611	35.6	60.96502 196	93.70370 376
25.8	59.60780 868	96.70413 685	35.8	61.07352 800	93.62812 867
26.0	59.57363 432	96.65357 273	36.0	61.18563 455	93.55172 362
26.2	59.54108 075	96.60262 251	36.2	61.30135 756	93.47446 131
26.4	59.51022 273	96.55128 483	36.4	61.42071 411	93.39631 286
26.6	59.48113 509	96.49955 823	36.6	61.54372 248	93.31724 775
26.8	59.45389 252	96.44744 110	36.8	61.67040 241	93.23723 371
27.0	59.42856 939	96.39493 173	37.0	61.80077 520	93.15623 660
27.2	59.40523 959	96.34202 824	37.2	61.93486 392	93.07422 028
27.4	59.38397 635	96.28872 864	37.4	62.07269 358	92.99114 652
27.6	59.36485 208	96.23503 075	37.6	62.21429 133	92.90697 480
27.8	59.34793 815	96.18093 225	37.8	62.35968 664	92.82166 221
28.0	59.33330 476	96.12643 065	38.0	62.50891 152	92.73516 325
28.2	59.32102 078	96.07152 326	38.2	62.66200 072	92.64742 967
28.4	59.31115 357	96.01620 722	38.4	62.81899 200	92.55841 027
28.6	59.30376 885	95.96047 947	38.6	62.97992 631	92.46805 064
28.8	59.29893 058	95.90433 673	38.8	63.14484 812	92.37629 301
29.0	59.29670 079	95.84777 549	39.0	63.31380 566	92.28307 589
29.2	59.29713 952	95.79079 204	39.2	63.48685 125	92.18833 388
29.4	59.30030 469	95.73338 240	39.4	63.66404 161	92.09199 727
29.6	59.30625 204	95.67554 232	39.6	63.84543 826	91.99399 175
29.8	59.31503 502	95.61726 731	39.8	64.03110 788	91.89423 800
30.0	59.32670 480	95.55855 258	40.0	64.22112 277	91.79265 127

$$FA(i\rho) = \tfrac{1}{2}(a_r + a_{r+2}), \quad FB(i\rho) = (a_{r+2} - a_r)^2$$

ρ	$a_r(i\rho)$	$a_{r+2}(i\rho)$	$FA(i\rho)$	$FB(i\rho)$
40.0	64.22112 277	91.79265 127	78.00688 702	760.18918 385
40.1	64.31778 394	91.74114 244	78.02946 319	752.04059 153
40.2	64.41556 135	91.68914 088	78.05235 112	743.84814 083
40.3	64.51446 582	91.63663 424	78.07555 003	735.61201 984
40.4	64.61450 867	91.58360 973	78.09905 920	727.33241 241
40.5	64.71570 165	91.53005 411	78.12287 788	719.00949 819
40.6	64.81805 703	91.47595 366	78.14700 535	710.64345 249
40.7	64.92158 760	91.42129 414	78.17144 087	702.23444 634
40.8	65.02630 668	91.36606 079	78.19618 373	693.78264 636
40.9	65.13222 816	91.31023 830	78.22123 323	685.28821 479
41.0	65.23936 653	91.25381 077	78.24658 865	676.75130 944
41.1	65.34773 689	91.19676 170	78.27224 930	668.17208 362
41.2	65.45735 503	91.13907 394	78.29821 449	659.55068 617
41.3	65.56823 740	91.08072 966	78.32448 353	650.88726 139
41.4	65.68040 117	91.02171 032	78.35105 574	642.18194 903
41.5	65.79386 431	90.96199 662	78.37793 047	633.43488 424
41.6	65.90864 556	90.90156 851	78.40510 703	624.64619 761
41.7	66.02476 451	90.84040 505	78.43258 478	615.81601 505
41.8	66.14224 168	90.77849 445	78.46036 306	606.94445 786
41.9	66.26109 849	90.71578 398	78.48844 123	598.03164 268
42.0	66.38135 738	90.65227 993	78.51681 866	589.07768 142
42.1	66.50304 186	90.58794 753	78.54549 470	580.08268 135
42.2	66.62617 654	90.52276 092	78.57446 873	571.04674 498
42.3	66.75078 724	90.45669 304	78.60374 014	561.96997 011
42.4	66.87690 102	90.38971 561	78.63330 831	552.85244 978
42.5	67.00454 630	90.32179 898	78.66317 264	543.69427 229
42.6	67.13375 293	90.25291 211	78.69333 252	534.49552 116
42.7	67.26455 227	90.18302 245	78.72378 736	525.25627 514
42.8	67.39697 732	90.11209 581	78.75453 657	515.97660 819
42.9	67.53106 281	90.04009 632	78.78557 956	506.65658 946
43.0	67.66684 532	89.96698 620	78.81691 576	497.29628 333
43.1	67.80436 345	89.89272 575	78.84854 460	487.89574 932
43.2	67.94365 790	89.81727 311	78.88046 550	478.45504 218
43.3	68.08477 170	89.74059 412	78.91267 791	468.97421 180
43.4	68.22775 033	89.66261 220	78.94518 127	459.45330 326
43.5	68.37264 196	89.58330 807	78.97797 502	449.89235 679
43.6	68.51949 763	89.50261 961	79.01105 862	440.29140 782
43.7	68.66837 150	89.42049 155	79.04443 153	430.65048 688
43.8	68.81932 110	89.33686 530	79.07809 320	420.96961 972
43.9	68.97240 767	89.25167 854	79.11204 311	411.24882 719
44.0	69.12769 642	89.16486 502	79.14628 072	401.48812 533
44.1	69.28525 695	89.07635 407	79.18080 551	391.68752 531
44.2	69.44516 362	88.98607 029	79.21561 696	381.84703 347
44.3	69.60749 606	88.89393 304	79.25071 455	371.96665 126
44.4	69.77233 963	88.79985 590	79.28609 776	362.04637 533
44.5	69.93978 606	88.70374 613	79.32176 610	352.08619 743
44.6	70.10993 411	88.60550 397	79.35771 904	342.08610 449
44.7	70.28289 032	88.50502 188	79.39395 610	332.04607 859
44.8	70.45876 988	88.40218 363	79.43047 676	321.96609 693
44.9	70.63769 770	88.29686 336	79.46728 053	311.84613 190
45.0	70.81980 949	88.18892 435	79.50436 692	301.68615 102

TABLE III. $a_r(i\rho)$, $a_{r+2}(i\rho)$ and Auxiliary Functions $\qquad r = 8$
$$FA(i\rho) = \tfrac{1}{2}(a_r + a_{r+2}), \quad FB(i\rho) = (a_{r+2} - a_r)^2$$

ρ	$a_r(i\rho)$	$a_{r+2}(i\rho)$	$FA(i\rho)$	$FB(i\rho)$
45.0	70.81980 949	88.18892 435	79.50436 692	301.68615 102
45.1	71.00525 318	88.07821 768	79.54173 543	291.48611 696
45.2	71.19419 048	87.96458 068	79.57938 558	281.24598 756
45.3	71.38679 874	87.84783 503	79.61731 688	270.96571 580
45.4	71.58327 313	87.72778 457	79.65552 885	260.64524 985
45.5	71.78382 927	87.60421 274	79.69402 100	250.28453 300
45.6	71.98870 635	87.47687 937	79.73279 286	239.88350 373
45.7	72.19817 086	87.34551 702	79.77184 394	229.44209 569
45.8	72.41252 124	87.20982 632	79.81117 378	218.96023 768
45.9	72.63209 340	87.06947 037	79.85078 188	208.43785 368
46.0	72.85726 778	86.92406 781	79.89066 780	197.87486 284
46.1	73.08847 801	86.77318 406	79.93083 104	187.27117 950
46.2	73.32622 198	86.61632 029	79.97127 113	176.62671 314
46.3	73.57107 603	86.45289 921	80.01198 762	165.94136 848
46.4	73.82371 351	86.28224 654	80.05298 002	155.21504 536
46.5	74.08492 931	86.10356 645	80.09424 788	144.44763 886
46.6	74.35567 309	85.91590 834	80.13579 072	133.63903 921
46.7	74.63709 519	85.71812 094	80.17760 806	122.78913 186
46.8	74.93061 170	85.50878 722	80.21969 946	111.89779 744
46.9	75.23799 955	85.28612 931	80.26206 443	100.96491 177
47.0	75.56154 044	85.04786 459	80.30470 251	89.99034 589
47.1	75.90424 835	84.79097 812	80.34761 323	78.97396 603
47.2	76.27024 903	84.51134 323	80.39079 613	67.91563 362
47.3	76.66545 763	84.20304 381	80.43425 072	56.81520 531
47.4	77.09890 371	83.85704 939	80.47797 655	45.67253 295
47.5	77.58567 174	83.45827 454	80.52197 314	34.48746 361
47.6	78.15481 722	82.97766 281	80.56624 001	23.25983 957
47.7	78.87948 396	82.34206 946	80.61077 671	11.98949 833
47.8	80.24440 376	81.06676 172	80.65558 274	0.67627 260

At $\rho = 47.80596570$

$a_8(i\rho) = a_{10}(i\rho) = 80.65826424$

(to 8D)

TABLE III. $a_r(i\rho)$, $a_{r+2}(i\rho)$ and Auxiliary Functions $\qquad r=8$
$$a_r(i\rho) = U+iV, \; a_{r+2}(i\rho) = U-iV, \; FB(i\rho) = (a_{r+2}-a_r)^2$$

ρ	U	V		$FB(i\rho)$
47.9	80.70065 764	-1.63401 420		-10.68000 967
48.0	80.74600 092	-2.34944 277		-22.07952 531
48.1	80.79161 211	-2.89492 901		-33.52245 595
48.2	80.83749 072	-3.35443 691		-45.00898 797
48.3	80.88363 628	-3.75963 138		-56.53931 250
48.4	80.93004 829	-4.12654 897		-68.11362 548
48.5	80.97672 626	-4.46464 242		-79.73212 759
48.6	81.02366 971	-4.78003 725		-91.39502 428
48.7	81.07087 814	-5.07697 070		-103.10252 576
48.8	81.11835 105	-5.35851 768		-114.85484 701
48.9	81.16608 795	-5.62699 315		-126.65220 775
49.0	81.21408 833	-5.88419 137		-138.49483 249
49.1	81.26235 168	-6.13153 632		-150.38295 046
49.2	81.31087 749	-6.37018 045		-162.31679 566
49.3	81.35966 526	-6.60107 201		-174.29660 685
49.4	81.40871 446	-6.82500 234		-186.32262 753
49.5	81.45802 457	-7.04263 988		-198.39510 595
49.6	81.50759 507	-7.25455 538		-210.51429 512
49.7	81.55742 543	-7.46124 073		-222.68045 279
49.8	81.60751 511	-7.66312 341		-234.89384 146
49.9	81.65786 357	-7.86057 772		-247.15472 835
50.0	81.70847 028	-8.05393 360		-259.46338 547
50.1	81.75933 467	-8.24348 363		-271.82008 952
50.2	81.81045 621	-8.42948 874		-284.22512 198
50.3	81.86183 433	-8.61218 278		-296.67876 905
50.4	81.91346 847	-8.79177 629		-309.18132 166
50.5	81.96535 806	-8.96845 967		-321.73307 550
50.6	82.01750 252	-9.14240 574		-334.33433 098
50.7	82.06990 127	-9.31377 197		-346.98539 323
50.8	82.12255 374	-9.48270 231		-359.68657 213
50.9	82.17545 931	-9.64932 876		-372.43818 229
51.0	82.22861 741	-9.81377 276		-385.24054 302
51.1	82.28202 742	-9.97614 628		-398.09397 838
51.2	82.33568 873	-10.13655 288		-410.99881 715
51.3	82.38960 072	-10.29508 855		-423.95539 282
51.4	82.44376 276	-10.45184 246		-436.96404 361
51.5	82.49817 424	-10.60689 767		-450.02511 244
51.6	82.55283 450	-10.76033 163		-463.13894 695
51.7	82.60774 290	-10.91221 677		-476.30589 949
51.8	82.66289 878	-11.06262 093		-489.52632 711
51.9	82.71830 149	-11.21160 773		-502.80059 157
52.0	82.77395 036	-11.35923 698		-516.12905 933

ρ	U	V	ρ	U	V
52.0	82.77395 036	−11.35923 698	57.0	85.85272 385	−17.75606 900
52.1	82.82984 471	−11.50556 497	57.2	85.98709 673	−17.99002 170
52.2	82.88598 385	−11.65064 477	57.4	86.12225 286	−18.23316 770
52.3	82.94236 710	−11.79452 646	57.6	86.25818 181	−18.45557 012
52.4	82.99899 374	−11.93725 740	57.8	86.39487 291	−18.68728 918
52.5	83.05586 307	−12.07888 242	58.0	86.53231 529	−18.91838 241
52.6	93.11297 438	−12.21944 401	58.2	86.67049 778	−19.14890 484
52.7	83.17032 693	−12.35898 249	58.4	86.80940 902	−19.37890 912
52.8	83.22791 999	−12.49753 617	58.6	86.94903 739	−19.60844 568
52.9	83.28575 281	−12.63514 149	58.8	87.08937 103	−19.83756 285
53.0	83.34382 464	−12.77183 315	59.0	87.23039 784	−20.06630 696
53.1	83.40213 471	−12.90764 422	59.2	87.37210 547	−20.29472 247
53.2	83.46068 225	−13.04260 625	59.4	87.51448 136	−20.52285 206
53.3	83.51946 648	−13.17674 939	59.6	87.65751 268	−20.75073 671
53.4	83.57848 661	−13.31010 245	59.8	87.80118 638	−20.97841 577
53.5	83.63774 183	−13.44269 300	60.0	87.94548 918	−21.20592 704
53.6	83.69723 132	−13.57454 744	60.2	88.09040 757	−21.43330 687
53.7	83.75695 427	−13.70569 107	60.4	88.23592 781	−21.66059 015
53.8	83.81690 985	−13.83614 819	60.6	88.38203 593	−21.88781 042
53.9	83.87709 719	−13.96594 208	60.8	88.52871 777	−22.11499 993
54.0	83.93751 547	−14.09509 515	61.0	88.67595 894	−22.34218 961
54.1	83.99816 379	−14.22362 893	61.2	88.82374 484	−22.56940 921
54.2	84.05904 130	−14.35156 413	61.4	88.97206 069	−22.79668 728
54.3	84.12014 710	−14.47892 070	61.6	89.12089 149	−23.02405 120
54.4	84.18148 028	−14.60571 785	61.8	89.27022 210	−23.25152 725
54.5	84.24303 995	−14.73197 413	62.0	89.42003 717	−23.47914 061
54.6	84.30482 518	−14.85770 740	62.2	89.57032 119	−23.70691 542
54.7	84.36683 503	−14.98293 492	62.4	89.72105 851	−23.93487 475
54.8	84.42906 856	−15.10767 337	62.6	89.87223 332	−24.16304 070
54.9	84.49152 481	−15.23193 885	62.8	90.02382 968	−24.39143 435
55.0	84.55420 281	−15.35574 696	63.0	90.17583 154	−24.62007 582
55.1	84.61710 158	−15.47911 275	63.2	90.32822 272	−24.84898 428
55.2	84.68022 012	−15.60205 084	63.4	90.48098 696	−25.07817 798
55.3	84.74355 743	−15.72457 535	63.6	90.63410 791	−25.30767 424
55.4	84.80711 249	−15.84670 000	63.8	90.78756 913	−25.53748 950
55.5	84.87088 425	−15.96843 805	64.0	90.94135 417	−25.76763 930
55.6	84.93487 169	−16.08980 240	64.2	91.09544 650	−25.99813 834
55.7	84.99907 374	−16.21080 556	64.4	91.24982 958	−26.22900 045
55.8	85.06348 932	−16.33145 967	64.6	91.40448 685	−26.46023 863
55.9	85.12811 736	−16.45177 651	64.8	91.55940 178	−26.69186 504
56.0	85.19295 675	−16.57176 757	65.0	91.71455 784	−26.92389 108
56.1	85.25800 639	−16.69144 397	65.2	91.86993 855	−27.15632 730
56.2	85.32326 515	−16.81081 656	65.4	92.02552 747	−27.38918 350
56.3	85.38873 188	−16.92989 588	65.6	92.18130 827	−27.62246 872
56.4	85.45440 544	−17.04869 219	65.8	92.33726 466	−27.85619 124
56.5	85.52028 467	−17.16721 550	66.0	92.49338 051	−28.09035 861
56.6	85.58636 837	−17.28547 552	66.2	92.64963 977	−28.32497 764
56.7	85.65265 535	−17.40348 176	66.4	92.80602 655	−28.56005 445
56.8	85.71914 441	−17.52124 344	66.6	92.96252 513	−28.79559 448
56.9	85.78583 433	−17.63876 959	66.8	93.11911 993	−29.03160 248
57.0	85.85272 385	−17.75606 900	67.0	93.27579 560	−29.26808 254

ρ	U	V	ρ	U	V
67.0	93.27579 560	−29.26808 254	77.0	100.96306 474	−41.65234 688
67.2	93.43253 698	−29.50503 813	77.5	101.33222 915	−42.29436 969
67.4	93.58932 911	−29.74247 209	78.0	101.69970 292	−42.93788 560
67.6	93.74615 731	−29.98038 663	78.5	102.06550 434	−43.58281 869
67.8	93.90300 712	−30.21878 340	79.0	102.42965 635	−44.22909 838
68.0	94.05986 437	−30.45766 347	79.5	102.79218 575	−44.87665 953
68.2	94.21671 515	−30.69702 738	80.0	103.15312 246	−45.52544 232
68.4	94.37354 585	−30.93687 510	80.5	103.51249 885	−46.17539 217
68.6	94.53034 317	−31.17720 613	81.0	103.87034 909	−46.82645 960
68.8	94.68709 413	−31.41801 946	81.5	104.22670 866	−47.47859 993
69.0	94.84378 606	−31.65931 361	82.0	104.58161 381	−48.13177 314
69.2	95.00040 665	−31.90108 665	82.5	104.93510 113	−48.78594 354
69.4	95.15694 393	−32.14333 622	83.0	105.28720 723	−49.44107 952
69.6	95.31338 626	−32.38605 956	83.5	105.63796 836	−50.09715 323
69.8	95.46972 241	−32.62925 353	84.0	105.98742 020	−50.75414 035
70.0	95.62594 147	−32.87291 459	84.5	106.33559 756	−51.41201 974
70.2	95.78203 295	−33.11703 889	85.0	106.68253 429	−52.07077 318
70.4	95.93798 671	−33.36162 224	85.5	107.02826 305	−52.73038 508
70.6	96.09379 299	−33.60666 016	86.0	107.37281 524	−53.39084 225
70.8	96.24944 245	−33.85214 786	86.5	107.71622 092	−54.05213 358
71.0	96.40492 610	−34.09808 033	87.0	108.05850 874	−54.71424 987
71.2	96.56023 536	−34.34445 228	87.5	108.39970 591	−55.37718 356
71.4	96.71536 205	−34.59125 821	88.0	108.73983 816	−56.04092 851
71.6	96.87029 835	−34.83849 245	88.5	109.07892 980	−56.70547 986
71.8	97.02503 685	−35.08614 910	89.0	109.41700 368	−57.37083 376
72.0	97.17957 053	−35.33422 214	89.5	109.75408 125	−58.03698 731
72.2	97.33389 273	−35.58270 538	90.0	110.09018 258	−58.70393 829
72.4	97.48799 719	−35.83159 252	90.5	110.42532 642	−59.37168 514
72.6	97.64187 803	−36.08087 713	91.0	110.75953 026	−60.04022 672
72.8	97.79552 972	−36.33055 272	91.5	111.09281 036	−60.70956 232
73.0	97.94894 712	−36.58061 271	92.0	111.42518 184	−61.37969 144
73.2	98.10212 541	−36.83105 047	92.5	111.75665 871	−62.05061 378
73.4	98.25506 017	−37.08185 930	93.0	112.08725 397	−62.72232 916
73.6	98.40774 729	−37.33303 252	93.5	112.41697 968	−63.39483 741
73.8	98.56018 301	−37.58456 340	94.0	112.74584 697	−64.06813 834
74.0	98.71236 390	−37.83644 522	94.5	113.07386 617	−64.74223 169
74.2	98.86428 684	−38.08867 127	95.0	113.40104 683	−65.41711 709
74.4	99.01594 905	−38.34124 488	95.5	113.72739 780	−66.09279 401
74.6	99.16734 801	−38.59412 940	96.0	114.05292 731	−66.76926 175
74.8	99.31848 153	−38.84734 822	96.5	114.37764 297	−67.44651 941
75.0	99.46934 769	−39.10088 482	97.0	114.70155 188	−68.12456 588
75.2	99.61994 484	−39.35473 271	97.5	115.02466 066	−68.80339 981
75.4	99.77027 159	−39.60888 549	98.0	115.34697 549	−69.48301 961
75.6	99.92032 682	−39.86333 686	98.5	115.66850 218	−70.16342 348
75.8	100.07010 965	−40.11808 058	99.0	115.98924 619	−70.84460 935
76.0	100.21961 942	−40.37311 053	99.5	116.30921 270	−71.52657 492
76.2	100.36885 571	−40.62842 069	100.0	116.62840 660	−72.20931 766
76.4	100.51781 830	−40.88400 514			
76.6	100.66650 718	−41.13985 809			
76.8	100.81492 254	−41.39597 385			
77.0	100.96306 474	−41.65234 688			

ρ	$a_r(i\rho)$	$a_{r+2}(i\rho)$	ρ	$a_r(i\rho)$	$a_{r+2}(i\rho)$
0.0	144.00000 000	196.00000 000	25.0	141.83574 314	194.40576 736
0.5	143.99912 588	195.99935 898	25.5	141.74916 786	194.34170 493
1.0	143.99650 355	195.99743 592	26.0	141.66094 540	194.27640 104
1.5	143.99213 315	195.99423 088	26.5	141.57107 960	194.20985 724
2.0	143.98601 487	195.98974 394	27.0	141.47957 435	194.14207 509
2.5	143.97814 902	195.98397 521	27.5	141.38643 366	194.07305 617
3.0	143.96853 596	195.97692 483	28.0	141.29166 159	194.00280 211
3.5	143.95717 615	195.96859 299	28.5	141.19526 232	193.93131 455
4.0	143.94407 014	195.95897 990	29.0	141.09724 013	193.85859 514
4.5	143.92921 854	195.94808 580	29.5	140.99759 939	193.78464 558
5.0	143.91262 205	195.93591 097	30.0	140.89634 460	193.70946 757
5.5	143.89428 148	195.92245 571	30.5	140.79348 039	193.63306 285
6.0	143.87419 767	195.90772 036	31.0	140.68901 154	193.55543 317
6.5	143.85237 159	195.89170 530	31.5	140.58294 295	193.47658 031
7.0	143.82880 425	195.87441 093	32.0	140.47527 972	193.39650 607
7.5	143.80349 679	195.85583 768	32.5	140.36602 714	193.31521 227
8.0	143.77645 038	195.83598 603	33.0	140.25519 068	193.23270 075
8.5	143.74766 629	195.81485 648	33.5	140.14277 607	193.14897 337
9.0	143.71714 589	195.79244 955	34.0	140.02878 929	193.06403 201
9.5	143.68489 060	195.76876 580	34.5	139.91323 660	192.97787 859
10.0	143.65090 192	195.74380 585	35.0	139.79612 460	192.89051 501
10.5	143.61518 144	195.71757 030	35.5	139.67746 023	192.80194 321
11.0	143.57773 084	195.69005 982	36.0	139.55725 085	192.71216 517
11.5	143.53855 184	195.66127 509	36.5	139.43550 425	192.62118 284
12.0	143.49764 626	195.63121 684	37.0	139.31222 875	192.52899 823
12.5	143.45501 600	195.59988 582	37.5	139.18743 321	192.43561 334
13.0	143.41066 303	195.56728 280	38.0	139.06112 714	192.34103 020
13.5	143.36458 939	195.53340 860	38.5	138.93332 075	192.24525 084
14.0	143.31679 718	195.49826 407	39.0	138.80402 503	192.14827 731
14.5	143.26728 861	195.46185 006	39.5	138.67325 186	192.05011 169
15.0	143.21606 592	195.42416 750	40.0	138.54101 409	191.95075 604
15.5	143.16313 146	195.38521 730	40.5	138.40732 567	191.85021 246
16.0	143.10848 762	195.34500 043	41.0	138.27220 178	191.74848 303
16.5	143.05213 689	195.30351 789	41.5	138.13565 895	191.64556 987
17.0	142.99408 179	195.26077 069	42.0	137.99771 521	191.54147 508
17.5	142.93432 495	195.21675 989	42.5	137.85839 028	191.43620 077
18.0	142.87286 905	195.17148 657	43.0	137.71770 574	191.32974 906
18.5	142.80971 682	195.12495 183	43.5	137.57568 524	191.22212 207
19.0	142.74487 109	195.07715 682	44.0	137.43235 470	191.11332 192
19.5	142.67833 474	195.02810 269	44.5	137.28774 258	191.00335 071
20.0	142.61011 070	194.97779 065	45.0	137.14188 014	190.89221 054
20.5	142.54020 201	194.92622 191	45.5	136.99480 172	190.77990 351
21.0	142.46861 172	194.87339 773	46.0	136.84654 506	190.66643 169
21.5	142.39534 299	194.81931 938	46.5	136.69715 165	190.55179 715
22.0	142.32039 903	194.76398 817	47.0	136.54666 709	190.43600 192
22.5	142.24378 310	194.70740 544	47.5	136.39514 150	190.31904 802
23.0	142.16549 854	194.64957 253	48.0	136.24262 997	190.20093 742
23.5	142.08554 876	194.59049 085	48.5	136.08919 299	190.08167 206
24.0	142.00393 723	194.53016 179	49.0	135.93489 701	189.96125 385
24.5	141.92066 749	194.46858 681	49.5	135.77981 494	189.83968 463
25.0	141.83574 314	194.40576 736	50.0	135.62402 673	189.71696 618

ρ	$a_r(i\rho)$	$a_{r+2}(i\rho)$	ρ	$a_r(i\rho)$	$a_{r+2}(i\rho)$
50.0	135.62402 673	189.71696 618	75.0	132.33987 556	182.06125 399
50.5	135.46761 999	189.59310 023	75.2	132.41263 700	181.98539 468
51.0	135.31069 066	189.46808 842	75.4	132.48783 762	181.90918 061
51.5	135.15334 368	189.34193 231	75.6	132.56548 543	181.83260 469
52.0	134.99569 369	189.21463 335	75.8	132.64558 824	181.75565 956
52.5	134.83786 584	189.08619 290	76.0	132.72815 364	181.67833 756
53.0	134.67999 652	188.95661 218	76.2	132.81318 910	181.60063 076
53.5	134.52223 420	188.82589 227	76.4	132.90070 195	181.52253 092
54.0	134.36474 023	188.69403 410	76.6	132.99069 946	181.44402 950
54.5	134.20768 970	188.56103 843	76.8	133.08318 881	181.36511 759
55.0	134.05127 227	188.42690 581	77.0	133.17817 718	181.28578 599
55.5	133.89569 297	188.29163 658	77.2	133.27567 174	181.20602 511
56.0	133.74117 305	188.15523 085	77.4	133.37567 974	181.12582 502
56.5	133.58795 070	188.01768 846	77.6	133.47820 846	181.04517 537
57.0	133.43628 179	187.87900 895	77.8	133.58326 532	180.96406 545
57.5	133.28644 049	187.73919 151	78.0	133.69085 788	180.88248 410
58.0	133.13871 977	187.59823 502	78.2	133.80099 388	180.80041 975
58.5	132.99343 187	187.45613 791	78.4	133.91368 127	180.71786 037
59.0	132.85090 852	187.31289 820	78.6	134.02892 827	180.63479 345
59.5	132.71150 102	187.16851 341	78.8	134.14674 336	180.55120 601
60.0	132.57558 019	187.02298 052	79.0	134.26713 537	180.46708 454
60.5	132.44353 595	186.87629 594	79.2	134.39011 348	180.38241 501
61.0	132.31577 680	186.72845 540	79.4	134.51568 728	180.29718 281
61.5	132.19272 892	186.57945 394	79.6	134.64386 677	180.21137 276
62.0	132.07483 508	186.42928 581	79.8	134.77466 247	180.12496 908
62.5	131.96255 314	186.27794 440	80.0	134.90808 539	180.03795 534
63.0	131.85635 436	186.12542 216	80.2	135.04414 712	179.95031 445
63.5	131.75672 131	185.97171 049	80.4	135.18285 983	179.86202 863
64.0	131.66414 563	185.81679 967	80.6	135.32423 637	179.77307 935
64.5	131.57912 538	185.66067 873	80.8	135.46829 026	179.68344 733
65.0	131.50216 228	185.50333 535	81.0	135.61503 576	179.59311 250
65.5	131.43375 872	185.34475 571	81.2	135.76448 793	179.50205 394
66.0	131.37441 468	185.18492 437	81.4	135.91666 267	179.41024 984
66.5	131.32462 457	185.02382 410	81.6	136.07157 676	179.31767 748
67.0	131.28487 407	184.86143 572	81.8	136.22924 794	179.22431 318
67.5	131.25563 708	184.69773 793	82.0	136.38969 494	179.13013 221
68.0	131.23737 282	184.53270 711	82.2	136.55293 757	179.03510 878
68.5	131.23052 314	184.36631 707	82.4	136.71899 676	178.93921 600
69.0	131.23551 013	184.19853 888	82.6	136.88789 462	178.84242 575
69.5	131.25273 412	184.02934 055	82.8	137.05965 455	178.74470 868
70.0	131.28257 202	183.85868 679	83.0	137.23430 128	178.64603 411
70.5	131.32537 612	183.68653 866	83.2	137.41186 094	178.54636 998
71.0	131.38147 340	183.51285 331	83.4	137.59236 118	178.44568 273
71.5	131.45116 519	183.33758 354	83.6	137.77583 123	178.34393 728
72.0	131.53472 743	183.16067 742	83.8	137.96230 201	178.24109 687
72.5	131.63241 127	182.98207 787	84.0	138.15180 623	178.13712 302
73.0	131.74444 415	182.80172 216	84.2	138.34437 847	178.03197 536
73.5	131.87103 125	182.61954 138	84.4	138.54005 534	177.92561 161
74.0	132.01235 728	182.43545 984	84.6	138.73887 559	177.81798 737
74.5	132.16858 860	182.24939 445	84.8	138.94088 023	177.70905 601
75.0	132.33987 556	182.06125 399	85.0	139.14611 269	177.59876 858

ρ	$a_r(i\rho)$	$a_{r+2}(i\rho)$	$FA(i\rho)$	$FB(i\rho)$
85.0	139.14611 269	177.59876 858	158.37244 063	1478.60674 477
85.2	139.35461 897	177.48707 357	158.42084 627	1454.08409 322
85.4	139.56644 783	177.37391 680	158.47018 232	1429.40470 981
85.6	139.78165 095	177.25924 123	158.52044 609	1404.56977 355
85.8	140.00028 313	177.14298 673	158.57163 493	1379.58043 097
86.0	140.22240 254	177.02508 989	158.62374 622	1354.43779 566
86.2	140.44807 096	176.90548 375	158.67677 735	1329.14294 772
86.4	140.67735 398	176.78409 758	158.73072 578	1303.69693 336
86.6	140.91032 139	176.66085 656	158.78558 897	1278.10076 443
86.8	141.14704 742	176.53568 144	158.84136 443	1252.35541 805
87.0	141.38761 111	176.40848 826	158.89804 968	1226.46183 619
87.2	141.63209 672	176.27918 788	158.95564 230	1200.42092 539
87.4	141.88059 415	176.14768 560	159.01413 988	1174.23355 635
87.6	142.13319 941	176.01388 068	159.07354 005	1147.90056 367
87.8	142.39001 514	175.87766 578	159.13384 046	1121.42274 555
88.0	142.65115 125	175.73892 639	159.19503 882	1094.80086 352
88.2	142.91672 555	175.59754 014	159.25713 284	1068.03564 218
88.4	143.18686 449	175.45337 606	159.32012 027	1041.12776 896
88.6	143.46170 404	175.30629 375	159.38399 890	1014.07789 396
88.8	143.74139 063	175.15614 241	159.44876 652	986.88662 965
89.0	144.02608 221	175.00275 974	159.51442 098	959.55455 076
89.2	144.31594 954	174.84597 074	159.58096 014	932.08219 408
89.4	144.61117 754	174.68558 624	159.64838 189	904.47005 830
89.6	144.91196 696	174.52140 133	159.71668 414	876.71860 383
89.8	145.21853 623	174.35319 347	159.78586 485	848.82825 272
90.0	145.53112 364	174.18072 029	159.85592 196	820.79938 849
90.2	145.84998 987	174.00371 708	159.92685 348	792.63235 601
90.4	146.17542 097	173.82189 383	159.99865 740	764.32746 141
90.6	146.50773 184	173.63493 170	160.07133 177	735.88497 197
90.8	146.84727 037	173.44247 889	160.14487 463	707.30511 604
91.0	147.19442 241	173.24414 569	160.21928 405	678.58808 291
91.2	147.54961 774	173.03949 853	160.29455 813	649.73402 281
91.4	147.91333 724	172.82805 271	160.37069 497	620.74304 677
91.6	148.28612 180	172.60926 359	160.44769 270	591.61522 655
91.8	148.66858 319	172.38251 570	160.52554 944	562.35059 466
92.0	149.06141 770	172.14710 903	160.60426 337	532.94914 420
92.2	149.46542 333	171.90224 193	160.68383 263	503.41082 890
92.4	149.88152 179	171.64698 901	160.76425 540	473.73556 300
92.6	150.31078 711	171.38027 265	160.84552 988	443.92322 125
92.8	150.75448 318	171.10082 533	160.92765 426	413.97363 886
93.0	151.21411 446	170.80713 902	161.01062 674	383.88661 148
93.2	151.69149 527	170.49739 581	161.09444 554	353.66189 511
93.4	152.18884 739	170.16937 036	161.17910 887	323.29920 614
93.6	152.70894 110	169.82028 883	161.26461 496	292.79822 129
93.8	153.25530 614	169.44661 794	161.35096 204	262.15857 755
94.0	153.83256 038	169.04373 628	161.43814 833	231.37987 223
94.2	154.44694 782	168.60539 629	161.52617 205	200.46166 286
94.4	155.10727 709	168.12278 581	161.61503 145	169.40346 723
94.6	155.82669 865	167.58275 085	161.70472 475	138.20476 332
94.8	156.62647 398	166.96402 636	161.79525 017	106.86498 930
95.0	157.54542 109	166.22779 078	161.88660 594	75.38354 354

ρ	$a_r(i\rho)$	$a_{r+2}(i\rho)$	$FA(i\rho)$	$FB(i\rho)$
95.0	157.54542 109	166.22779 078	161.88660 594	75.38354 354
95.1	158.07288 303	165.79230 625	161.93259 464	59.58949 485
95.2	158.67123 132	165.28634 920	161.97879 026	43.75978 454
95.3	159.38443 860	164.66594 655	162.02519 258	27.89432 621
95.4	160.34025 357	163.80334 915	162.07180 136	11.99303 094

At ρ = 95.47527271

$a_{12}(i\rho) = a_{14}(i\rho) = 162.10702112$

(to 8D)

ρ	U	V		$FB(i\rho)$
95.5	162.11861 639	−0.99299 958		−3.94419 266
95.6	162.16563 743	−2.23144 788		−19.91743 849
95.7	162.21286 427	−2.99694 857		−35.92680 294
95.8	162.26029 667	−3.60459 377		−51.97238 490
95.9	162.30793 441	−4.12475 108		−68.05428 573
96.0	162.35577 725	−4.58728 158		−84.17260 932
96.1	162.40382 498	−5.00817 986		−100.32746 203
96.2	162.45207 736	−5.39719 725		−116.51895 274
96.3	162.50053 415	−5.76079 840		−132.74719 281
96.4	162.54919 514	−6.10352 964		−149.01229 609
96.5	162.59806 008	−6.42873 197		−165.31437 895
96.6	162.64712 875	−6.73894 577		−181.65356 024
96.7	162.69640 090	−7.03615 593		−198.02996 133
96.8	162.74587 631	−7.32194 827		−214.44370 607
96.9	162.79555 473	−7.59761 345		−230.89492 082
97.0	162.84543 593	−7.86421 856		−247.38373 443
97.1	162.89551 967	−8.12265 779		−263.91027 827
97.2	162.94580 571	−8.37368 924		−280.47468 619
97.3	162.99629 382	−8.61796 227		−297.07709 456
97.4	163.04698 373	−8.85603 808		−313.71764 224
97.5	163.09787 522	−9.08840 567		−330.39647 060
97.6	163.14896 804	−9.31549 413		−347.11372 352
97.7	163.20026 194	−9.53768 247		−363.86954 735
97.8	163.25175 667	−9.75530 741		−380.66409 099
97.9	163.30345 198	−9.96866 974		−397.49750 583
98.0	163.35534 763	−10.17803 942		−414.36994 573
98.1	163.40744 336	−10.38365 985		−431.28156 712
98.2	163.45973 891	−10.58575 138		−448.23252 887
98.3	163.51223 403	−10.78451 427		−465.22299 241
98.4	163.56492 847	−10.98013 117		−482.25312 164
98.5	163.61782 195	−11.17276 916		−499.32308 299
98.6	163.67091 423	−11.36258 163		−516.43304 538
98.7	163.72420 504	−11.54970 974		−533.58318 026
98.8	163.77769 411	−11.73428 376		−550.77366 156
98.9	163.83138 117	−11.91642 423		−568.00466 575
99.0	163.88526 597	−12.09624 293		−585.27637 178
99.1	163.93934 822	−12.27384 375		−602.58896 113
99.2	163.99362 766	−12.44932 345		−619.94261 778
99.3	164.04810 401	−12.62277 236		−637.33752 823
99.4	164.10277 700	−12.79427 491		−654.77388 146
99.5	164.15764 633	−12.96391 018		−672.25186 901
99.6	164.21271 174	−13.13175 240		−689.77168 488
99.7	164.26797 295	−13.29787 131		−707.33352 561
99.8	164.32342 965	−13.46233 255		−724.93759 025
99.9	164.37908 157	−13.62519 798		−742.58408 035
100.0	164.43492 842	−13.78652 603		−760.27319 997

TABLE IV. VALUES OF $b_r(q)$, $b_{r+2}(q)$

And other related functions

$$b_r(q) = U + iV, \qquad b_{r+2}(q) = U - iV$$

$$FA(q) = \tfrac{1}{2}[b_r(q) + b_{r+2}(q)], \qquad FB(q) = [b_{r+2}(q) - b_r(q)]^2$$

$$q = i\rho$$

$$r = 2, 6, 10, 14; \qquad r + 2 = 4, 8, 12, 16$$

ρ	$b_r(i\rho)$	$b_{r+2}(i\rho)$	$FA(i\rho)$	$FB(i\rho)$
0.0	4.00000 000	16.00000 000	10.00000 000	144.00000 000
0.1	4.00083 337	15.99966 663	10.00025 000	143.97199 961
0.2	4.00333 391	15.99866 608	10.00100 000	143.88799 380
0.3	4.00750 293	15.99699 703	10.00224 998	143.74796 861
0.4	4.01334 261	15.99465 726	10.00399 993	143.55190 078
0.5	4.02085 600	15.99164 368	10.00624 984	143.29975 772
0.6	4.03004 705	15.98795 228	10.00899 966	142.99149 753
0.7	4.04092 060	15.98357 814	10.01224 937	142.62706 894
0.8	4.05348 244	15.97851 541	10.01599 893	142.20641 130
0.9	4.06773 925	15.97275 730	10.02024 827	141.72945 457
1.0	4.08369 870	15.96629 603	10.02499 736	141.19611 928
1.1	4.10136 941	15.95912 285	10.03024 613	140.60631 648
1.2	4.12076 104	15.95122 797	10.03599 451	139.95994 771
1.3	4.14188 426	15.94260 056	10.04224 241	139.25690 499
1.4	4.16475 084	15.93322 868	10.04898 976	138.49707 071
1.5	4.18937 363	15.92309 928	10.05623 646	137.68031 762
1.6	4.21576 668	15.91219 813	10.06398 240	136.80650 876
1.7	4.24394 521	15.90050 977	10.07222 749	135.87549 742
1.8	4.27392 571	15.88801 746	10.08097 159	134.88712 705
1.9	4.30572 602	15.87470 312	10.09021 457	133.84123 120
2.0	4.33936 533	15.86054 728	10.09995 631	132.73763 344
2.1	4.37486 432	15.84552 896	10.11019 664	131.57614 732
2.2	4.41224 518	15.82962 562	10.12093 540	130.35657 622
2.3	4.45153 176	15.81281 309	10.13217 243	129.07871 334
2.4	4.49274 965	15.79506 541	10.14390 753	127.74234 157
2.5	4.53592 625	15.77635 477	10.15614 051	126.34723 337
2.6	4.58109 095	15.75665 137	10.16887 116	124.89315 074
2.7	4.62827 524	15.73592 328	10.18209 926	123.37984 506
2.8	4.67751 284	15.71413 629	10.19582 456	121.80705 702
2.9	4.72883 992	15.69125 372	10.21004 682	120.17451 647
3.0	4.78229 522	15.66723 630	10.22476 576	118.48194 234
3.1	4.83792 033	15.64204 188	10.23998 110	116.72904 251
3.2	4.89575 985	15.61562 522	10.25569 254	114.91551 368
3.3	4.95586 172	15.58793 777	10.27189 974	113.04104 123
3.4	5.01827 747	15.55892 731	10.28860 239	111.10529 913
3.5	5.08306 256	15.52853 765	10.30580 011	109.10794 976
3.6	5.15027 679	15.49670 824	10.32349 252	107.04864 379
3.7	5.21998 468	15.46337 377	10.34167 922	104.92702 002
3.8	5.29225 598	15.42846 361	10.36035 980	102.74270 526
3.9	5.36716 623	15.39190 135	10.37953 379	100.49531 414
4.0	5.44479 741	15.35360 405	10.39920 073	98.18444 899
4.1	5.52523 866	15.31348 158	10.41936 012	95.80969 963
4.2	5.60858 713	15.27143 574	10.44001 143	93.37064 327
4.3	5.69494 902	15.22735 922	10.46115 412	90.86684 428
4.4	5.78444 070	15.18113 448	10.48278 759	88.29785 405
4.5	5.87719 013	15.13263 236	10.50491 124	85.66321 081
4.6	5.97333 845	15.08171 039	10.52752 442	82.96243 944
4.7	6.07304 197	15.02821 094	10.55062 645	80.19505 129
4.8	6.17647 448	14.97195 877	10.57421 663	77.36054 400
4.9	6.28383 011	14.91275 828	10.59829 419	74.45840 131
5.0	6.39532 679	14.85038 994	10.62285 836	71.48809 284

TABLE IV. $b_r(i\rho)$, $b_{r+2}(i\rho)$ and Auxiliary Functions $r=2$

$$FA(i\rho) = \tfrac{1}{2}(b_r + b_{r+2}), \quad FB(i\rho) = (b_{r+2} - b_r)^2$$

ρ	$b_r(i\rho)$	$b_{r+2}(i\rho)$	$FA(i\rho)$	$FB(i\rho)$
5.0	6.39532 679	14.85038 994	10.62285 836	71.48809 284
5.1	6.51121 054	14.78460 609	10.64790 832	68.44907 394
5.2	6.63176 082	14.71512 556	10.67344 319	65.34078 544
5.3	6.75729 727	14.64162 688	10.69946 207	62.16265 351
5.4	6.88818 831	14.56373 972	10.72596 402	58.91408 937
5.5	7.02486 242	14.48103 363	10.75294 802	55.59448 917
5.6	7.16782 278	14.39300 332	10.78041 305	52.20323 372
5.7	7.31766 723	14.29904 878	10.80835 801	48.73968 833
5.8	7.47511 540	14.19844 810	10.83678 175	45.20320 255
5.9	7.64104 706	14.09031 911	10.86568 308	41.59310 999
6.0	7.81655 754	13.97356 396	10.89506 075	37.90872 808
6.1	8.00304 086	13.84678 606	10.92491 346	34.14935 789
6.2	8.20231 939	13.70816 028	10.95523 983	30.31428 390
6.3	8.41685 698	13.55521 992	10.98603 845	26.40277 378
6.4	8.65013 238	13.38448 325	11.01730 782	22.41407 816
6.5	8.90735 136	13.19074 142	11.04904 639	18.34743 049
6.6	9.19697 239	12.96553 269	11.08125 254	14.20204 672
6.7	9.53459 520	12.69325 396	11.11392 458	9.97712 521
6.8	9.95627 882	12.33784 268	11.14706 075	5.67184 643
6.9	10.61378 779	11.74753 063	11.18065 921	1.28537 281

At ρ = 6.92895476

$b_2(i\rho) = b_4(i\rho) = 11.19047360$

(to 8D)

TABLE IV. $b_r(i\rho)$, $b_{r+2}(i\rho)$ and Auxiliary Functions $\quad r=2$

$$b_r(i\rho) = U+iV, \; b_{r+2}(i\rho) = U-iV, \; FB(i\rho) = (b_{r+2}-b_r)^2$$

ρ	U	V		$FB(i\rho)$
7.0	11.21471 805	−0.89206 943		−3.18315 146
7.1	11.24923 528	−1.39055 750		−7.73460 064
7.2	11.28420 883	−1.75854 113		−12.36986 763
7.3	11.31963 654	−2.06699 444		−17.08986 411
7.4	11.35551 617	−2.33963 249		−21.89552 078
7.5	11.39184 540	−2.58784 599		−26.78778 745
7.6	11.42862 179	−2.81813 916		−31.76763 327
7.7	11.46584 284	−3.03463 535		−36.83604 683
7.8	11.50350 592	−3.24014 029		−41.99403 631
7.9	11.54160 834	−3.43666 370		−47.24262 961
8.0	11.58014 729	−3.62570 250		−52.58287 447
8.1	11.61911 983	−3.80840 644		−58.01583 854
8.2	11.65852 296	−3.98568 092		−63.54260 950
8.3	11.69835 354	−4.15825 369		−69.16429 513
8.4	11.73860 832	−4.32671 998		−74.88202 331
8.5	11.77928 396	−4.49157 384		−80.69694 213
8.6	11.82037 697	−4.65323 059		−86.61021 985
8.7	11.86188 376	−4.81204 335		−92.62304 490
8.8	11.90380 062	−4.96831 525		−98.73662 588
8.9	11.94612 371	−5.12230 884		−104.95219 148
9.0	11.98884 907	−5.27425 327		−111.27099 043
9.1	12.03197 259	−5.42434 999		−117.69429 136
9.2	12.07549 006	−5.57277 720		−124.22338 271
9.3	12.11939 713	−5.71969 345		−130.85957 254
9.4	12.16368 929	−5.86524 058		−137.60418 836
9.5	12.20836 193	−6.00954 609		−144.45857 691
9.6	12.25341 029	−6.15272 509		−151.42410 390
9.7	12.29882 945	−6.29488 192		−158.50215 371
9.8	12.34461 438	−6.43611 158		−165.69412 908
9.9	12.39075 990	−6.57650 079		−173.00145 075
10.0	12.43726 066	−6.71612 904		−180.42555 706

$$b_r(i\rho) = U + iV, \quad b_{r+2}(i\rho) = U - iV, \quad FB(i\rho) = (b_{r+2} - b_r)^2$$

ρ	U	V		$FB(i\rho)$
10.0	12.43726 066	−6.71612 904		−180.42555 706
10.1	12.48411 122	−6.85506 936		−187.96790 351
10.2	12.53130 594	−6.99338 906		−195.62996 227
10.3	12.57883 908	−7.13115 036		−203.41322 167
10.4	12.62670 473	−7.26841 086		−211.31918 566
10.5	12.67489 685	−7.40522 405		−219.34937 314
10.6	12.72340 924	−7.54163 970		−227.50531 738
10.7	12.77223 557	−7.67770 417		−235.78856 528
10.8	12.82136 937	−7.81346 077		−244.20067 667
10.9	12.87080 403	−7.94894 999		−252.74322 348
11.0	12.92053 279	−8.08420 975		−261.41778 893
11.1	12.97054 876	−8.21927 562		−270.22596 667
11.2	13.02084 492	−8.35418 099		−279.16935 986
11.3	13.07141 412	−8.48895 724		−288.24958 016
11.4	13.12224 906	−8.62363 390		−297.46824 679
11.5	13.17334 234	−8.75823 877		−306.82698 545
11.6	13.22468 643	−8.89279 803		−316.32742 720
11.7	13.27627 368	−9.02733 637		−325.97120 739
11.8	13.32809 633	−9.16187 705		−335.75996 444
11.9	13.38014 651	−9.29644 204		−345.69533 868
12.0	13.43241 626	−9.43105 205		−355.77897 105
12.1	13.48489 749	−9.56572 660		−366.01250 190
12.2	13.53758 207	−9.70048 413		−376.39756 966
12.3	13.59046 174	−9.83534 201		−386.93580 949
12.4	13.64352 818	−9.97031 659		−397.62885 200
12.5	13.69677 302	−10.10542 332		−408.47832 183
12.6	13.75018 779	−10.24067 669		−419.48583 627
12.7	13.80376 399	−10.37609 035		−430.65300 393
12.8	13.85749 306	−10.51167 712		−441.98142 328
12.9	13.91136 643	−10.64744 901		−453.47268 127
13.0	13.96537 547	−10.78341 727		−465.12835 196
13.1	14.01951 154	−10.91959 243		−476.94999 509
13.2	14.07376 599	−11.05598 429		−488.93915 474
13.3	14.12813 016	−11.19260 200		−501.09735 794
13.4	14.18259 543	−11.32945 402		−513.42611 336
13.5	14.23715 316	−11.46654 819		−525.92690 996
13.6	14.29179 475	−11.60389 176		−538.60121 575
13.7	14.34651 164	−11.74149 135		−551.45047 652
13.8	14.40129 533	−11.87935 304		−564.47611 464
13.9	14.45613 736	−12.01748 235		−577.67952 790
14.0	14.51102 934	−12.15588 426		−591.06208 843
14.1	14.56596 296	−12.29456 325		−604.62514 162
14.2	14.62093 001	−12.43352 329		−618.37000 512
14.3	14.67592 235	−12.57276 787		−632.29796 793
14.4	14.73093 197	−12.71230 004		−646.41028 953
14.5	14.78595 096	−12.85212 238		−660.70819 910
14.6	14.84097 155	−12.99223 705		−675.19289 475
14.7	14.89598 608	−13.13264 580		−689.86554 292
14.8	14.95098 706	−13.27334 997		−704.72727 780
14.9	15.00596 713	−13.41435 053		−719.77920 080
15.0	15.06091 908	−13.55564 809		−735.02238 020

ρ	U	V	ρ	U	V
15.0	15.06091 908	−13.55564 809	20.0	17.66988 175	−20.95019 033
15.1	15.11583 589	−13.69724 289	20.2	17.76659 887	−21.25630 933
15.2	15.17071 070	−13.83913 485	20.4	17.86271 581	−21.56298 393
15.3	15.22553 680	−13.98132 357	20.6	17.95824 134	−21.87019 370
15.4	15.28030 771	−14.12380 836	20.8	18.05318 479	−22.17791 936
15.5	15.33501 710	−14.26658 820	21.0	18.14755 600	−22.48614 277
15.6	15.38965 885	−14.40966 185	21.2	18.24136 517	−22.79484 688
15.7	15.44422 704	−14.55302 777	21.4	18.33462 278	−23.10401 570
15.8	15.49871 595	−14.69668 420	21.6	18.42733 954	−23.41363 428
15.9	15.55312 005	−14.84062 913	21.8	18.51952 627	−23.72368 864
16.0	15.60743 403	−14.98486 037	22.0	18.61119 385	−24.03416 575
16.1	15.66165 279	−15.12937 549	22.2	18.70235 315	−24.34505 346
16.2	15.71577 144	−15.27417 189	22.4	18.79301 500	−24.65634 047
16.3	15.76978 530	−15.41924 682	22.6	18.88319 015	−24.96801 629
16.4	15.82368 990	−15.56459 733	22.8	18.97288 917	−25.28007 117
16.5	15.87748 099	−15.71022 035	23.0	19.06212 249	−25.59249 606
16.6	15.93115 452	−15.85611 268	23.2	19.15090 034	−25.90528 257
16.7	15.98470 667	−16.00227 097	23.4	19.23923 271	−26.21842 294
16.8	16.03813 382	−16.14869 180	23.6	19.32712 936	−26.53190 995
16.9	16.09143 255	−16.29537 163	23.8	19.41459 979	−26.84573 694
17.0	16.14459 967	−16.44230 684	24.0	19.50165 324	−27.15989 771
17.1	16.19763 216	−16.58949 373	24.2	19.58829 865	−27.47438 653
17.2	16.25052 724	−16.73692 854	24.4	19.67454 469	−27.78919 808
17.3	16.30328 229	−16.88460 747	24.6	19.76039 974	−28.10432 741
17.4	16.35589 492	−17.03252 667	24.8	19.84587 189	−28.41976 993
17.5	16.40836 290	−17.18068 223	25.0	19.93096 895	−28.73552 137
17.6	16.46068 421	−17.32907 026	25.2	20.01569 843	−29.05157 773
17.7	16.51285 698	−17.47768 682	25.4	20.10006 756	−29.36793 529
17.8	16.56487 955	−17.62652 797	25.6	20.18408 331	−29.68459 057
17.9	16.61675 042	−17.77558 978	25.8	20.26775 235	−30.00154 028
18.0	16.66846 826	−17.92486 831	26.0	20.35108 110	−30.31878 135
18.1	16.72003 188	−18.07435 965	26.2	20.43407 573	−30.63631 088
18.2	16.77144 028	−18.22405 989	26.4	20.51674 213	−30.95412 611
18.3	16.82269 259	−18.37396 517	26.6	20.59908 599	−31.27222 443
18.4	16.87378 809	−18.52407 165	26.8	20.68111 272	−31.59060 336
18.5	16.92472 620	−18.67437 551	27.0	20.76282 755	−31.90926 051
18.6	16.97550 647	−18.82487 300	27.2	20.84423 546	−32.22819 360
18.7	17.02612 860	−18.97556 040	27.4	20.92534 124	−32.54740 043
18.8	17.07659 239	−19.12643 405	27.6	21.00614 947	−32.86687 889
18.9	17.12689 776	−19.27749 032	27.8	21.08666 456	−33.18662 691
19.0	17.17704 476	−19.42872 565	28.0	21.16689 071	−33.50664 249
19.1	17.22703 352	−19.58013 656	28.2	21.24683 199	−33.82692 368
19.2	17.27686 429	−19.73171 960	28.4	21.32649 227	−34.14746 856
19.3	17.32653 742	−19.88347 140	28.6	21.40587 528	−34.46827 526
19.4	17.37605 334	−20.03538 866	28.8	21.48498 460	−34.78934 194
19.5	17.42541 257	−20.18746 813	29.0	21.56382 368	−35.11066 676
19.6	17.47461 569	−20.33970 665	29.2	21.64239 582	−35.43224 794
19.7	17.52366 340	−20.49210 113	29.4	21.72070 422	−35.75408 369
19.8	17.57255 642	−20.64464 852	29.6	21.79875 193	−36.07617 224
19.9	17.62129 559	−20.79734 588	29.8	21.87654 193	−36.39851 183
20.0	17.66988 175	−20.95019 033	30.0	21.95407 707	−36.72110 072

ρ	U	V	ρ	U	V
30.0	21.95407 707	−36.72110 072	40.0	25.55160 504	−53.13089 578
30.2	22.03136 011	−37.04393 716	40.2	25.61869 106	−53.46398 822
30.4	22.10839 370	−37.36701 942	40.4	25.68561 007	−53.79724 738
30.6	22.18518 044	−37.69034 576	40.6	25.75236 327	−54.13067 198
30.8	22.26172 281	−38.01391 446	40.8	25.81895 185	−54.46426 078
31.0	22.33802 324	−38.33772 379	41.0	25.88537 696	−54.79801 252
31.2	22.41408 409	−38.66177 202	41.2	25.95163 979	−55.13192 598
31.4	22.48990 762	−38.98605 744	41.4	26.01774 147	−55.46599 995
31.6	22.56549 606	−39.31057 832	41.6	26.08368 314	−55.80023 324
31.8	22.64085 157	−39.63533 293	41.8	26.14946 594	−56.13462 466
32.0	22.71597 627	−39.96031 956	42.0	26.21509 097	−56.46917 304
32.2	22.79087 219	−40.28553 649	42.2	26.28055 936	−56.80387 723
32.4	22.86554 135	−40.61098 200	42.4	26.34587 219	−57.13873 609
32.6	22.93998 571	−40.93665 437	42.6	26.41103 055	−57.47374 850
32.8	23.01420 718	−41.26255 189	42.8	26.47603 551	−57.80891 335
33.0	23.08820 764	−41.58867 285	43.0	26.54088 814	−58.14422 953
33.2	23.16198 894	−41.91501 555	43.2	26.60558 950	−58.47969 596
33.4	23.23555 287	−42.24157 826	43.4	26.67014 062	−58.81531 157
33.6	23.30890 121	−42.56835 930	43.6	26.73454 254	−59.15107 531
33.8	23.38203 569	−42.89535 698	43.8	26.79879 628	−59.48698 614
34.0	23.45495 804	−43.22256 959	44.0	26.86290 286	−59.82304 301
34.2	23.52766 993	−43.54999 546	44.2	26.92686 327	−60.15924 491
34.4	23.60017 303	−43.87763 292	44.4	26.99067 852	−60.49559 083
34.6	23.67246 895	−44.20548 028	44.6	27.05434 957	−60.83207 978
34.8	23.74455 933	−44.53353 590	44.8	27.11787 741	−61.16871 079
35.0	23.81644 574	−44.86179 811	45.0	27.18126 299	−61.50548 287
35.2	23.88812 974	−45.19026 528	45.2	27.24450 727	−61.84239 507
35.4	23.95961 290	−45.51893 577	45.4	27.30761 119	−62.17944 644
35.6	24.03089 673	−45.84780 796	45.6	27.37057 569	−62.51663 605
35.8	24.10198 275	−46.17688 023	45.8	27.43340 168	−62.85396 297
36.0	24.17287 244	−46.50615 099	46.0	27.49609 008	−63.19142 629
36.2	24.24356 729	−46.83561 863	46.2	27.55864 180	−63.52902 510
36.4	24.31406 875	−47.16528 160	46.4	27.62105 773	−63.86675 853
36.6	24.38437 827	−47.49513 831	46.6	27.68333 875	−64.20462 567
36.8	24.45449 728	−47.82518 721	46.8	27.74548 575	−64.54262 567
37.0	24.52442 718	−48.15542 678	47.0	27.80749 959	−64.88075 766
37.2	24.59416 939	−48.48585 547	47.2	27.86938 113	−65.21902 079
37.4	24.66372 528	−48.81647 179	47.4	27.93113 121	−65.55741 422
37.6	24.73309 624	−49.14727 422	47.6	27.99275 068	−65.89593 711
37.8	24.80228 362	−49.47826 130	47.8	28.05424 038	−66.23458 865
38.0	24.87128 877	−49.80943 154	48.0	28.11560 112	−66.57336 803
38.2	24.94011 301	−50.14078 350	48.2	28.17683 372	−66.91227 443
38.4	25.00875 769	−50.47231 574	48.4	28.23793 898	−67.25130 706
38.6	25.07722 409	−50.80402 682	48.6	28.29891 771	−67.59046 514
38.8	25.14551 354	−51.13591 535	48.8	28.35977 069	−67.92974 788
39.0	25.21362 729	−51.46797 992	49.0	28.42049 871	−68.26915 453
39.2	25.28156 664	−51.80021 916	49.2	28.48110 254	−68.60868 432
39.4	25.34933 285	−52.13263 171	49.4	28.54158 294	−68.94833 649
39.6	25.41692 716	−52.46521 622	49.6	28.60194 067	−69.28811 031
39.8	25.48435 081	−52.79797 134	49.8	28.66217 649	−69.62800 503
40.0	25.55160 504	−53.13089 578	50.0	28.72229 114	−69.96801 993

ρ	U	V	ρ	U	V
50.0	28.72229 114	−69.96801 993	75.0	35.46958 251	−113.23218 082
50.5	28.87205 241	−70.81857 823	75.5	35.59192 770	−114.11000 304
51.0	29.02107 220	−71.66987 210	76.0	35.71386 796	−114.98822 849
51.5	29.16936 149	−72.52189 074	76.5	35.83540 730	−115.86685 321
52.0	29.31693 101	−73.37462 366	77.0	35.95654 963	−116.74587 329
52.5	29.46379 122	−74.22806 060	77.5	36.07729 881	−117.62528 490
53.0	29.60995 231	−75.08219 156	78.0	36.19765 866	−118.50508 425
53.5	29.75542 424	−75.93700 679	78.5	36.31763 292	−119.38526 764
54.0	29.90021 673	−76.79249 677	79.0	36.43722 526	−120.26583 140
54.5	30.04433 925	−77.64865 219	79.5	36.55643 931	−121.14677 193
55.0	30.18780 106	−78.50546 397	80.0	36.67527 864	−122.02808 569
55.5	30.33061 121	−79.36292 321	80.5	36.79374 676	−122.90976 919
56.0	30.47277 852	−80.22102 126	81.0	36.91184 712	−123.79181 900
56.5	30.61431 163	−81.07974 961	81.5	37.02958 313	−124.67423 174
57.0	30.75521 897	−81.93909 997	82.0	37.14695 815	−125.55700 407
57.5	30.89550 878	−82.79906 422	82.5	37.26397 546	−126.44013 272
58.0	31.03518 914	−83.65963 442	83.0	37.38063 833	−127.32361 446
58.5	31.17426 791	−84.52080 279	83.5	37.49694 995	−128.20744 611
59.0	31.31275 283	−85.38256 172	84.0	37.61291 348	−129.09162 453
59.5	31.45065 143	−86.24490 375	84.5	37.72853 203	−129.97614 664
60.0	31.58797 110	−87.10782 160	85.0	37.84380 864	−130.86100 939
60.5	31.72471 908	−87.97130 811	85.5	37.95874 635	−131.74620 980
61.0	31.86090 245	−88.83535 629	86.0	38.07334 812	−132.63174 490
61.5	31.99652 813	−89.69995 927	86.5	38.18761 689	−133.51761 178
62.0	32.13160 293	−90.56511 033	87.0	38.30155 553	−134.40380 759
62.5	32.26613 350	−91.43080 288	87.5	38.41516 689	−135.29032 948
63.0	32.40012 636	−92.29703 045	88.0	38.52845 378	−136.17717 468
63.5	32.53358 790	−93.16378 673	88.5	38.64141 896	−137.06434 044
64.0	32.66652 439	−94.03106 549	89.0	38.75406 515	−137.95182 404
64.5	32.79894 197	−94.89886 065	89.5	38.86639 505	−138.83962 282
65.0	32.93084 666	−95.76716 623	90.0	38.97841 130	−139.72773 415
65.5	33.06224 438	−96.63597 637	90.5	39.09011 652	−140.61615 542
66.0	33.19314 091	−97.50528 532	91.0	39.20151 328	−141.50488 408
66.5	33.32354 196	−98.37508 743	91.5	39.31260 412	−142.39391 760
67.0	33.45345 308	−99.24537 718	92.0	39.42339 156	−143.28325 348
67.5	33.58287 977	−100.11614 912	92.5	39.53387 805	−144.17288 928
68.0	33.71182 739	−100.98739 793	93.0	39.64406 605	−145.06282 256
68.5	33.84030 123	−101.85911 835	93.5	39.75395 795	−145.95305 093
69.0	33.96830 646	−102.73130 525	94.0	39.86355 614	−146.84357 203
69.5	34.09584 816	−103.60395 358	94.5	39.97286 295	−147.73438 354
70.0	34.22293 134	−104.47705 837	95.0	40.08188 069	−148.62548 315
70.5	34.34956 091	−105.35061 476	95.5	40.19061 166	−149.51686 860
71.0	34.47574 167	−106.22461 795	96.0	40.29905 809	−150.40853 764
71.5	34.60147 837	−107.09906 325	96.5	40.40722 221	−151.30048 807
72.0	34.72677 567	−107.97394 603	97.0	40.51510 622	−152.19271 771
72.5	34.85163 812	−108.84926 174	97.5	40.62271 228	−153.08522 440
73.0	34.97607 024	−109.72500 593	98.0	40.73004 252	−153.97800 602
73.5	35.10007 643	−110.60117 422	98.5	40.83709 906	−154.87106 047
74.0	35.22366 103	−111.47776 227	99.0	40.94388 397	−155.76438 568
74.5	35.34682 833	−112.35476 586	99.5	41.05039 933	−156.65797 960
75.0	35.46958 251	−113.23218 082	100.0	41.15664 715	−157.55184 021

ρ	$b_r(i\rho)$	$b_{r+2}(i\rho)$	ρ	$b_r(i\rho)$	$b_{r+2}(i\rho)$
0.0	36.00000 000	64.00000 000	10.0	34.68787 845	63.21271 968
0.2	35.99942 858	63.99968 254	10.2	34.64336 149	63.18115 004
0.4	35.99771 440	63.99873 018	10.4	34.59895 655	63.14897 047
0.6	35.99485 770	63.99714 295	10.6	34.55475 840	63.11618 127
0.8	35.99085 890	63.99492 091	10.8	34.51086 644	63.08278 267
1.0	35.98571 861	63.99206 417	11.0	34.46738 470	63.04877 483
1.2	35.97943 759	63.98857 284	11.2	34.42442 173	63.01415 781
1.4	35.97201 684	63.98444 706	11.4	34.38209 044	62.97893 155
1.6	35.96345 755	63.97968 700	11.6	34.34050 796	62.94309 590
1.8	35.95376 116	63.97429 286	11.8	34.29979 543	62.90665 057
2.0	35.94292 936	63.96826 485	12.0	34.26007 768	62.86959 517
2.2	35.93096 414	63.96160 323	12.2	34.22148 298	62.83192 912
2.4	35.91786 779	63.95430 827	12.4	34.18414 261	62.79365 170
2.6	35.90364 295	63.94638 027	12.6	34.14819 049	62.75476 203
2.8	35.88829 265	63.93781 954	12.8	34.11376 271	62.71525 902
3.0	35.87182 035	63.92862 644	13.0	34.08099 703	62.67514 139
3.2	35.85422 996	63.91880 135	13.2	34.05003 235	62.63440 764
3.4	35.83552 592	63.90834 465	13.4	34.02100 813	62.59305 603
3.6	35.81571 324	63.89725 677	13.6	33.99406 382	62.55108 457
3.8	35.79479 755	63.88553 816	13.8	33.96933 824	62.50849 099
4.0	35.77278 519	63.87318 929	14.0	33.94696 897	62.46527 272
4.2	35.74968 323	63.86021 065	14.2	33.92709 173	62.42142 688
4.4	35.72549 957	63.84660 276	14.4	33.90983 979	62.37695 026
4.6	35.70024 302	63.83236 616	14.6	33.89534 339	62.33183 925
4.8	35.67392 339	63.81750 139	14.8	33.88372 916	62.28608 988
5.0	35.64655 154	63.80200 906	15.0	33.87511 963	62.23969 775
5.2	35.61813 951	63.78588 975	15.2	33.86963 274	62.19265 801
5.4	35.58870 060	63.76914 408	15.4	33.86738 148	62.14496 533
5.6	35.55824 948	63.75177 270	15.6	33.86847 346	62.09661 386
5.8	35.52680 231	63.73377 626	15.8	33.87301 066	62.04759 721
6.0	35.49437 683	63.71515 543	16.0	33.88108 922	61.99790 840
6.2	35.46099 254	63.69591 090	16.2	33.89279 927	61.94753 982
6.4	35.42667 074	63.67604 337	16.4	33.90822 484	61.89648 319
6.6	35.39143 477	63.65555 355	16.6	33.92744 387	61.84472 953
6.8	35.35531 005	63.63444 215	16.8	33.95052 826	61.79226 910
7.0	35.31832 431	63.61270 992	17.0	33.97754 397	61.73909 132
7.2	35.28050 770	63.59035 760	17.2	34.00855 121	61.68518 478
7.4	35.24189 294	63.56738 591	17.4	34.04360 470	61.63053 714
7.6	35.20251 551	63.54379 560	17.6	34.08275 388	61.57513 506
7.8	35.16241 380	63.51958 742	17.8	34.12604 332	61.51896 418
8.0	35.12162 925	63.49476 211	18.0	34.17351 299	61.46200 900
8.2	35.08020 657	63.46932 040	18.2	34.22519 871	61.40425 284
8.4	35.03819 388	63.44326 300	18.4	34.28113 257	61.34567 775
8.6	34.99564 287	63.41659 063	18.6	34.34134 330	61.28626 443
8.8	34.95260 897	63.38930 398	18.8	34.40585 677	61.22599 213
9.0	34.90915 150	63.36140 373	19.0	34.47469 641	61.16483 857
9.2	34.86533 386	63.33289 051	19.2	34.54788 371	61.10277 980
9.4	34.82122 362	63.30376 493	19.4	34.62543 862	61.03979 013
9.6	34.77689 267	63.27402 759	19.6	34.70738 007	60.97584 199
9.8	34.73241 733	63.24367 901	19.8	34.79372 640	60.91090 580
10.0	34.68787 845	63.21271 968	20.0	34.88449 579	60.84494 982

ρ	$b_r(i\rho)$	$b_{r+2}(i\rho)$	$FA(i\rho)$	$FB(i\rho)$
20.0	34.88449 579	60.84494 982	47.86472 280	673.94517 346
20.2	34.97970 676	60.77794 002	47.87882 339	665.54883 958
20.4	35.07937 856	60.70983 989	47.89460 923	656.92054 825
20.6	35.18353 166	60.64061 029	47.91207 097	648.06285 244
20.8	35.29218 814	60.57020 921	47.93119 867	638.97834 908
21.0	35.40537 216	60.49859 159	47.95198 187	629.66966 157
21.2	35.52311 036	60.42570 909	47.97440 973	620.13942 344
21.4	35.64543 236	60.35150 982	47.99847 109	610.39026 337
21.6	35.77237 113	60.27593 804	48.02415 458	600.42479 144
21.8	35.90396 351	60.19893 390	48.05144 871	590.24558 653
22.0	36.04025 066	60.12043 307	48.08034 186	579.85518 493
22.2	36.18127 854	60.04036 633	48.11082 243	569.25606 998
22.4	36.32709 848	59.95865 921	48.14287 885	558.45066 277
22.6	36.47776 768	59.87523 151	48.17649 959	547.44131 376
22.8	36.63334 984	59.78999 673	48.21167 328	536.23029 537
23.0	36.79391 580	59.70286 154	48.24838 867	524.81979 532
23.2	36.95954 425	59.61372 512	48.28663 468	513.21191 079
23.4	37.13032 253	59.52247 837	48.32640 045	501.40864 327
23.6	37.30634 747	59.42900 314	48.36767 530	489.41189 407
23.8	37.48772 639	59.33317 123	48.41044 881	477.22346 037
24.0	37.67457 823	59.23484 334	48.45471 078	464.84503 191
24.2	37.86703 474	59.13386 779	48.50045 126	452.27818 801
24.4	38.06524 200	59.03007 911	48.54766 055	439.52439 519
24.6	38.26936 201	58.92329 638	48.59632 920	426.58500 506
24.8	38.47957 468	58.81332 132	48.64644 800	413.46125 262
25.0	38.69608 001	58.69993 601	48.69800 801	400.15425 483
25.2	38.91910 078	58.58290 025	48.75100 052	386.66500 954
25.4	39.14888 565	58.46194 845	48.80541 705	372.99439 453
25.6	39.38571 288	58.33678 586	48.86124 937	359.14316 691
25.8	39.62989 481	58.20708 412	48.91848 946	345.11196 259
26.0	39.88178 324	58.07247 581	48.97712 952	330.90129 600
26.2	40.14177 607	57.93254 783	49.03716 195	316.51155 987
26.4	40.41032 542	57.78683 327	49.09857 935	301.94302 522
26.6	40.68794 776	57.63480 120	49.16137 448	287.19584 138
26.8	40.97523 672	57.47584 387	49.22554 030	272.27003 613
27.0	41.27287 940	57.30926 041	49.29106 991	257.16551 590
27.2	41.58167 747	57.13423 565	49.35795 656	241.88206 605
27.4	41.90257 498	56.94981 231	49.42619 364	226.41935 118
27.6	42.23669 560	56.75485 373	49.49577 467	210.77691 543
27.8	42.58539 353	56.54799 296	49.56669 324	194.95418 294
28.0	42.95032 481	56.32756 138	49.63894 309	178.95045 816

TABLE IV. $b_r(i\rho)$, $b_{r+2}(i\rho)$ and Auxiliary Functions $\qquad$ $r = 6$

$$FA(i\rho) = \tfrac{1}{2}(b_r + b_{r+2}), \quad FB(i\rho) = (b_{r+2} - b_r)^2$$

ρ	$b_r(i\rho)$	$b_{r+2}(i\rho)$	$FA(i\rho)$	$FB(i\rho)$
28.0	42.95032 481	56.32756 138	49.63894 309	178.95045 816
28.1	43.13950 239	56.21162 822	49.67556 530	170.88047 370
28.2	43.33355 010	56.09148 592	49.71251 801	162.76492 634
28.3	43.53281 373	55.96678 717	49.74980 045	154.60369 566
28.4	43.73768 762	55.83713 611	49.78741 186	146.39665 385
28.5	43.94862 481	55.70207 817	49.82535 149	138.14366 572
28.6	44.16615 009	55.56108 707	49.86361 858	129.84458 867
28.7	44.39087 695	55.41354 781	49.90221 238	121.49927 278
28.8	44.62353 022	55.25873 406	49.94113 214	113.10756 075
28.9	44.86497 664	55.09577 758	49.98037 711	104.66928 796
29.0	45.11626 725	54.92362 584	50.01994 654	96.18428 244
29.1	45.37869 761	54.74098 179	50.05983 970	87.65236 493
29.2	45.65389 600	54.54621 565	50.10005 583	79.07334 884
29.3	45.94395 743	54.33723 094	50.14059 418	70.44704 033
29.4	46.25165 638	54.11125 167	50.18145 402	61.77323 823
29.5	46.58080 354	53.86446 567	50.22263 460	53.05173 413
29.6	46.93688 735	53.59138 300	50.26413 517	44.28231 235
29.7	47.32834 059	53.28356 938	50.30595 499	35.46474 996
29.8	47.76939 126	52.92679 533	50.34809 329	26.59881 681
29.9	48.28791 555	52.49318 314	50.39054 934	17.68427 548
30.0	48.95676 546	51.90987 930	50.43332 238	8.72088 136

At $\rho = 30.09677284$

$b_6(i\rho) = b_8(i\rho) = 50.47501616$

(to 8D)

TABLE IV. $b_r(i\rho)$, $b_{r+2}(i\rho)$ and Auxiliary Functions $\qquad$ r=6

$$b_r(i\rho) = U+iV, \quad b_{r+2}(i\rho) = U-iV, \quad FB(i\rho) = (b_{r+2}-b_r)^2$$

ρ	U	V		$FB(i\rho)$
30.1	50.47641 165	-0.27000 805		-0.29161 738
30.2	50.51981 638	-1.52917 296		-9.35347 978
30.3	50.56353 583	-2.14854 439		-18.46497 206
30.4	50.60756 921	-2.62803 956		-27.62636 765
30.5	50.65191 576	-3.03471 363		-36.83794 716
30.6	50.69657 471	-3.39484 898		-46.09999 834
30.7	50.74154 526	-3.72198 926		-55.41281 614
30.8	50.78682 664	-4.02419 876		-64.77670 265
30.9	50.83241 804	-4.30673 795		-74.19196 713
31.0	50.87831 868	-4.57326 267		-83.65892 597
31.1	50.92452 774	-4.82643 509		-93.17790 270
31.2	50.97104 443	-5.06826 469		-102.74922 800
31.3	51.01786 790	-5.30031 225		-112.37323 967
31.4	51.06499 735	-5.52381 849		-122.05028 262
31.5	51.11243 193	-5.73978 895		-131.78070 891
31.6	51.16017 081	-5.94905 198		-141.56487 767
31.7	51.20821 314	-6.15229 947		-151.40315 517
31.8	51.25655 804	-6.35011 643		-161.29591 478
31.9	51.30520 466	-6.54300 269		-171.24353 695
32.0	51.35415 212	-6.73138 933		-181.24640 923
32.1	51.40339 953	-6.91565 120		-191.30492 627
32.2	51.45294 598	-7.09611 672		-201.41948 979
32.3	51.50279 058	-7.27307 549		-211.59050 858
32.4	51.55293 240	-7.44678 452		-221.81839 852
32.5	51.60337 051	-7.61747 305		-232.10358 255
32.6	51.65410 396	-7.78534 666		-242.44649 065
32.7	51.70513 181	-7.95059 054		-252.84755 990
32.8	51.75645 308	-8.11337 221		-263.30723 438
32.9	51.80806 680	-8.27384 381		-273.82596 524
33.0	51.85997 196	-8.43214 401		-284.40421 066
33.1	51.91216 757	-8.58839 967		-295.04243 585
33.2	51.96465 261	-8.74272 716		-305.74111 303
33.3	52.01742 604	-8.89523 358		-316.50072 144
33.4	52.07048 681	-9.04601 773		-327.32174 732
33.5	52.12383 386	-9.19517 107		-338.20468 390
33.6	52.17746 611	-9.34277 838		-349.15003 141
33.7	52.23138 248	-9.48891 850		-360.15829 702
33.8	52.28558 184	-9.63366 486		-371.22999 489
33.9	52.34006 307	-9.77708 604		-382.36564 612
34.0	52.39482 504	-9.91924 618		-393.56577 872
34.1	52.44986 658	-10.06020 536		-404.83092 766
34.2	52.50518 652	-10.20002 003		-416.16163 477
34.3	52.56078 367	-10.33874 326		-427.55844 880
34.4	52.61665 682	-10.47642 503		-439.02192 536
34.5	52.67280 473	-10.61311 249		-450.55262 689
34.6	52.72922 616	-10.74885 020		-462.15112 269
34.7	52.78591 985	-10.88368 032		-473.81798 885
34.8	52.84288 451	-11.01764 276		-485.55380 823
34.9	52.90011 884	-11.15077 543		-497.35917 047
35.0	52.95762 151	-11.28311 429		-509.23467 193

ρ	U	V	ρ	U	V
35.0	52.95762 151	−11.28311 429	40.0	56.13906 945	−17.37409 921
35.1	53.01539 119	−11.41469 355	40.1	56.20796 421	−17.49158 078
35.2	53.07342 650	−11.54554 580	40.2	56.27702 585	−17.60905 156
35.3	53.13172 607	−11.67570 207	40.3	56.34625 175	−17.72651 773
35.4	53.19028 849	−11.80519 199	40.4	56.41563 928	−17.84398 528
35.5	53.24911 233	−11.93404 382	40.5	56.48518 578	−17.96146 006
35.6	53.30819 616	−12.06228 462	40.6	56.55488 856	−18.07894 777
35.7	53.36753 848	−12.18994 026	40.7	56.62474 491	−18.19645 395
35.8	53.42713 783	−12.31703 552	40.8	56.69475 211	−18.31398 402
35.9	53.48699 268	−12.44359 416	40.9	56.76490 742	−18.43154 323
36.0	53.54710 150	−12.56963 896	41.0	56.83520 805	−18.54913 673
36.1	53.60746 273	−12.69519 180	41.1	56.90565 124	−18.66676 950
36.2	53.66807 479	−12.82027 373	41.2	56.97623 417	−18.78444 641
36.3	53.72893 607	−12.94490 495	41.3	57.04695 402	−18.90217 218
36.4	53.79004 495	−13.06910 494	41.4	57.11780 796	−19.01995 142
36.5	53.85139 978	−13.19289 243	41.5	57.18879 312	−19.13778 861
36.6	53.91299 887	−13.31628 548	41.6	57.25990 664	−19.25568 810
36.7	53.97484 053	−13.43930 153	41.7	57.33114 563	−19.37365 412
36.8	54.03692 303	−13.56195 737	41.8	57.40250 718	−19.49169 078
36.9	54.09924 462	−13.68426 924	41.9	57.47398 838	−19.60980 209
37.0	54.16180 353	−13.80625 281	42.0	57.54558 631	−19.72799 190
37.1	54.22459 797	−13.92792 324	42.1	57.61729 801	−19.84626 400
37.2	54.28762 609	−14.04929 520	42.2	57.68912 055	−19.96462 203
37.3	54.35088 606	−14.17038 288	42.3	57.76105 096	−20.08306 954
37.4	54.41437 601	−14.29120 000	42.4	57.83308 627	−20.20160 994
37.5	54.47809 401	−14.41175 987	42.5	57.90522 350	−20.32024 656
37.6	54.54203 816	−14.53207 538	42.6	57.97745 966	−20.43898 262
37.7	54.60620 650	−14.65215 905	42.7	58.04979 176	−20.55782 123
37.8	54.67059 704	−14.77202 299	42.8	58.12221 679	−20.67676 539
37.9	54.73520 779	−14.89167 897	42.9	58.19473 177	−20.79581 800
38.0	54.80003 671	−15.01113 842	43.0	58.26733 367	−20.91498 186
38.1	54.86508 174	−15.13041 241	43.1	58.34001 949	−21.03425 968
38.2	54.93034 080	−15.24951 174	43.2	58.41278 622	−21.15365 405
38.3	54.99581 178	−15.36844 686	43.3	58.48563 084	−21.27316 748
38.4	55.06149 254	−15.48722 797	43.4	58.55855 034	−21.39280 238
38.5	55.12738 092	−15.60586 494	43.5	58.63154 172	−21.51256 104
38.6	55.19347 473	−15.72436 741	43.6	58.70460 196	−21.63244 570
38.7	55.25977 175	−15.84274 474	43.7	58.77772 807	−21.75245 847
38.8	55.32626 974	−15.96100 605	43.8	58.85091 704	−21.87260 139
38.9	55.39296 643	−16.07916 020	43.9	58.92416 588	−21.99287 638
39.0	55.45985 952	−16.19721 582	44.0	58.99747 161	−22.11328 532
39.1	55.52694 670	−16.31518 132	44.1	59.07083 125	−22.23382 994
39.2	55.59422 562	−16.43306 490	44.2	59.14424 183	−22.35451 193
39.3	55.66169 390	−16.55087 452	44.3	59.21770 040	−22.47533 288
39.4	55.72934 915	−16.66861 796	44.4	59.29120 400	−22.59629 428
39.5	55.79718 894	−16.78630 277	44.5	59.36474 972	−22.71739 756
39.6	55.86521 083	−16.90393 635	44.6	59.43833 462	−22.83864 404
39.7	55.93341 233	−17.02152 586	44.7	59.51195 581	−22.96003 499
39.8	56.00179 096	−17.13907 832	44.8	59.58561 040	−23.08157 156
39.9	56.07034 418	−17.25660 056	44.9	59.65929 553	−23.20325 486
40.0	56.13906 945	−17.37409 921	45.0	59.73300 833	−23.32508 589

ρ	U	V	ρ	U	V
45.0	59.73300 833	−23.32508 589	55.0	66.90020 905	−36.20259 293
45.2	59.88050 566	−23.56919 483	55.2	67.03578 210	−36.47087 329
45.4	60.02808 000	−23.81390 497	55.4	67.17102 123	−36.73943 152
45.6	60.17570 932	−24.05922 172	55.6	67.30592 914	−37.00826 144
45.8	60.32337 197	−24.30514 935	55.8	67.44050 869	−37.27735 715
46.0	60.47104 675	−24.55169 102	56.0	67.57476 284	−37.54671 295
46.2	60.61871 291	−24.79884 887	56.2	67.70869 467	−37.81632 339
46.4	60.76635 019	−25.04662 401	56.4	67.84230 736	−38.08618 325
46.6	60.91393 884	−25.29501 657	56.6	67.97560 415	−38.35628 754
46.8	61.06145 966	−25.54402 577	56.8	68.10858 836	−38.62663 146
47.0	61.20889 403	−25.79364 996	57.0	68.24126 337	−38.89721 046
47.2	61.35622 388	−26.04388 663	57.2	68.37363 261	−39.16802 019
47.4	61.50343 179	−26.29473 251	57.4	68.50569 954	−39.43905 651
47.6	61.65050 095	−26.54618 357	57.6	68.63746 764	−39.71031 547
47.8	61.79741 517	−26.79823 509	57.8	68.76894 042	−39.98179 332
48.0	61.94415 895	−27.05088 170	58.0	68.90012 140	−40.25348 649
48.2	62.09071 742	−27.30411 743	58.2	69.03101 409	−40.52539 163
48.4	62.23707 643	−27.55793 574	58.4	69.16162 201	−40.79750 551
48.6	62.38322 246	−27.81232 959	58.6	69.29194 866	−41.06982 513
48.8	62.52914 271	−28.06729 148	58.8	69.42199 753	−41.34234 760
49.0	62.67482 504	−28.32281 347	59.0	69.55177 206	−41.61507 023
49.2	62.82025 803	−28.57888 725	59.2	69.68127 570	−41.88799 047
49.4	62.96543 091	−28.83550 418	59.4	69.81051 185	−42.16110 590
49.6	63.11033 360	−29.09265 530	59.6	69.93948 385	−42.43441 427
49.8	63.25495 669	−29.35033 142	59.8	70.06819 504	−42.70791 344
50.0	63.39929 145	−29.60852 313	60.0	70.19664 869	−42.98160 140
50.2	63.54332 979	−29.86722 082	60.2	70.32484 801	−43.25547 629
50.4	63.68706 425	−30.12641 477	60.4	70.45279 620	−43.52953 634
50.6	63.83048 803	−30.38609 512	60.6	70.58049 636	−43.80377 989
50.8	63.97359 492	−30.64625 196	60.8	70.70795 156	−44.07820 540
51.0	64.11637 931	−30.90687 532	61.0	70.83516 482	−44.35281 142
51.2	64.25883 620	−31.16795 522	61.2	70.96213 908	−44.62759 661
51.4	64.40096 110	−31.42948 169	61.4	71.08887 723	−44.90255 970
51.6	64.54275 013	−31.69144 480	61.6	71.21538 210	−45.17769 952
51.8	64.68419 988	−31.95383 469	61.8	71.34165 646	−45.45301 498
52.0	64.82530 749	−32.21664 157	62.0	71.46770 300	−45.72850 506
52.2	64.96607 054	−32.47985 578	62.2	71.59352 436	−46.00416 880
52.4	65.10648 713	−32.74346 775	62.4	71.71912 313	−46.28000 532
52.6	65.24655 574	−33.00746 810	62.6	71.84450 182	−46.55601 382
52.8	65.38627 533	−33.27184 757	62.8	71.96966 287	−46.83219 353
53.0	65.52564 523	−33.53659 708	63.0	72.09460 867	−47.10854 373
53.2	65.66466 514	−33.80170 775	63.2	72.21934 154	−47.38506 379
53.4	65.80333 515	−34.06717 089	63.4	72.34386 375	−47.66175 308
53.6	65.94165 566	−34.33297 800	63.6	72.46817 748	−47.93861 105
53.8	66.07962 739	−34.59912 082	63.8	72.59228 488	−48.21563 718
54.0	66.21725 138	−34.86559 130	64.0	72.71618 803	−48.49283 097
54.2	66.35452 891	−35.13238 161	64.2	72.83988 894	−48.77019 198
54.4	66.49146 155	−35.39948 417	64.4	72.96338 957	−49.04771 978
54.6	66.62805 107	−35.66689 161	64.6	73.08669 182	−49.32541 398
54.8	66.76429 950	−35.93459 682	64.8	73.20979 754	−49.60327 422
55.0	66.90020 905	−36.20259 293	65.0	73.33270 851	−49.88130 015

ρ	U	V	ρ	U	V
65.0	73.33270 851	−49.88130 015	75.0	79.25721 577	−63.98828 352
65.2	73.45542 648	−50.15949 146	75.5	79.54304 689	−64.70388 578
65.4	73.57795 311	−50.43784 784	76.0	79.82795 587	−65.42042 198
65.6	73.70029 004	−50.71636 900	76.5	80.11194 990	−66.13788 492
65.8	73.82243 886	−50.99505 468	77.0	80.39503 602	−66.85626 724
66.0	73.94440 108	−51.27390 461	77.5	80.67722 118	−67.57556 142
66.2	74.06617 820	−51.55291 855	78.0	80.95851 223	−68.29575 984
66.4	74.18777 164	−51.83209 626	78.5	81.23891 596	−69.01685 479
66.6	74.30918 280	−52.11143 752	79.0	81.51843 912	−69.73883 845
66.8	74.43041 303	−52.39094 210	79.5	81.79708 840	−70.46170 297
67.0	74.55146 361	−52.67060 977	80.0	82.07487 047	−71.18544 047
67.2	74.67233 583	−52.95044 034	80.5	82.35179 199	−71.91004 301
67.4	74.79303 089	−53.23043 358	81.0	82.62785 958	−72.63550 269
67.6	74.91354 999	−53.51058 929	81.5	82.90307 987	−73.36181 159
67.8	75.03389 427	−53.79090 726	82.0	83.17745 946	−74.08896 184
68.0	75.15406 483	−54.07138 727	82.5	83.45100 495	−74.81694 560
68.2	75.27406 275	−54.35202 911	83.0	83.72372 294	−75.54575 507
68.4	75.39388 908	−54.63283 258	83.5	83.99561 999	−76.27538 252
68.6	75.51354 481	−54.91379 744	84.0	84.26670 269	−77.00582 030
68.8	75.63303 094	−55.19492 350	84.5	84.53697 757	−77.73706 082
69.0	75.75234 840	−55.47621 051	85.0	84.80645 117	−78.46909 658
69.2	75.87149 811	−55.75765 824	85.5	85.07513 002	−79.20192 018
69.4	75.99048 098	−56.03926 647	86.0	85.34302 058	−79.93552 431
69.6	76.10929 785	−56.32103 496	86.5	85.61012 933	−80.66990 175
69.8	76.22794 957	−56.60296 345	87.0	85.87646 270	−81.40504 540
70.0	76.34643 696	−56.88505 169	87.5	86.14202 708	−82.14094 826
70.2	76.46476 081	−57.16729 942	88.0	86.40682 883	−82.87760 342
70.4	76.58292 189	−57.44970 638	88.5	86.67087 426	−83.61500 411
70.6	76.70092 094	−57.73227 229	89.0	86.93416 964	−84.35314 365
70.8	76.81875 871	−58.01499 687	89.5	87.19672 120	−85.09201 548
71.0	76.93643 588	−58.29787 982	90.0	87.45853 511	−85.83161 312
71.2	77.05395 317	−58.58092 086	90.5	87.71961 747	−86.57193 023
71.4	77.17131 124	−58.86411 967	91.0	87.97997 437	−87.31296 057
71.6	77.28851 075	−59.14747 594	91.5	88.23961 178	−88.05469 800
71.8	77.40555 234	−59.43098 936	92.0	88.49853 567	−88.79713 649
72.0	77.52243 664	−59.71465 959	92.5	88.75675 190	−89.54027 010
72.2	77.63916 426	−59.99848 629	93.0	89.01426 630	−90.28409 301
72.4	77.75573 581	−60.28246 912	93.5	89.27108 461	−91.02859 947
72.6	77.87215 186	−60.56660 774	94.0	89.52721 252	−91.77378 387
72.8	77.98841 301	−60.85090 177	94.5	89.78265 564	−92.51964 064
73.0	78.10451 980	−61.13535 085	95.0	90.03741 953	−93.26616 435
73.2	78.22047 279	−61.41995 461	95.5	90.29150 966	−94.01334 962
73.4	78.33627 253	−61.70471 266	96.0	90.54493 144	−94.76119 118
73.6	78.45191 955	−61.98962 462	96.5	90.79769 023	−95.50968 384
73.8	78.56741 438	−62.27469 008	97.0	91.04979 130	−96.25882 249
74.0	78.68275 753	−62.55990 865	97.5	91.30123 985	−97.00860 209
74.2	78.79794 952	−62.84527 992	98.0	91.55204 102	−97.75901 768
74.4	78.91299 084	−63.13080 346	98.5	91.80219 989	−98.51006 440
74.6	79.02788 200	−63.41647 887	99.0	92.05172 144	−99.26173 742
74.8	79.14262 348	−63.70230 570	99.5	92.30061 064	−100.01403 201
75.0	79.25721 577	−63.98828 352	100.0	92.54887 233	−100.76694 350

ρ	$b_r(i\rho)$	$b_{r+2}(i\rho)$	ρ	$b_r(i\rho)$	$b_{r+2}(i\rho)$
0.0	100.00000 000	144.00000 000	25.0	96.90919 878	141.83572 332
0.5	99.99873 738	143.99912 588	25.2	96.86073 925	141.80128 909
1.0	99.99494 967	143.99650 355	25.4	96.81194 236	141.76659 076
1.5	99.98863 722	143.99213 315	25.6	96.76281 027	141.73162 855
2.0	99.97980 070	143.98601 487	25.8	96.71334 522	141.69640 269
2.5	99.96844 098	143.97814 902	26.0	96.66354 955	141.66091 341
3.0	99.95455 922	143.96853 596	26.2	96.61342 573	141.62516 093
3.5	99.93815 680	143.95717 615	26.4	96.56297 631	141.58914 548
4.0	99.91923 539	143.94407 014	26.6	96.51220 398	141.55286 729
4.5	99.89779 687	143.92921 854	26.8	96.46111 155	141.51632 659
5.0	99.87384 340	143.91262 205	27.0	96.40970 197	141.47952 360
5.5	99.84737 737	143.89428 148	27.2	96.35797 829	141.44245 855
6.0	99.81840 142	143.87419 767	27.4	96.30594 376	141.40513 167
6.5	99.78691 844	143.85237 159	27.6	96.25360 173	141.36754 319
7.0	99.75293 155	143.82880 425	27.8	96.20095 574	141.32969 334
7.5	99.71644 411	143.80349 679	28.0	96.14800 949	141.29158 235
8.0	99.67745 973	143.77645 038	28.2	96.09476 684	141.25321 044
8.5	99.63598 224	143.74766 629	28.4	96.04123 185	141.21457 785
9.0	99.59201 571	143.71714 589	28.6	95.98740 876	141.17568 481
9.5	99.54556 444	143.68489 060	28.8	95.93330 201	141.13653 153
10.0	99.49663 297	143.65090 192	29.0	95.87891 627	141.09711 826
10.5	99.44522 605	143.61518 144	29.2	95.82425 640	141.05744 521
11.0	99.39134 867	143.57773 083	29.4	95.76932 750	141.01751 261
11.5	99.33500 603	143.53855 183	29.6	95.71413 492	140.97732 069
12.0	99.27620 358	143.49764 626	29.8	95.65868 425	140.93686 967
12.5	99.21494 700	143.45501 600	30.0	95.60298 135	140.89615 978
13.0	99.15124 218	143.41066 302	30.2	95.54703 235	140.85519 123
13.5	99.08509 527	143.36458 937	30.4	95.49084 365	140.81396 425
14.0	99.01651 265	143.31679 716	30.6	95.43442 198	140.77247 905
14.5	98.94550 096	143.26728 858	30.8	95.37777 435	140.73073 586
15.0	98.87206 712	143.21606 588	31.0	95.32090 811	140.68873 488
15.5	98.79621 830	143.16313 140	31.2	95.26383 094	140.64647 633
16.0	98.71796 199	143.10848 754	31.4	95.20655 089	140.60396 043
16.5	98.63730 601	143.05213 676	31.6	95.14907 636	140.56118 737
17.0	98.55425 852	142.99408 161	31.8	95.09141 611	140.51815 737
17.5	98.46882 807	142.93432 469	32.0	95.03357 934	140.47487 062
18.0	98.38102 364	142.87286 868	32.2	94.97557 504	140.43132 733
18.5	98.29085 468	142.80971 631	32.4	94.91741 501	140.38752 770
19.0	98.19833 121	142.74487 039	32.6	94.85910 792	140.34347 190
19.5	98.10346 383	142.67833 377	32.8	94.80066 529	140.29916 014
20.0	98.00626 384	142.61010 939	33.0	94.74209 852	140.25459 260
20.5	97.90674 335	142.54020 024	33.2	94.68341 949	140.20976 946
21.0	97.80491 533	142.46860 935	33.4	94.62464 062	140.16469 089
21.5	97.70079 380	142.39533 984	33.6	94.56577 482	140.11935 706
22.0	97.59439 398	142.32039 485	33.8	94.50683 559	140.07376 814
22.5	97.48573 240	142.24377 761	34.0	94.44783 696	140.02792 428
23.0	97.37482 715	142.16549 137	34.2	94.38879 356	139.98182 564
23.5	97.26169 810	142.08553 944	34.4	94.32972 063	139.93547 237
24.0	97.14636 712	142.00392 519	34.6	94.27063 402	139.88886 460
24.5	97.02885 840	141.92065 200	34.8	94.21155 021	139.84200 247
25.0	96.90919 878	141.83572 332	35.0	94.15248 636	139.79488 609

ρ	$b_r(i\rho)$	$b_{r+2}(i\rho)$	ρ	$b_r(i\rho)$	$b_{r+2}(i\rho)$
35.0	94.15248 636	139.79488 609	45.0	91.83280 344	137.11322 533
35.2	94.09346 030	139.74751 560	45.2	91.81562 646	137.05288 758
35.4	94.03449 053	139.69989 108	45.4	91.80035 632	136.99226 975
35.6	93.97559 629	139.65201 265	45.6	91.78703 679	136.93136 997
35.8	93.91679 754	139.60388 039	45.8	91.77571 091	136.87018 627
36.0	93.85811 499	139.55549 437	46.0	91.76642 104	136.80871 659
36.2	93.79957 012	139.50685 468	46.2	91.75920 869	136.74695 875
36.4	93.74118 516	139.45796 135	46.4	91.75411 456	136.68491 046
36.6	93.68298 317	139.40881 444	46.6	91.75117 843	136.62256 931
36.8	93.62498 801	139.35941 397	46.8	91.75043 915	136.55993 277
37.0	93.56722 435	139.30975 997	47.0	91.75193 456	136.49699 819
37.2	93.50971 772	139.25985 244	47.2	91.75570 150	136.43376 276
37.4	93.45249 448	139.20969 137	47.4	91.76177 573	136.37022 358
37.6	93.39558 185	139.15927 672	47.6	91.77019 192	136.30637 755
37.8	93.33900 793	139.10860 847	47.8	91.78098 362	136.24222 146
38.0	93.28280 168	139.05768 655	48.0	91.79418 326	136.17775 192
38.2	93.22699 296	139.00651 088	48.2	91.80982 210	136.11296 539
38.4	93.17161 250	138.95508 136	48.4	91.82793 025	136.04785 815
38.6	93.11669 192	138.90339 789	48.6	91.84853 663	135.98242 630
38.8	93.06226 374	138.85146 031	48.8	91.87166 903	135.91666 577
39.0	93.00836 136	138.79926 847	49.0	91.89735 404	135.85057 228
39.2	92.95501 905	138.74682 220	49.2	91.92561 711	135.78414 134
39.4	92.90227 198	138.69412 127	49.4	91.95648 254	135.71736 828
39.6	92.85015 616	138.64116 547	49.6	91.98997 351	135.65024 819
39.8	92.79870 847	138.58795 453	49.8	92.02611 210	135.58277 593
40.0	92.74796 663	138.53448 817	50.0	92.06491 930	135.51494 612
40.2	92.69796 919	138.48076 607	50.2	92.10641 508	135.44675 315
40.4	92.64875 547	138.42678 788	50.4	92.15061 837	135.37819 112
40.6	92.60036 560	138.37255 324	50.6	92.19754 714	135.30925 388
40.8	92.55284 046	138.31806 172	50.8	92.24721 841	135.23993 500
41.0	92.50622 163	138.26331 289	51.0	92.29964 832	135.17022 774
41.2	92.46055 140	138.20830 626	51.2	92.35485 217	135.10012 505
41.4	92.41587 270	138.15304 131	51.4	92.41284 445	135.02961 959
41.6	92.37222 907	138.09751 748	51.6	92.47363 891	134.95870 364
41.8	92.32966 465	138.04173 417	51.8	92.53724 862	134.88736 916
42.0	92.28822 407	137.98569 073	52.0	92.60368 600	134.81560 773
42.2	92.24795 244	137.92938 647	52.2	92.67296 289	134.74341 057
42.4	92.20889 533	137.87282 065	52.4	92.74509 061	134.67076 847
42.6	92.17109 863	137.81599 249	52.6	92.82008 004	134.59767 181
42.8	92.13460 857	137.75890 113	52.8	92.89794 162	134.52411 056
43.0	92.09947 165	137.70154 569	53.0	92.97868 549	134.45007 421
43.2	92.06573 453	137.64392 521	53.2	93.06232 149	134.37555 178
43.4	92.03344 401	137.58603 868	53.4	93.14885 928	134.30053 178
43.6	92.00264 696	137.52788 503	53.6	93.23830 833	134.22500 222
43.8	91.97339 024	137.46946 311	53.8	93.33067 808	134.14895 055
44.0	91.94572 065	137.41077 172	54.0	93.42597 791	134.07236 366
44.2	91.91968 482	137.35180 958	54.2	93.52421 728	133.99522 782
44.4	91.89532 921	137.29257 534	54.4	93.62540 576	133.91752 870
44.6	91.87269 997	137.23306 757	54.6	93.72955 312	133.83925 130
44.8	91.85184 292	137.17328 477	54.8	93.83666 936	133.76037 992
45.0	91.83280 344	137.11322 533	55.0	93.94676 482	133.68089 816

322-566 O - 69 - 17

ρ	$b_r(i\rho)$	$b_{r+2}(i\rho)$	$FA(i\rho)$	$FB(i\rho)$
55.0	93.94676 482	133.68089 816	113.81383 149	1578.80135 226
55.2	94.05985 025	133.60078 885	113.83031 955	1563.48582 558
55.4	94.17593 684	133.52003 402	113.84798 543	1547.95798 350
55.6	94.29503 632	133.43861 488	113.86682 560	1532.21974 210
55.8	94.41716 105	133.35651 173	113.88683 639	1516.27303 118
56.0	94.54232 406	133.27370 398	113.90801 402	1500.11979 030
56.2	94.67053 914	133.19017 005	113.93035 460	1483.76196 507
56.4	94.80182 093	133.10588 734	113.95385 413	1467.20150 351
56.6	94.93618 496	133.02083 217	113.97850 857	1450.44035 259
56.8	95.07364 780	132.93497 972	114.00431 376	1433.48045 498
57.0	95.21422 707	132.84830 399	114.03126 553	1416.32374 582
57.2	95.35794 158	132.76077 769	114.05935 963	1398.97214 974
57.4	95.50481 138	132.67237 221	114.08859 180	1381.42757 803
57.6	95.65485 792	132.58305 752	114.11895 772	1363.69192 584
57.8	95.80810 407	132.49280 210	114.15045 309	1345.76706 967
58.0	95.96457 427	132.40157 284	114.18307 356	1327.65486 487
58.2	96.12429 463	132.30933 496	114.21681 480	1309.35714 335
58.4	96.28729 306	132.21605 189	114.25167 248	1290.87571 136
58.6	96.45359 935	132.12168 519	114.28764 227	1272.21234 743
58.8	96.62324 537	132.02619 440	114.32471 988	1253.36880 044
59.0	96.79626 512	131.92953 692	114.36290 102	1234.34678 775
59.2	96.97269 496	131.83166 788	114.40218 142	1215.14799 350
59.4	97.15257 372	131.73253 999	114.44255 686	1195.77406 695
59.6	97.33594 292	131.63210 336	114.48402 314	1176.22662 102
59.8	97.52284 687	131.53030 533	114.52657 610	1156.50723 080
60.0	97.71333 298	131.42709 029	114.57021 164	1136.61743 226
60.2	97.90745 189	131.32239 945	114.61492 567	1116.55872 098
60.4	98.10525 774	131.21617 061	114.66071 417	1096.33255 103
60.6	98.30680 845	131.10833 789	114.70757 317	1075.94033 383
60.8	98.51216 597	130.99883 150	114.75549 874	1055.38343 718
61.0	98.72139 662	130.88757 737	114.80448 700	1034.66318 435
61.2	98.93457 140	130.77449 685	114.85453 413	1013.78085 314
61.4	99.15176 639	130.65950 632	114.90563 635	992.73767 515
61.6	99.37306 319	130.54251 675	114.95778 997	971.53483 502
61.8	99.59854 934	130.42343 328	115.01099 131	950.17346 970
62.0	99.82831 888	130.30215 467	115.06523 678	928.65466 789
62.2	100.06247 290	130.17857 273	115.12052 281	906.97946 941
62.4	100.30112 019	130.05257 167	115.17684 593	885.14886 466
62.6	100.54437 803	129.92402 735	115.23420 269	863.16379 419
62.8	100.79237 290	129.79280 649	115.29258 969	841.02514 819
63.0	101.04524 153	129.65876 571	115.35200 362	818.73376 611
63.2	101.30313 188	129.52175 049	115.41244 119	796.29043 629
63.4	101.56620 439	129.38159 393	115.47389 916	773.69589 561
63.6	101.83463 334	129.23811 540	115.53637 437	750.95082 921
63.8	102.10860 845	129.09111 890	115.59986 368	728.05587 017
64.0	102.38833 674	128.94039 126	115.66436 400	705.01159 930
64.2	102.67404 464	128.78569 998	115.72987 231	681.81854 491
64.4	102.96598 049	128.62679 074	115.79638 561	658.47718 257
64.6	103.26441 749	128.46338 443	115.86390 096	634.98793 499
64.8	103.56965 713	128.29517 374	115.93241 544	611.35117 183
65.0	103.88203 335	128.12181 902	116.00192 619	587.56720 956

ρ	$b_r(i\rho)$	$b_{r+2}(i\rho)$	$FA(i\rho)$	$FB(i\rho)$
65.0	103.88203 335	128.12181 902	116.00192 619	587.56720 956
65.2	104.20191 742	127.94294 333	116.07243 037	563.63631 133
65.4	104.52972 391	127.75812 650	116.14392 521	539.55868 688
65.6	104.86591 794	127.56689 792	116.21640 793	515.33449 244
65.8	105.21102 399	127.36872 763	116.28987 581	490.96383 063
66.0	105.56563 699	127.16301 531	116.36432 615	466.44675 042
66.2	105.93043 605	126.94907 651	116.43975 628	441.78324 706
66.4	106.30620 198	126.72612 514	116.51616 356	416.97326 201
66.6	106.69383 977	126.49325 095	116.59354 536	392.01668 292
66.8	107.09440 799	126.24939 020	116.67189 909	366.91334 358
67.0	107.50915 768	125.99328 666	116.75122 217	341.66302 393
67.2	107.93958 522	125.72343 885	116.83151 203	316.26544 999
67.4	108.38750 523	125.43802 704	116.91276 613	290.72029 387
67.6	108.85515 433	125.13480 954	116.99498 194	265.02717 375
67.8	109.34534 284	124.81097 099	117.07815 691	239.18565 388
68.0	109.86168 508	124.46289 203	117.16228 855	213.19524 456
68.2	110.40896 440	124.08578 428	117.24737 434	187.05540 215
68.4	110.99374 440	123.67307 913	117.33341 177	160.76552 908
68.6	111.62546 576	123.21533 090	117.42039 833	134.32497 382
68.8	112.31860 535	122.69805 769	117.50833 152	107.73303 091
69.0	113.09751 603	122.09690 162	117.59720 882	80.98894 094
69.2	114.00966 826	121.36438 719	117.68702 772	54.09189 059
69.4	115.17773 702	120.37783 438	117.77778 570	27.04101 259

At ρ = 69.59879328

$b_{10}(i\rho) = b_{12}(i\rho) = 117.86892416$

(to 8D)

ρ	U	V		$FB(i\rho)$
69.6	117.86948 021	-0.20286 340		-0.16461 424
69.8	117.96210 872	-2.62325 966		-27.52596 500
70.0	118.05566 864	-3.70958 450		-55.04406 870
70.2	118.15015 741	-4.54752 703		-82.72000 828
70.4	118.24557 243	-5.25725 500		-110.55492 058
70.6	118.34191 106	-5.88536 312		-138.54999 634
70.8	118.43917 066	-6.45574 318		-166.70648 020
71.0	118.53734 856	-6.98257 959		-195.02567 072
71.2	118.63644 204	-7.47510 736		-223.50892 034
71.4	118.73644 839	-7.93973 607		-252.15763 543
71.6	118.83736 481	-8.38112 875		-280.97327 624
71.8	118.93918 851	-8.80280 292		-309.95735 693
72.0	119.04191 664	-9.20748 942		-339.11144 554
72.2	119.14554 631	-9.59735 854		-368.43716 404
72.4	119.25007 460	-9.97416 899		-397.93618 829
72.6	119.35549 851	-10.33936 952		-427.61024 804
72.8	119.46181 504	-10.69417 046		-457.46112 692
73.0	119.56902 109	-11.03959 536		-487.49066 248
73.2	119.67711 354	-11.37651 909		-517.70074 613
73.4	119.78608 921	-11.70569 651		-548.09332 313
73.6	119.89594 484	-12.02778 442		-578.67039 264
73.8	120.00667 713	-12.34335 862		-609.43400 760
74.0	120.11828 272	-12.65292 728		-640.38627 482
74.2	120.23075 817	-12.95694 172		-671.52935 485
74.4	120.34409 996	-13.25580 497		-702.86546 202
74.6	120.45830 455	-13.54987 882		-734.39686 436
74.8	120.57336 826	-13.83948 955		-766.12588 357
75.0	120.68928 739	-14.12493 270		-798.05489 496
75.2	120.80605 813	-14.40647 708		-830.18632 738
75.4	120.92367 660	-14.68436 808		-862.52266 314
75.6	121.04213 884	-14.95883 049		-895.06643 794
75.8	121.16144 080	-15.23007 092		-927.82024 076
76.0	121.28157 833	-15.49827 985		-960.78671 376
76.2	121.40254 722	-15.76363 340		-993.96855 211
76.4	121.52434 314	-16.02629 483		-1027.36850 391
76.6	121.64696 167	-16.28641 589		-1060.98937 000
76.8	121.77039 831	-16.54413 796		-1094.83400 376
77.0	121.89464 843	-16.79959 308		-1128.90531 095
77.2	122.01970 731	-17.05290 481		-1163.20624 949
77.4	122.14557 014	-17.30418 901		-1197.73982 918
77.6	122.27223 198	-17.55355 457		-1232.50911 148
77.8	122.39968 779	-17.80110 396		-1267.51720 920
78.0	122.52793 242	-18.04693 385		-1302.76728 620
78.2	122.65696 061	-18.29113 554		-1338.26255 700
78.4	122.78676 695	-18.53379 539		-1374.00628 647
78.6	122.91734 596	-18.77499 527		-1410.00178 938
78.8	123.04869 199	-19.01481 284		-1446.25242 997
79.0	123.18079 931	-19.25332 193		-1482.76162 149

ρ	U	V	ρ	U	V
79.0	123.18079 931	−19.25332 193	89.0	130.58904 723	−30.51542 863
79.2	123.31366 204	−19.49059 277	89.5	130.98968 674	−31.07762 045
79.4	123.44727 416	−19.72669 227	90.0	131.39193 183	−31.64168 131
79.6	123.58162 955	−19.96168 428	90.5	131.79559 432	−32.20774 525
79.8	123.71672 194	−20.19562 977	91.0	132.20048 675	−32.77592 762
80.0	123.85254 493	−20.42858 701	91.5	132.60642 323	−33.34632 574
80.2	123.98909 197	−20.66061 179	92.0	133.01322 032	−33.91901 957
80.4	124.12635 640	−20.89175 756	92.5	133.42069 794	−34.49407 242
80.6	124.26433 140	−21.12207 556	93.0	133.82868 020	−35.07153 173
80.8	124.40301 001	−21.35161 498	93.5	134.23699 624	−35.65142 988
81.0	124.54238 514	−21.58042 307	94.0	134.64548 106	−36.23378 504
81.2	124.68244 954	−21.80854 526	94.5	135.05397 622	−36.81860 207
81.4	124.82319 583	−22.03602 524	95.0	135.46233 052	−37.40587 354
81.6	124.96461 646	−22.26290 510	95.5	135.87040 062	−37.99558 070
81.8	125.10670 377	−22.48922 537	96.0	136.27805 153	−38.58769 450
82.0	125.24944 992	−22.71502 514	96.5	136.68515 702	−39.18217 668
82.2	125.39284 693	−22.94034 210	97.0	137.09159 997	−39.77898 083
82.4	125.53688 668	−23.16521 263	97.5	137.49727 256	−40.37805 346
82.6	125.68156 089	−23.38967 186	98.0	137.90207 641	−40.97933 503
82.8	125.82686 112	−23.61375 372	98.5	138.30592 260	−41.58276 104
83.0	125.97277 880	−23.83749 101	99.0	138.70873 160	−42.18826 297
83.2	126.11930 521	−24.06091 544	99.5	139.11043 313	−42.79576 928
83.4	126.26643 146	−24.28405 766	100.0	139.51096 593	−43.40520 625
83.6	126.41414 852	−24.50694 733			
83.8	126.56244 722	−24.72961 314			
84.0	126.71131 823	−24.95208 288			
84.2	126.86075 208	−25.17438 340			
84.4	127.01073 915	−25.39654 073			
84.6	127.16126 969	−25.61858 006			
84.8	127.31233 378	−25.84052 575			
85.0	127.46392 140	−26.06240 142			
85.2	127.61602 235	−26.28422 990			
85.4	127.76862 632	−26.50603 329			
85.6	127.92172 287	−26.72783 298			
85.8	128.07530 142	−26.94964 966			
86.0	128.22935 127	−27.17150 334			
86.2	128.38386 161	−27.39341 337			
86.4	128.53882 148	−27.61539 843			
86.6	128.69421 984	−27.83747 659			
86.8	128.85004 553	−28.05966 527			
87.0	129.00628 728	−28.28198 129			
87.2	129.16293 374	−28.50444 088			
87.4	129.31997 343	−28.72705 966			
87.6	129.47739 483	−28.94985 267			
87.8	129.63518 631	−29.17283 441			
88.0	129.79333 617	−29.39601 877			
88.2	129.95183 263	−29.61941 912			
88.4	130.11066 388	−29.84304 828			
88.6	130.26981 802	−30.06691 851			
88.8	130.42928 313	−30.29104 155			
89.0	130.58904 723	−30.51542 863			

ρ	$b_r(i\rho)$	$b_{r+2}(i\rho)$	ρ	$b_r(i\rho)$	$b_{r+2}(i\rho)$
0.0	196.00000 000	256.00000 000	25.0	194.40576 739	254.77823 571
0.5	195.99935 898	255.99950 980	25.5	194.34170 497	254.72903 158
1.0	195.99743 592	255.99803 923	26.0	194.27640 110	254.67886 540
1.5	195.99423 088	255.99558 828	26.5	194.20985 731	254.62773 787
2.0	195.98974 394	255.99215 702	27.0	194.14207 518	254.57564 973
2.5	195.98397 521	255.98774 547	27.5	194.07305 629	254.52260 170
3.0	195.97692 483	255.98235 372	28.0	194.00280 227	254.46859 453
3.5	195.96859 299	255.97598 184	28.5	193.93131 475	254.41362 898
4.0	195.95897 990	255.96862 991	29.0	193.85859 539	254.35770 582
4.5	195.94808 580	255.96029 806	29.5	193.78464 590	254.30082 583
5.0	195.93591 097	255.95098 641	30.0	193.70946 798	254.24298 980
5.5	195.92245 571	255.94069 508	30.5	193.63306 336	254.18419 854
6.0	195.90772 036	255.92942 423	31.0	193.55543 382	254.12445 287
6.5	195.89170 530	255.91717 403	31.5	193.47658 112	254.06375 363
7.0	195.87441 093	255.90394 466	32.0	193.39650 708	254.00210 164
7.5	195.85583 768	255.88973 631	32.5	193.31521 353	253.93949 777
8.0	195.83598 603	255.87454 919	33.0	193.23270 231	253.87594 287
8.5	195.81485 648	255.85838 352	33.5	193.14897 530	253.81143 783
9.0	195.79244 955	255.84123 955	34.0	193.06403 440	253.74598 353
9.5	195.76876 580	255.82311 751	34.5	192.97788 153	253.67958 087
10.0	195.74380 585	255.80401 768	35.0	192.89051 862	253.61223 076
10.5	195.71757 030	255.78394 034	35.5	192.80194 763	253.54393 412
11.0	195.69005 982	255.76288 577	36.0	192.71217 056	253.47469 189
11.5	195.66127 509	255.74085 429	36.5	192.62118 941	253.40450 499
12.0	195.63121 684	255.71784 623	37.0	192.52900 621	253.33337 440
12.5	195.59988 582	255.69386 190	37.5	192.43562 300	253.26130 107
13.0	195.56728 280	255.66890 168	38.0	192.34104 187	253.18828 598
13.5	195.53340 860	255.64296 591	38.5	192.24526 491	253.11433 011
14.0	195.49826 407	255.61605 498	39.0	192.14829 424	253.03943 446
14.5	195.46185 006	255.58816 928	39.5	192.05013 200	252.96360 004
15.0	195.42416 750	255.55930 921	40.0	191.95078 036	252.88682 785
15.5	195.38521 730	255.52947 519	40.5	191.85024 151	252.80911 894
16.0	195.34500 043	255.49866 766	41.0	191.74851 767	252.73047 432
16.5	195.30351 789	255.46688 706	41.5	191.64561 109	252.65089 506
17.0	195.26077 069	255.43413 386	42.0	191.54152 402	252.57038 221
17.5	195.21675 989	255.40040 852	42.5	191.43625 878	252.48893 683
18.0	195.17148 657	255.36571 154	43.0	191.32981 769	252.40656 000
18.5	195.12495 183	255.33004 341	43.5	191.22220 310	252.32325 281
19.0	195.07715 682	255.29340 465	44.0	191.11341 742	252.23901 635
19.5	195.02810 269	255.25579 579	44.5	191.00346 307	252.15385 172
20.0	194.97779 065	255.21721 736	45.0	190.89234 252	252.06776 004
20.5	194.92622 191	255.17766 993	45.5	190.78005 826	251.98074 243
21.0	194.87339 773	255.13715 406	46.0	190.66661 285	251.89280 002
21.5	194.81931 938	255.09567 034	46.5	190.55200 888	251.80393 395
22.0	194.76398 818	255.05321 934	47.0	190.43624 899	251.71414 538
22.5	194.70740 545	255.00980 169	47.5	190.31933 588	251.62343 545
23.0	194.64957 254	254.96541 800	48.0	190.20127 230	251.53180 535
23.5	194.59049 086	254.92006 891	48.5	190.08206 108	251.43925 623
24.0	194.53016 181	254.87375 505	49.0	189.96170 509	251.34578 929
24.5	194.46858 683	254.82647 710	49.5	189.84020 731	251.25140 571
25.0	194.40576 739	254.77823 571	50.0	189.71757 077	251.15610 670

ρ	$b_r(i\rho)$	$b_{r+2}(i\rho)$	ρ	$b_r(i\rho)$	$b_{r+2}(i\rho)$
50.0	189.71757 077	251.15610 670	75.0	182.29833 646	245.25193 022
50.5	189.59379 862	251.05989 346	75.5	182.13292 762	245.11161 153
51.0	189.46889 410	250.96276 721	76.0	181.96768 421	244.97043 879
51.5	189.34286 054	250.86476 916	76.5	181.80271 136	244.82841 247
52.0	189.21570 141	250.76578 056	77.0	181.63812 191	244.68553 289
52.5	189.08742 031	250.66592 263	77.5	181.47403 692	244.54180 031
53.0	188.95802 099	250.56515 662	78.0	181.31058 606	244.39721 484
53.5	188.82750 734	250.46348 379	78.5	181.14790 807	244.25177 648
54.0	188.69588 344	250.36090 538	79.0	180.98615 121	244.10548 507
54.5	188.56315 357	250.25742 266	79.5	180.82547 364	243.95834 031
55.0	188.42932 221	250.15303 690	80.0	180.66604 389	243.81034 173
55.5	188.29439 407	250.04774 938	80.5	180.50804 121	243.66148 867
56.0	188.15837 412	249.94156 138	81.0	180.35165 593	243.51178 028
56.5	188.02126 763	249.83447 418	81.5	180.19708 980	243.36121 548
57.0	187.88308 017	249.72648 908	82.0	180.04455 624	243.20979 297
57.5	187.74381 764	249.61760 737	82.5	179.89428 060	243.05751 118
58.0	187.60348 632	249.50783 035	83.0	179.74650 028	242.90436 827
58.5	187.46209 292	249.39715 933	83.5	179.60146 481	242.75036 210
59.0	187.31964 458	249.28559 562	84.0	179.45943 588	242.59549 018
59.5	187.17614 895	249.17314 052	84.5	179.32068 722	242.43974 970
60.0	187.03161 421	249.05979 535	85.0	179.18550 439	242.28313 743
60.5	186.89604 916	248.94556 142	85.5	179.05418 449	242.12564 975
61.0	186.73946 322	248.83044 005	86.0	178.92703 568	241.96728 256
61.5	186.59186 655	248.71443 257	86.5	178.80437 666	241.80803 129
62.0	186.44327 008	248.59754 027	87.0	178.68653 595	241.64789 082
62.5	186.29368 559	248.47976 450	87.5	178.57385 105	241.48685 549
63.0	186.14312 582	248.36110 655	88.0	178.46666 747	241.32491 896
63.5	185.99160 450	248.24156 774	88.5	178.36533 763	241.16207 428
64.0	185.83913 647	248.12114 938	89.0	178.27021 966	240.99831 372
64.5	185.68573 781	247.99985 278	89.5	178.18167 599	240.83362 878
65.0	185.53142 591	247.87767 923	90.0	178.10007 197	240.66801 013
65.5	185.37621 958	247.75463 004	90.5	178.02577 426	240.50144 749
66.0	185.22013 922	247.63070 648	91.0	177.95914 929	240.33392 960
66.5	185.06320 691	247.50590 982	91.5	177.90056 157	240.16544 412
67.0	184.90544 662	247.38024 134	92.0	177.85037 203	239.99597 756
67.5	184.74688 427	247.25370 229	92.5	177.80893 633	239.82551 518
68.0	184.58754 801	247.12629 389	93.0	177.77660 328	239.65404 086
68.5	184.42746 832	246.99801 738	93.5	177.75371 324	239.48153 705
69.0	184.26667 824	246.86887 394	94.0	177.74059 663	239.30798 461
69.5	184.10521 359	246.73886 475	94.5	177.73757 262	239.13336 270
70.0	183.94311 315	246.60799 098	95.0	177.74494 789	238.95764 865
70.5	183.78041 896	246.47625 374	95.5	177.76301 558	238.78081 779
71.0	183.61717 651	246.34365 413	96.0	177.79205 444	238.60284 331
71.5	183.45343 505	246.21019 322	96.5	177.83232 815	238.42369 611
72.0	183.28924 788	246.07587 202	97.0	177.88408 489	238.24334 456
72.5	183.12467 260	245.94069 151	97.5	177.94755 705	238.06175 436
73.0	182.95977 150	245.80465 264	98.0	178.02296 123	237.87888 827
73.5	182.79461 184	245.66775 627	98.5	178.11049 842	237.69470 592
74.0	182.62926 622	245.53000 325	99.0	178.21035 437	237.50916 352
74.5	182.46381 296	245.39139 434	99.5	178.32270 017	237.32221 362
75.0	182.29833 646	245.25193 022	100.0	178.44769 300	237.13380 477

ρ	$b_r(i\rho)$	$b_{r+2}(i\rho)$	ρ	$b_r(i\rho)$	$b_{r+2}(i\rho)$
100.0	178.44769 300	237.13380 477	110.0	183.77700 617	232.92542 730
100.2	178.50126 402	237.05802 038	110.2	183.94183 482	232.82864 740
100.4	178.55689 045	236.98198 993	110.4	184.10912 519	232.73113 246
100.6	178.61458 068	236.90570 950	110.6	184.27889 403	232.63286 136
100.8	178.67434 281	236.82917 509	110.8	184.45115 888	232.53381 220
101.0	178.73618 469	236.75238 253	111.0	184.62593 819	232.43396 222
101.2	178.80011 390	236.67532 753	111.2	184.80325 126	232.33328 774
101.4	178.86613 778	236.59800 568	111.4	184.98311 840	232.23176 416
101.6	178.93426 345	236.52041 238	111.6	185.16556 087	232.12936 589
101.8	179.00449 782	236.44254 292	111.8	185.35060 102	232.02606 630
102.0	179.07684 760	236.36439 243	112.0	185.53826 230	231.92183 767
102.2	179.15131 932	236.28595 585	112.2	185.72856 933	231.81665 112
102.4	179.22791 934	236.20722 800	112.4	185.92154 795	231.71047 660
102.6	179.30665 389	236.12820 349	112.6	186.11722 532	231.60328 276
102.8	179.38752 904	236.04887 677	112.8	186.31562 993	231.49503 691
103.0	179.47055 078	235.96924 212	113.0	186.51679 174	231.38570 497
103.2	179.55572 495	235.88929 361	113.2	186.72074 224	231.27525 136
103.4	179.64305 737	235.80902 513	113.4	186.92751 449	231.16363 892
103.6	179.73255 374	235.72843 036	113.6	187.13714 328	231.05082 883
103.8	179.82421 976	235.64750 278	113.8	187.34966 519	230.93678 051
104.0	179.91806 106	235.56623 563	114.0	187.56511 870	230.82145 151
104.2	180.01408 330	235.48462 197	114.2	187.78354 431	230.70479 740
104.4	180.11229 210	235.40265 459	114.4	188.00498 464	230.58677 164
104.6	180.21269 316	235.32032 605	114.6	188.22948 462	230.46732 549
104.8	180.31529 219	235.23762 867	114.8	188.45709 156	230.34640 778
105.0	180.42009 496	235.15455 451	115.0	188.68785 535	230.22396 487
105.2	180.52710 735	235.07109 536	115.2	188.92182 864	230.09994 037
105.4	180.63633 532	234.98724 275	115.4	189.15906 697	229.97427 504
105.6	180.74778 496	234.90298 789	115.6	189.39962 901	229.84690 655
105.8	180.86146 250	234.81832 172	115.8	189.64357 677	229.71776 927
106.0	180.97737 433	234.73323 488	116.0	189.89097 584	229.58679 404
106.2	181.09552 703	234.64771 766	116.2	190.14189 563	229.45390 790
106.4	181.21592 738	234.56176 005	116.4	190.39640 968	229.31903 383
106.6	181.33858 238	234.47535 168	116.6	190.65459 596	229.18209 039
106.8	181.46349 926	234.38848 182	116.8	190.91653 720	229.04299 143
107.0	181.59068 556	234.30113 938	117.0	191.18232 132	228.90164 567
107.2	181.72014 906	234.21331 289	117.2	191.45204 179	228.75795 627
107.4	181.85189 788	234.12499 045	117.4	191.72579 814	228.61182 041
107.6	181.98594 048	234.03615 979	117.6	192.00369 645	228.46312 874
107.8	182.12228 565	233.94680 816	117.8	192.28584 998	228.31176 477
108.0	182.26094 259	233.85692 240	118.0	192.57237 974	228.15760 429
108.2	182.40192 089	233.76648 886	118.2	192.86341 529	228.00051 459
108.4	182.54523 058	233.67549 341	118.4	193.15909 551	227.84035 365
108.6	182.69088 215	233.58392 141	118.6	193.45956 956	227.67696 923
108.8	182.83888 658	233.49175 768	118.8	193.76499 789	227.51019 782
109.0	182.98925 536	233.39898 652	119.0	194.07555 343	227.33986 346
109.2	183.14200 050	233.30559 162	119.2	194.39142 297	227.16577 636
109.4	183.29713 463	233.21155 610	119.4	194.71280 868	226.98773 138
109.6	183.45467 094	233.11686 244	119.6	195.03992 991	226.80550 624
109.8	183.61462 328	233.02149 245	119.8	195.37302 524	226.61885 945
110.0	183.77700 617	232.92542 730	120.0	195.71235 485	226.42752 794

ρ	$b_r(i\rho)$	$b_{r+2}(i\rho)$	$FA(i\rho)$	$FB(i\rho)$
120.0	195.71235 485	226.42752 794	211.06994 139	943.42185 741
120.2	196.05820 337	226.23122 423	211.14471 380	910.41118 778
120.4	196.41088 305	226.02963 321	211.22025 813	877.27036 110
120.6	196.77073 772	225.82240 827	211.29657 299	843.99956 172
120.8	197.13814 731	225.60916 668	211.37365 699	810.59894 420
121.0	197.51353 334	225.38948 414	211.45150 874	777.06863 325
121.2	197.89736 556	225.16288 818	211.53012 687	743.40872 372
121.4	198.29016 992	224.92885 008	211.60951 000	709.61928 048
121.6	198.69253 847	224.68677 511	211.68965 679	675.70033 841
121.8	199.10514 148	224.43599 031	211.77056 589	641.65190 234
122.0	199.52874 267	224.17572 924	211.85223 595	607.47394 701
122.2	199.96421 853	223.90511 277	211.93466 565	573.16641 703
122.4	200.41258 300	223.62312 429	212.01785 364	538.72922 683
122.6	200.87501 969	223.32857 755	212.10179 862	504.16226 063
122.8	201.35292 445	223.02007 406	212.18649 925	469.46537 239
123.0	201.84796 285	222.69594 562	212.27195 423	434.63838 580
123.2	202.36214 936	222.35417 513	212.35816 225	399.68109 423
123.4	202.89795 931	221.99228 466	212.44512 199	364.59326 069
123.6	203.45849 170	221.60717 259	212.53283 215	329.37461 783
123.8	204.04771 474	221.19486 809	212.62129 142	294.02486 788
124.0	204.67085 169	220.75014 529	212.71049 849	258.54368 264
124.2	205.33502 001	220.26588 413	212.80045 207	222.93070 344
124.4	206.05036 249	219.73193 920	212.89115 084	187.18554 113
124.6	206.83223 221	219.13295 479	212.98259 350	151.30777 604
124.8	207.70595 769	218.44359 979	213.07477 874	115.29695 797
125.0	208.71931 771	217.61609 276	213.16770 523	79.15260 615
125.2	209.98745 165	216.53529 170	213.26137 167	42.87420 923
125.4	212.08482 972	214.62672 375	213.35577 674	6.46122 527

At ρ = 125.43541131

$b_{14}(i\rho) = b_{16}(i\rho) = 213.37256864$

(to 8D)

ρ	U	V		$FB(i\rho)$
125.6	213.45091 909	−2.74257 718		−30.08691 833
125.8	213.54679 740	−4.08567 084		−66.77082 481
126.0	213.64341 033	−5.08898 634		−103.59112 807
126.2	213.74075 654	−5.92765 748		−140.54849 270
126.4	213.83883 465	−6.66415 062		−177.64361 403
126.6	213.93764 331	−7.32934 544		−214.87721 810
126.8	214.03718 115	−7.94119 106		−252.25006 172
127.0	214.13744 677	−8.51121 220		−289.76293 244
127.2	214.23843 877	−9.04732 901		−327.41664 865
127.4	214.34015 576	−9.55526 111		−365.21205 951
127.6	214.44259 630	−10.03929 835		−403.15004 505
127.8	214.54575 896	−10.50275 578		−441.23151 611
128.0	214.64964 228	−10.94825 802		−479.45741 442
128.2	214.75424 481	−11.37792 504		−517.82871 260
128.4	214.85956 505	−11.79349 836		−556.34641 417
128.6	214.96560 151	−12.19642 933		−595.01155 356
128.8	215.07235 268	−12.58794 261		−633.82519 616
129.0	215.17981 701	−12.96908 283		−672.78843 829
129.2	215.28799 295	−13.34074 967		−711.90240 725
129.4	215.39687 894	−13.70372 451		−751.16826 134
129.6	215.50647 336	−14.05869 117		−790.58718 984
129.8	215.61677 462	−14.40625 223		−830.16041 305
130.0	215.72778 106	−14.74694 191		−869.88918 231

TABLE V. VALUES OF $a_r(q)$ AND $b_r(q)$

$$a_r(q) = U + iV, \qquad b_r(q) = U - iV$$

$$q = i\rho$$

$$r = 1(2)15$$

ρ	U	V	ρ	U	V
0.0	1.00000 000	0.00000 000	5.0	2.92805 120	6.75549 918
0.1	1.00124 993	0.10001 563	5.1	2.96275 207	6.92924 037
0.2	1.00499 895	0.20012 510	5.2	2.99662 008	7.10318 881
0.3	1.01124 467	0.30042 260	5.3	3.02970 865	7.27730 613
0.4	1.01998 299	0.40100 305	5.4	3.06206 918	7.45156 032
0.5	1.03120 800	0.50196 240	5.5	3.09375 073	7.62592 495
0.6	1.04491 171	0.60339 803	5.6	3.12479 978	7.80037 844
0.7	1.06108 378	0.70540 901	5.7	3.15526 021	7.97490 345
0.8	1.07971 117	0.80809 645	5.8	3.18517 319	8.14948 623
0.9	1.10077 772	0.91156 372	5.9	3.21457 720	8.32411 616
1.0	1.12426 362	1.01591 674	6.0	3.24350 815	8.49878 522
1.1	1.15014 482	1.12126 413	6.1	3.27199 938	8.67348 765
1.2	1.17839 238	1.22771 731	6.2	3.30008 182	8.84821 957
1.3	1.20897 164	1.33539 055	6.3	3.32778 408	9.02297 867
1.4	1.24184 142	1.44440 092	6.4	3.35513 260	9.19776 394
1.5	1.27695 306	1.55486 799	6.5	3.38215 174	9.37257 544
1.6	1.31424 939	1.66691 355	6.6	3.40886 395	9.54741 412
1.7	1.35366 366	1.78066 098	6.7	3.43528 985	9.72228 164
1.8	1.39511 848	1.89623 446	6.8	3.46144 841	9.89718 021
1.9	1.43852 466	2.01375 792	6.9	3.48735 700	10.07211 249
2.0	1.48378 025	2.13335 367	7.0	3.51303 157	10.24708 148
2.1	1.53076 958	2.25514 068	7.1	3.53848 670	10.42209 039
2.2	1.57936 263	2.37923 262	7.2	3.56373 576	10.59714 263
2.3	1.62941 460	2.50573 553	7.3	3.58879 094	10.77224 171
2.4	1.68076 597	2.63474 518	7.4	3.61366 339	10.94739 118
2.5	1.73324 309	2.76634 425	7.5	3.63836 328	11.12259 460
2.6	1.78665 929	2.90059 948	7.6	3.66289 987	11.29785 550
2.7	1.84081 683	3.03755 879	7.7	3.68728 160	11.47317 734
2.8	1.89550 942	3.17724 866	7.8	3.71151 617	11.64856 350
2.9	1.95052 559	3.31967 205	7.9	3.73561 056	11.82401 725
3.0	2.00565 250	3.46480 686	8.0	3.75957 111	11.99954 174
3.1	2.06068 032	3.61260 537	8.1	3.78340 357	12.17513 998
3.2	2.11540 670	3.76299 457	8.2	3.80711 318	12.35081 483
3.3	2.16964 117	3.91587 761	8.3	3.83070 466	12.52656 900
3.4	2.22320 922	4.07113 616	8.4	3.85418 229	12.70240 505
3.5	2.27595 566	4.22863 374	8.5	3.87754 994	12.87832 537
3.6	2.32774 712	4.38821 958	8.6	3.90081 110	13.05433 219
3.7	2.37847 363	4.54973 295	8.7	3.92396 891	13.23042 758
3.8	2.42804 911	4.71300 752	8.8	3.94702 623	13.40661 345
3.9	2.47641 091	4.87787 554	8.9	3.96998 560	13.58289 154
4.0	2.52351 859	5.04417 164	9.0	3.99284 933	13.75926 346
4.1	2.56935 197	5.21173 601	9.1	4.01561 947	13.93573 064
4.2	2.61390 882	5.38041 698	9.2	4.03829 789	14.11229 437
4.3	2.65720 228	5.55007 289	9.3	4.06088 624	14.28895 580
4.4	2.69925 818	5.72057 330	9.4	4.08338 603	14.46571 593
4.5	2.74011 252	5.89179 969	9.5	4.10579 857	14.64257 565
4.6	2.77980 903	6.06364 561	9.6	4.12812 507	14.81953 570
4.7	2.81839 708	6.23601 647	9.7	4.15036 661	14.99659 669
4.8	2.85592 978	6.40882 907	9.8	4.17252 413	15.17375 912
4.9	2.89246 244	6.58201 086	9.9	4.19459 851	15.35102 339
5.0	2.92805 120	6.75549 918	10.0	4.21659 052	15.52838 978

TABLE V. $a_r(i\rho) = U + iV, b_r(i\rho) = U - iV$ $r = 1$

ρ	U	V	ρ	U	V
10.0	4.21659 052	15.52838 978	20.0	6.06983 699	33.66952 935
10.2	4.26033 011	15.88342 950	20.2	6.10141 603	34.03804 472
10.4	4.30374 771	16.23887 860	20.4	6.13283 658	34.40671 434
10.6	4.34684 726	16.59473 597	20.6	6.16410 113	34.77553 587
10.8	4.38963 209	16.95099 931	20.8	6.19521 214	35.14450 703
11.0	4.43210 507	17.30766 525	21.0	6.22617 198	35.51362 562
11.2	4.47426 877	17.66472 949	21.2	6.25698 296	35.88288 949
11.4	4.51612 560	18.02218 694	21.4	6.28764 735	36.25229 657
11.6	4.55767 785	18.38003 188	21.6	6.31816 732	36.62184 483
11.8	4.59892 779	18.73825 800	21.8	6.34854 503	36.99153 232
12.0	4.63987 776	19.09685 856	22.0	6.37878 255	37.36135 712
12.2	4.68053 015	19.45582 649	22.2	6.40888 192	37.73131 737
12.4	4.72088 747	19.81515 443	22.4	6.43884 509	38.10141 126
12.6	4.76095 234	20.17483 484	22.6	6.46867 401	38.47163 703
12.8	4.80072 755	20.53486 004	22.8	6.49837 053	38.84199 295
13.0	4.84021 600	20.89522 232	23.0	6.52793 650	39.21247 735
13.2	4.87942 076	21.25591 391	23.2	6.55737 368	39.58308 858
13.4	4.91834 503	21.61692 710	23.4	6.58668 383	39.95382 504
13.6	4.95699 214	21.97825 424	23.6	6.61586 862	40.32468 516
13.8	4.99536 554	22.33988 778	23.8	6.64492 972	40.69566 742
14.0	5.03346 880	22.70182 029	24.0	6.67386 873	41.06677 032
14.2	5.07130 558	23.06404 450	24.2	6.70268 723	41.43799 239
14.4	5.10887 962	23.42655 328	24.4	6.73138 676	41.80933 219
14.6	5.14619 474	23.78933 971	24.6	6.75996 881	42.18078 833
14.8	5.18325 482	24.15239 705	24.8	6.78843 486	42.55235 943
15.0	5.22006 376	24.51571 875	25.0	6.81678 633	42.92404 413
15.2	5.25662 551	24.87929 847	25.2	6.84502 463	43.29584 112
15.4	5.29294 404	25.24313 007	25.4	6.87315 112	43.66774 911
15.6	5.32902 332	25.60720 763	25.6	6.90116 715	44.03976 681
15.8	5.36486 731	25.97152 542	25.8	6.92907 402	44.41189 298
16.0	5.40047 997	26.33607 794	26.0	6.95687 302	44.78412 639
16.2	5.43586 523	26.70085 986	26.2	6.98456 540	45.15646 586
16.4	5.47102 699	27.06586 607	26.4	7.01215 239	45.52891 018
16.6	5.50596 911	27.43109 165	26.6	7.03963 519	45.90145 821
16.8	5.54069 539	27.79653 185	26.8	7.06701 499	46.27410 881
17.0	5.57520 961	28.16218 214	27.0	7.09429 294	46.64686 086
17.2	5.60951 547	28.52803 812	27.2	7.12147 017	47.01971 326
17.4	5.64361 662	28.89409 558	27.4	7.14854 779	47.39266 493
17.6	5.67751 665	29.26035 049	27.6	7.17552 689	47.76571 481
17.8	5.71121 906	29.62679 894	27.8	7.20240 854	48.13886 185
18.0	5.74472 730	29.99343 720	28.0	7.22919 379	48.51210 503
18.2	5.77804 476	30.36026 166	28.2	7.25588 366	48.88544 335
18.4	5.81117 474	30.72726 887	28.4	7.28247 916	49.25887 580
18.6	5.84412 045	31.09445 548	28.6	7.30898 130	49.63240 141
18.8	5.87688 507	31.46181 828	28.8	7.33539 103	50.00601 924
19.0	5.90947 166	31.82935 418	29.0	7.36170 932	50.37972 831
19.2	5.94188 325	32.19706 020	29.2	7.38793 710	50.75352 773
19.4	5.97412 275	32.56493 346	29.4	7.41407 530	51.12741 655
19.6	6.00619 302	32.93297 117	29.6	7.44012 482	51.50139 390
19.8	6.03809 686	33.30117 067	29.8	7.46608 655	51.87545 888
20.0	6.06983 699	33.66952 935	30.0	7.49196 138	52.24961 062

TABLE V. $a_r(i\rho) = U + iV, b_r(i\rho) = U - iV$ $r = 1$

ρ	U	V	ρ	U	V
30.0	7.49196 138	52.24961 062	40.0	8.69079 734	71.05192 071
30.2	7.51775 016	52.62384 826	40.2	8.71313 887	71.42959 824
30.4	7.54345 374	52.99817 097	40.4	8.73542 484	71.80733 117
30.6	7.56907 296	53.37257 790	40.6	8.75765 567	72.18511 911
30.8	7.59460 862	53.74706 825	40.8	8.77983 176	72.56296 164
31.0	7.62006 155	54.12164 121	41.0	8.80195 352	72.94085 837
31.2	7.64543 253	54.49629 597	41.2	8.82402 133	73.31880 889
31.4	7.67072 234	54.87103 178	41.4	8.84603 560	73.69681 282
31.6	7.69593 176	55.24584 785	41.6	8.86799 672	74.07486 977
31.8	7.72106 154	55.62074 342	41.8	8.88990 505	74.45297 935
32.0	7.74611 242	55.99571 776	42.0	8.91176 100	74.83114 119
32.2	7.77108 514	56.37077 013	42.2	8.93356 492	75.20935 492
32.4	7.79598 042	56.74589 980	42.4	8.95531 719	75.58762 017
32.6	7.82079 898	57.12110 606	42.6	8.97701 818	75.96593 657
32.8	7.84554 150	57.49638 822	42.8	8.99866 824	76.34430 377
33.0	7.87020 869	57.87174 557	43.0	9.02026 773	76.72272 141
33.2	7.89480 122	58.24717 744	43.2	9.04181 701	77.10118 913
33.4	7.91931 976	58.62268 316	43.4	9.06331 642	77.47970 659
33.6	7.94376 498	58.99826 206	43.6	9.08476 631	77.85827 345
33.8	7.96813 752	59.37391 349	43.8	9.10616 703	78.23688 937
34.0	7.99243 802	59.74963 681	44.0	9.12751 889	78.61555 401
34.2	8.01666 712	60.12543 139	44.2	9.14882 225	78.99426 704
34.4	8.04082 544	60.50129 661	44.4	9.17007 743	79.37302 813
34.6	8.06491 359	60.87723 184	44.6	9.19128 475	79.75183 696
34.8	8.08893 218	61.25323 648	44.8	9.21244 454	80.13069 320
35.0	8.11288 181	61.62930 993	45.0	9.23355 711	80.50959 655
35.2	8.13676 305	62.00545 161	45.2	9.25462 279	80.88854 668
35.4	8.16057 650	62.38166 093	45.4	9.27564 187	81.26754 330
35.6	8.18432 273	62.75793 732	45.6	9.29661 468	81.64658 608
35.8	8.20800 229	63.13428 022	45.8	9.31754 151	82.02567 472
36.0	8.23161 575	63.51068 906	46.0	9.33842 266	82.40480 894
36.2	8.25516 365	63.88716 330	46.2	9.35925 844	82.78398 843
36.4	8.27864 654	64.26370 240	46.4	9.38004 913	83.16321 289
36.6	8.30206 496	64.64030 583	46.6	9.40079 503	83.54248 204
36.8	8.32541 941	65.01697 304	46.8	9.42149 643	83.92179 559
37.0	8.34871 044	65.39370 353	47.0	9.44215 361	84.30115 325
37.2	8.37193 855	65.77049 679	47.2	9.46276 686	84.68055 475
37.4	8.39510 424	66.14735 230	47.4	9.48333 646	85.05999 981
37.6	8.41820 802	66.52426 956	47.6	9.50386 267	85.43948 815
37.8	8.44125 038	66.90124 809	47.8	9.52434 578	85.81901 950
38.0	8.46423 180	67.27828 740	48.0	9.54478 605	86.19859 359
38.2	8.48715 277	67.65538 700	48.2	9.56518 375	86.57821 015
38.4	8.51001 376	68.03254 643	48.4	9.58553 916	86.95786 892
38.6	8.53281 524	68.40976 522	48.6	9.60585 252	87.33756 964
38.8	8.55555 767	68.78704 290	48.8	9.62612 410	87.71731 205
39.0	8.57824 151	69.16437 902	49.0	9.64635 415	88.09709 589
39.2	8.60086 720	69.54177 314	49.2	9.66654 294	88.47692 091
39.4	8.62343 519	69.91922 480	49.4	9.68669 071	88.85678 687
39.6	8.64594 592	70.29673 357	49.6	9.70679 771	89.23669 350
39.8	8.66839 983	70.67429 902	49.8	9.72686 418	89.61664 058
40.0	8.69079 734	71.05192 071	50.0	9.74689 038	89.99662 784

TABLE V. $a_r(i\rho) = U + iV, b_r(i\rho) = U - iV$ $r = 1$

ρ	U	V	ρ	U	V
50.0	9.74689 038	89.99662 784	75.0	11.99490 506	137.74983 650
50.5	9.79678 124	90.94677 029	75.5	12.03567 046	138.70908 905
51.0	9.84642 557	91.89715 874	76.0	12.07630 104	139.66847 624
51.5	9.89582 699	92.84778 961	76.5	12.11679 813	140.62799 674
52.0	9.94498 904	93.79865 938	77.0	12.15716 304	141.58764 925
52.5	9.99391 516	94.74976 460	77.5	12.19739 705	142.54743 248
53.0	10.04260 871	95.70110 193	78.0	12.23750 143	143.50734 517
53.5	10.09107 299	96.65266 809	78.5	12.27747 743	144.46738 608
54.0	10.13931 119	97.60445 989	79.0	12.31732 626	145.42755 399
54.5	10.18732 646	98.55647 420	79.5	12.35704 915	146.38784 769
55.0	10.23512 186	99.50870 796	80.0	12.39664 726	147.34826 600
55.5	10.28270 038	100.46115 821	80.5	12.43612 178	148.30880 776
56.0	10.33006 494	101.41382 201	81.0	12.47547 384	149.26947 181
56.5	10.37721 841	102.36669 653	81.5	12.51470 459	150.23025 702
57.0	10.42416 359	103.31977 896	82.0	12.55381 514	151.19116 229
57.5	10.47090 321	104.27306 658	82.5	12.59280 658	152.15218 651
58.0	10.51743 994	105.22655 673	83.0	12.63168 001	153.11332 861
58.5	10.56377 641	106.18024 679	83.5	12.67043 647	154.07458 753
59.0	10.60991 518	107.13413 421	84.0	12.70907 703	155.03596 221
59.5	10.65585 876	108.08821 649	84.5	12.74760 272	155.99745 163
60.0	10.70160 960	109.04249 117	85.0	12.78601 455	156.95905 476
60.5	10.74717 011	109.99695 585	85.5	12.82431 353	157.92077 062
61.0	10.79254 265	110.95160 820	86.0	12.86250 065	158.88259 821
61.5	10.83772 953	111.90644 590	86.5	12.90057 688	159.84453 655
62.0	10.88273 299	112.86146 671	87.0	12.93854 318	160.80658 469
62.5	10.92755 527	113.81666 841	87.5	12.97640 050	161.76874 169
63.0	10.97219 853	114.77204 884	88.0	13.01414 977	162.73100 661
63.5	11.01666 489	115.72760 588	88.5	13.05179 191	163.69337 854
64.0	11.06095 645	116.68333 744	89.0	13.08932 783	164.65585 657
64.5	11.10507 525	117.63924 149	89.5	13.12675 843	165.61843 981
65.0	11.14902 329	118.59531 603	90.0	13.16408 458	166.58112 737
65.5	11.19280 255	119.55155 909	90.5	13.20130 715	167.54391 840
66.0	11.23641 495	120.50796 875	91.0	13.23842 701	168.50681 202
66.5	11.27986 238	121.46454 312	91.5	13.27544 499	169.46980 741
67.0	11.32314 671	122.42128 035	92.0	13.31236 194	170.43290 373
67.5	11.36626 976	123.37817 861	92.5	13.34917 867	171.39610 015
68.0	11.40923 331	124.33523 613	93.0	13.38589 599	172.35939 587
68.5	11.45203 913	125.29245 115	93.5	13.42251 471	173.32279 009
69.0	11.49468 893	126.24982 195	94.0	13.45903 562	174.28628 201
69.5	11.53718 442	127.20734 685	94.5	13.49545 950	175.24987 086
70.0	11.57952 725	128.16502 417	95.0	13.53178 711	176.21355 587
70.5	11.62171 905	129.12285 230	95.5	13.56801 922	177.17733 629
71.0	11.66376 144	130.08082 964	96.0	13.60415 657	178.14121 137
71.5	11.70565 599	131.03895 460	96.5	13.64019 991	179.10518 036
72.0	11.74740 425	131.99722 565	97.0	13.67614 996	180.06924 254
72.5	11.78900 773	132.95564 126	97.5	13.71200 744	181.03339 719
73.0	11.83046 794	133.91419 995	98.0	13.74777 307	181.99764 360
73.5	11.87178 635	134.87290 025	98.5	13.78344 755	182.96198 106
74.0	11.91296 439	135.83174 072	99.0	13.81903 157	183.92640 890
74.5	11.95400 350	136.79071 993	99.5	13.85452 582	184.89092 641
75.0	11.99490 506	137.74983 650	100.0	13.88993 097	185.85553 294

TABLE V. $a_r(i\rho) = U + iV, b_r(i\rho) = U - iV$ $r = 3$

ρ	U	V	ρ	U	V
0.0	9.00000 000	0.00000 000	5.0	8.62470 211	-1.77826 441
0.1	8.99937 506	-0.00001 563	5.1	8.65232 476	-1.85444 502
0.2	8.99750 102	-0.00012 510	5.2	8.68197 993	-1.93104 197
0.3	8.99438 020	-0.00042 262	5.3	8.71361 160	-2.00803 060
0.4	8.99001 659	-0.00100 312	5.4	8.74716 565	-2.08539 330
0.5	8.98441 598	-0.00196 261	5.5	8.78259 007	-2.16311 870
0.6	8.97758 618	-0.00339 856	5.6	8.81983 522	-2.24120 099
0.7	8.96953 732	-0.00541 015	5.7	8.85885 386	-2.31963 927
0.8	8.96028 217	-0.00809 867	5.8	8.89960 116	-2.39843 702
0.9	8.94983 662	-0.01156 773	5.9	8.94203 471	-2.47760 154
1.0	8.93822 015	-0.01592 354	6.0	8.98611 437	-2.55714 356
1.1	8.92545 642	-0.02127 509	6.1	9.03180 220	-2.63707 680
1.2	8.91157 400	-0.02773 425	6.2	9.07906 227	-2.71741 771
1.3	8.89660 708	-0.03541 586	6.3	9.12786 057	-2.79818 509
1.4	8.88059 637	-0.04443 760	6.4	9.17816 477	-2.87939 991
1.5	8.86359 002	-0.05491 983	6.5	9.22994 409	-2.96108 504
1.6	8.84564 464	-0.06698 520	6.6	9.28316 910	-3.04326 512
1.7	8.82682 640	-0.08075 809	6.7	9.33781 157	-3.12596 635
1.8	8.80721 206	-0.09636 384	6.8	9.39384 424	-3.20921 636
1.9	8.78689 016	-0.11392 765	6.9	9.45124 064	-3.29304 410
2.0	8.76596 196	-0.13357 326	7.0	9.50997 495	-3.37747 974
2.1	8.74454 238	-0.15542 127	7.1	9.57002 180	-3.46255 457
2.2	8.72276 070	-0.17958 715	7.2	9.63135 604	-3.54830 087
2.3	8.70076 092	-0.20617 888	7.3	9.69395 263	-3.63475 191
2.4	8.67870 171	-0.23529 441	7.4	9.75778 642	-3.72194 181
2.5	8.65675 589	-0.26701 881	7.5	9.82283 200	-3.80990 545
2.6	8.63510 921	-0.30142 141	7.6	9.88906 347	-3.89867 848
2.7	8.61395 850	-0.33855 294	7.7	9.95645 434	-3.98829 714
2.8	8.59350 907	-0.37844 298	7.8	10.02497 728	-4.07879 822
2.9	8.57397 142	-0.42109 777	7.9	10.09460 403	-4.17021 896
3.0	8.55555 733	-0.46649 883	8.0	10.16530 513	-4.26259 696
3.1	8.53847 558	-0.51460 229	8.1	10.23704 987	-4.35597 004
3.2	8.52292 745	-0.56533 929	8.2	10.30980 604	-4.45037 611
3.3	8.50910 225	-0.61861 744	8.3	10.38353 981	-4.54585 307
3.4	8.49717 333	-0.67432 318	8.4	10.45821 559	-4.64243 860
3.5	8.48729 469	-0.73232 512	8.5	10.53379 589	-4.74017 003
3.6	8.47959 845	-0.79247 795	8.6	10.61024 191	-4.83908 412
3.7	8.47419 331	-0.85462 674	8.7	10.68750 984	-4.93921 686
3.8	8.47116 404	-0.91861 133	8.8	10.76555 795	-5.04060 325
3.9	8.47057 190	-0.98427 052	8.9	10.84433 938	-5.14327 704
4.0	8.47245 595	-1.05144 591	9.0	10.92380 562	-5.24727 051
4.1	8.47683 489	-1.11998 508	9.1	11.00390 582	-5.35261 412
4.2	8.48370 944	-1.18974 415	9.2	11.08458 679	-5.45933 631
4.3	8.49306 491	-1.26058 974	9.3	11.16579 309	-5.56746 312
4.4	8.50487 381	-1.33240 014	9.4	11.24746 704	-5.67701 796
4.5	8.51909 846	-1.40506 604	9.5	11.32954 895	-5.78802 126
4.6	8.53569 334	-1.47849 070	9.6	11.41197 719	-5.90049 019
4.7	8.55460 722	-1.55258 977	9.7	11.49468 851	-6.01443 837
4.8	8.57578 503	-1.62729 080	9.8	11.57761 823	-6.12987 563
4.9	8.59916 944	-1.70253 261	9.9	11.66070 055	-6.24680 771
5.0	8.62470 211	-1.77826 441	10.0	11.74386 894	-6.36523 611

ρ	U	V	ρ	U	V
10.0	11.74386 894	−6.36523 611	20.0	17.69166 538	−20.99373 219
10.2	11.91019 629	−6.60656 556	20.2	17.78462 975	−21.29896 613
10.4	12.07606 799	−6.85378 542	20.4	17.87725 431	−21.60457 517
10.6	12.24096 665	−7.10674 344	20.6	17.96954 342	−21.91056 549
10.8	12.40440 436	−7.36521 616	20.8	18.06150 065	−22.21694 250
11.0	12.56593 649	−7.62891 536	21.0	18.15312 895	−22.52371 080
11.2	12.72517 350	−7.89749 798	21.2	18.24443 068	−22.83087 424
11.4	12.88178 973	−8.17057 873	21.4	18.33540 776	−23.13843 594
11.6	13.03552 853	−8.44774 430	21.6	18.42606 166	−23.44639 834
11.8	13.18620 360	−8.72856 788	21.8	18.51639 354	−23.75476 323
12.0	13.33369 672	−9.01262 287	22.0	18.60640 428	−24.06353 180
12.2	13.47795 262	−9.29949 488	22.2	18.69609 453	−24.37270 463
12.4	13.61897 160	−9.58879 140	22.4	18.78546 478	−24.68228 180
12.6	13.75680 107	−9.88014 888	22.6	18.87451 539	−24.99226 287
12.8	13.89152 651	10.17323 732	22.8	18.96324 661	−25.30264 692
13.0	14.02326 272	10.46776 259	23.0	19.05165 866	−25.61343 262
13.2	14.15214 576	10.76346 691	23.2	19.13975 171	−25.92461 823
13.4	14.27832 578	11.06012 784	23.4	19.22752 594	−26.23620 166
13.6	14.40196 103	11.35755 632	23.6	19.31498 156	−26.54818 047
13.8	14.52321 289	11.65559 399	23.8	19.40211 881	−26.86055 193
14.0	14.64224 208	11.95411 019	24.0	19.48893 798	−27.17331 305
14.2	14.75920 565	12.25299 891	24.2	19.57543 945	−27.48646 058
14.4	14.87425 484	12.55217 561	24.4	19.66162 366	−27.79999 105
14.6	14.98753 363	12.85157 441	24.6	19.74749 115	−28.11390 083
14.8	15.09917 778	13.15114 531	24.8	19.83304 255	−28.42818 611
15.0	15.20931 428	13.45085 181	25.0	19.91827 861	−28.74284 292
15.2	15.31806 117	13.75066 870	25.2	20.00320 016	−29.05786 721
15.4	15.42552 754	14.05058 017	25.4	20.08780 815	−29.37325 478
15.6	15.53181 374	14.35057 813	25.6	20.17210 364	−29.68900 140
15.8	15.63701 175	14.65066 078	25.8	20.25608 779	−30.00510 274
16.0	15.74120 548	14.95083 141	26.0	20.33976 187	−30.32155 444
16.2	15.84447 133	15.25109 730	26.2	20.42312 725	−30.63835 210
16.4	15.94687 860	15.55146 885	26.4	20.50618 540	−30.95549 130
16.6	16.04848 999	15.85195 886	26.6	20.58893 790	−31.27296 763
16.8	16.14936 209	16.15258 187	26.8	20.67138 640	−31.59077 666
17.0	16.24954 586	16.45335 364	27.0	20.75353 266	−31.90891 401
17.2	16.34908 703	16.75429 072	27.2	20.83537 851	−32.22737 528
17.4	16.44802 658	17.05541 008	27.4	20.91692 586	−32.54615 615
17.6	16.54640 115	17.35672 881	27.6	20.99817 670	−32.86525 230
17.8	16.64424 335	17.65826 389	27.8	21.07913 310	−33.18465 950
18.0	16.74158 220	17.96003 198	28.0	21.15979 715	−33.50437 354
18.2	16.83844 339	18.26204 927	28.2	21.24017 105	−33.82439 029
18.4	16.93484 966	18.56433 132	28.4	21.32025 702	−34.14470 566
18.6	17.03082 099	18.86689 303	28.6	21.40005 733	−34.46531 566
18.8	17.12637 494	19.16974 851	28.8	21.47957 431	−34.78621 633
19.0	17.22152 687	19.47291 103	29.0	21.55881 030	−35.10740 383
19.2	17.31629 013	19.77639 299	29.2	21.63776 769	−35.42887 435
19.4	17.41067 632	20.08020 593	29.4	21.71644 889	−35.75062 419
19.6	17.50469 542	20.38436 045	29.6	21.79485 634	−36.07264 970
19.8	17.59835 600	20.68886 626	29.8	21.87299 249	−36.39494 733
20.0	17.69166 538	20.99373 219	30.0	21.95085 980	−36.71751 360

322-566 O - 69 - 18

TABLE V. $a_r(i\rho) = U+iV, b_r(i\rho) = U-iV$ $r=3$

ρ	U	V	ρ	U	V
30.0	21.95085 980	-36.71751 360	40.0	25.55223 829	-53.13096 750
30.2	22.02846 076	-37.04034 511	40.2	25.61929 686	-53.46408 457
30.4	22.10579 784	-37.36343 853	40.4	25.68618 846	-53.79736 617
30.6	22.18287 353	-37.68679 063	40.6	25.75291 440	-54.13081 112
30.8	22.25969 032	-38.01039 823	40.8	25.81947 594	-54.46441 826
31.0	22.33625 067	-38.33425 825	41.0	25.88587 432	-54.79818 644
31.2	22.41255 707	-38.65836 767	41.2	25.95211 078	-55.13211 454
31.4	22.48861 197	-38.98272 354	41.4	26.01818 653	-55.46620 143
31.6	22.56441 784	-39.30732 300	41.6	26.08410 277	-55.80044 601
31.8	22.63997 710	-39.63216 326	41.8	26.14986 066	-56.13484 718
32.0	22.71529 217	-39.95724 158	42.0	26.21546 138	-56.46940 387
32.2	22.79036 545	-40.28255 531	42.2	26.28090 606	-56.80411 501
32.4	22.86519 933	-40.60810 185	42.4	26.34619 584	-57.13897 954
32.6	22.93979 616	-40.93387 866	42.6	26.41133 182	-57.47399 642
32.8	23.01415 827	-41.25988 329	42.8	26.47631 510	-57.80916 461
33.0	23.08828 799	-41.58611 333	43.0	26.54114 677	-58.14448 310
33.2	23.16218 758	-41.91256 644	43.2	26.60582 789	-58.47995 087
33.4	23.23585 931	-42.23924 031	43.4	26.67035 952	-58.81556 692
33.6	23.30930 541	-42.56613 271	43.6	26.73474 269	-59.15133 027
33.8	23.38252 808	-42.89324 147	43.8	26.79897 844	-59.48723 994
34.0	23.45552 950	-43.22056 445	44.0	26.86306 777	-59.82329 495
34.2	23.52831 179	-43.54809 958	44.2	26.92701 169	-60.15949 435
34.4	23.60087 709	-43.87584 481	44.4	26.99081 119	-60.49583 719
34.6	23.67322 746	-44.20379 817	44.6	27.05446 724	-60.83232 253
34.8	23.74536 497	-44.53195 772	44.8	27.11798 080	-61.16894 944
35.0	23.81729 163	-44.86032 154	45.0	27.18135 282	-61.50571 700
35.2	23.88900 943	-45.18888 779	45.2	27.24458 426	-61.84262 430
35.4	23.96052 034	-45.51765 466	45.4	27.30767 603	-62.17967 044
35.6	24.03182 628	-45.84662 035	45.6	27.37062 905	-62.51685 452
35.8	24.10292 916	-46.17578 312	45.8	27.43344 424	-62.85417 565
36.0	24.17383 084	-46.50514 128	46.0	27.49612 249	-63.19163 297
36.2	24.24453 317	-46.83469 315	46.2	27.55866 469	-63.52922 560
36.4	24.31503 794	-47.16443 708	46.4	27.62107 170	-63.86695 269
36.6	24.38534 695	-47.49437 147	46.6	27.68334 442	-64.20481 339
36.8	24.45546 194	-47.82449 474	46.8	27.74548 367	-64.54280 684
37.0	24.52538 464	48.15480 534	47.0	27.80749 033	-64.88093 223
37.2	24.59511 674	-48.48530 174	47.2	27.86936 522	-65.21918 872
37.4	24.66465 990	-48.81598 247	47.4	27.93110 918	-65.55757 549
37.6	24.73401 576	-49.14684 603	47.6	27.99272 302	-65.89609 174
37.8	24.80318 595	-49.47789 100	47.8	28.05420 756	-66.23473 665
38.0	24.87217 203	-49.80911 595	48.0	28.11556 360	-66.57350 945
38.2	24.94097 557	-50.14051 948	48.2	28.17679 194	-66.91240 933
38.4	25.00959 811	-50.47210 022	48.4	28.23789 337	-67.25143 552
38.6	25.07804 116	-50.80385 682	48.6	28.29886 865	-67.59058 724
38.8	25.14630 619	-51.13578 795	48.8	28.35971 857	-67.92986 374
39.0	25.21439 466	-51.46789 228	49.0	28.42044 389	-68.26926 424
39.2	25.28230 803	-51.80016 853	49.2	28.48104 535	-68.60878 801
39.4	25.35004 769	-52.13261 543	49.4	28.54152 372	-68.94843 430
39.6	25.41761 505	-52.46523 171	49.6	28.60187 972	-69.28820 236
39.8	25.48501 147	-52.79801 614	49.8	28.66211 409	-69.62809 148
40.0	25.55223 829	-53.13096 750	50.0	28.72222 757	-69.96810 092

TABLE V. $a_r(i\rho) = U+iV, b_r(i\rho) = U-iV$ $r=3$

ρ	U	V	ρ	U	V
50.0	28.72222 757	−69.96810 092	75.0	35.46958 424	−113.23218 169
50.5	28.87198 699	−70.81864 628	75.5	35.59192 924	−114.11000 398
51.0	29.02100 629	−71.66992 822	76.0	35.71386 932	−114.98822 948
51.5	29.16929 622	−72.52193 599	76.5	35.83540 848	−115.86685 423
52.0	29.31686 730	−73.37465 907	77.0	35.95655 064	−116.74587 432
52.5	29.46372 982	−74.22808 721	77.5	36.07729 968	−117.62528 593
53.0	29.60989 381	−75.08221 038	78.0	36.19765 939	−118.50508 528
53.5	29.75536 907	−75.93701 878	78.5	36.31763 352	−119.38526 864
54.0	29.90016 520	−76.79250 283	79.0	36.43722 574	−120.26583 237
54.5	30.04429 156	−77.64865 317	79.5	36.55643 968	−121.14677 287
55.0	30.18775 732	−78.50546 066	80.0	36.67527 892	−122.02808 659
55.5	30.33057 144	−79.36291 635	80.5	36.79374 695	−122.90977 005
56.0	30.47274 269	−80.22101 149	81.0	36.91184 723	−123.79181 981
56.5	30.61427 965	−81.07973 754	81.5	37.02958 318	−124.67423 250
57.0	30.75519 070	−81.93908 613	82.0	37.14695 814	−125.55700 478
57.5	30.89548 405	−82.79904 909	82.5	37.26397 540	−126.44013 338
58.0	31.03516 775	−83.65961 841	83.0	37.38063 822	−127.32361 507
58.5	31.17424 966	−84.52078 627	83.5	37.49694 981	−128.20744 667
59.0	31.31273 748	−85.38254 499	84.0	37.61291 331	−129.09162 504
59.5	31.45063 875	−86.24488 709	84.5	37.72853 183	−129.97614 710
60.0	31.58796 087	−87.10780 523	85.0	37.84380 843	−130.86100 981
60.5	31.72471 106	−87.97129 221	85.5	37.95874 612	−131.74621 017
61.0	31.86089 641	−88.83534 099	86.0	38.07334 788	−132.63174 522
61.5	31.99652 386	−89.69994 470	86.5	38.18761 664	−133.51761 207
62.0	32.13160 022	−90.56509 657	87.0	38.30155 528	−134.40380 784
62.5	32.26613 214	−91.43078 999	87.5	38.41516 664	−135.29032 970
63.0	32.40012 617	−92.29701 849	88.0	38.52845 353	−136.17717 486
63.5	32.53358 872	−93.16377 570	88.5	38.64141 871	−137.06434 059
64.0	32.66652 604	−94.03105 540	89.0	38.75406 491	−137.95182 417
64.5	32.79894 432	−94.89885 149	89.5	38.86639 482	−138.83962 292
65.0	32.93084 957	−95.76715 798	90.0	38.97841 108	−139.72773 423
65.5	33.06224 773	−96.63596 900	90.5	39.09011 631	−140.61615 548
66.0	33.19314 460	−97.50527 879	91.0	39.20151 308	−141.50488 412
66.5	33.32354 588	−98.37508 172	91.5	39.31260 393	−142.39391 762
67.0	33.45345 717	−99.24537 222	92.0	39.42339 137	−143.28325 349
67.5	33.58288 393	−100.11614 488	92.5	39.53387 788	−144.17288 927
68.0	33.71183 158	−100.98739 434	93.0	39.64406 589	−145.06282 254
68.5	33.84030 538	−101.85911 537	93.5	39.75395 780	−145.95305 090
69.0	33.96831 052	−102.73130 283	94.0	39.86355 600	−146.84357 200
69.5	34.09585 211	−103.60395 166	94.5	39.97286 282	−147.73438 350
70.0	34.22293 514	−104.47705 691	95.0	40.08188 058	−148.62548 310
70.5	34.34956 453	−105.35061 371	95.5	40.19061 156	−149.51686 855
71.0	34.47574 510	−106.22461 726	96.0	40.29905 800	−150.40853 759
71.5	34.60148 160	−107.09906 288	96.5	40.40722 213	−151.30048 802
72.0	34.72677 868	−107.97394 593	97.0	40.51510 615	−152.19271 765
72.5	34.85164 092	108.84926 189	97.5	40.62271 221	−153.08522 434
73.0	34.97607 281	−109.72500 629	98.0	40.73004 246	−153.97800 596
73.5	35.10007 878	−110.60117 474	98.5	40.83709 901	−154.87106 041
74.0	35.22366 318	−111.47776 294	99.0	40.94388 393	−155.76438 562
74.5	35.34683 026	−112.35476 664	99.5	41.05039 930	−156.65797 954
75.0	35.46958 424	113.23218 169	100.0	41.15664 712	−157.55184 015

TABLE V. $a_r(i\rho) = U + iV, b_r(i\rho) = U - iV$ $\qquad$ $r = 5$

ρ	U	V	ρ	U	V
0.0	25.00000 000	0.00000 000	5.0	24.48763 532	0.02280 290
0.1	24.99979 167	0.00000 000	5.1	24.46729 038	0.02524 798
0.2	24.99916 669	0.00000 000	5.2	24.44657 283	0.02790 284
0.3	24.99812 512	0.00000 002	5.3	24.42548 501	0.03078 129
0.4	24.99666 703	0.00000 007	5.4	24.40402 944	0.03389 780
0.5	24.99479 255	0.00000 021	5.5	24.38220 881	0.03726 754
0.6	24.99250 184	0.00000 053	5.6	24.36002 599	0.04090 634
0.7	24.98979 507	0.00000 114	5.7	24.33748 413	0.04483 077
0.8	24.98667 248	0.00000 223	5.8	24.31458 660	0.04905 814
0.9	24.98313 430	0.00000 401	5.9	24.29133 706	0.05360 652
1.0	24.97918 083	0.00000 680	6.0	24.26773 949	0.05849 474
1.1	24.97481 240	0.00001 096	6.1	24.24379 820	0.06374 246
1.2	24.97002 934	0.00001 695	6.2	24.21951 791	0.06937 012
1.3	24.96483 205	0.00002 531	6.3	24.19490 374	0.07539 902
1.4	24.95922 095	0.00003 669	6.4	24.16996 131	0.08185 127
1.5	24.95319 647	0.00005 185	6.5	24.14469 672	0.08874 988
1.6	24.94675 911	0.00007 166	6.6	24.11911 668	0.09611 870
1.7	24.93990 937	0.00009 714	6.7	24.09322 849	0.10398 249
1.8	24.93264 779	0.00012 941	6.8	24.06704 017	0.11236 688
1.9	24.92497 495	0.00016 976	6.9	24.04056 047	0.12129 840
2.0	24.91689 145	0.00021 965	7.0	24.01379 897	0.13080 445
2.1	24.90839 792	0.00028 068	7.1	23.98676 615	0.14091 335
2.2	24.89949 502	0.00035 464	7.2	23.95947 347	0.15165 427
2.3	24.89018 345	0.00044 351	7.3	23.93193 347	0.16305 725
2.4	24.88046 391	0.00054 945	7.4	23.90415 980	0.17515 315
2.5	24.87033 717	0.00067 485	7.5	23.87616 742	0.18797 365
2.6	24.85980 399	0.00082 231	7.6	23.84797 259	0.20155 119
2.7	24.84886 518	0.00099 465	7.7	23.81959 304	0.21591 891
2.8	24.83752 156	0.00119 495	7.8	23.79104 807	0.23111 062
2.9	24.82577 401	0.00142 654	7.9	23.76235 864	0.24716 070
3.0	24.81362 341	0.00169 301	8.0	23.73354 748	0.26410 402
3.1	24.80107 068	0.00199 823	8.1	23.70463 922	0.28197 584
3.2	24.78811 676	0.00234 636	8.2	23.67566 049	0.30081 170
3.3	24.77476 263	0.00274 186	8.3	23.64664 004	0.32064 728
3.4	24.76100 930	0.00318 952	8.4	23.61760 881	0.34151 825
3.5	24.74685 780	0.00369 445	8.5	23.58860 007	0.36346 010
3.6	24.73230 922	0.00426 211	8.6	23.55964 948	0.38650 794
3.7	24.71736 464	0.00489 832	8.7	23.53079 518	0.41069 632
3.8	24.70202 523	0.00560 927	8.8	23.50207 782	0.43605 899
3.9	24.68629 216	0.00640 154	8.9	23.47354 064	0.46262 863
4.0	24.67016 665	0.00728 211	9.0	23.44522 946	0.49043 663
4.1	24.65364 998	0.00825 839	9.1	23.41719 267	0.51951 279
4.2	24.63674 346	0.00933 821	9.2	23.38948 123	0.54988 503
4.3	24.61944 846	0.01052 988	9.3	23.36214 855	0.58157 908
4.4	24.60176 642	0.01184 216	9.4	23.33525 038	0.61461 822
4.5	24.58369 883	0.01328 429	9.5	23.30884 472	0.64902 291
4.6	24.56524 725	0.01486 603	9.6	23.28299 157	0.68481 053
4.7	24.54641 333	0.01659 766	9.7	23.25775 272	0.72199 510
4.8	24.52719 880	0.01849 000	9.8	23.23319 150	0.76058 697
4.9	24.50760 548	0.02055 443	9.9	23.20937 240	0.80059 261
5.0	24.48763 532	0.02280 290	10.0	23.18636 078	0.84201 437

TABLE V.　$a_r(i\rho) = U + iV, b_r(i\rho) = U - iV$　　　　$r = 5$

ρ	U	V	ρ	U	V
10.0	23.18636 078	0.84201 437	20.0	27.50973 110	8.15329 309
10.2	23.14302 323	0.92909 418	20.2	27.69290 075	8.35199 748
10.4	23.10370 295	1.02175 781	20.4	27.87745 826	8.55447 480
10.6	23.06890 990	1.11986 524	20.6	28.06317 027	8.76080 707
10.8	23.03912 513	1.22320 748	20.8	28.24979 328	8.97105 858
11.0	23.01478 675	1.33151 291	21.0	28.43707 545	9.18527 380
11.2	22.99627 803	1.44445 711	21.2	28.62475 870	9.40347 539
11.4	22.98391 842	1.56167 544	21.4	28.81258 146	9.62566 266
11.6	22.97795 836	1.68277 721	21.6	29.00028 157	9.85181 040
11.8	22.97857 782	1.80736 013	21.8	29.18759 965	10.08186 824
12.0	22.98588 853	1.93502 407	22.0	29.37428 255	10.31576 065
12.2	22.99993 905	2.06538 303	22.2	29.56008 688	10.55338 759
12.4	23.02072 206	2.19807 479	22.4	29.74478 240	10.79462 580
12.6	23.04818 280	2.33276 810	22.6	29.92815 523	11.03933 074
12.8	23.08222 809	2.46916 725	22.8	30.11001 057	11.28733 908
13.0	23.12273 498	2.60701 448	23.0	30.29017 497	11.53847 171
13.2	23.16955 884	2.74609 052	23.2	30.46849 798	11.79253 698
13.4	23.22254 043	2.88621 366	23.4	30.64485 317	12.04933 425
13.6	23.28151 186	3.02723 787	23.6	30.81913 848	12.30865 735
13.8	23.34630 149	3.16905 026	23.8	30.99127 597	12.57029 807
14.0	23.41673 768	3.31156 818	24.0	31.16121 095	12.83404 932
14.2	23.49265 172	3.45473 626	24.2	31.32891 075	13.09970 799
14.4	23.57387 984	3.59852 344	24.4	31.49436 296	13.36707 750
14.6	23.66026 461	3.74292 021	24.6	31.65757 354	13.63596 980
14.8	23.75165 575	3.88793 605	24.8	31.81856 469	13.90620 701
15.0	23.84791 053	4.03359 715	25.0	31.97737 264	14.17762 263
15.2	23.94889 382	4.17994 440	25.2	32.13404 551	14.45006 227
15.4	24.05447 786	4.32703 162	25.4	32.28864 115	14.72338 414
15.6	24.16454 187	4.47492 407	25.6	32.44122 523	14.99745 912
15.8	24.27897 142	4.62369 715	25.8	32.59186 934	15.27217 062
16.0	24.39765 781	4.77343 533	26.0	32.74064 942	15.54741 426
16.2	24.52049 728	4.92423 123	26.2	32.88764 424	15.82309 733
16.4	24.64739 014	5.07618 485	26.4	33.03293 422	16.09913 820
16.6	24.77823 996	5.22940 294	26.6	33.17660 027	16.37546 556
16.8	24.91295 254	5.38399 843	26.8	33.31872 295	16.65201 774
17.0	25.05143 503	5.54008 991	27.0	33.45938 168	16.92874 192
17.2	25.19359 488	5.69780 124	27.2	33.59865 419	17.20559 334
17.4	25.33933 884	5.85726 111	27.4	33.73661 599	17.48253 459
17.6	25.48857 188	6.01860 259	27.6	33.87334 004	17.75953 487
17.8	25.64119 612	6.18196 269	27.8	34.00889 649	18.03656 931
18.0	25.79710 973	6.34748 190	28.0	34.14335 245	18.31361 836
18.2	25.95620 579	6.51530 354	28.2	34.27677 191	18.59066 714
18.4	26.11837 119	6.68557 318	28.4	34.40921 565	18.86770 494
18.6	26.28348 550	6.85843 779	28.6	34.54074 123	19.14472 470
18.8	26.45141 988	7.03404 488	28.8	34.67140 302	19.42172 255
19.0	26.62203 605	7.21254 137	29.0	34.80125 223	19.69869 737
19.2	26.79518 529	7.39407 234	29.2	34.93033 697	19.97565 048
19.4	26.97070 762	7.57877 965	29.4	35.05870 236	20.25258 521
19.6	27.14843 109	7.76680 020	29.6	35.18639 063	20.52950 669
19.8	27.32817 129	7.95826 419	29.8	35.31344 122	20.80642 149
20.0	27.50973 110	8.15329 309	30.0	35.43989 089	21.08333 744

TABLE V. $a_r(i\rho) = U + iV, b_r(i\rho) = U - iV$ $r = 5$

ρ	U	V	ρ	U	V
30.0	35.43989 089	21.08333 744	40.0	41.34370 859	35.13945 193
30.2	35.56577 385	21.36026 339	40.2	41.45553 967	35.42742 524
30.4	35.69112 187	21.63720 903	40.4	41.56713 079	35.71569 850
30.6	35.81596 444	21.91418 468	40.6	41.67848 131	36.00427 038
30.8	35.94032 882	22.19120 120	40.8	41.78959 065	36.29313 943
31.0	36.06424 022	22.46826 981	41.0	41.90045 830	36.58230 407
31.2	36.18772 188	22.74540 198	41.2	42.01108 381	36.87176 264
31.4	36.31079 522	23.02260 936	41.4	42.12146 678	37.16151 336
31.6	36.43347 988	23.29990 364	41.6	42.23160 689	37.45155 439
31.8	36.55579 391	23.57729 653	41.8	42.34150 391	37.74188 380
32.0	36.67775 379	23.85479 962	42.0	42.45115 763	38.03249 959
32.2	36.79937 459	24.13242 438	42.2	42.56056 796	38.32339 969
32.4	36.92067 002	24.41018 210	42.4	42.66973 485	38.61458 198
32.6	37.04165 254	24.68808 380	42.6	42.77865 834	38.90604 431
32.8	37.16233 341	24.96614 027	42.8	42.88733 851	39.19778 446
33.0	37.28272 283	25.24436 195	43.0	42.99577 553	39.48980 020
33.2	37.40282 994	25.52275 898	43.2	43.10396 965	39.78208 925
33.4	37.52266 296	25.80134 114	43.4	43.21192 115	40.07464 932
33.6	37.64222 921	26.08011 784	43.6	43.31963 040	40.36747 808
33.8	37.76153 520	26.35909 808	43.8	43.42709 783	40.66057 323
34.0	37.88058 667	26.63829 051	44.0	43.53432 392	40.95393 241
34.2	37.99938 868	26.91770 333	44.2	43.64130 922	41.24755 329
34.4	38.11794 562	27.19734 436	44.4	43.74805 433	41.54143 353
34.6	38.23626 130	27.47722 099	44.6	43.85455 991	41.83557 078
34.8	38.35433 897	27.75734 021	44.8	43.96082 668	42.12996 272
35.0	38.47218 140	28.03770 860	45.0	44.06685 538	42.42460 702
35.2	38.58979 089	28.31833 231	45.2	44.17264 685	42.71950 137
35.4	38.70716 933	28.59921 710	45.4	44.27820 192	43.01464 347
35.6	38.82431 820	28.88036 832	45.6	44.38352 149	43.31003 105
35.8	38.94123 869	29.16179 093	45.8	44.48860 652	43.60566 185
36.0	39.05793 164	29.44348 951	46.0	44.59345 797	43.90153 364
36.2	39.17439 764	29.72546 826	46.2	44.69807 687	44.19764 421
36.4	39.29063 701	30.00773 098	46.4	44.80246 427	44.49399 136
36.6	39.40664 986	30.29028 116	46.6	44.90662 123	44.79057 294
36.8	39.52243 612	30.57312 190	46.8	45.01054 889	45.08738 683
37.0	39.63799 553	30.85625 598	47.0	45.11424 838	45.38443 092
37.2	39.75332 771	31.13968 585	47.2	45.21772 086	45.68170 313
37.4	39.86843 213	31.42341 364	47.4	45.32096 752	45.97920 144
37.6	39.98330 817	31.70744 117	47.6	45.42398 957	46.27692 383
37.8	40.09795 513	31.99176 997	47.8	45.52678 825	46.57486 834
38.0	40.21237 223	32.27640 130	48.0	45.62936 479	46.87303 301
38.2	40.32655 863	32.56133 614	48.2	45.73172 046	47.17141 594
38.4	40.44051 347	32.84657 522	48.4	45.83385 653	47.47001 525
38.6	40.55423 586	33.13211 901	48.6	45.93577 430	47.76882 911
38.8	40.66772 489	33.41796 776	48.8	46.03747 505	48.06785 570
39.0	40.78097 964	33.70412 149	49.0	46.13896 011	48.36709 324
39.2	40.89399 923	33.99058 004	49.2	46.24023 077	48.66654 001
39.4	41.00678 276	34.27734 301	49.4	46.34128 835	48.96619 429
39.6	41.11932 937	34.56440 983	49.6	46.44213 419	49.26605 440
39.8	41.23163 825	34.85177 977	49.8	46.54276 960	49.56611 871
40.0	41.34370 859	35.13945 193	50.0	46.64319 592	49.86638 559

TABLE V. $a_r(i\rho) = U + iV, b_r(i\rho) = U - iV$ $\qquad$ $r = 5$

ρ	U	V	ρ	U	V
50.0	46.64319 592	49.86638 559	75.0	57.89953 435	88.65926 665
50.5	46.89335 563	50.61792 882	75.5	58.10360 005	89.45586 947
51.0	47.14223 749	51.37070 458	76.0	58.30698 977	90.25314 232
51.5	47.38986 209	52.12469 021	76.5	58.50971 011	91.05107 861
52.0	47.63624 978	52.87986 418	77.0	58.71176 759	91.84967 187
52.5	47.88142 065	53.63620 601	77.5	58.91316 860	92.64891 572
53.0	48.12539 444	54.39369 620	78.0	59.11391 946	93.44880 387
53.5	48.36819 049	55.15231 616	78.5	59.31402 637	94.24933 015
54.0	48.60982 774	55.91204 819	79.0	59.51349 547	95.05048 846
54.5	48.85032 463	56.67287 536	79.5	59.71233 277	95.85227 281
55.0	49.08969 918	57.43478 148	80.0	59.91054 421	96.65467 731
55.5	49.32796 888	58.19775 105	80.5	60.10813 563	97.45769 615
56.0	49.56515 075	58.96176 917	81.0	60.30511 281	98.26132 361
56.5	49.80126 132	59.72682 152	81.5	60.50148 141	99.06555 406
57.0	50.03631 661	60.49289 429	82.0	60.69724 702	99.87038 196
57.5	50.27033 218	61.25997 417	82.5	60.89241 516	100.67580 186
58.0	50.50332 311	62.02804 825	83.0	61.08699 125	101.48180 838
58.5	50.73530 402	62.79710 405	83.5	61.28098 064	102.28839 622
59.0	50.96628 908	63.56712 943	84.0	61.47438 859	103.09556 018
59.5	51.19629 206	64.33811 260	84.5	61.66722 031	103.90329 512
60.0	51.42532 628	65.11004 207	85.0	61.85948 092	104.71159 598
60.5	51.65340 468	65.88290 662	85.5	62.05117 544	105.52045 778
61.0	51.88053 983	66.65669 530	86.0	62.24230 887	106.32987 562
61.5	52.10674 394	67.43139 740	86.5	62.43288 609	107.13984 465
62.0	52.33202 887	68.20700 243	87.0	62.62291 194	107.95036 011
62.5	52.55640 614	68.98350 011	87.5	62.81239 118	108.76141 731
63.0	52.77988 700	69.76088 035	88.0	63.00132 849	109.57301 162
63.5	53.00248 236	70.53913 326	88.5	63.18972 852	110.38513 847
64.0	53.22420 289	71.31824 910	89.0	63.37759 583	111.19779 336
64.5	53.44505 898	72.09821 831	89.5	63.56493 490	112.01097 188
65.0	53.66506 076	72.87903 149	90.0	63.75175 018	112.82466 963
65.5	53.88421 813	73.66067 939	90.5	63.93804 603	113.63888 233
66.0	54.10254 078	74.44315 290	91.0	64.12382 678	114.45360 571
66.5	54.32003 816	75.22644 305	91.5	64.30909 668	115.26883 558
67.0	54.53671 953	76.01054 102	92.0	64.49385 993	116.08456 782
67.5	54.75259 395	76.79543 813	92.5	64.67812 065	116.90079 835
68.0	54.96767 030	77.58112 581	93.0	64.86188 294	117.71752 314
68.5	55.18195 729	78.36759 563	93.5	65.04515 082	118.53473 823
69.0	55.39546 344	79.15483 929	94.0	65.22792 826	119.35243 971
69.5	55.60819 713	79.94284 862	94.5	65.41021 919	120.17062 371
70.0	55.82016 657	80.73161 556	95.0	65.59202 747	120.98928 643
70.5	56.03137 982	81.52113 218	95.5	65.77335 693	121.80842 410
71.0	56.24184 481	82.31139 066	96.0	65.95421 131	122.62803 301
71.5	56.45156 933	83.10238 331	96.5	66.13459 435	123.44810 951
72.0	56.66056 102	83.89410 256	97.0	66.31450 971	124.26864 997
72.5	56.86882 740	84.68654 094	97.5	66.49396 102	125.08965 083
73.0	57.07637 587	85.47969 111	98.0	66.67295 184	125.91110 856
73.5	57.28321 370	86.27354 583	98.5	66.85148 571	126.73301 969
74.0	57.48934 805	87.06809 799	99.0	67.02956 610	127.55538 078
74.5	57.69478 596	87.86334 056	99.5	67.20719 646	128.37818 844
75.0	57.89953 435	88.65926 665	100.0	67.38438 019	129.20143 932

TABLE V. $a_r(i\rho) = U + iV, b_r(i\rho) = U - iV$ $r = 7$

ρ	U	V	ρ	U	V
0.0	49.00000 000	0.00000 000	5.0	48.74055 959	-0.00003 770
0.1	48.99989 583	-0.00000 000	5.1	48.73011 869	-0.00004 334
0.2	48.99958 334	-0.00000 000	5.2	48.71947 423	-0.00004 970
0.3	48.99906 251	-0.00000 000	5.3	48.70862 640	-0.00005 685
0.4	48.99833 337	-0.00000 000	5.4	48.69757 538	-0.00006 486
0.5	48.99739 593	0.00000 000	5.5	48.68632 136	-0.00007 383
0.6	48.99625 021	0.00000 000	5.6	48.67486 454	-0.00008 384
0.7	48.99489 621	-0.00000 000	5.7	48.66320 510	-0.00009 500
0.8	48.99333 398	-0.00000 000	5.8	48.65134 325	-0.00010 742
0.9	48.99156 354	-0.00000 000	5.9	48.63927 919	-0.00012 121
1.0	48.98958 491	-0.00000 000	6.0	48.62701 312	-0.00013 650
1.1	48.98739 815	-0.00000 000	6.1	48.61454 525	-0.00015 342
1.2	48.98500 328	-0.00000 000	6.2	48.60187 578	-0.00017 212
1.3	48.98240 035	-0.00000 000	6.3	48.58900 493	-0.00019 275
1.4	48.97958 941	-0.00000 000	6.4	48.57593 292	-0.00021 547
1.5	48.97657 050	-0.00000 001	6.5	48.56265 996	-0.00024 047
1.6	48.97334 369	-0.00000 001	6.6	48.54918 628	-0.00026 792
1.7	48.96990 903	-0.00000 002	6.7	48.53551 209	-0.00029 804
1.8	48.96626 658	-0.00000 003	6.8	48.52163 762	-0.00033 103
1.9	48.96241 642	-0.00000 004	6.9	48.50756 311	-0.00036 713
2.0	48.95835 860	-0.00000 006	7.0	48.49328 878	-0.00040 657
2.1	48.95409 320	-0.00000 009	7.1	48.47881 487	-0.00044 961
2.2	48.94962 031	-0.00000 012	7.2	48.46414 162	-0.00049 653
2.3	48.94493 999	-0.00000 016	7.3	48.44926 926	-0.00054 761
2.4	48.94005 234	-0.00000 022	7.4	48.43419 803	-0.00060 317
2.5	48.93495 744	-0.00000 029	7.5	48.41892 819	-0.00066 352
2.6	48.92965 539	-0.00000 038	7.6	48.40345 997	-0.00072 902
2.7	48.92414 627	-0.00000 050	7.7	48.38779 364	-0.00080 003
2.8	48.91843 020	-0.00000 064	7.8	48.37192 943	-0.00087 694
2.9	48.91250 726	-0.00000 082	7.9	48.35586 761	-0.00096 015
3.0	48.90637 757	-0.00000 104	8.0	48.33960 843	-0.00105 009
3.1	48.90004 124	-0.00000 131	8.1	48.32315 216	-0.00114 723
3.2	48.89349 837	-0.00000 163	8.2	48.30649 904	-0.00125 204
3.3	48.88674 909	-0.00000 203	8.3	48.28964 936	-0.00136 502
3.4	48.87979 352	-0.00000 250	8.4	48.27260 337	-0.00148 671
3.5	48.87263 178	-0.00000 307	8.5	48.25536 134	-0.00161 767
3.6	48.86526 399	-0.00000 374	8.6	48.23792 356	-0.00175 850
3.7	48.85769 029	-0.00000 453	8.7	48.22029 028	-0.00190 981
3.8	48.84991 081	-0.00000 546	8.8	48.20246 178	-0.00207 225
3.9	48.84192 568	-0.00000 656	8.9	48.18443 836	-0.00224 652
4.0	48.83373 506	-0.00000 784	9.0	48.16622 028	-0.00243 334
4.1	48.82533 908	-0.00000 932	9.1	48.14780 783	-0.00263 346
4.2	48.81673 789	-0.00001 104	9.2	48.12920 130	-0.00284 767
4.3	48.80793 164	-0.00001 303	9.3	48.11040 097	-0.00307 682
4.4	48.79892 048	-0.00001 532	9.4	48.09140 714	-0.00332 177
4.5	48.78970 458	-0.00001 795	9.5	48.07222 011	-0.00358 345
4.6	48.78028 409	-0.00002 095	9.6	48.05284 016	-0.00386 280
4.7	48.77065 918	-0.00002 438	9.7	48.03326 760	-0.00416 084
4.8	48.76083 001	-0.00002 827	9.8	48.01350 272	-0.00447 861
4.9	48.75079 676	-0.00003 269	9.9	47.99354 585	-0.00481 722
5.0	48.74055 959	-0.00003 770	10.0	47.97339 727	-0.00517 782

TABLE V. $a_r(i\rho) = U+iV, b_r(i\rho) = U-iV$ $\qquad$ $r=7$

ρ	U	V	ρ	U	V
10.0	47.97339 727	−0.00517 782	20.0	45.15494 244	−0.83474 432
10.2	47.93252 626	−0.00596 984	20.2	45.09555 155	−0.89727 934
10.4	47.89089 223	−0.00686 496	20.4	45.03768 672	−0.96341 399
10.6	47.84849 775	−0.00787 438	20.6	44.98157 292	−1.03322 537
10.8	47.80534 545	−0.00901 033	20.8	44.92744 609	−1.10677 398
11.0	47.76143 803	−0.01028 607	21.0	44.87555 122	−1.18410 158
11.2	47.71677 827	−0.01171 604	21.2	44.82614 009	−1.26522 928
11.4	47.67136 901	−0.01331 588	21.4	44.77946 858	−1.35015 584
11.6	47.62521 321	−0.01510 254	21.6	44.73579 354	−1.43885 659
11.8	47.57831 391	−0.01709 437	21.8	44.69536 946	−1.53128 271
12.0	47.53067 429	−0.01931 119	22.0	44.65844 487	−1.62736 123
12.2	47.48229 765	−0.02177 443	22.2	44.62525 885	−1.72699 565
12.4	47.43318 749	−0.02450 717	22.4	44.59603 746	−1.83006 721
12.6	47.38334 746	−0.02753 431	22.6	44.57099 062	−1.93643 680
12.8	47.33278 145	−0.03088 264	22.8	44.55030 925	−2.04594 748
13.0	47.28149 360	−0.03458 098	23.0	44.53416 300	−2.15842 741
13.2	47.22948 837	−0.03866 028	23.2	44.52269 857	−2.27369 313
13.4	47.17677 053	−0.04315 377	23.4	44.51603 862	−2.39155 307
13.6	47.12334 529	−0.04809 709	23.6	44.51428 145	−2.51181 101
13.8	47.06921 832	−0.05352 841	23.8	44.51750 119	−2.63426 955
14.0	47.01439 585	−0.05948 860	24.0	44.52574 864	−2.75873 330
14.2	46.95888 474	−0.06602 136	24.2	44.53905 250	−2.88501 171
14.4	46.90269 259	−0.07317 338	24.4	44.55742 111	−3.01292 163
14.6	46.84582 787	−0.08099 449	24.6	44.58084 430	−3.14228 932
14.8	46.78830 004	−0.08953 784	24.8	44.60929 553	−3.27295 210
15.0	46.73011 973	−0.09886 005	25.0	44.64273 407	−3.40475 952
15.2	46.67129 886	−0.10902 134	25.2	44.68110 715	−3.53757 419
15.4	46.61185 092	−0.12008 578	25.4	44.72435 205	−3.67127 223
15.6	46.55179 113	−0.13212 134	25.6	44.77239 806	−3.80574 336
15.8	46.49113 674	−0.14520 014	25.8	44.82516 832	−3.94089 079
16.0	46.42990 729	−0.15939 855	26.0	44.88258 140	−4.07663 095
16.2	46.36812 498	−0.17479 735	26.2	44.94455 276	−4.21289 291
16.4	46.30581 498	−0.19148 180	26.4	45.01099 601	−4.34961 789
16.6	46.24300 590	−0.20954 183	26.6	45.08182 391	−4.48675 851
16.8	46.17973 020	−0.22907 201	26.8	45.15694 931	−4.62427 811
17.0	46.11602 471	−0.25017 167	27.0	45.23628 583	−4.76215 005
17.2	46.05193 120	−0.27294 483	27.2	45.31974 848	−4.90035 693
17.4	45.98749 696	−0.29750 019	27.4	45.40725 404	−5.03888 993
17.6	45.92277 544	−0.32395 096	27.6	45.49872 145	−5.17774 810
17.8	45.85782 704	−0.35241 467	27.8	45.59407 199	−5.31693 777
18.0	45.79271 974	−0.38301 287	28.0	45.69322 948	−5.45647 192
18.2	45.72753 001	−0.41587 073	28.2	45.79612 029	−5.59636 966
18.4	45.66234 354	−0.45111 646	28.4	45.90267 343	−5.73665 570
18.6	45.59725 613	−0.48888 068	28.6	46.01282 044	−5.87735 995
18.8	45.53237 447	−0.52929 554	28.8	46.12649 534	−6.01851 705
19.0	45.46781 701	−0.57249 372	29.0	46.24363 451	−6.16016 608
19.2	45.40371 465	−0.61860 719	29.2	46.36417 653	−6.30235 016
19.4	45.34021 139	−0.66776 582	29.4	46.48806 203	−6.44511 622
19.6	45.27746 488	−0.72009 575	29.6	46.61523 344	−6.58851 472
19.8	45.21564 669	−0.77571 756	29.8	46.74563 484	−6.73259 944
20.0	45.15494 244	−0.83474 432	30.0	46.87921 167	−6.87742 725

TABLE V. $a_r(i\rho) = U + iV, b_r(i\rho) = U - iV$ $\qquad r = 7$

ρ	U	V	ρ	U	V
30.0	46.87921 167	−6.87742 725	40.0	55.94867 218	−16.54815 461
30.2	47.01591 052	−7.02305 798	40.2	56.12997 814	−16.80164 636
30.4	47.15567 885	−7.16955 422	40.4	56.30959 507	−17.05648 522
30.6	47.29846 472	−7.31698 120	40.6	56.48751 664	−17.31255 545
30.8	47.44421 651	−7.46540 668	40.8	56.66374 494	−17.56974 521
31.0	47.59288 261	−7.61490 076	41.0	56.83828 983	−17.82794 715
31.2	47.74441 115	−7.76553 582	41.2	57.01116 810	−18.08705 891
31.4	47.89874 962	−7.91738 638	41.4	57.18240 272	−18.34698 346
31.6	48.05584 460	−8.07052 899	41.6	57.35202 212	−18.60762 935
31.8	48.21564 140	−8.22504 205	41.8	57.52005 934	−18.86891 092
32.0	48.37808 370	−8.38100 574	42.0	57.68655 142	−19.13074 832
32.2	48.54311 325	−8.53850 179	42.2	57.85153 864	−19.39306 756
32.4	48.71066 941	−8.69761 334	42.4	58.01506 394	−19.65580 040
32.6	48.88068 888	−8.85842 475	42.6	58.17717 233	−19.91888 423
32.8	49.05310 529	−9.02102 130	42.8	58.33791 032	−20.18226 193
33.0	49.22784 884	−9.18548 899	43.0	58.49732 549	−20.44588 165
33.2	49.40484 590	−9.35191 420	43.2	58.65546 604	−20.70969 656
33.4	49.58401 873	−9.52038 335	43.4	58.81238 042	−20.97366 464
33.6	49.76528 507	−9.69098 249	43.6	58.96811 700	−21.23774 838
33.8	49.94855 784	−9.86379 691	43.8	59.12272 376	−21.50191 453
34.0	50.13374 487	10.03891 057	44.0	59.27624 808	−21.76613 383
34.2	50.32074 864	−10.21640 562	44.2	59.42873 653	−22.03038 070
34.4	50.50946 603	10.39636 176	44.4	59.58023 467	−22.29463 304
34.6	50.69978 823	10.57885 562	44.6	59.73078 695	−22.55887 193
34.8	50.89160 063	10.76396 005	44.8	59.88043 654	−22.82308 136
35.0	51.08478 280	−10.95174 338	45.0	60.02922 530	−23.08724 806
35.2	51.27920 860	−11.14226 866	45.2	60.17719 368	−23.35136 119
35.4	51.47474 638	−11.33559 283	45.4	60.32438 070	−23.61541 218
35.6	51.67125 922	11.53176 597	45.6	60.47082 386	−23.87939 452
35.8	51.86860 543	11.73083 045	45.8	60.61655 919	−24.14330 354
36.0	52.06663 902	11.93282 017	46.0	60.76162 121	−24.40713 628
36.2	52.26521 037	−12.13775 985	46.2	60.90604 292	−24.67089 126
36.4	52.46416 708	12.34566 431	46.4	61.04985 586	−24.93456 840
36.6	52.66335 478	12.55653 795	46.6	61.19309 009	−25.19816 882
36.8	52.86261 824	12.77037 424	46.8	61.33577 421	−25.46169 471
37.0	53.06180 240	12.98715 540	47.0	61.47793 543	−25.72514 927
37.2	53.26075 358	13.20685 223	47.2	61.61959 959	−25.98853 650
37.4	53.45932 069	13.42942 406	47.4	61.76079 116	−26.25186 118
37.6	53.65735 648	13.65481 894	47.6	61.90153 335	−26.51512 875
37.8	53.85471 875	13.88297 393	47.8	62.04184 807	−26.77834 519
38.0	54.05127 155	14.11381 567	48.0	62.18175 605	−27.04151 699
38.2	54.24688 629	14.34726 104	48.2	62.32127 682	−27.30465 104
38.4	54.44144 273	14.58321 797	48.4	62.46042 880	−27.56775 459
38.6	54.63482 987	14.82158 649	48.6	62.59922 932	−27.83083 518
38.8	54.82694 668	−15.06225 976	48.8	62.73769 465	−28.09390 055
39.0	55.01770 265	15.30512 525	49.0	62.87584 008	−28.35695 867
39.2	55.20701 817	15.55006 597	49.2	63.01367 994	−28.62001 761
39.4	55.39482 474	15.79696 174	49.4	63.15122 763	−28.88308 555
39.6	55.58106 504	16.04569 036	49.6	63.28849 568	−29.14617 074
39.8	55.76569 272	16.29612 886	49.8	63.42549 579	−29.40928 142
40.0	55.94867 218	16.54815 461	50.0	63.56223 885	−29.67242 585

TABLE V. $a_r(i\rho) = U + iV, b_r(i\rho) = U - iV$ $r = 7$

ρ	U	V	ρ	U	V
50.0	63.56223 885	−29.67242 585	75.0	79.25841 972	−63.98329 144
50.5	63.90303 663	30.33048 839	75.5	79.54455 635	−64.69932 045
51.0	64.24242 839	−30.98893 944	76.0	79.82971 654	−65.41627 732
51.5	64.58052 825	−31.64790 115	76.5	80.11391 189	−66.13415 109
52.0	64.91742 836	−32.30748 988	77.0	80.39715 381	−66.85293 126
52.5	65.25320 164	32.96781 517	77.5	80.67945 351	−67.57260 777
53.0	65.58790 437	−33.62897 890	78.0	80.96082 202	−68.29317 094
53.5	65.92157 846	34.29107 485	78.5	81.24127 011	−69.01461 146
54.0	66.25425 355	−34.95418 840	79.0	81.52080 835	−69.73692 041
54.5	66.58594 885	35.61839 638	79.5	81.79944 707	−70.46008 913
55.0	66.91667 490	36.28376 717	80.0	82.07719 636	−71.18410 929
55.5	67.24643 498	36.95036 081	80.5	82.35406 606	−71.90897 282
56.0	67.57522 658	37.61822 925	81.0	82.63006 578	−72.63467 192
56.5	67.90304 250	38.28741 669	81.5	82.90520 489	−73.36119 898
57.0	68.22987 197	38.95795 993	82.0	83.17949 252	−74.08854 662
57.5	68.55570 160	39.62988 881	82.5	83.45293 757	−74.81670 767
58.0	68.88051 614	−40.30322 664	83.0	83.72554 872	−75.54567 509
58.5	69.20429 925	40.97799 070	83.5	83.99733 443	−76.27544 203
59.0	69.52703 411	41.65419 271	84.0	84.26830 293	−77.00600 179
59.5	69.84870 390	−42.33183 930	84.5	84.53846 227	−77.73734 779
60.0	70.16929 224	43.01093 256	85.0	84.80782 028	−78.46947 356
60.5	70.48878 361	43.69147 043	85.5	85.07638 462	−79.20237 277
61.0	70.80716 355	44.37344 724	86.0	85.34416 275	−79.93603 918
61.5	71.12441 893	45.05685 414	86.5	85.61116 195	−80.67046 663
62.0	71.44053 814	45.74167 949	87.0	85.87738 936	−81.40564 908
62.5	71.75551 115	46.42790 933	87.5	86.14285 193	−82.14158 054
63.0	72.06932 962	47.11552 768	88.0	86.40755 647	−82.87825 511
63.5	72.38198 695	47.80451 697	88.5	86.67150 965	−83.61566 697
64.0	72.69347 823	48.49485 831	89.0	86.93471 799	−84.35381 034
64.5	73.00380 026	49.18653 179	89.5	87.19718 788	−85.09267 954
65.0	73.31295 150	49.87951 677	90.0	87.45892 561	−85.83226 891
65.5	73.62093 195	50.57379 213	90.5	87.71993 731	−86.57257 288
66.0	73.92774 316	51.26933 641	91.0	87.98022 902	−87.31358 593
66.5	74.23338 805	51.96612 809	91.5	88.23980 668	−88.05530 258
67.0	74.53787 084	52.66414 568	92.0	88.49867 610	−88.79771 741
67.5	74.84119 697	53.36336 791	92.5	88.75684 303	−89.54082 506
68.0	75.14337 295	54.06377 380	93.0	89.01431 308	−90.28462 021
68.5	75.44440 627	54.76534 280	93.5	89.27109 182	−91.02909 759
69.0	75.74430 530	55.46805 484	94.0	89.52718 469	−91.77425 199
69.5	76.04307 916	56.17189 040	94.5	89.78259 709	−92.52007 825
70.0	76.34073 763	56.87683 057	95.0	90.03733 431	−93.26657 124
70.5	76.63729 105	57.58285 707	95.5	90.29140 159	−94.01372 589
71.0	76.93275 023	58.28995 227	96.0	90.54480 407	−94.76153 719
71.5	77.22712 637	58.99809 921	96.5	90.79754 686	−95.51000 016
72.0	77.52043 095	59.70728 161	97.0	91.04963 496	−96.25910 989
72.5	77.81267 570	60.41748 387	97.5	91.30107 333	−97.00886 149
73.0	78.10387 249	61.12869 101	98.0	91.55186 687	−97.75925 014
73.5	78.39403 328	61.84088 874	98.5	91.80202 042	−98.51027 108
74.0	78.68317 009	62.55406 335	99.0	92.05153 874	−99.26191 956
74.5	78.97129 492	63.26820 175	99.5	92.30042 656	−100.01419 092
75.0	79.25841 972	63.98329 144	100.0	92.54868 853	−100.76708 052

ρ	U	V	ρ	U	V
0.0	81.00000 000	0.00000 000	5.0	80.84395 326	0.00000 002
0.1	80.99993 750	0.00000 000	5.1	80.83765 748	0.00000 002
0.2	80.99975 000	0.00000 000	5.2	80.83123 770	0.00000 003
0.3	80.99943 750	0.00000 000	5.3	80.82469 398	0.00000 003
0.4	80.99900 001	0.00000 000	5.4	80.81802 634	0.00000 004
0.5	80.99843 752	0.00000 000	5.5	80.81123 483	0.00000 004
0.6	80.99775 004	0.00000 000	5.6	80.80431 950	0.00000 005
0.7	80.99693 758	0.00000 000	5.7	80.79728 037	0.00000 006
0.8	80.99600 013	0.00000 000	5.8	80.79011 750	0.00000 007
0.9	80.99493 771	0.00000 000	5.9	80.78283 093	0.00000 008
1.0	80.99375 033	0.00000 000	6.0	80.77542 071	0.00000 010
1.1	80.99243 798	0.00000 000	6.1	80.76788 688	0.00000 011
1.2	80.99100 068	0.00000 000	6.2	80.76022 948	0.00000 013
1.3	80.98943 843	0.00000 000	6.3	80.75244 856	0.00000 015
1.4	80.98775 125	0.00000 000	6.4	80.74454 418	0.00000 017
1.5	80.98593 915	0.00000 000	6.5	80.73651 637	0.00000 020
1.6	80.98400 214	0.00000 000	6.6	80.72836 519	0.00000 023
1.7	80.98194 023	0.00000 000	6.7	80.72009 069	0.00000 026
1.8	80.97975 343	0.00000 000	6.8	80.71169 291	0.00000 030
1.9	80.97744 175	0.00000 000	6.9	80.70317 191	0.00000 034
2.0	80.97500 522	0.00000 000	7.0	80.69452 774	0.00000 039
2.1	80.97244 385	0.00000 000	7.1	80.68576 046	0.00000 044
2.2	80.96975 764	0.00000 000	7.2	80.67687 010	0.00000 050
2.3	80.96694 663	0.00000 000	7.3	80.66785 674	0.00000 057
2.4	80.96401 082	0.00000 000	7.4	80.65872 042	0.00000 064
2.5	80.96095 024	0.00000 000	7.5	80.64946 119	0.00000 072
2.6	80.95776 491	0.00000 000	7.6	80.64007 913	0.00000 081
2.7	80.95445 483	0.00000 000	7.7	80.63057 427	0.00000 092
2.8	80.95102 005	0.00000 000	7.8	80.62094 667	0.00000 103
2.9	80.94746 057	0.00000 000	7.9	80.61119 641	0.00000 116
3.0	80.94377 641	0.00000 000	8.0	80.60132 353	0.00000 129
3.1	80.93996 761	0.00000 000	8.1	80.59132 809	0.00000 145
3.2	80.93603 419	0.00000 000	8.2	80.58121 015	0.00000 162
3.3	80.93197 616	0.00000 000	8.3	80.57096 977	0.00000 181
3.4	80.92779 356	0.00000 000	8.4	80.56060 703	0.00000 201
3.5	80.92348 641	0.00000 000	8.5	80.55012 196	0.00000 224
3.6	80.91905 473	0.00000 000	8.6	80.53951 465	0.00000 249
3.7	80.91449 857	0.00000 000	8.7	80.52878 514	0.00000 277
3.8	80.90981 793	0.00000 000	8.8	80.51793 352	0.00000 307
3.9	80.90501 286	0.00000 000	8.9	80.50695 983	0.00000 340
4.0	80.90008 338	0.00000 000	9.0	80.49586 414	0.00000 376
4.1	80.89502 952	0.00000 000	9.1	80.48464 653	0.00000 416
4.2	80.88985 132	0.00000 000	9.2	80.47330 706	0.00000 459
4.3	80.88454 881	0.00000 000	9.3	80.46184 579	0.00000 507
4.4	80.87912 201	0.00000 001	9.4	80.45026 279	0.00000 558
4.5	80.87357 096	0.00000 001	9.5	80.43855 813	0.00000 615
4.6	80.86789 571	0.00000 001	9.6	80.42673 187	0.00000 676
4.7	80.86209 627	0.00000 001	9.7	80.41478 410	0.00000 743
4.8	80.85617 269	0.00000 001	9.8	80.40271 488	0.00000 815
4.9	80.85012 501	0.00000 002	9.9	80.39052 427	0.00000 894
5.0	80.84395 326	0.00000 002	10.0	80.37821 235	0.00000 979

TABLE V. $a_r(i\rho) = U + iV, b_r(i\rho) = U - iV$ $r = 9$

ρ	U	V	ρ	U	V
10.0	80.37821 235	0.00000 979	20.0	78.54907 844	0.00567 024
10.2	80.35322 488	0.00001 172	20.2	78.50076 170	0.00622 136
10.4	80.32775 304	0.00001 399	20.4	78.45199 997	0.00682 021
10.6	80.30179 743	0.00001 663	20.6	78.40279 422	0.00747 045
10.8	80.27535 864	0.00001 972	20.8	78.35314 542	0.00817 596
11.0	80.24843 729	0.00002 330	21.0	78.30305 456	0.00894 090
11.2	80.22103 400	0.00002 745	21.2	78.25252 264	0.00976 969
11.4	80.19314 940	0.00003 225	21.4	78.20155 067	0.01066 704
11.6	80.16478 413	0.00003 779	21.6	78.15013 967	0.01163 798
11.8	80.13593 884	0.00004 416	21.8	78.09829 067	0.01268 783
12.0	80.10661 418	0.00005 148	22.0	78.04600 474	0.01382 228
12.2	80.07681 082	0.00005 985	22.2	77.99328 293	0.01504 737
12.4	80.04652 944	0.00006 943	22.4	77.94012 633	0.01636 949
12.6	80.01577 071	0.00008 035	22.6	77.88653 606	0.01779 548
12.8	79.98453 533	0.00009 278	22.8	77.83251 325	0.01933 255
13.0	79.95282 401	0.00010 690	23.0	77.77805 905	0.02098 839
13.2	79.92063 744	0.00012 291	23.2	77.72317 465	0.02277 113
13.4	79.88797 635	0.00014 104	23.4	77.66786 127	0.02468 940
13.6	79.85484 146	0.00016 152	23.6	77.61212 017	0.02675 235
13.8	79.82123 350	0.00018 462	23.8	77.55595 265	0.02896 966
14.0	79.78715 321	0.00021 062	24.0	77.49936 006	0.03135 159
14.2	79.75260 134	0.00023 986	24.2	77.44234 378	0.03390 901
14.4	79.71757 866	0.00027 268	24.4	77.38490 528	0.03665 339
14.6	79.68208 591	0.00030 946	24.6	77.32704 609	0.03959 690
14.8	79.64612 387	0.00035 062	24.8	77.26876 779	0.04275 237
15.0	79.60969 332	0.00039 662	25.0	77.21007 207	0.04613 338
15.2	79.57279 504	0.00044 794	25.2	77.15096 070	0.04975 427
15.4	79.53542 984	0.00050 514	25.4	77.09143 557	0.05363 019
15.6	79.49759 849	0.00056 878	25.6	77.03149 866	0.05777 712
15.8	79.45930 182	0.00063 952	25.8	76.97115 213	0.06221 192
16.0	79.42054 064	0.00071 805	26.0	76.91039 823	0.06695 238
16.2	79.38131 576	0.00080 511	26.2	76.84923 944	0.07201 726
16.4	79.34162 801	0.00090 151	26.4	76.78767 838	0.07742 633
16.6	79.30147 823	0.00100 813	26.6	76.72571 789	0.08320 041
16.8	79.26086 725	0.00112 592	26.8	76.66336 108	0.08936 142
17.0	79.21979 592	0.00125 591	27.0	76.60061 127	0.09593 246
17.2	79.17826 509	0.00139 921	27.2	76.53747 212	0.10293 780
17.4	79.13627 563	0.00155 700	27.4	76.47394 760	0.11040 300
17.6	79.09382 839	0.00173 058	27.6	76.41004 204	0.11835 491
17.8	79.05092 424	0.00192 134	27.8	76.34576 020	0.12682 175
18.0	79.00756 407	0.00213 076	28.0	76.28110 727	0.13583 317
18.2	78.96374 876	0.00236 044	28.2	76.21608 899	0.14542 027
18.4	78.91947 920	0.00261 212	28.4	76.15071 162	0.15561 572
18.6	78.87475 628	0.00288 765	28.6	76.08498 209	0.16645 375
18.8	78.82958 090	0.00318 901	28.8	76.01890 801	0.17797 025
19.0	78.78395 398	0.00351 833	29.0	75.95249 775	0.19020 282
19.2	78.73787 642	0.00387 790	29.2	75.88576 059	0.20319 081
19.4	78.69134 916	0.00427 016	29.4	75.81870 670	0.21697 539
19.6	78.64437 312	0.00469 774	29.6	75.75134 737	0.23159 962
19.8	78.59694 923	0.00516 343	29.8	75.68369 500	0.24710 844
20.0	78.54907 844	0.00567 024	30.0	75.61576 332	0.26354 878

TABLE V. $a_r(i\rho) = U + iV, b_r(i\rho) = U - iV$ $r = 9$

ρ	U	V	ρ	U	V
30.0	75.61576 332	0.26354 878	40.0	73.08971 510	3.53019 483
30.2	75.54756 745	0.28096 958	40.2	73.10086 748	3.65368 871
30.4	75.47912 408	0.29942 182	40.4	73.11606 631	3.77847 796
30.6	75.41045 163	0.31895 854	40.6	73.13531 572	3.90445 437
30.8	75.34157 039	0.33963 489	40.8	73.15861 129	4.03151 412
31.0	75.27250 271	0.36150 811	41.0	73.18594 083	4.15955 828
31.2	75.20327 324	0.38463 754	41.2	73.21728 507	4.28849 339
31.4	75.13390 905	0.40908 463	41.4	73.25261 850	4.41823 177
31.6	75.06443 992	0.43491 286	41.6	73.29191 008	4.54869 181
31.8	74.99489 858	0.46218 771	41.8	73.33512 401	4.67979 813
32.0	74.92532 089	0.49097 658	42.0	73.38222 043	4.81148 166
32.2	74.85574 618	0.52134 872	42.2	73.43315 609	4.94367 968
32.4	74.78621 748	0.55337 505	42.4	73.48788 499	5.07633 568
32.6	74.71678 178	0.58712 804	42.6	73.54635 893	5.20939 935
32.8	74.64749 039	0.62268 151	42.8	73.60852 804	5.34282 634
33.0	74.57839 913	0.66011 036	43.0	73.67434 129	5.47657 811
33.2	74.50956 873	0.69949 034	43.2	73.74374 686	5.61062 168
33.4	74.44106 500	0.74089 768	43.4	73.81669 251	5.74492 942
33.6	74.37295 921	0.78440 876	43.6	73.89312 596	5.87947 882
33.8	74.30532 828	0.83009 965	43.8	73.97299 507	6.01425 216
34.0	74.23825 500	0.87804 565	44.0	74.05624 818	6.14923 635
34.2	74.17182 831	0.92832 072	44.2	74.14283 422	6.28442 258
34.4	74.10614 335	0.98099 695	44.4	74.23270 291	6.41980 616
34.6	74.04130 164	1.03614 386	44.6	74.32580 488	6.55538 620
34.8	73.97741 105	1.09382 773	44.8	74.42209 177	6.69116 545
35.0	73.91458 583	1.15411 086	45.0	74.52151 629	6.82715 003
35.2	73.85294 639	1.21705 080	45.2	74.62403 231	6.96334 924
35.4	73.79261 917	1.28269 956	45.4	74.72959 481	7.09977 536
35.6	73.73373 621	1.35110 280	45.6	74.83815 998	7.23644 349
35.8	73.67643 478	1.42229 900	45.8	74.94968 515	7.37337 135
36.0	73.62085 672	1.49631 871	46.0	75.06412 880	7.51057 916
36.2	73.56714 784	1.57318 381	46.2	75.18145 054	7.64808 944
36.4	73.51545 703	1.65290 683	46.4	75.30161 103	7.78592 696
36.6	73.46593 534	1.73549 036	46.6	75.42457 195	7.92411 853
36.8	73.41873 497	1.82092 659	46.8	75.55029 594	8.06269 296
37.0	73.37400 810	1.90919 697	47.0	75.67874 654	8.20168 093
37.2	73.33190 572	2.00027 200	47.2	75.80988 809	8.34111 490
37.4	73.29257 638	2.09411 123	47.4	75.94368 566	8.48102 904
37.6	73.25616 492	2.19066 340	47.6	76.08010 498	8.62145 914
37.8	73.22281 123	2.28986 676	47.8	76.21911 231	8.76244 254
38.0	73.19264 905	2.39164 960	48.0	76.36067 439	8.90401 810
38.2	73.16580 484	2.49593 091	48.2	76.50475 829	9.04622 611
38.4	73.14239 676	2.60262 125	48.4	76.65133 134	9.18910 823
38.6	73.12253 378	2.71162 366	48.6	76.80036 099	9.33270 749
38.8	73.10631 491	2.82283 484	48.8	76.95181 474	9.47706 820
39.0	73.09382 870	2.93614 620	49.0	77.10565 994	9.62223 589
39.2	73.08515 275	3.05144 520	49.2	77.26186 377	9.76825 733
39.4	73.08035 357	3.16861 650	49.4	77.42039 302	9.91518 042
39.6	73.07948 650	3.28754 321	49.6	77.58121 402	10.06305 417
39.8	73.08259 584	3.40810 813	49.8	77.74429 246	10.21192 865
40.0	73.08971 510	3.53019 483	50.0	77.90959 330	10.36185 494

ρ	U	V	ρ	U	V
50.0	77.90959 330	10.36185 494	75.0	99.57316 664	39.21674 075
50.5	78.33232 975	10.74161 587	75.5	99.93349 683	39.85271 151
51.0	78.76813 501	11.12911 361	76.0	100.29310 270	40.48924 855
51.5	79.21635 978	11.52521 031	76.5	100.65200 831	41.12642 156
52.0	79.67628 402	11.93078 471	77.0	101.01023 071	41.76429 534
52.5	80.14710 201	12.34671 899	77.5	101.36778 078	42.40292 972
53.0	80.62790 854	12.77388 175	78.0	101.72466 407	43.04237 948
53.5	81.11768 738	13.21310 668	78.5	102.08088 154	43.68269 446
54.0	81.61530 338	13.66516 680	79.0	102.43643 027	44.32391 960
54.5	82.11950 026	14.13074 459	79.5	102.79130 407	44.96609 502
55.0	82.62890 581	14.61039 920	80.0	103.14549 406	45.60925 624
55.5	83.14204 628	15.10453 254	80.5	103.49898 922	46.25343 427
56.0	83.65737 119	15.61335 733	81.0	103.85177 680	46.89865 583
56.5	84.17328 849	16.13687 055	81.5	104.20384 283	47.54494 357
57.0	84.68820 890	16.67483 608	82.0	104.55517 244	48.19231 627
57.5	85.20059 615	17.22678 011	82.5	104.90575 021	48.84078 905
58.0	85.70901 898	17.79200 116	83.0	105.25556 050	49.49037 364
58.5	86.21219 941	18.36959 531	83.5	105.60458 771	50.14107 860
59.0	86.70905 233	18.95849 450	84.0	105.95281 647	50.79290 954
59.5	87.19871 233	19.55751 417	84.5	106.30023 187	51.44586 939
60.0	87.68054 578	20.16540 520	85.0	106.64681 964	52.09995 863
60.5	88.15414 821	20.78090 493	85.5	106.99256 625	52.75517 549
61.0	88.61932 895	21.40278 273	86.0	107.33745 906	53.41151 619
61.5	89.07608 630	22.02987 712	86.5	107.68148 638	54.06897 520
62.0	89.52457 703	22.66112 283	87.0	108.02463 757	54.72754 535
62.5	89.96508 373	23.29556 787	87.5	108.36690 305	55.38721 815
63.0	90.39798 287	23.93238 166	88.0	108.70827 435	56.04798 387
63.5	90.82371 569	24.57085 575	88.5	109.04874 413	56.70983 176
64.0	91.24276 292	25.21039 920	89.0	109.38830 619	57.37275 026
64.5	91.65562 408	25.85053 023	89.5	109.72695 541	58.03672 706
65.0	92.06280 096	26.49086 574	90.0	110.06468 779	58.70174 933
65.5	92.46478 523	27.13110 985	90.5	110.40150 037	59.36780 380
66.0	92.86204 945	27.77104 236	91.0	110.73739 123	60.03487 688
66.5	93.25504 089	28.41050 769	91.5	111.07235 940	60.70295 481
67.0	93.64417 774	29.04940 465	92.0	111.40640 485	61.37202 370
67.5	94.02984 695	29.68767 721	92.5	111.73952 844	62.04206 966
68.0	94.41240 353	30.32530 637	93.0	112.07173 183	62.71307 887
68.5	94.79217 069	30.96230 306	93.5	112.40301 743	63.38503 761
69.0	95.16944 073	31.59870 204	94.0	112.73338 838	64.05793 238
69.5	95.54447 640	32.23455 671	94.5	113.06284 843	64.73174 987
70.0	95.91751 247	32.86993 473	95.0	113.39140 194	65.40647 710
70.5	96.28875 752	33.50491 431	95.5	113.71905 379	66.08210 136
71.0	96.65839 582	34.13958 113	96.0	114.04580 932	66.75861 029
71.5	97.02658 916	34.77402 581	96.5	114.37167 430	67.43599 189
72.0	97.39347 869	35.40834 175	97.0	114.69665 486	68.11423 453
72.5	97.75918 668	36.04262 344	97.5	115.02075 744	68.79332 698
73.0	98.12381 823	36.67696 498	98.0	115.34398 876	69.47325 839
73.5	98.48746 282	37.31145 898	98.5	115.66635 576	70.15401 830
74.0	98.85019 585	37.94619 558	99.0	115.98786 555	70.83559 666
74.5	99.21208 002	38.58126 177	99.5	116.30852 542	71.51798 379
75.0	99.57316 664	39.21674 075	100.0	116.62834 274	72.20117 041

ρ	U	V	ρ	U	V
0.0	121.00000 000	0.00000 000	25.0	118.43126 190	-0.00019 812
0.5	120.99895 834	-0.00000 000	25.5	118.32891 165	-0.00024 768
1.0	120.99583 343	-0.00000 000	26.0	118.22464 393	-0.00030 835
1.5	120.99062 548	-0.00000 000	26.5	118.11846 464	-0.00038 237
2.0	120.98333 485	-0.00000 000	27.0	118.01037 972	-0.00047 234
2.5	120.97396 203	0.00000 000	27.5	117.90039 520	-0.00058 134
3.0	120.96250 766	-0.00000 000	28.0	117.78851 717	-0.00071 296
3.5	120.94897 252	-0.00000 000	28.5	117.67475 178	-0.00087 141
4.0	120.93335 752	-0.00000 000	29.0	117.55910 524	-0.00106 156
4.5	120.91566 374	-0.00000 000	29.5	117.44158 382	-0.00128 911
5.0	120.89589 235	-0.00000 000	30.0	117.32219 385	-0.00156 064
5.5	120.87404 471	-0.00000 000	30.5	117.20094 171	-0.00188 377
6.0	120.85012 229	-0.00000 000	31.0	117.07783 383	-0.00226 729
6.5	120.82412 669	-0.00000 000	31.5	116.95287 672	-0.00272 134
7.0	120.79605 968	-0.00000 000	32.0	116.82607 693	-0.00325 757
7.5	120.76592 313	-0.00000 000	32.5	116.69744 105	-0.00388 935
8.0	120.73371 907	-0.00000 000	33.0	116.56697 577	-0.00463 200
8.5	120.69944 964	-0.00000 000	33.5	116.43468 780	-0.00550 301
9.0	120.66311 714	-0.00000 000	34.0	116.30058 394	-0.00652 238
9.5	120.62472 398	-0.00000 000	34.5	116.16467 106	-0.00771 288
10.0	120.58427 271	-0.00000 001	35.0	116.02695 611	-0.00910 040
10.5	120.54176 601	-0.00000 001	35.5	115.88744 615	-0.01071 436
11.0	120.49720 668	-0.00000 002	36.0	115.74614 832	-0.01258 812
11.5	120.45059 765	-0.00000 003	36.5	115.60306 994	-0.01475 946
12.0	120.40194 198	-0.00000 006	37.0	115.45821 846	-0.01727 109
12.5	120.35124 285	0.00000 009	37.5	115.31160 158	-0.02017 123
13.0	120.29850 355	-0.00000 013	38.0	115.16322 722	-0.02351 424
13.5	120.24372 751	-0.00000 020	38.5	115.01310 365	-0.02736 135
14.0	120.18691 827	-0.00000 031	39.0	114.86123 955	-0.03178 140
14.5	120.12807 949	-0.00000 045	39.5	114.70764 411	-0.03685 171
15.0	120.06721 493	-0.00000 066	40.0	114.55232 721	-0.04265 898
15.5	120.00432 849	-0.00000 095	40.5	114.39529 953	-0.04930 036
16.0	119.93942 415	-0.00000 135	41.0	114.23657 284	-0.05688 454
16.5	119.87250 603	-0.00000 190	41.5	114.07616 025	-0.06553 298
17.0	119.80357 833	-0.00000 265	42.0	113.91407 655	-0.07538 124
17.5	119.73264 539	-0.00000 366	42.5	113.75033 868	-0.08658 045
18.0	119.65971 163	-0.00000 500	43.0	113.58496 627	-0.09929 886
18.5	119.58478 157	-0.00000 679	43.5	113.41798 233	-0.11372 359
19.0	119.50785 985	-0.00000 914	44.0	113.24941 412	-0.13006 242
19.5	119.42895 118	-0.00001 222	44.5	113.07929 416	-0.14854 579
20.0	119.34806 039	-0.00001 621	45.0	112.90766 162	-0.16942 889
20.5	119.26519 241	-0.00002 136	45.5	112.73456 385	-0.19299 390
21.0	119.18035 223	-0.00002 797	46.0	112.56005 841	-0.21955 227
21.5	119.09354 496	-0.00003 640	46.5	112.38421 546	-0.24944 717
22.0	119.00477 578	-0.00004 710	47.0	112.20712 071	-0.28305 584
22.5	118.91404 998	-0.00006 060	47.5	112.02887 893	-0.32079 204
23.0	118.82137 291	-0.00007 756	48.0	111.84961 829	-0.36310 823
23.5	118.72675 000	-0.00009 875	48.5	111.66949 542	-0.41049 762
24.0	118.63018 679	-0.00012 512	49.0	111.48870 147	-0.46349 568
24.5	118.53168 887	-0.00015 780	49.5	111.30746 920	-0.52268 104
25.0	118.43126 190	-0.00019 812	50.0	111.12608 124	-0.58867 544

TABLE V. $a_r(i\rho) = U + iV, b_r(i\rho) = U - iV$ $r = 11$

ρ	U	V	ρ	U	V
50.0	111.12608 124	-0.58867 544	75.0	117.10033 901	-14.59628 904
50.5	110.94487 945	-0.66214 229	75.5	117.58604 918	-15.00806 222
51.0	110.76427 543	-0.74378 349	76.0	118.08004 407	-15.42929 066
51.5	110.58476 201	-0.83433 391	76.5	118.58158 990	-15.86055 619
52.0	110.40692 530	-0.93455 291	77.0	119.08988 117	-16.30240 307
52.5	110.23145 683	-1.04521 229	77.5	119.60403 959	-16.75532 283
53.0	110.05916 488	-1.16708 020	78.0	120.12311 612	-17.21973 792
53.5	109.89098 379	-1.30090 030	78.5	120.64609 680	-17.69598 464
54.0	109.72797 972	-1.44736 646	79.0	121.17191 281	-18.18429 628
54.5	109.57135 104	-1.60709 307	79.5	121.69945 505	-18.68478 778
55.0	109.42242 148	-1.78058 234	80.0	122.22759 306	-19.19744 313
55.5	109.28262 413	-1.96819 040	80.5	122.75519 774	-19.72210 699
56.0	109.15347 535	-2.17009 531	81.0	123.28116 660	-20.25848 163
56.5	109.03653 832	-2.38627 030	81.5	123.80445 016	-20.80613 016
57.0	108.93337 764	-2.61646 638	82.0	124.32407 745	-21.36448 624
57.5	108.84550 810	-2.86020 742	82.5	124.83917 891	-21.93286 993
58.0	108.77434 182	-3.11680 014	83.0	125.34900 472	-22.51050 874
58.5	108.72113 920	-3.38535 909	83.5	125.85293 753	-23.09656 212
59.0	108.68696 866	-3.66484 483	84.0	126.35049 872	-23.69014 784
59.5	108.67267 921	-3.95411 145	84.5	126.84134 842	-24.29036 810
60.0	108.67888 783	-4.25195 842	85.0	127.32527 971	-24.89633 372
60.5	108.70598 167	-4.55718 158	85.5	127.80220 815	-25.50718 530
61.0	108.75413 298	-4.86861 876	86.0	128.27215 798	-26.12211 019
61.5	108.82332 356	-5.18518 695	86.5	128.73524 630	-26.74035 527
62.0	108.91337 492	-5.50590 952	87.0	129.19166 647	-27.36123 533
62.5	109.02398 065	-5.82993 354	87.5	129.64167 184	-27.98413 771
63.0	109.15473 805	-6.15653 812	88.0	130.08556 051	-28.60852 359
63.5	109.30517 690	-6.48513 562	88.5	130.52366 163	-29.23392 666
64.0	109.47478 442	-6.81526 742	89.0	130.95632 353	-29.85994 988
64.5	109.66302 569	-7.14659 612	89.5	131.38390 376	-30.48626 093
65.0	109.86935 963	-7.47889 567	90.0	131.80676 097	-31.11258 675
65.5	110.09325 105	-7.81204 066	90.5	132.22524 850	-31.73870 779
66.0	110.33417 903	-8.14599 556	91.0	132.63970 947	-32.36445 213
66.5	110.59164 241	-8.48080 452	91.5	133.05047 314	-32.98968 971
67.0	110.86516 287	-8.81658 209	92.0	133.45785 242	-33.61432 691
67.5	111.15428 609	-9.15350 499	92.5	133.86214 218	-34.23830 154
68.0	111.45858 134	-9.49180 506	93.0	134.26361 833	-34.86157 821
68.5	111.77764 000	-9.83176 325	93.5	134.66253 743	-35.48414 418
69.0	112.11107 307	-10.17370 459	94.0	135.05913 673	-36.10600 571
69.5	112.45850 796	-10.51799 414	94.5	135.45363 446	-36.72718 478
70.0	112.81958 466	-10.86503 355	95.0	135.84623 049	-37.34771 624
70.5	113.19395 139	-11.21525 831	95.5	136.23710 700	-37.96764 535
71.0	113.58125 974	-11.56913 540	96.0	136.62642 934	-38.58702 557
71.5	113.98115 940	-11.92716 114	96.5	137.01434 695	-39.20591 675
72.0	114.39329 236	-12.28985 918	97.0	137.40099 429	-39.82438 348
72.5	114.81728 681	-12.65777 833	97.5	137.78649 177	-40.44249 377
73.0	115.25275 046	-13.03149 004	98.0	138.17094 671	-41.06031 785
73.5	115.69926 364	-13.41158 539	98.5	138.55445 425	-41.67792 714
74.0	116.15637 200	-13.79867 117	99.0	138.93709 826	-42.29539 348
74.5	116.62357 911	-14.19336 500	99.5	139.31895 213	-42.91278 834
75.0	117.10033 901	-14.59628 904	100.0	139.70007 969	-43.53018 225

TABLE V. $a_r(i\rho) = U + iV, b_r(i\rho) = U - iV$ $r = 13$

ρ	U	V	ρ	U	V
0.0	169.00000 000	0.00000 000	25.0	167.15289 527	0.00000 042
0.5	168.99925 595	0.00000 000	25.5	167.07880 744	0.00000 055
1.0	168.99702 384	0.00000 000	26.0	167.00329 439	0.00000 070
1.5	168.99330 374	0.00000 000	26.5	166.92635 846	0.00000 091
2.0	168.98809 578	0.00000 000	27.0	166.84800 205	0.00000 116
2.5	168.98140 014	0.00000 000	27.5	166.76822 758	0.00000 148
3.0	168.97321 704	0.00000 000	28.0	166.68703 751	0.00000 187
3.5	168.96354 677	0.00000 000	28.5	166.60443 433	0.00000 236
4.0	168.95238 966	0.00000 000	29.0	166.52042 056	0.00000 298
4.5	168.93974 609	0.00000 000	29.5	166.43499 878	0.00000 373
5.0	168.92561 649	0.00000 000	30.0	166.34817 156	0.00000 466
5.5	168.91000 135	0.00000 000	30.5	166.25994 154	0.00000 580
6.0	168.89290 119	0.00000 000	31.0	166.17031 137	0.00000 719
6.5	168.87431 661	0.00000 000	31.5	166.07928 374	0.00000 889
7.0	168.85424 824	0.00000 000	32.0	165.98686 136	0.00001 095
7.5	168.83269 675	0.00000 000	32.5	165.89304 698	0.00001 345
8.0	168.80966 289	0.00000 000	33.0	165.79784 339	0.00001 647
8.5	168.78514 744	0.00000 000	33.5	165.70125 339	0.00002 011
9.0	168.75915 123	0.00000 000	34.0	165.60327 980	0.00002 449
9.5	168.73167 513	0.00000 000	34.5	165.50392 550	0.00002 974
10.0	168.70272 009	0.00000 000	35.0	165.40319 337	0.00003 601
10.5	168.67228 708	0.00000 000	35.5	165.30108 633	0.00004 350
11.0	168.64037 713	0.00000 000	36.0	165.19760 733	0.00005 241
11.5	168.60699 131	0.00000 000	36.5	165.09275 932	0.00006 299
12.0	168.57213 075	0.00000 000	37.0	164.98654 531	0.00007 553
12.5	168.53579 661	0.00000 000	37.5	164.87896 832	0.00009 035
13.0	168.49799 013	0.00000 000	38.0	164.77003 138	0.00010 784
13.5	168.45871 256	0.00000 000	38.5	164.65973 756	0.00012 842
14.0	168.41796 521	0.00000 000	39.0	164.54808 996	0.00015 262
14.5	168.37574 945	0.00000 000	39.5	164.43509 168	0.00018 099
15.0	168.33206 669	0.00000 000	40.0	164.32074 586	0.00021 421
15.5	168.28691 836	0.00000 000	40.5	164.20505 565	0.00025 302
16.0	168.24030 597	0.00000 000	41.0	164.08802 424	0.00029 829
16.5	168.19223 106	0.00000 000	41.5	163.96965 481	0.00035 099
17.0	168.14269 521	0.00000 000	42.0	163.84995 059	0.00041 226
17.5	168.09170 005	0.00000 000	42.5	163.72891 481	0.00048 335
18.0	168.03924 727	0.00000 001	43.0	163.60655 074	0.00056 571
18.5	167.98533 857	0.00000 001	43.5	163.48286 163	0.00066 097
19.0	167.92997 572	0.00000 001	44.0	163.35785 080	0.00077 100
19.5	167.87316 051	0.00000 002	44.5	163.23152 155	0.00089 788
20.0	167.81489 480	0.00000 002	45.0	163.10387 720	0.00104 398
20.5	167.75518 048	0.00000 003	45.5	162.97492 110	0.00121 198
21.0	167.69401 946	0.00000 004	46.0	162.84465 663	0.00140 487
21.5	167.63141 373	0.00000 006	46.5	162.71308 714	0.00162 605
22.0	167.56736 528	0.00000 008	47.0	162.58021 605	0.00187 932
22.5	167.50187 618	0.00000 011	47.5	162.44604 675	0.00216 896
23.0	167.43494 851	0.00000 014	48.0	162.31058 268	0.00249 976
23.5	167.36658 439	0.00000 019	48.5	162.17382 728	0.00287 710
24.0	167.29678 600	0.00000 025	49.0	162.03578 401	0.00330 700
24.5	167.22555 555	0.00000 032	49.5	161.89645 634	0.00379 618
25.0	167.15289 527	0.00000 042	50.0	161.75584 777	0.00435 217

TABLE V. $a_r(i\rho) = U + iV, b_r(i\rho) = U - iV$ $r = 13$

ρ	U	V	ρ	U	V
50.0	161.75584 777	0.00435 217	75.0	153.28766 197	1.19613 237
50.5	161.61396 180	0.00498 336	75.5	153.10956 354	1.31106 488
51.0	161.47080 197	0.00569 910	76.0	152.93460 150	1.43553 082
51.5	161.32637 183	0.00650 983	76.5	152.76345 711	1.57004 679
52.0	161.18067 495	0.00742 715	77.0	152.59689 076	1.71509 813
52.5	161.03371 493	0.00846 397	77.5	152.43574 212	1.87112 398
53.0	160.88549 539	0.00963 463	78.0	152.28092 726	2.03850 099
53.5	160.73602 000	0.01095 506	78.5	152.13343 213	2.21752 622
54.0	160.58529 245	0.01244 292	79.0	151.99430 179	2.40840 038
54.5	160.43331 650	0.01411 779	79.5	151.86462 517	2.61121 245
55.0	160.28009 593	0.01600 135	80.0	151.74551 558	2.82592 701
55.5	160.12563 462	0.01811 759	80.5	151.63808 746	3.05237 580
56.0	159.96993 650	0.02049 306	81.0	151.54343 064	3.29025 468
56.5	159.81300 561	0.02315 705	81.5	151.46258 349	3.53912 669
57.0	159.65484 611	0.02614 194	82.0	151.39650 699	3.79843 178
57.5	159.49546 229	0.02948 343	82.5	151.34606 153	4.06750 255
58.0	159.33485 860	0.03322 089	83.0	151.31198 814	4.34558 524
58.5	159.17303 973	0.03739 767	83.5	151.29489 556	4.63186 425
59.0	159.01001 058	0.04206 153	84.0	151.29525 362	4.92548 841
59.5	158.84577 639	0.04726 497	84.5	151.31339 305	5.22559 711
60.0	158.68034 276	0.05306 574	85.0	151.34951 099	5.53134 457
60.5	158.51371 576	0.05952 724	85.5	151.40368 127	5.84192 093
61.0	158.34590 200	0.06671 912	86.0	151.47586 806	6.15656 938
61.5	158.17690 878	0.07471 774	86.5	151.56594 147	6.47459 896
62.0	158.00674 421	0.08360 687	87.0	151.67369 395	6.79539 315
62.5	157.83541 739	0.09347 822	87.5	151.79885 646	7.11841 458
63.0	157.66293 864	0.10443 222	88.0	151.94111 353	7.44320 657
63.5	157.48931 973	0.11657 876	88.5	152.10011 674	7.76939 202
64.0	157.31457 417	0.13003 792	89.0	152.27549 644	8.09667 043
64.5	157.13871 762	0.14494 090	89.5	152.46687 153	8.42481 365
65.0	156.96176 829	0.16143 088	90.0	152.67385 729	8.75366 079
65.5	156.78374 745	0.17966 402	90.5	152.89607 161	9.08311 284
66.0	156.60468 009	0.19981 045	91.0	153.13313 958	9.41312 717
66.5	156.42459 560	0.22205 538	91.5	153.38469 677	9.74371 231
67.0	156.24352 871	0.24660 019	92.0	153.65039 137	10.07492 295
67.5	156.06152 047	0.27366 364	92.5	153.92988 539	10.40685 549
68.0	155.87861 948	0.30348 301	93.0	154.22285 509	10.73964 395
68.5	155.69488 338	0.33631 536	93.5	154.52899 070	11.07345 645
69.0	155.51038 046	0.37243 873	94.0	154.84799 574	11.40849 210
69.5	155.32519 173	0.41215 327	94.5	155.17958 581	11.74497 838
70.0	155.13941 313	0.45578 238	95.0	155.52348 705	12.08316 886
70.5	154.95315 829	0.50367 363	95.5	155.87943 430	12.42334 136
71.0	154.76656 153	0.55619 958	96.0	156.24716 901	12.76579 628
71.5	154.57978 143	0.61375 824	96.5	156.62643 686	13.11085 529
72.0	154.39300 479	0.67677 320	97.0	157.01698 520	13.45886 011
72.5	154.20645 114	0.74569 325	97.5	157.41856 025	13.81017 142
73.0	154.02037 766	0.82099 132	98.0	157.83090 407	14.16516 785
73.5	153.83508 467	0.90316 263	98.5	158.25375 130	14.52424 487
74.0	153.65092 139	0.99272 176	99.0	158.68682 578	14.88781 361
74.5	153.46829 204	1.09019 855	99.5	159.12983 684	15.25629 942
75.0	153.28766 197	1.19613 237	100.0	159.58247 553	15.63014 023

ρ	U	V	ρ	U	V
0.0	225.00000 000	0.00000 000	25.0	223.61040 859	-0.00000 000
0.5	224.99944 197	-0.00000 000	25.5	223.55449 738	-0.00000 000
1.0	224.99776 787	-0.00000 000	26.0	223.49749 705	-0.00000 000
1.5	224.99497 775	-0.00000 000	26.5	223.43940 863	-0.00000 000
2.0	224.99107 166	-0.00000 000	27.0	223.38023 318	-0.00000 000
2.5	224.98604 966	-0.00000 000	27.5	223.31997 175	-0.00000 000
3.0	224.97991 187	-0.00000 000	28.0	223.25862 545	-0.00000 000
3.5	224.97265 839	-0.00000 000	28.5	223.19619 536	-0.00000 000
4.0	224.96428 936	-0.00000 000	29.0	223.13268 262	-0.00000 000
4.5	224.95480 494	-0.00000 000	29.5	223.06808 836	-0.00000 001
5.0	224.94420 533	-0.00000 000	30.0	223.00241 374	-0.00000 001
5.5	224.93249 070	-0.00000 000	30.5	222.93565 991	-0.00000 001
6.0	224.91966 130	-0.00000 000	31.0	222.86782 808	-0.00000 001
6.5	224.90571 737	-0.00000 000	31.5	222.79891 945	-0.00000 002
7.0	224.89065 916	-0.00000 000	32.0	222.72893 522	-0.00000 002
7.5	224.87448 698	-0.00000 000	32.5	222.65787 665	-0.00000 003
8.0	224.85720 112	-0.00000 000	33.0	222.58574 498	-0.00000 003
8.5	224.83880 192	-0.00000 000	33.5	222.51254 148	-0.00000 004
9.0	224.81928 972	-0.00000 000	34.0	222.43826 743	-0.00000 005
9.5	224.79866 491	-0.00000 000	34.5	222.36292 413	-0.00000 006
10.0	224.77692 786	-0.00000 000	35.0	222.28651 289	-0.00000 008
10.5	224.75407 899	-0.00000 000	35.5	222.20903 505	-0.00000 010
11.0	224.73011 875	-0.00000 000	36.0	222.13049 194	-0.00000 012
11.5	224.70504 757	-0.00000 000	36.5	222.05088 492	-0.00000 015
12.0	224.67886 593	-0.00000 000	37.0	221.97021 536	-0.00000 018
12.5	224.65157 434	-0.00000 000	37.5	221.88848 466	-0.00000 022
13.0	224.62317 331	-0.00000 000	38.0	221.80569 422	-0.00000 028
13.5	224.59366 336	-0.00000 000	38.5	221.72184 544	-0.00000 034
14.0	224.56304 507	-0.00000 000	39.0	221.63693 976	-0.00000 041
14.5	224.53131 900	-0.00000 000	39.5	221.55097 863	-0.00000 050
15.0	224.49848 576	-0.00000 000	40.0	221.46396 350	-0.00000 060
15.5	224.46454 596	-0.00000 000	40.5	221.37589 584	-0.00000 073
16.0	224.42950 024	-0.00000 000	41.0	221.28677 713	-0.00000 088
16.5	224.39334 925	-0.00000 000	41.5	221.19660 887	-0.00000 105
17.0	224.35609 368	-0.00000 000	42.0	221.10539 258	-0.00000 127
17.5	224.31773 421	-0.00000 000	42.5	221.01312 977	-0.00000 152
18.0	224.27827 158	-0.00000 000	43.0	220.91982 199	-0.00000 182
18.5	224.23770 650	-0.00000 000	43.5	220.82547 077	-0.00000 217
19.0	224.19603 974	-0.00000 000	44.0	220.73007 768	-0.00000 258
19.5	224.15327 208	-0.00000 000	44.5	220.63364 429	-0.00000 307
20.0	224.10940 430	-0.00000 000	45.0	220.53617 219	-0.00000 364
20.5	224.06443 723	-0.00000 000	45.5	220.43766 298	-0.00000 431
21.0	224.01837 168	-0.00000 000	46.0	220.33811 825	-0.00000 510
21.5	223.97120 852	-0.00000 000	46.5	220.23753 964	-0.00000 602
22.0	223.92294 862	-0.00000 000	47.0	220.13592 877	-0.00000 710
22.5	223.87359 286	-0.00000 000	47.5	220.03328 729	-0.00000 835
23.0	223.82314 214	-0.00000 000	48.0	219.92961 684	-0.00000 981
23.5	223.77159 741	-0.00000 000	48.5	219.82491 910	-0.00001 150
24.0	223.71895 959	-0.00000 000	49.0	219.71919 573	-0.00001 347
24.5	223.66522 966	-0.00000 000	49.5	219.61244 843	-0.00001 575
25.0	223.61040 859	-0.00000 000	50.0	219.50467 889	-0.00001 838

ρ	U	V	ρ	U	V
50.0	219.50467 889	−0.00001 838	75.0	212.85285 443	−0.01026 846
50.5	219.39588 881	−0.00002 143	75.5	212.69539 334	−0.01140 938
51.0	219.28607 991	−0.00002 494	76.0	212.53700 898	−0.01266 912
51.5	219.17525 391	−0.00002 899	76.5	212.37770 348	−0.01405 924
52.0	219.06341 256	−0.00003 365	77.0	212.21747 897	−0.01559 236
52.5	218.95055 760	−0.00003 901	77.5	212.05633 762	−0.01728 224
53.0	218.83669 078	−0.00004 516	78.0	211.89428 163	−0.01914 388
53.5	218.72181 387	−0.00005 221	78.5	211.73131 322	−0.02119 362
54.0	218.60592 863	−0.00006 028	79.0	211.56743 467	−0.02344 923
54.5	218.48903 685	−0.00006 952	79.5	211.40264 830	−0.02593 007
55.0	218.37114 032	−0.00008 007	80.0	211.23695 649	−0.02865 720
55.5	218.25224 085	−0.00009 212	80.5	211.07036 169	−0.03165 350
56.0	218.13234 023	−0.00010 585	81.0	210.90286 644	−0.03494 387
56.5	218.01144 028	−0.00012 149	81.5	210.73447 337	−0.03855 532
57.0	217.88954 283	−0.00013 928	82.0	210.56518 522	−0.04251 720
57.5	217.76664 970	−0.00015 950	82.5	210.39500 488	−0.04686 137
58.0	217.64276 275	−0.00018 245	83.0	210.22393 539	−0.05162 239
58.5	217.51788 380	−0.00020 847	83.5	210.05197 999	−0.05683 774
59.0	217.39201 473	−0.00023 796	84.0	209.87914 216	−0.06254 804
59.5	217.26515 739	−0.00027 133	84.5	209.70542 562	−0.06879 732
60.0	217.13731 365	−0.00030 907	85.0	209.53083 443	−0.07563 325
60.5	217.00848 538	−0.00035 170	85.5	209.35537 303	−0.08310 745
61.0	216.87867 447	−0.00039 981	86.0	209.17904 628	−0.09127 579
61.5	216.74788 281	−0.00045 406	86.5	209.00185 957	−0.10019 867
62.0	216.61611 230	−0.00051 519	87.0	208.82381 893	−0.10994 143
62.5	216.48336 483	−0.00058 399	87.5	208.64493 109	−0.12057 467
63.0	216.34964 232	−0.00066 136	88.0	208.46520 364	−0.13217 465
63.5	216.21494 669	−0.00074 830	88.5	208.28464 516	−0.14482 372
64.0	216.07927 984	−0.00084 592	89.0	208.10326 543	−0.15861 074
64.5	215.94264 372	−0.00095 542	89.5	207.92107 558	−0.17363 158
65.0	215.80504 025	−0.00107 816	90.0	207.73808 839	−0.18998 957
65.5	215.66647 137	−0.00121 563	90.5	207.55431 851	−0.20779 607
66.0	215.52693 902	−0.00136 947	91.0	207.36978 280	−0.22717 099
66.5	215.38644 516	−0.00154 151	91.5	207.18450 072	−0.24824 337
67.0	215.24499 175	−0.00173 374	92.0	206.99849 475	−0.27115 200
67.5	215.10258 073	−0.00194 838	92.5	206.81179 089	−0.29604 603
68.0	214.95921 409	−0.00218 787	93.0	206.62441 922	−0.32308 561
68.5	214.81489 378	−0.00245 487	93.5	206.43641 461	−0.35244 256
69.0	214.66962 180	−0.00275 234	94.0	206.24781 746	−0.38430 106
69.5	214.52340 011	−0.00308 354	94.5	206.05867 460	−0.41885 828
70.0	214.37623 071	−0.00345 201	95.0	205.86904 027	−0.45632 507
70.5	214.22811 558	−0.00386 168	95.5	205.67897 732	−0.49692 659
71.0	214.07905 675	−0.00431 684	96.0	205.48855 851	−0.54090 293
71.5	213.92905 619	−0.00482 221	96.5	205.29786 802	−0.58850 959
72.0	213.77811 594	−0.00538 296	97.0	205.10700 311	−0.64001 799
72.5	213.62623 801	−0.00600 477	97.5	204.91607 604	−0.69571 572
73.0	213.47342 442	−0.00669 383	98.0	204.72521 620	−0.75590 676
73.5	213.31967 722	−0.00745 694	98.5	204.53457 247	−0.82091 137
74.0	213.16499 845	−0.00830 153	99.0	204.34431 577	−0.89106 580
74.5	213.00939 016	−0.00923 574	99.5	204.15464 196	−0.96672 158
75.0	212.85285 443	−0.01026 846	100.0	203.96577 479	−1.04824 447

TABLE VI. DOUBLE POINTS OF MATHIEU'S EQUATION

TABLE VI. Double Points of Mathieu's Equation
$$a_r(q) = a_{r+2}(q) = U + iV, \quad q = \rho e^{i\phi}$$

r	ϕ, in degrees	ρ	U	V	$r+2$
0	90.00000 000	1.46876 861	2.08869 890	0.00000 000	2
1	59.18208 061	3.76995 749	6.17647 404	1.23177 966	3
2	44.60975 039	7.26814 689	12.79971 624	2.76304 492	4
3	36.02304 851	11.97821 151	21.92533 616	4.49002 890	5
4	90.00000 000	16.47116 589	27.31912 767	0.00000 000	6
4	30.32903 891	17.90770 960	33.54015 643	6.36251 878	6
5	77.74433 895	22.85524 712	38.40883 857	2.53293 279	7
5	26.26120 049	25.06087 566	47.63741 382	8.35068 598	7
6	68.63569 460	30.42738 210	52.02534 500	5.55189 444	8
6	23.20168 627	33.44030 379	64.21313 050	10.43474 552	8
7	61.57215 455	39.19378 450	68.15680 853	8.96150 250	9
7	20.81211 404	.43.04769 498	83.26475 268	12.60061 661	9
8	90.00000 000	47.80596 570	80.65826 424	0.00000 000	10
8	55.91955 555	49.16014 417	86.79479 850	12.69861 754	10
8	18.89115 596	53.88422 425	104.79053 631	14.83777 144	10
9	82.35333 500	58.27413 845	98.76912 388	3.83025 506	11
9	51.28456 166	60.33123 310	107.93306 428	16.71813 422	11
9	17.31131 065	65.95073 725	128.78923 395	17.13804 526	11
10	76.00421 757	69.92930 518	119.40038 738	8.20296 334	12
10	47.40927 141	72.71097 078	131.56682 190	20.98611 513	12
10	15.98778 925	79.24786 295	155.25992 075	19.49492 409	12
11	70.63818 332	82.77468 530	142.54619 965	13.04302 555	13
11	44.11709 801	86.30257 222	157.69231 520	25.47604 566	13
11	14.86194 679	93.77608 193	184.20189 088	21.90309 228	13
12	90.00000 000	95.47527 271	162.10702 112	0.00000 000	14
12	66.03683 674	96.81379 444	168.20157 306	18.29431 821	14
12	41.28283 447	101.10868 908	186.30653 256	30.16660 867	14
12	13.89188 815	109.53576 981	215.61459 283	24.35813 133	14
13	84.44343 693	110.02736 921	187.24248 763	5.12750 451	15
13	62.04316 195	112.05003 644	196.36226 473	23.91319 567	15
13	38.81510 667	117.13152 570	217.40701 681	35.04027 512	15
13	13.04686 266	126.52722 577	249.49758 698	26.85631 162	15
14	79.59090 305	125.76627 897	214.89467 225	10.82481 143	16
14	58.54107 283	128.48655 463	227.02465 063	29.86467 710	16
14	36.64559 325	134.37293 031	250.99173 315	40.08236 608	16
14	12.30377 417	144.75069 208	285.85051 698	29.39444 380	16
15	75.31192 241	142.69395 383	245.06010 153	17.03092 757	17
15	55.44272 850	146.12619 098	260.18561 672	36.12005 618	17
15	34.72213 986	152.83446 572	287.05897 499	45.28040 307	17
15	11.64492 867	164.20636 770	324.67308 978	31.96977 006	17

TABLE VI.   Double Points of Mathieu's Equation
$$b_r(q) = b_{r+2}(q) = U + iV, \quad q = \rho e^{i\phi}$$

r	ϕ, in degrees	ρ	U	V	$r+2$
2	90.00000 000	6.92895 476	11.19047 360	0.00000 000	4
3	72.46057 467	11.27098 527	18.77370 055	1.88381 571	5
4	60.97874 908	16.80308 983	28.88860 879	4.19467 426	6
5	52.82618 856	23.53467 876	41.51634 588	6.82630 952	7
6	90.00000 000	30.09677 284	50.47501 616	0.00000 000	8
6	46.71423 788	31.47295 165	56.64571 353	9.71571 559	8
7	80.58233 121	38.52292 501	65.07456 904	3.18163 148	9
7	41.94897 328	40.62318 483	74.26939 582	12.82090 012	9
8	73.08912 353	48.13638 186	82.19724 671	6.88343 235	10
8	38.12170 543	50.98928 567	94.38230 111	16.11176 782	10
9	66.96914 596	58.94150 633	101.83496 931	11.02097 811	11
9	34.97532 055	62.57420 650	116.98071 992	19.56564 754	11
10	90.00000 000	69.59879 328	117.86892 416	0.00000 000	12
10	61.86698 774	70.94273 869	123.98133 068	15.53425 785	12
10	32.33961 544	75.38022 473	142.06185 385	23.16482 626	12
11	83.56378 920	82.10894 361	139.49186 015	4.47887 410	13
11	57.54201 185	84.14413 219	148.63118 156	20.37826 431	13
11	30.09725 025	89.40913 113	169.62353 277	26.89507 274	13
12	78.06133 695	95.80595 671	163.63313 127	9.51589 661	14
12	53.82495 450	98.54925 096	175.78032 210	25.51790 587	14
12	28.16459 857	104.66235 807	199.66403 556	30.74469 753	14
13	73.29652 000	110.69230 161	190.28830 309	15.04368 354	15
13	50.59302 351	114.16118 710	205.42527 964	30.92500 454	15
13	26.48038 795	121.14106 880	232.18197 149	34.70392 490	15
14	90.00000 000	125.43541 131	213.37256 864	0.00000 000	16
14	69.12577 961	126.77081 443	219.45339 815	21.00996 902	16
14	47.75482 811	130.98261 358	237.56314 715	36.57640 523	16
14	24.99865 911	138.84622 074	267.17619 891	38.76445 692	16
15	85.11157 324	142.02943 128	242.02085 606	5.77614 871	17
15	65.44128 256	144.04436 333	251.12488 713	27.37294 857	17
15	45.24085 886	149.01584 316	272.19146 415	42.45272 306	17
15	23.68423 768	157.77861 135	304.64576 791	42.91916 094	17

U. S. GOVERNMENT PRINTING OFFICE : 1969 O - 322-566